Environmental Science

Principles and Practices

Frank R. Spellman
Melissa L. Stoudt

THE SCARECROW PRESS, INC.
Lanham • Toronto • Plymouth, UK
2013

Published by Scarecrow Press, Inc.
A wholly owned subsidiary of The Rowman & Littlefield Publishing Group, Inc.
4501 Forbes Boulevard, Suite 200, Lanham, Maryland 20706
www.rowman.com

10 Thornbury Road, Plymouth PL6 7PP, United Kingdom

British Library Cataloguing in Publication Information Available

Library of Congress Cataloging-in-Publication Data
Spellman, Frank R.
  Environmental science : principles and practices / Frank R. Spellman, Melissa Stoudt.
      p. cm.
  Includes bibliographical references and index.
  ISBN 978-0-8108-8610-0 (cloth : alk. paper) — ISBN 978-0-8108-8611-7 (ebook)
  1. Environmental sciences. I. Stoudt, Melissa L. II. Title.
  GE105.S74 2013
  363.7—dc23

                                                                        2012029047

♾️™ The paper used in this publication meets the minimum requirements of American National Standard for Information Sciences—Permanence of Paper for Printed Library Materials, ANSI/NISO Z39.48-1992. Printed in the United States of America.

For
Nancy Lee Velasquez
and
Ryan Cooper Bonsett

Tell me and I might forget. Show me and I can remember. Involve me and I will understand.

—Confucius, 450 BC

Contents

Preface   xix

PART I: THE BASICS   1

1   The Environment and Environmental Science   3
    Killing the Wolf   3
    Chapter Objectives   3
    Chapter Outline   4
    Key Terms   4
    Introduction   5
    What Is Environmental Science?   6
    Key Terms and Introductory Principles   10
    Sound Science versus Voodoo (Junk) Science   11
    Scientists' Toolbox: Additional Tools   13
    Science and Environmental Science   28
    Good Science versus Feel-Good Science   28
    Good Science versus Feel-Good Science: The Difference   29
    Environmental Science and Technology   35
    Chapter Summary   39
    Discussion Questions   40
    Suggested Research Topics and Projects   40
    Notes   41
    References and Recommended Reading   41

2   Environmental Science: The Fundamentals   45
    Chapter Objectives   45
    Chapter Outline   45
    Key Terms   46
    Introduction   46
    Biogeochemical Cycles   47
    Energy Flow through an Ecosystem and the Biosphere   53
    Ecological Pyramids   62

Productivity   64
Population Ecology   66
Ecological Succession   82
Units of Measurement   83
Chapter Summary   88
Discussion Questions and Problems   89
Suggested Research Topics and Projects   89
Notes   90
References and Recommended Reading   90

3   Environmental Chemistry   93
    Chapter Objectives   93
    Chapter Outline   93
    Key Terms   94
    Introduction   95
    What Is Chemistry?   96
    Elements and Compounds   97
    Classification of Elements   97
    Physical and Chemical Changes   98
    Periodic Classification of the Elements   99
    Molecules and Ions   102
    Chemical Bonding   102
    Chemical Formulas and Equations   103
    Molecular Weights, Formulas, and the Mole   104
    Density   105
    States of Matter   105
    Gas Laws   106
    Liquids and Solutions   106
    Thermal Properties   107
    Acids + Bases → Salts   109
    pH Scale   110
    Organic Chemistry   111
    Environmental Chemistry: Environmental Media   114
    Chapter Summary   172
    Discussion Questions and Problems   172
    Suggested Research Topics and Projects   172
    Note   173
    References and Recommended Reading   173

4   Environmental Biology   175
    Chapter Objectives   175
    Chapter Outline   176
    Key Terms   176
    Introduction   179
    Microbiology   181
    The Cell   182
    Bacteria   184

Viruses   199
Fungi   201
Algae   206
Protozoa and Other Microorganisms   211
Enzymes   219
Metabolic Transformations   225
Bacterial Growth   233
Pathogenicity   240
Chapter Summary   255
Discussion Questions and Problems   255
Suggested Research Topics and Projects   255
Notes   256
References and Recommended Reading   256

5   Environmental Toxicology   261
    "Don't Eat the Lettuce!"   261
    Chapter Objectives   262
    Chapter Outline   262
    Key Terms   262
    Introduction   263
    Dose–Response   263
    Environmental Toxicology: Practical Applications   265
    Chapter Summary   279
    Discussion Questions and Problems   279
    Suggested Research Topics and Projects   279
    Note   280
    References and Recommended Reading   280

6   Environmental Geology and Groundwater Hydrology   281
    Chapter Objectives   281
    Chapter Outline   282
    Key Terms   282
    Introduction   282
    What Is Geology?   284
    Formation and Types of Rocks   284
    Formation of Soil   284
    Soil Enhancement and Rebuilding   287
    Soil Characteristics   287
    Soil Profile   288
    Functions of Soils   289
    Groundwater Hydrology   291
    Chapter Summary   293
    Plausible Answers to Response Scenario 6.1   293
    Discussion Questions and Problems   294
    Suggested Research Topics and Projects   294
    References and Recommended Reading   294

7   Environmental Sampling and Analyses   297
     Chapter Objectives   297
     Chapter Outline   298
     Key Terms   298
     Introduction   298
     Environmental Sampling and Analysis: What's It All About?   299
     General Considerations for a Sampling Program   300
     General Evaluation Methods for Environmental Media   305
     Chapter Summary   309
     Discussion Questions and Problems   309
     Suggested Research Topics and Projects   309
     References and Recommended Reading   310

8   Technology and the Environment   311
     Chapter Objectives   311
     Chapter Outline   312
     Key Terms   312
     Weathering the Storm   313
     Modern Technology   317
     The Impact of Technology on Air Quality   319
     Sources of Water Pollution   329
     Sources of Soil Pollution   336
     Alternative/Renewable Energy   339
     Chapter Summary   354
     Discussion Questions and Problems   355
     Suggested Research Topics and Projects   355
     Notes   355
     References and Recommended Reading   356

PART II: AIR QUALITY   359

9   The Atmosphere: Basic Air Quality   361
     Chapter Objectives   362
     Chapter Outline   363
     Key Terms   363
     Introduction   363
     What Is Air?   364
     The Atmosphere   372
     Chapter Summary   388
     Discussion Questions and Problems   388
     Suggested Research Topics and Projects   389
     References and Recommended Reading   389

10   Meteorology   391
     Chapter Objectives   391
     Chapter Outline   392
     Key Terms   392

Introduction   392
Weather   402
Meteorology: The Science of Weather   403
Thermal Inversion and Air Pollution   408
Chapter Summary   409
Discussion Questions and Problems   409
Suggested Research Topics and Projects   410
Note   410
References and Recommended Reading   410

11 Atmospheric Pollutants   411
    Chapter Objectives   412
    Chapter Outline   413
    Key Terms   413
    Introduction   413
    Major Air Pollutants   414
    Volatile Organic Compounds (VOC—Hydrocarbons)   416
    Ozone and Photochemical Smog   417
    Carbon Dioxide   420
    Particulate Matter   420
    Lead   422
    Chapter Summary   422
    Discussion Questions and Problems   424
    Suggested Research Topics and Projects   424
    References and Recommended Reading   425

12 Atmospheric Air Dispersion   427
    Chapter Objectives   427
    Chapter Outline   428
    Key Terms   428
    Introduction   428
    The Atmosphere and Meteorology   429
    Chapter Summary   437
    Discussion Questions and Problems   437
    Suggested Research Topics and Projects   437
    References and Recommended Reading   438

13 Atmospheric Change   439
    Chapter Objectives   439
    Chapter Outline   440
    Key Terms   440
    Introduction   440
    Global Warming   441
    Acid Precipitation   457
    Stratospheric Ozone Depletion   459
    Air Pollution Control Technology   460
    Chapter Summary   466

Discussion Questions and Problems   466
Suggested Research Topics and Projects   466
References and Recommended Reading   467

PART III: WATER QUALITY   471

14 All about Water: Earth's Blood   473
    Chapter Objectives   474
    Chapter Outline   475
    Key Terms   476
    Introduction   477
    Water Resources   478
    Water Use   484
    Characteristics of Water   486
    Chapter Summary   502
    Discussion Questions and Problems   502
    Suggested Research Topics and Projects   503
    References and Recommended Reading   503

15 Freshwater: Surface and Ground Sources   505
    Chapter Objectives   505
    Chapter Outline   506
    Key Terms   507
    Introduction   508
    Surface Water   509
    Groundwater   535
    Chapter Summary   537
    Discussion Questions and Problems   537
    Suggested Research Topics and Projects   538
    References and Recommended Reading   538

16 Water Pollution and Control   541
    Chapter Objectives   541
    Chapter Outline   542
    Key Terms   543
    Introduction   543
    Sick Water   544
    Point and Nonpoint Sources of Pollution   547
    Industrial Sources of Water Pollution   549
    Hazardous Waste Disposal   550
    Acid Mine Drainage   551
    Agricultural Sources of Surface Water Pollution   552
    Acid Rain   557
    Groundwater Pollution   558
    Water Pollution Control   560
    Effect of Regulations on Preventing Water Pollution   561
    Water Treatment   563

Wastewater Treatment   564
Thermal Pollution Treatment   568
Underground Storage Tanks (USTs)   568
Groundwater Remediation   572
Chapter Summary   574
Discussion Questions and Problems   575
Suggested Research Topics and Projects   575
References and Recommended Reading   576

PART IV: SOIL QUALITY   579

17   Soil Characteristics, Pollution, and Pollution Control   581
     Chapter Objectives   581
     Chapter Outline   583
     Key Terms   584
     Introduction   585
     Soil: What Is It?   587
     Soil Basics   589
     Soil Pollution   592
     Industrial Practices and Soil Contamination   598
     Soil Pollution Control Technology   602
     Risk Assessment   610
     Exposure Pathways   611
     Remediation of UST-Contaminated Soils   611
     Chapter Summary   622
     Discussion Questions and Problems   623
     Suggested Research Topics and Projects   623
     References and Recommended Reading   624

PART V: SOLID AND HAZARDOUS WASTES   627

18   Solid/Hazardous Wastes and Control   629
     Chapter Objectives   629
     Chapter Outline   630
     Key Terms   631
     Introduction   632
     Solid Waste Regulatory History (United States)   632
     Solid Waste Characteristics   634
     Sources of Municipal Solid Wastes (MSW)   637
     America: A Throwaway Society   639
     What Is a Hazardous Substance? A Hazardous Waste?   639
     Again, What Is a Hazardous Substance?   642
     What Is Hazardous Waste?   643
     Where Do Hazardous Wastes Come From?   645
     Why Are We Concerned about Hazardous Wastes?   645
     Hazardous Waste Legislation   646

Waste Control Technology   648
Waste Minimization   648
Recycling   650
Treatment Technologies   650
Ultimate Disposal   654
Chapter Summary   658
Discussion Questions and Problems   659
Suggested Research Topics and Projects   659
References and Recommended Reading   661

Glossary   663

Index   699

About the Authors   709

Figures

1.1   Components of environmental science.   7
1.2   Classic representation of the scientific method.   10
1.3   The scientific method simplified.   10
1.4   Devil's Tower, Wyoming. Photo courtesy of Frank Spellman   19
1.5   Two young women climbing the columnar sides of Devil's Tower,
        Wyoming. Photo courtesy of Frank Spellman   19
1.6   Major components of a freshwater pond ecosystem. Adapted from
        Spellman, 1996   25

2.1   The carbon cycle.   49
2.2   The nitrogen cycle.   51
2.3   The phosphorus cycle.   52
2.4   The sulfur cycle.   53
2.5   Any system requires inputs of energy and matter from the
        environment. These resources flowing through the economy
        are converted to low-quality heat energy, wastes, and pollutants.   55
2.6   Illustration for example 2.1   56
2.7   Materials balance diagram.   57
2.8   Flow of energy to and from the Earth.   59
2.9   Aquatic food chain.   61
2.10   Energy-flow pyramid. Adapted from Odum, 1971, 80   63
2.11   Diurnal oxygen curve for an aquatic ecosystem.   65
2.12   Population ecology relative to other ecological disciplines.
        Adapted from Alexi Sharov, Department of Entomology,
        Virginia Tech, Virginia, 1966, 1   68
2.13   Basic patterns of distribution. Adapted from Odum, 1971, 205   74
2.14a   Black bear in Sequoia National Park, California. Photo courtesy
        of Frank Spellman   76
2.14b   Black bear in Sequoia National Park, California. Photo courtesy
        of Frank Spellman   76
2.15   J-shaped growth curve.   77

2.16	S-shaped (sigmoidal) growth curve.	78
2.17	Length.	85
3.1	The element sodium as it is commonly shown in one of the horizontal boxes in the periodic table.	100
3.2	Carbon atoms sharing their electrons with the electrons of other nonmetallic atoms such as hydrogen, chlorine, and oxygen. The compounds that result from such electron sharing are methane, carbon tetrachloride, and carbon monoxide, respectively.	112
3.3	Two carbon atoms may share their own electrons in any of the three ways noted. When these carbon atoms further bond to hydrogen atoms, the resulting compounds are ethane, ethene, and acetylene, respectively.	112
3.4	Structure of benzene.	113
3.5	Water strider. Adapted from *Standard Methods*, 15th ed. Copyright © 1981 by the American Public Health Association, the American Water Works Association, and the Water Pollution Control Federation	127
3.6	The numbers are representative values of the concentration of DDT and its derivatives in tissues (in parts per million, ppm).	135
4.1	Basic features of a cell.	183
4.2	Bacterial shapes and arrangements.	194
4.3	Bacterial cell.	194
4.4	Autotrophic and heterotrophic organism in relation to their means of obtaining energy.	198
4.5	Virus shapes	201
4.6	Nomenclature of fungi. Adapted from McKinney, 1962, 36	203
4.7	Asexual life of penicillum sp. Adapted from Wistreich and Lechtman, 1980, 163	205
4.8	Amoebae and other protozoa.	214
4.9	Philodina, a common rotifer.	218
4.10	Holoenzymes showing apoenzymes and various types of cofactor. Adapted from Witkowski and Power, 1975, 7	221
4.11	Enzyme function showing the interaction of the substrate and enzyme with the resulting product. Adapted from Prescott et al., 1993, 141	222
4.12	The effect of substrate concentration: the dependence of velocity on substrate concentration for a simple one-substrate enzyme-catalyzed reaction. This substrate curve fits the Michaelis equation, which relates reaction velocity (v) to the substrate concentration (S).	224
4.13	A simplified view of cell metabolism. Adapted from Brock & Madigan, 1991	226
4.14	Aerobic respiration: the process by which a compound is oxidized using oxygen as an external electron acceptor.	229
4.15	Summary of the overall reaction of the Krebs cycle.	230

4.16   The formation of ATP, a substance that fuels all living organisms. By
        means of phosphorylation, energy-rich bonds (* * *) are formed and
        used to combine ADP and Pi into ATP, which is used to fuel the life
        processes. Then Pi and ADP are used again in a continuous cycle.
        Adapted from Wistreich and Lechtman, 1980, 273   231
4.17   Bacterial growth curve. The four phases of the growth curve are
        identified on the curve and discussed in the text. Adapted from
        McKinney, 1962, 118   234
4.18   Effect of temperature on growth rate and the enzymic-reaction
        activity that occurs as the temperature increases.   236
4.19   Potable water collector in Amazonia, Ecuadorian jungle. Photo by
        Frank R. Spellman   249

5.1   Dose–response curve for a typical chemical.   264
5.2   Variation of dose–response curve for the same chemical in
        two different species.   265

6.1   Typical volume concentration of a loam surface soil. The curved
        line between water and air indicates that the proportion of these
        two components fluctuates as soil becomes wetter or drier.   283
6.2   Water cycle. Adapted from Spellman, 1999   292

8.1   Wind turbine farm in cornfield in Indiana. Photo by
        Frank R. Spellman   344

9.1   Gaseous components of air.   373
9.2   The Earth's atmosphere and incoming solar radiation.   375
9.3   Insolation distribution.   377
9.4   Isobars drawn though locations having equal atmospheric pressures.
        The air motion, or wind direction, is at right angles to the isobars and
        movers from a region of high pressure to a region of low pressure.   378
9.5   Thermal circulation of air. Localized heating, which causes air in the
        region to rise, initiates the circulation. As the warm air rises and cools,
        cool air near the surface moves horizontally into the region vacated by
        the rising air. The upper, still cooler, air then descends to occupy the
        region vacated by the cool air.   382

10.1   Global wind directions in the Northern Hemisphere.   407
10.2   Normal conditions: (A) Air at Earth's surface is heated by the sun and
        rises to mix with the cooler air above it. In thermal inversion (B), a layer
        of warm air forms a lid above the Earth, and the cooler air at the surface
        is unable to mix with the warm air above. Pollutants are trapped.   408

11.1   Annual emissions of SO_2 and NO_x in the United States, 1940–1987.
        From U.S. EPA, 1989   416

11.2   Trends in carbon monoxide emissions, 1940–1986. Adapted from
        U.S. EPA, 1988b   417
11.3   Average concentration of various air pollutants in the atmosphere of
        Los Angeles during days of eye irritation. Adapted from Haagen-Smit
        & Wayne, 1976, 235–88   419

13.1   Greenhouse effect.   454
13.2   Measuring activity: pH scale. Adapted from USGS, 1987   457
13.3   Acid rain cycle.   458
13.4   Profile of acid rain deposition in the United States. USGS, 1987   459

15.1   An example of a lotic water systems.   510
15.2   (A) Vertical section of pond showing major zones. (B) View looking
        down on concentric zones that make up the littoral zone.   513
15.3   A Secchi disk, used to measure turbidity or water clarity. The disk
        is lowered into the water until it can no longer be seen from the surface.
        The depth of visual disappearance becomes the Secchi Disk Transparency
        Extinction Coefficient, which will range from a few centimeters in very
        turbid waters to 35 m in a very clear lake.   516
15.4   Thermal stratification of a temperate lake.   519
15.5   Waterfall in a river system, aiding re-aeration of water. Dawn Mist
        Falls, Belly River, Glacier National Park. Photo by F. R. Spellman   533
15.6   (A) Changes that occur in a river after it receives excessive amounts
        of raw sewage. (B) Effects of waste on DO. Adapted from Enger et al.,
        1989, 411   533
15.7   An unconfined aquifer with its saturated and unsaturated zones.
        To remove water from the water table, a well would have to penetrate
        the saturated zone.   536

16.1   Origins and fate of PPCPs in the environment. From U.S. EPA,
        http://epa.gov/nerlesd1/chemistry/pharma/.   545
16.2   Common activities that can lead to groundwater contamination:
        leaky underground storage tank; surface pits, ponds, or lagoons;
        and mining tailings contributing to acid mine discharge.   559

17.1   Soil profiles on residual and transported parent materials.   591

18.1   Composition of municipal solid waste discarded in a typical day
        by each American. From U.S. EPA, 2009a, 2009b   635
18.2   Cross-section of a surface liquid waste impoundment.   655
18.3   Cross-section of a secure landfill double liner system.   657

Preface

The goal of *Environmental Science: Principles and Practices* is to provide general students and anyone outside of a formal classroom setting with the scientific principles, concepts, applications, and methodologies required to understand the interrelationships of the natural world; to identify and analyze environmental problems, both natural and human-made; to evaluate the relative risks associated with these problems; and to examine alternative solutions, such as renewable energy sources, for resolving and/or preventing them. Moreover, this text is intended to introduce the science related to all of the environmental mediums—air, water, soil, and biota—to the undergraduate student in environmental science and related disciplines. The text includes recent improvements in our understanding of fundamental phenomena and applications of new technologies and materials, including preparation for current advanced placement (AP) environmental science exams, which help you earn college credit and advanced placement, and/or to stand out in the college admission process.

Environmental science is interdisciplinary; it embraces a wide variety of topics from different areas of study. Yet, there are several major unifying themes that cut across the many topics included in the study of environmental science. The following themes provide a foundation for the structure of this text:

- Environmental science is a process and method of learning more about the natural world.
- Energy conversions underlie all ecological processes.
- Earth's environment is one interconnected system.
- Humans alter natural systems.
- Understanding the role of culture and social and economic factors is vital to the development of solutions.
- Human survival depends on stewardship and sustainability.

Moreover, the major overriding theme professed by the authors of this text is the inherent right of nature. In light of this, this text, in its presentation of those practices by humans that are harmful to the environment, does not gloss over these facts, but rather presents them clearly, without smoke and mirrors, and without kid gloves;

unlike many other environmental science texts that are currently available, we pull no punches in presenting our take on current and future problems facing our environment. Why? It's simple. Without a healthy environment, everything else is microminiature or nonexistent.

To the Instructor

As mentioned, the study of environmental science is interdisciplinary. It includes aspects of basic Earth science, ecology, biology, geology, engineering, and chemistry, among others. Environmental science is also interwoven with technology. This interconnection, often overlooked, is critically important, because without making the connections apparent to students of environmental science, students lose sight of the usefulness—the utility—of environmental science. In short, a gap has formed between environmental science and environmental technology—and this gap impacts the environment.

Do we need to fill this gap? Yes. Many traditional undergraduate texts on environmental science fail in (or avoid) discussing and developing the natural interconnection between environmental science and technology. Consider this: The underlying principles governing the function of the physical and biological systems (basic concepts) that make up the environment do not change. A student's grounding in basic concepts can be provided by any good text currently available in the field. Since environmental science is a dynamic discipline, ever changing, students must be well-grounded in the basic concepts to adjust to these changes. But most environmental science texts fail in their most important mission. They do not deliver to the student the reasons that the subject should matter to him or her. What good is environmental science? Students learn much of the same information by studying basic Earth science, ecology, biology, geology, hydrology, or other related subject areas.

Remember this: Students today aren't the same as the ones we taught 10 or 15 years ago. Today's students want to *see* the usefulness of the material they study. They drag their feet at learning for the sake of learning. They don't want to hear, "Learn it— you'll see how it helps you later, maybe." They have a touchstone question: *How will learning this subject matter help me in the future?* This text clearly answers this question.

Undergraduate students in environmental science naturally develop a curiosity for some of the areas included in the curriculum—because these areas have a direct impact on their lives and livelihoods. This text expands upon this natural desire to find out what's going on —and why—with the air, water, soil, and biota we depend on for our existence. While *Environmental Science: Principles and Practices* discusses these four environmental media in detail, it also fills the gap that stands between environmental science and humankind's technological impact, with clear explanations and illustrations of the interconnection between the basics (principles) and actual use (practices).

To the Student and the Rest of Us

You have undoubtedly heard about, read about, or witnessed the horrific impact that technology, used to produce the "good life," has had on the environment. You may have observed or heard about rivers so oil-laden that they actually burned. Or perhaps you've observed, heard, or read about skies above metropolitan areas that were red with soot. Some of you may have breathed air you could actually see. You may have walked alongside lakes choked with algae or lakes so poisoned that they could no longer support life (but might still be a source of drinking water). Or you may have seen the flip side of this coin—a place so pristine, so unlittered, so filled with abounding life—that you recognize it as special, as different, as a priceless treasure.

You may have seen Earth-moving machines enter what appeared to be pristine wilderness areas to gouge out huge, gaping masses from the face of the Earth to remove the soil to a segregated holding area, because the soil was contaminated, polluted by hazardous materials, and dumped there by environmental criminals. These criminals, by wont of their greed, their unconcern, and their thoughtlessness, have committed an ultimate crime: They have poisoned us all by poisoning what we all must have to live. They have fouled our Earth.

You are certainly aware of such travesties, such total disregard for the source of our being, for the basis of our very survival. And in the past, as well as in the present (we hope not in the future), we have directed the blame toward a consistent culprit: people using (without complete knowledge of the consequences), misusing, or abusing technology and technological advances.

In *Environmental Science: Principles and Practices*, we examine the many environmental problems that beset us, the dimensions of those problems, and their varied and interrelated causes. We discuss in detail the three environmental media that we are wholly dependent upon: air, water, and soil. The text examines data on the ecological relationships of endangered species (are we one of them?); the impact of toxic materials on air, water, and soil (and ultimately on human health); the dispersal of pollutants in the atmosphere, bodies of water, and soil; the accumulation of persistent chemicals in aquatic food webs; and the control of agricultural pests with pesticides. We study acid rain and the management of hazardous wastes and also look at wastewater treatment plants that have significantly lessened the impact of some water pollutants. The groundwater problem and the ozone depletion problem are also examined. We look at advancements made in reusing and recycling contaminated soils. All of these many problems can, will, and do affect us all—and they are all related to the environment.

Are you wondering, "So what else is new? We've heard all this before." You have seen, heard, read about, and studied these topics. But consider this: A fundamental knowledge of environmental science is a prerequisite to meeting the environmental and natural resource challenges that will face us all in the 21st century. Granted, this is an old concept, but we must go beyond concepts to the connections those concepts can lead us to make—a realistic view, clearly presented, that shows the environmental effects of human activity (primarily technological advances), which, when constructively directed, can have a beneficial impact on the Earth.

This text analyzes environmental problems related to air, water, and soil as objectively as possible. We leave you to form your own opinion on many of the controversial issues, which means you're going to have to think about them—a worthy goal for any learning activity. In short, the primary message in this text is that while we have environmental problems and challenges, the news is not all bad. Remember that every problem has a solution. This solution is critically important.

For environmental challenges, the solution is the use of the proper technology to minimize environmental disruption.

Organization and Content

Environmental Science: Principles and Practices is divided into five parts and eighteen chapters and is organized to provide an even and logical flow of concepts. It provides the student with a clear and thoughtful picture of this complex field.

Part I provides the foundation for the underlying theme of this book—the connections between environmental science and technological innovation. We augment the philosophical with more practical aspects, which include a presentation of fundamentals: energy, materials balance, and units of measurement. We present our materials simply, in a down-to-Earth, user-friendly format. Concepts of environmental chemistry, biology/ecology, toxicology, geology and groundwater hydrology, environmental processes, and technology and engineering are also presented as part of these introductory chapters, all germane to the foundation-building process, and presented in an understandable format.

Part II develops the principles basic to an understanding of air quality. Meteorology, air pollution, atmospheric air dispersion, atmospheric change (the greenhouse effect and global climate change), and air pollution control are discussed in detail.

Part III focuses on water quality and the characteristics of water and water bodies, sciences, pollution, and treatment.

Part IV deals with soil science and emphasizes soil as a natural resource, highlighting the many interactions between soil and other components of the ecosystem.

Part V is devoted to showing how decisions regarding handling solid and hazardous waste have had or can have a profound impact on the environment and air, water, and soil.

Special Features

Environmental Science: Principles and Practices asks readers to examine their worldview before they begin to study environmental issues. Features of the text include the following:

- Chapter objectives
- Key terms
- Discussion questions
- Bibliography for further readings and research
- Current, real-life examples illustrating principles
- Suggested topics for students to pursue in research papers and projects

Part I

THE BASICS

For every complex question there is a simple and wrong solution.

—Albert Einstein

CHAPTER 1

The Environment and Environmental Science

Killing the Wolf

We were eating lunch on a high rimrock, at the foot of which a turbulent river elbowed its way. We saw what we thought was a doe fording the torrent, her breast awash in white water. When she climbed the bank toward us and shook out her tail, we realized our error: It was a wolf. A half-dozen others, evidently grown pups, sprang from the willows and all joined in a welcoming melee of wagging tails and playful maulings. What was literally a pile of wolves writhed and tumbled in the center of an open flat at the foot of our rimrock.

In those days we had never heard of passing up a chance to kill a wolf. In a second we were pumping lead into the pack, but with more excitement than accuracy; how to aim a steep downhill shot is always confusing. When our rifles were empty, the old wolf was down, and a pup was dragging a leg into impassable side-rocks.

We reached the old wolf in time to watch a fierce green fire dying in her eyes. I realized then, and have known ever since, that there was something new to me in those eyes—something known only to her and the mountain. I was young then, and full of trigger-itch; I thought that because few wolves mean more deer, that no wolves would mean hunters' paradise. But after seeing the green fire die, I sensed that neither the wolf nor the mountain agreed with such a view.—Aldo Leopold, 1948

Chapter Objectives

After studying this chapter, you should be able to:

- Identify the concepts basic to the study of environmental science.
- Discuss environmental science's roots, the area of study it involves, and its function within our society.

3

- Define and discuss the advantages and problems inherent in the use of technology in individual environmental circumstances.
- Define and discuss such concepts as maximum sustainable yield, sustainable society, natural capital, Earth's capital, environmental globalization, biological diversity, "grasshopper generation," and voodoo science.
- Gain an understanding of the "good life" in relationship to the environment.
- Gain an understanding of inference and modeling.

Chapter Outline

- Definition and discussion: environmental science and technology
- Definitions: environment and science
- Definitions: key concepts and vocabulary
- Definitions: pure science, applied science, voodoo science, and environmental science
- The scientist's toolbox
- Discussion: societal demands, environmental needs, resources, and technological advantages
- Discussion: technological solutions to environmental problems
- Response scenarios: student response

Key Terms

abiotic
air pollution
atmosphere
biogeochemical cycles
biological diversity
biosphere
biotic
consumers
decomposers
desertification
Earth's natural capital
ecology
ecosystem
environment
environmental degradation
environmental science
geosphere
"grasshopper generation"
habitat
hydrosphere
Laws of Thermodynamics
lithosphere

maximum sustainable yield
niche
nonpoint-source pollution
nonrenewable resources
overgrazing
perpetual resources
point-source pollution
pollute
producers
recycling
renewable resources
resource
reuse
science
scientific method
stewardship
sustainable societies
thermal pollution
tragedy of the commons
voodoo science
water pollution

Introduction

Leopold's account of killing wolves, and, by extension, the entire species, has a profound impact on our surroundings, our environment, and our river of life; we—as representatives of but a few of the organisms who depend on the river for life, and for survival—are tied to it, the component and portion of the environment that we influence and are influenced by. The point is that what we do to one part of our environment has a profound effect on another part of the environment. The killing off of wolves, a natural predator, affects the balance of nature. Leopold makes this point clear in his later statement, which reads as follows: "I have watched the face of many a newly wolfless mountain, and seen the south-facing slopes wrinkle with a maze of new deer trails. I have seen every edible bush and seedling browsed, first to anaemic desuetude, and then to death" (Leopold, 1948, 132).

This text examines four specific areas: air, water, soil, and biota. However, our principal focus is on the first three—because without air, water, or soil, no biota can exist. Without them, the planet would be a sterile hunk of orbiting rock. Without air, water, and soil, nothing is left that we can—or could—relate to.

Along with the standard focus on air, water, soil, and biota, many environmental science texts leave out a crucial element related to all of them—one that impacts all of them: technology. This should come as no surprise to anyone concerned about the environment and environmental issues, especially since technology and the use of technology is usually blamed for the degradation of the Earth's environment.

We damage the environment through the use, misuse, and abuse of technology. We frequently use technological advances before we fully understand their long-term effects on the environment. We weigh the advantages a technological advance can give us against the environment and discount the importance of the environment, through greed, hubris, or simply a lack of knowledge of what that new technology will do to our surroundings. We often only examine short-term plans, without fully developing how problems may be handled years later. We assume that when the situation becomes critical, technology will be there to fix it and scientists will be able to figure it out; we believe and, in turn, ignore the immediate consequences of our technological abuse.

Consider this: While technological advances have provided us with nuclear power, the light bulb and its energy source, plastics, the internal combustion engine, air conditioning and refrigeration, genetic engineering, stem cell treatment, DNA analysis, artificial intelligence, machine vision, computers, LEDs (light emitting diodes), digital cameras, iPods, cell phones, BlackBerry phones, GPS devices, flat screen TVs, and scores of other advances that make our modern lives more pleasant and comfortable, many of these advances, especially when not properly used and/or disposed of (e.g., nuclear waste), have affected the Earth's environment in ways we did not expect, in ways we deplore, and in ways we may not be able to live with. Note, however, that technology is also a double-edged sword. On one side it can do great damage to the environment, but, on the other edge, it can remediate or prevent environmental damage; therefore, in this text, the argument is made that the same technology that can destroy the environment can also be used to mitigate the consequences of technological misuse.

In this chapter, we set out on a journey that begins with the basics, the building blocks that enable us to pursue and understand difficult concepts. We develop clearer perceptions about ideas that some people view as controversial concerns (although almost everyone will agree that our environment is not as pristine and unspoiled as we want—and expect it to be) that impact us all. Most importantly, we offer insights that will enable you, the reader, to make up your mind on what needs to be done, on what needs to be undone, and on what mankind's focus should be on maintaining life as we know it, as we want it, as we deserve it. Have a smooth and enlightening journey.

What Is Environmental Science?

To precisely define **environmental science** as an interdisciplinary study of how the Earth works, how we are affecting the Earth's life-support systems (environment), and how to deal with the environmental problems we face, we must first break down the phrase and look at both terms separately. When we say the "environment," what exactly do we mean? Think about it. The word *environment* can mean many different things to many different people. For example, some may view "environment" as the office environment, creative environment, learning environment, corporate environment, virtual environment, aquatic environment, tropical environment, social environment, conservation environment, or, in this digital age, the desktop environment, integrated development environment, or runtime environment, and so forth. Obviously, when we use the term *environment*, we need to be more specific.

In this text, we are specific, actually more specific, by defining the **environment** as the natural environment, which includes all living and nonliving (e.g., air, soil, and water) things that influence organisms. Unlike the term *environment*, the word **science** is rather straightforward in meaning. Simply, "science" is the observation, identification, description, experimental investigation, and theoretical explanation of natural phenomena. When we combine the two, we are left with a complex interdisciplinary study that must be defined both narrowly and broadly—and then combined—to allow us an accurate definition.

The narrow definition of *environmental science* is the study of the human impact on the physical and biological environment of an organism. In this sense, environmental scientists are interested in determining the effects of pesticides on croplands, in learning how acid rain affects vegetation, or determining the impact of introducing an exotic species of game fish into a pond or lake, and so on.

Beginning in the early 1960s, environmental science became an active field of scientific investigation driven by both events and needs. The events that spurred environmental awareness include the publication of Rachel Carson's flagship environmental book, *Silent Spring* (1962), along with major environmental issues becoming very public, such as the Cuyahoga River in Cleveland, Ohio, catching fire in 1969. The pressing need to educate personnel in proper environmental **stewardship** (i.e., justice and equity) practices related to the environment and the proper protocols to employ to mitigate environmental disasters drove the discipline of environmental science to evolve out of the studies of natural science, biology, ecology, conservation, and geography. Moreover, increasing awareness of the interdependence that exists among all the disparate elements that make up our environment led to the field of study that contains aspects of all of those elements. Biological and physical ideas were combined with ideas from the social sciences—sociology, economics, and political science—into a new, interdisciplinary field: environmental science (see Figure 1.1).

Did You Know?

The terms *environmental science* and *ecology* are often used interchangeably, but technically ecology refers only to the study of organisms and their interactions with each other and their environment. Ecology could be considered a subset of environmental science. In practice, there is considerable overlap between the work of ecologists and other environmental scientists.

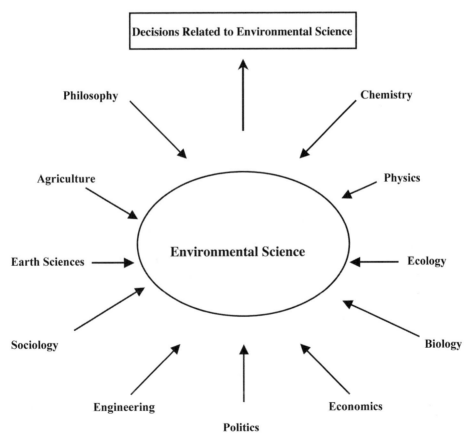

Figure 1.1.   Components of Environmental Science.

Many environmental scientists have widely varying, diverse backgrounds. A well-trained environmentalist is a generalist, trained as a biologist, ecologist (formerly known as a natural scientist), geologist, and environmental engineer, and in many other related areas. While environmental scientists are generalists (i.e., they have a broad view based on knowledge gained from several subject areas, including the arts), and while they may have concentrated their study on a particular specialty, solidly trained environmental scientists have one thing in common: They are well-grounded in several different branches of science.

Did You Know?

The National Center for Education Statistics (2011) defines an academic program in environmental science as a program that focuses on the application of biological, chemical, and physical principles to the study of the physical environment and the solution of environmental problems, including subjects such as abating or controlling environmental pollution and degradation, the interaction between human society and the natural environment, and natural resources management. It includes instruction in biology, chemistry, physics, geosciences, climatology, statistics, and mathematical modeling.

In its broadest sense, environmental science also encompasses the social and cultural aspects of the environment. As a mixture of several traditional sciences, political awareness, and societal values, environmental science demands examination of more than the concrete physical aspects of the world around us—and many of those political, societal, and cultural aspects are far more slippery than what we can prove as scientific fact.

Did You Know?

In the early 1980s, the California Waste Management Board was concerned about siting municipal landfills. It contracted with a consulting firm to help it determine how to successfully site landfills. The consultant's report suggested siting landfills in minority neighborhoods, because these individuals were less apt to know how to stop the building of such facilities in their neighborhoods.

In short, we can accurately say that environmental science is a pure science, because it includes study of all the mechanisms of environmental processes: the study of the air, water, and soil. But it is also an applied science, because it examines problems with the goal of contributing to their solution: the study of the effects of technology thereon. As mentioned, to solve environmental problems and understand the issues, environmental scientists need a broad base of information from which to draw.

The environment in which we live has been irreversibly affected by advancements in technology, and it has been affected for as long as humans have wielded tools to alter their circumstances. We will continue to alter our environment to suit ourselves as long as we remain a viable species, but to do so wisely, we need to closely examine what we do and how we do it. We need to build a bridge between science and technology, with science on the one side, and technology on the other.

Why is environmental science necessary? We can all see the signs of decay around us. The air we breathe is filthy, the water we drink has a foul odor and taste, and the landfill (not in my backyard!—NIMBY) is overflowing, but why do we need science to tell us that? We need environmental science (and science in general) first for quantitative analysis. We use science to obtain basic information of existing conditions of air, water, and soil. We need to know what causes the problem and to define its severity. We also need science to show us the hidden problems—the ones we can't see: the lake that appears normal on the surface, but is, in fact, sterile from acid rain (and yet may remain a source of drinking water). We rely on scientific measurements and computer models to help us define, understand, and affect change on these problems. The environmental challenges we face today are often less visible to the unaware and more global in scope—and have longer response times. We can solve these problems only through scientific methods.

We use technology to address environmental problems of air and water quality, soil contamination, and solid and hazardous waste—the technology to clean up the environment. Technology? Didn't we say that technology has caused our present environmental problems in the first place? Why do we want to make a bad situation worse by throwing more technology at it?

For better or worse, technology has changed our environment. And while technology has contributed to our environmental problems, remember that the human element must bear the brunt of the blame. People must use technology to repair the damage as well. For example, water and wastewater treatment technologies have made enormous strides in the task of purifying the water we drink (water treatment technology) and treating the water we waste (wastewater treatment technology). Whether we agree or disagree with the advantages or disadvantages of technology, to sustain life on our planet, we must learn that the marriage between environmental science and technology is not only compatible, it is also critically important. In short, we can't simply mitigate the anthropogenic effects on the natural environment without using technology. What are the issues environmental scientists use technology and technological advances to mitigate? The following is a short list:

- anoxic waters
- climate change
- energy
- environmental degradation
- environmental health
- genetic engineering
- land degradation
- nanotechnology
- nuclear issues
- overpopulation
- ozone depletion
- pollution
- resource depletion

Key Terms and Introductory Principles

To understand the basic concepts of environmental science, we need to learn the core vocabulary. The following are some of the key terms used in this chapter. Environmental scientists gather information and draw conclusions about the workings of the environment by applying the scientific method.[1] The *scientific method* (the scientist's toolbox) is an orderly method—a set of techniques (we call them tools)—generally used in scientific research to investigate natural phenomena. The method consists of identifying the problem, gathering data, formulating hypotheses, performing experiments, interpreting results, and reaching a conclusion. Generally speaking, the scientific method is often used to define science. We have no problem with this approach, provided that, when illustrating or describing the scientific method to the uninitiated, we point out and make clear that the methodology won't necessarily fit perfectly into any round or square hole; it is not a perfect cookie cutter mold (Trefil, 2008). This makes sense when you consider our earlier definition of science, where we pointed out that it is an investigation into the natural world and the knowledge gained through the process; science is not a collection of facts or a fact-finding methodology. The scientific method is classically portrayed as the steps shown in Figure 1.2 and linearly portrayed in Figure 1.3 (Carpi & Egger, 2009).

Observation → Question → Hypothesis → Experiment → Data Collection → Conclusion
Figure 1.2.   Classic representation of the scientific method.

The problem with the classical scientific method exemplified in Figure 1.2 is that the reader may assume that this representation, because of its linearity, is written in stone and therefore is to be followed step by step. In the real world, however, this is not the case. Science is not a linear process, because it does not have to start with an observation or a question. Moreover, science often does not include experiments. Science is more fluid and dynamic (never static), and it evolves around input obtained from the natural world, from studying the work of others, from interfacing with colleagues, or from experience (Capri & Egger, 2009). Thus, Figure 1.3, the simplified scientific method, is probably a more practical methodology, one that is constantly being reevaluated and adjusted as per requirement(s).

Make observations and gather data

Figure 1.3.   The Scientific Method simplified. This process is reevaluated on an ongoing basis.

Hypothesize an explanation

Test hypothesis

Sound Science versus Voodoo (Junk) Science[2]

> He had a natural appetite for the wonders of the universe. He wanted to know about science. It's just that all the science had gotten filtered out before it reached him. Our cultural motifs, our educational system, our communications media had failed this man. What the society allowed to trickle through was mainly pretense and confusion. It had never taught him how to distinguish real science from the cheap imitation. He knew nothing about how science works.
>
> —Carl Sagan, *The Demon-Haunted World* (1996)

The difference between real or sound science and voodoo or junk science can be summed up quite succinctly. Sound science is peer-reviewed findings that are verified as true. On the other hand, voodoo science involves the presentation of shaky data, with selective presentation results that are politically motivated distortions of scientifically sound papers or findings attributed to false information by or to a respected researcher or research organization.

Response Scenario 1.1
Snake Oil by Any Other Name Is . . .

The applause, hoots, and shouts were thunderous and continuous while camera bulbs popped and television cameras rolled. The presenter stood tall on the stage, dignified in demeanor and appearance, taking in the adoration he told himself he so richly deserved. The ever-present smile with perfectly implanted white teeth shone through like the perfect spotlight drenching his perfect presence in halolike light. Of course, the halolike appearance was accentuated by his $3,000.00 snow-white suit, with matching shirt and tie, and the coiffed snowy hair that, in volume and density, certainly matched that of disgraced former Illinois governor Ron Blagojevich (Blago). It was a hairstyle psychologists might characterize as a sign of narcissistic personality disorder (and in the presenter's case, they'd be absolutely correct). On the left lapel of that flawless suit rested the perfectly white flower, of course. Ah, and we must not forget the ubiquitous pink ribbon, signifying his absolute support for the fight against breast cancer. The presenter had a soft spot for women—all women.

He scanned the audience of 3,655 souls (or as P. T. Barnum might comment, 3,655 suckers—the presenter preferred to call them his "guppies"). Quick of mind, the presenter was just as quick in calculating 3,655 attendees times the $15 entrance fee ($54,825). Not quite what he was really worth, he told himself, but a good start to what would be a very profitable evening. As the frigid green eyes in his handsome, smiling, charismatic face swept the audience in front of him, it was the women that held his momentary interest. He made a mental note of which of those beauties he would seduce later.

(continued)

Response Scenario 1.1 (*continued*)

"Standing room only tonight," the presenter told himself. "Heck, why not . . . they are here because of the promise . . . the promise and hope that we all have . . . and when offered, none will be able to turn it down or turn away. Thank you Lord, for making so many gullible guppies for me to fleece! Amen."

The applause seemed interminable. Finally, after at least a minute of steady clapping, hooting, hollering, yelling, and gleeful laughing, the greedy middle-aged presenter motioned them back in their seats and convinced them to settle in and hear what he had to say.

Before he began his standard presentation, a large, round, happy face flashed onto the oversized movie screen behind him. He looked around the over-crowded auditorium and stood smiling, taking it all in. He was sure this momentary pause mesmerized the audience, increasing their sharp excitement. He spoke into the microphone he held in his right hand while pointing to the audience with the foot-long gold-clad scepter in his left hand (a scepter he personally designed and adorned with a miniature golden crown at one end). Those first words and that Darth Vaderlike deep, penetrating voice brought them to total silence, full attention, and made many a heart quiver.

The presenter had the gift, the golden voice that no one could ignore, a charismatic presence that you had to experience to believe. The combination of his appearance, his manner, and that voice reached out and grabbed you, whether you wanted it to or not, harnessing your full, undivided attention.

Of course, his message wasn't exactly boring, either. When someone so plausible, so golden, so utterly believable offers someone, anyone, everyone, eternal life, how would you expect them to react?

He always began by shouting out the same question.

"Are you happy to be here?"

It was followed by maximum applause and a resounding, "Yes, we are!"

"Are you excited about the possibility of living your life disease free?"

Again, "Yes, we are!"

"Can anyone think of anything more terrible, more evil, more despicable than illness, disease, disability, or autism causing suffering for a helpless, aging adult or an innocent child?"

In unison they answered, "No, we can't!"

Knowing that he was winding them to the level of frenzy that he wanted (the maximum level of donation), he went on, saying, "Can anyone think of why any of us should have to suffer through life with illnesses, disease, disabilities, or aging?"

"No," they chorused.

"Then let's stop death in its tracks! Let's throw all those wrinkles to the wind! Or better yet, give all the wrinkles and dying to child molesters and women beaters and animal haters . . . let those evildoers shrivel up and feed the worms!"

He paused again, lifting his head earnestly to the rafters. "Thank God for science and scientists!" Then he directed that powerful, penetrating gaze back to the crowd hanging on his every word and continued. "My research team is just a few months away . . . they tell me the Ray will not only cure whatever ails you . . . including diabetes (audience roars in approval), kidney stones (still roaring), autism (roar getting louder), Alzheimer's . . . I've been told rayology will cure every disease known to man! . . . Moreover, rayology is a fountain of youth and will take us all back to our mid-20s . . . ah, physically that is."

Now the approving roar was so loud the rafters in the ancient auditorium were starting to rattle.

Finally, in his best Elmer Gantry manner, he shouted "Do you B-E-L-I-E-V-E?"

It's a good thing the fire marshall and building codes people weren't around; the auditorium was rocking under the foot stomping and the resounding "Yes!"

"Now here is the plan. We will rent the Alamo Dome, place the Ray machine on the main floor, and allow as many of the faithful to get a dose of the Ray . . . and then all their problems will be over."

The roar was deafening.

When it quieted down a bit (below 85 decibels), the presenter continued, saying, "Look, people, we are going to do all this two months from today . . . but we need your help to make it happen. This kind of progress doesn't come without a price. My science team is on the brink of success. Don't let the lack of a few dollars hold us back! And when you make a donation, and please, we need your donations to make this happen . . . please leave your phone number so we can let you know the time and the exact date of your rejuvenation."

And with that, the presenter stepped out of that halolike spotlight and down to the front of the stage. With his face in full smile mode, he performed the necessary, but distasteful, contact with the populace, and he walked out of the auditorium through the crowded house, shaking every hand, his arm around every offered shoulder, with the sound of *cha ching* ringing in his head.

RESPONSE

This sidebar, case study, vignette, or whatever you wish to call it has been a favorite of our college 300-level science students from day one. We usually present this short account to the students early in our introductory courses. We have found that not only do the students like to ponder this story, but they also enjoy commenting on it both in written analysis and oral discussions. We have found their analyses penetrating, scathing, and humorous.

(a) The jury is still out on definitively defining what the previous story is really about. Respond to each of the following:
  (i) Some say that it is a classic portrayal of the conflict between religion and science.
  (ii) Others find that religion is used to sell science and vice versa.
  (iii) Some argue that this is an example of voodoo science at its best.

Scientists' Toolbox: Additional Tools

We previously stated that, in our opinion, the scientific method is the scientists' toolbox. So, the obvious question is, What is in the toolbox? Not only are the standard tools diagrammed in Figure 1.2 included (observations, questions, hypotheses, experiments, data collection, and conclusions), but also several others. These additional tools include facts, deductive inferences, inductive inferences, statistical inferences, hypotheses, multiple working hypotheses, theories, evidence, Ockham's Razor, natural law, paradigm, serendipity, luck, the unknown, the unanticipated, and the unexpected. Wow! Sounds like a heavy toolbox, doesn't it? While it is heavy, skill gained through experience lightens the load and makes lifting it easier. Let's take a closer look at these tools and see how they are applied by the scientist in the performance of his or her endeavors.

FACTS

A fact is a truth known by actual experience or observation. The luster of gold, the electrical conductivity of copper, the number of bones in the human spine, the existence of fossil dinosaurs, and the like are all facts. Is it a fact that an atom consists of protons, neutrons, and electrons? Is it a fact that Leonardo da Vinci painted the *Mona Lisa*? Is it a fact that the sun will set tomorrow? None of us has observed any of these things. The first is an inference from a variety of different observations. The second is reported by those who lived close enough in time and space to the event that we trust their account. And the third is an inductive inference after repeated observations.

DEDUCTIVE INFERENCES

A deductive inference is a process by which a conclusion is logically inferred from certain premises. This is an important tool in the scientific method toolbox, because it is often more accurate than the six major tools of the scientific method alone; it allows for mistakes to be quickly detected and corrected. The great mathematician Euclid developed many mathematical proofs with mistakes in them that have been detected and corrected, but the theorems of Euclid—all of them—have stood the test of time for more than 2,000 years (Euclid, 1956). Inferences are valid or invalid—never both!

Greek philosophers defined a number of three-part inferences, or syllogisms, that can be used as building blocks for more complex reasoning. Many readers may be familiar with the examples given below. You may have seen syllogisms on college entrance examinations. We begin with the most famous of them all.

Syllogism 1
All men are mortal.
Socrates is a man.
Therefore Socrates is mortal.

For an argument to be valid, it must be impossible for both its premises to be true and its conclusion to be false (a fallacy). An argument can be valid even though the premises are false. Note, for example, that the conclusion of the following argument would have to be true if the premises were true (even though they are, in fact, false).

Syllogism 2
Everyone who eats lobster is from Maine.
Alice eats lobster.
Therefore, Alice is from Maine.

The argument is not sound. For a deductive argument to be sound, it must not only be valid, the premises must be true as well.

INDUCTIVE INFERENCES

An inductive inference is a conclusion based on (i.e., inferred from) multiple observations. Shoot a particular kind of artillery shell at a particular target at a particular barrel elevation numerous (n) times, and you can, by induction from those examples, make an inference and a prediction about what will happen the next time you fire the artillery piece. However, your prediction is not a fact, in that you won't know by actual observation the result of the $n+1$ drop until it has happened.

STATISTICAL INFERENCES

Statistical inference is the process of drawing conclusions from data that are subject to random variation (Upton & Cook, 2008). An understanding of statistical inference is important to practitioners of environmental science and to discussing the role of sampling in the inferential process. Scientific inference becomes statistical inference when the connection between the unknown "state of nature" and the observed information is expressed in probabilistic terms (Dawid, 1983).

Statistical inference comprises the whole field of statistics, its focus being what is logically implied by the information available (Frazer, 1983). Cramer (1946) summarizes the role of statistical inference as having three functions: description, analysis, and prediction. Description is the reduction of data sets to as small a set of numbers as possible, such as the mean, variance, skewness of a distribution, and so forth. This enables one to describe a population as concisely and as briefly as possible and can allow for comparison between populations. Analysis is the summarization of data for a particular purpose or objective. Examples include the following: What are the estimates of certain population characteristics? Did the sample arise from a given distribution? Given two samples, did they arise from the same population? Statistics provides methods of how to do such analyses. Statistical methods are used to predict and explain phenomena, which is often a challenging task.

Scientific databases can be used by different users in applying different priorities to make their decisions. Ideally, statistical inference would always be based on Bayes' Theorem, which combines prior information with information from surveys or experiments, and would be acceptable to many statisticians if the prior belief is objective. The problem is that prior information is usually subjective, where subjective indicates that the information available varies from person to person. Objective prior information indicates that people would normally agree on it. As an example of subjective prior information, a person working in the forest industry could believe that there is plenty of old growth distributed nicely over the forest habitat for endangered species, whereas an environmental scientist could believe equally strongly that the old growth in the forest is limited and badly distributed. People willing to accept prior subjective information are called Bayesians and rely on Bayes' Theorem for inference.

Non-Bayesians, or frequentists (an alternative name is frequentist statistics, the inference framework in which the well-established methodologies of statistical hypothesis testing and confidence intervals are based), a majority, use classical inference procedures relying only on objective data often based on normality assumptions and large sample theory based on the central limit theorem and related statistical properties. Many believe that Bayesian procedures should be used when immediate logically defensible decisions need to be made and that classical ones should be utilized when building a body of scientific knowledge. A forest manager who has to make decisions about whether to cut old growth and where, for management purposes, may well choose to use all his prior information to construct a (subjective) prior distribution to combine with actual sample data to use Bayes' Theorem to make such decisions. Such decisions can be defended at least on the basis of a systematic approach.

Statistical inference from sample surveys can be either model-based or design-based. In model-based sampling, inference relies on a statistical model to describe how the probability structure of the observed data depends on uncontrollable change variables and, frequently, on other unknown nuisance variables. Such models can be based on a theoretical understanding of the process by which the data were generated, experimental techniques used, or past experience with similar processes. For inference in design-based sampling, reliance is placed on probabilistic sampling. It is currently the most widely accepted approach.

In regard to which single method of inference is best, Smith (1994) states that,

> My view is that there is no single right method of inference. All inferences are the product of man's imagination, and there can be no absolutely correct method of inductive reasoning. Different types of inference are relevant for different problems, and frequently the approach recommended reflects the statistician's background, such as science, industry, social sciences, or government. . . . I now find the case for hard-line randomization inference based on the unconditional distribution to be acceptable. . . . Complete reconciliation is neither possible nor desirable. Vive la difference. (p. 17)

HYPOTHESES

A hypothesis is a proposed explanation for an observable phenomenon. For a hypothesis to be put forward as a scientific hypothesis, the scientific method (the toolbox) requires that one can test it. Two important words in the definition of hypothesis are *observed* and *testable*. If you want to know about something, you need to look at it (if possible) and see how it operates. If you are able to observe the operation of something, will it always operate in this manner? It must be testable; others must observe and test and come to the same conclusion that you did. Otherwise, it did not occur as you assumed it did. After shooting the artillery piece from the same barrel elevation several times, you may think shooting it from a greater barrel elevation will lead to a different response, and you may predict that different response. Your response is a hypothesis, and you can test it by changing the elevation of the barrel and observing the result. At that point you will have conducted an experiment to test your hypothesis.

MULTIPLE WORKING HYPOTHESES

Multiple working hypotheses make up a method of research where one considers not just a single hypothesis, but multiple hypotheses that might explain the phenomenon under study. Each hypothesis is then tested. The development of multiple hypotheses prior to the research lets one avoid the trap of narrow-mindedly focusing on just one hypothesis; however, absence of an alternative explanation is no assurance that the truth has been discovered, for example, your boat is missing from where you docked it.

What happened to the boat?
It sank.
It drifted out to sea.
It was stolen.
Your friend borrowed it.

Everyone loves dinosaurs, so let's use them as an example of multiple working hypotheses.

What happened to the dinosaurs?
They died from an asteroid impact.
They died from disease.
They died as a result of climate change.
They died from volcanic eruptions.
They died because of competition with mammals.

THEORIES

A theory is a coherent set of propositions that explain a class of phenomena supported by extensive factual evidence and that may be used for prediction of future observations. For our artillery piece example, a theory would emerge only after a large number of tests of different kinds of artillery shells at different elevations. The theory would try to explain why assorted varieties of shells strike the target differently (wind effect, aerodynamics, etc.), and it ought to be useful in predicting how different shells would behave if fired at different elevations the same way. Over time, scientists have predicted numerous familiar theories, including the following:

• Darwin's theory of natural selection
• Copernicus's theory of the heliocentric solar system
• Newton's theory of gravity
• Einstein's theory of relativity

In regard to theories, it seems like everyone has one. Because of our tendency to state our opinion on just about everything and anything, we often hear, "That's just a theory." In discussions about evolution, natural selection, predicted sea level rise, global climate change, and global warming, "That's just a theory" is stated even more forcefully—sometimes vehemently. At least, that's our theory.

EVIDENCE

Evidence is one of the principal underpinnings of a theory. It consists of the physical observations and measurements made to understand a phenomenon. Keep in mind that opinions and theories are not evidence.

OCKHAM'S RAZOR

For those familiar with the 1950s classic television show *Dragnet*, Joe Friday's standard saying, "Just the facts, ma'am," is the gist of Ockham's Razor. William of Ockham, an English monk who died in 1349, developed, in regards to theories and hypotheses, the following philosophical statement: "Our explanations of things should minimize unsupported assumptions."

Some have reduced Ockham's Razor to the acronym KISS—keep it simple stupid! Others have interpreted Ockham's Razor as stating that the "simplest explanation is the best explanation." Both of these interpretations are incorrect. The easiest or simplest explanation is not always accurate. Let's say we see a large house standing in the middle of a river. One of our hypotheses for the presence of the house might be that the Abominable Snowperson picked it up off its foundation, carried it to the river, and set it down in the middle of the river. Another hypothesis might be that the river overflowed its banks, flooded the floodplain, floated the house, and set it down in the middle of the river. Ockham's Razor tells us to reject the first and retain the second for further consideration. Because we have no evidence for the Abominable Snowperson, he/she is an unsupported assumption. We do, however, have modern evidence that overflowing rivers can transport large houses.

Another classic example often used to make the same point concerns Devil's Tower in Wyoming (see Figure 1.4). Native American legend (20 tribes have potential cultural affiliation with Devil's Tower) tells that this landform originated when a huge bear's claws scraped away the sides of the mountain when the bear tried to attack an Indian maiden. This is a simple explanation, for sure, but it assumes the existence of a huge bear capable of clawing the sides of a mountain (see Figure 1.5) to carve something like Devil's Tower. We reject the Native American story as nothing more than folklore or myth because the existence of such a bear is an unsupported assumption.

NATURAL LAW

Natural law is based on 19th-century science, which presumed that it could arrive at absolutely true, immutable, and universal statements about nature (natural laws). For example, Newton's studies and conclusions about gravity led to what were considered

Figure 1.4.   Devil's Tower, Wyoming. Photo courtesy of Frank Spellman

Figure 1.5.   Two young women climb the columnar sides of Devil's Tower, Wyoming. Photo courtesy of Frank Spellman

"laws of gravity." However, in the 20th century, Einstein's theory of relativity showed that Newton's findings needed slight corrections. Thus it became apparent that it would be wisest to treat even our most trusted ideas, of which Newton's had been one, as theories rather than absolute laws. It may very well be that another scientist, the likes of Newton and/or Einstein, will come along in the future to prove many of our other most trusted scientific ideas or findings incorrect.

Did You Know?

Albert Einstein said, "Make your theory as simple as possible, but no simpler."

ENVIRONMENTAL MODELS/MODELING[3]

Environmental models/modeling is a representation of structure in an environmental or physical system and/or its properties. Hestenes (2011) points out that scientific models are coherent units of structured knowledge. They are used to organize factual information into coherent wholes, often by the coordinated use of general laws or principles.

Notwithstanding the statement by Box and Draper (1987) that "all models are wrong," models and modeling in the practice of environmental science (and other sciences) are important tools. Box and Draper also ask, "how wrong do [models] have to be to not be useful?" This viewpoint is generally accepted in the statistical world and can be paraphrased as "all models are wrong and some are useful." It is the "useful part" that practitioners of environmental science are concerned with. Note that the actual utility of models is often assessed by the degree of correlation between the variables of interest and covariates, but note that correlation does not prove causation (Kish, 1967).

Also note that anyone who has worked in any scientific field or researched any scientific topic knows that much, if not all, of research revolves around model building, and the potential misuse of models has been greatly facilitated by the ready availability of computers and easy use of regression programs. Ideally, an environmental researcher observes the real world or carefully studies substantive scientific theories. Models are then developed on the basis of the insights accorded, recognizing the fact that, besides the explanatory variables, there are other sources of variation to be considered. Kish (1967) separates all sources of variation into the following four classes:

1. The explanatory or experimental variables that are the objectives of the research in explaining or establishing a relationship between both the dependent (often called the response variables in this context) and the independent (often called the predictor variables in this context) variables
2. Extraneous variables that can be controlled either in sample selection or estimation
3. Extraneous (unmeasured, often unmeasurable) variables that may be confounded with the variables in class 1 above

4. Extraneous, difficult to control, or uncontrollable variables that have to be treated as randomized errors. In ideal experiments, they can be randomized, whereas in surveys they can only be assumed to be randomized.

In all research, one wants to place as many extraneous variables as possible in class 2. Since this usually cannot be done, we have experiments and surveys. Experiments, the conduct of a systematic, controlled test or investigation, try to control the variables in class 3 as much as possible by trying to place all of the third class of variation into the fourth through randomization. In an ideal experiment, there are no variables in the third class. In an ideal survey, all variables in class 3 are separated from those in class 1 through regression adjustments, matching of units, and standardization.

Did You Know?

In statistics used in environmental science (and elsewhere), regression and regression analysis include any techniques for modeling and analyzing several variables, when the focus is on the relationship between a dependent variable and one or more independent variable. In other words, regression analysis helps one understand how the typical value of the dependent variable changes when any of the independent variables is varied, while the other independent variables are held fixed.

SAMPLING

Sampling is a means by which inferences about a planned community can be made based on information from an examination of a small proportion of that community. The most complete way to determine the characteristics of a population is to conduct a complete census enumeration. In a census, each individual unit in the population is sampled to provide the data for the aggregate. This process is both time-consuming and costly. It may also result in inaccurate values when individual sampling units are difficult to identify. Therefore, the best way to collect vegetation data, for example, is to sample a small subset of the population. If the population is uniform, sampling can be conducted anywhere in the population; however, most vegetation populations are not uniform. It is important that data be collected so that the sample represents the entire population. Sample design is an important consideration in collected representative data.

PARADIGM AND PARADIGM SHIFT

We view paradigm as a model, exemplar, prototype, or way of thinking so ingrained in people's thoughts and behavior that they aren't even conscious of it. In science, historian Thomas Kuhn (1996) gave the word *paradigm* its contemporary meaning when he adopted it to refer to the set of practices that define a scientific discipline during a particular period of time. In his book *The Structure of Scientific Revolutions*, Kuhn defines a scientific paradigm as the following:

- *What* is to be observed and scrutinized?
- *What* kinds of questions are to be asked and probed for answers in relation to this subject?
- *How* are these questions to be structured?
- *How* should the results of scientific investigations be interpreted?
- *How* is an experiment to be conducted, and what equipment is available to conduct the experiment?

How do paradigms and the scientific method interrelate or mix? Keep in mind that, in our opinion, a paradigm is just one of the tools in the scientific method's toolbox. This makes sense when you consider that paradigm is a more specific approach (a tool) to viewing reality than the much more generalized scientific method (the toolbox).

With time and experience, things change. Science, like life, is dynamic and constantly changing or adapting. So, when in 1900, Lord Kelvin famously stated, "There is nothing new to be discovered in physics now. All that remains is more and more precise measurement," he was a bit premature. Just five years later, Albert Einstein published his paper on special relativity, which challenged the very simple set of rules laid down by Newtonian mechanics, which had been used to describe force and motion for more than 200 years. Einstein's special relativity paper is an example of a paradigm shift. According to Kuhn (1996), other paradigm shifts in science include the following:

- The transition from a Ptolemaic cosmology (Earth is the center of the universe) to a Copernican one (the Sun is the center of the universe).
- The unification of classical physics by Newton into a coherent mechanical worldview.
- The transition between the Maxwellian electromagnetic worldview and the Einsteinian relativistic worldview.
- The transition between the worldview of Newtonian physics and the Einsteinian relativistic worldview.
- The development of quantum mechanics, which overthrew classical mechanics.
- The development of Darwin's theory of evolution by natural selection, which overturned Lamarckian theories of evolution by inheritance of acquired characteristics.
- The acceptance of plate tectonics as the explanation for large-scale geologic changes.

You might think that the scientist's toolbox, the scientific method, and other tools are for scientists only. Not true! We all use the toolbox all the time. For example, in the following instances:

- Observe: The car won't start.
- Think of a question: What is wrong with the car?
- Predict the answer (hypothesis): The car won't start because the battery is dead.
- Plan the experiment: I will have the battery tested.

- Collect data: The car battery is dead.
- Analyze results: The car won't start because the battery is dead.

Just as with mechanics and carpenters, scientists don't always use the same tools. Individual scientific toolboxes are stocked to fit the situation and the person. Almost always, however, they contain the basic six ingredients—observation, forming the question, presenting the hypothesis, experimentation, results, and analyzing the results—or modifications or variations of these components. Keep in mind, however, that observation and testing are the key tools in the scientist's toolbox.

We all know that in the wrong hands, mechanical tools can be dangerous to the operator or damaging to whatever is being worked on. The same is true when using tools in the scientific toolbox. To ensure that the results are valid to the natural world, the toolbox must be used objectively to remove personal and cultural biases. In addition, the tools must be used consistently and allow for observable and measurable results. All tools should be focused on describing and explaining observed phenomena. Finally, the test should enable researchers to prove it incorrect by observable data within the experiment, and it must be reproducible.

As mentioned, environmental science may be divided among the study of air (atmosphere), water (hydrosphere), soil (geosphere), and life (biota; biosphere). Again, we discuss these four media throughout the text, but the emphasis is on the first three (air, water, and soil), because without any of these, biota, biosphere, or any form of life as we know it is impossible.

ENVIRONMENTAL MEDIA

The *atmosphere* is the envelope of thin air that surrounds the Earth. The role of the atmosphere is multifaceted: (1) it serves as a reservoir of gases; (2) it moderates the Earth's temperature; (3) it absorbs energy and damaging ultraviolet (UV) radiation from the sun; (4) it transports energy away from equatorial regions; and (5) it serves as a pathway for vapor-phase movement of water in the hydrologic cycle. Air, the mixture of gases that constitutes the Earth's **atmosphere**, is by volume at sea level 78.0% nitrogen, 21.0% oxygen, 0.93% argon, and 0.03% carbon dioxide, together with very small amounts of numerous other constituents. The **hydrosphere** is the water component of the Earth, encompassing the oceans, seas, rivers, streams, swamps, lakes, groundwater, and atmospheric water vapor. Water (H_2O) is a liquid that, when pure, is without color, taste, or odor. It covers 70% of the Earth's surface and occurs as standing (oceans, lakes) and running (rivers, streams) water, rain, and vapor. It supports all forms of Earth's life. The **geosphere** consists of the solid Earth, including soil—the **lithosphere**, the topmost layer of decomposed rock and organic matter, which usually contains air, moisture, and nutrients, and can therefore support life. The **biosphere** is the region of the Earth and its atmosphere in which life exists, an envelope extending from up to 6,000 meters above sea level to 10,000 meters below sea level. Living organisms and the aspects of the environment pertaining directly to them are called **biotic** (biota), and other portions, the nonliving part, of the physical environment are **abiotic**.

BIOGEOCHEMICAL CYCLES

Biogeochemical cycles are a series of biological, chemical, and geological processes by which materials cycle through ecosystems. We are concerned with two types, the *gaseous* and the *sedimentary*. Gaseous cycles include the carbon and nitrogen cycles. The main sink (the main receiving area for material: for example, plants are sinks for carbon dioxide) of nutrients in the gaseous cycle is the atmosphere and the ocean. The sedimentary cycles include sulfur and phosphorus cycles. The main sink for sedimentary cycles is soil and rocks of the Earth's crust.

ECOLOGY

Formerly known as natural science, **ecology** is critical to the study of environmental science, as the study of the structure, function, and behavior of the natural systems that comprise the biosphere. The terms *ecology* and *interrelationship* are interchangeable; they mean the same thing. In fact, ecology is the scientific study of the interrelationships among organisms and between organisms, and all aspects, living and nonliving, of their environment.

Ecology is normally approached from two viewpoints: (1) the environment and the demands it places on the organisms in it, or (2) organisms and how they adapt to their environmental conditions. An **ecosystem**, a cyclic mechanism, describes the interdependence of species in the living world (the biome or community) on one another and on their nonliving (abiotic) environment. An ecosystem has physical, chemical, and biological components, as well as energy sources and pathways.

An ecosystem can be analyzed from a functional viewpoint in terms of several factors. The factors important in this discussion include biogeochemical cycles, *energy*, and *food chains* (all discussed in detail in Chapter 2). Each ecosystem is bound together by biogeochemical cycles through which living organisms use energy from the sun to obtain or "fix" nonliving inorganic elements, like carbon, oxygen, and hydrogen, from the environment and transform them into vital food, which is then used and recycled. The environment in which a particular organism lives is a **habitat**. The role of an organism in a habitat is its **niche**.

Figure 1.6 depicts an ecosystem where biotic and abiotic materials are constantly exchanged. **Producers** construct organic substances through photosynthesis and chemosynthesis. **Consumers** and **decomposers** use organic matter as their food and convert it into abiotic components—that is, they dissipate energy fixed by producers through food chains. The abiotic part of the pond in Figure 1.6 is formed of inorganic and organic compounds, including carbon, oxygen, nitrogen, sulfur, calcium, hydrogen, and humic acids. Producers—rooted plants and phytoplankton—represent the biotic. Fish, crustaceans, and insect larvae make up the consumers. Mayfly nymphs, for example, are detritivores, feeding on organic detritus. Decomposers (aquatic bacteria and fungi) make up the final biotic element.

In short, while many branches of science help us understand the physical, chemical, and biological processes of our environment, ecology concentrates on the way these

---

Did You Know?

Aquatic plants are an important link in a pond ecosystem. Algae are the foundation of the food chain for fish. Free-floating and rooted aquatic plants provide escape cover and shelter for fish and wildlife; however, too many aquatic plants can kill fish. How much is too much? Healthy ponds normally have a faint, green color from algae, but water with a bright pea-soup color indicates an algae bloom and imminent fish kill (U.S. Department of Agriculture, 2011).

---

processes interact as systems. A well-grounded knowledge of ecology is fundamental to gaining knowledge of environmental science. Ecology and the holistic approach are also interchangeable, because ecologists study nature as a functioning system, instead of as a collection of distinct, unrelated parts.

SUSTAINABILITY

One major goal for environmentalists and ecologists alike is the goal of a **sustainable society**. "A society that manages its economy and population without harming the environment by regulating population growth, uses renewable resources at a rate at which they can be replenished, and encourages Earth-sustaining forms of economic development is known as a *sustainable society*" (Miller, 2004).

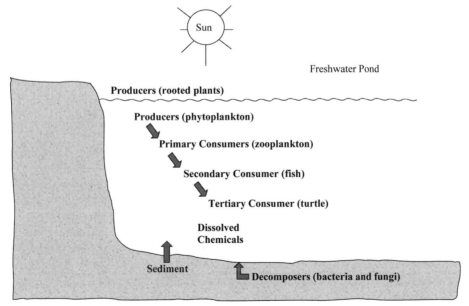

Figure 1.6.   Major components of a freshwater pond ecosystem. Adapted from Spellman, F. R., 1996. *Stream Ecology & Self-Purification*. Lancaster, PA: Technomic

Some argue that sustainability and living the "good life" are diametrically opposed and when discussed tend to ignite and feed argument and conflict between the opposing parties involved. Actually, the goal of sustainability, as established by the 1970 National Environmental Policy Act (NEPA) was crafted to nip argument and conflict in the bud (to the extent possible) by establishing a national goal under which humans and nature "can exist in productive harmony, and fulfill the social, economic, and other requirements of present and future generations of Americans" (Environmental Protection Agency, 2011).

Response Scenario 1.2. The Appalachian Trail

We had not walked any part of the Appalachian Trail for more than several years. Although we had never walked its entire 2,160-mile length, from Springer Mountain, in Georgia, to Katahdin, Maine, at once, during the course of several years, we had, in piecemeal fashion, covered most of it and hiked many of the several hundred trails that parallel, bisect, and join it. But we had moved out of easy reach of the trail and for years had only our memories of it.

For us, the lure of sojourning the Appalachian Trail had always been more than just an excuse to get away from it all—whatever "it" happened to be at the time. The draw, the magnetism of the trail was more—much more to us than that, although we have always found its magic difficult to define. Maybe it was a combination of elements—recollections, ephemeral surprises found and never forgotten, pleasant memories—memories waking from the miles-deep sleep of earned exhaustion to the awareness of peace . . . inhaling deep draughts of cool, clean mountain air, breathing through nostrils tickled with the pungency of pure, sweet pine . . . eardrums soothed by the light tattoo of fresh rain pattering against taut nylon . . . watching darkness lifted, then suddenly replaced with cloud-filtered daylight, spellbound by the sudden, ordinary miracle of a new morning . . . anticipating our expected adventure and realizing the pure, unadulterated treasure of pristine wilderness we momentarily owned, with minds not weighed down by the everyday mundanities of existence. That is what we took away from our trail experiences, years ago, what we remembered about living on the trail, on our untroubled sojourn through one of the last pure wilderness areas left in the United States. Those memories were magnets. They drew us inexorably to the trail—back again and again.

But, of course, the trail for us had another drawing card—the natural world and all its glory. The trail defined that for us. The flora that surrounds you on the trail literally encapsulates you as it does in any dense forest and brings you fully into its own world, shutting out all the other worlds of your life. For a brief span of time, along the trail, the office was gone, and cities, traffic, and the buzz and grind of work melted away into forest. But this forest was different, and its floral inhabitants created the difference. Not only the thickets of rhododendrons and azaleas (in memory, always in full bloom), the other forest growths drew us there: the magnificent trees, that wild assortment of incomparable beauty that stood as if for forever that was the Trail.

This was how it had been—no more than 25 years ago. But now things were different; things had changed. To say that we were shocked at what we found along the trail—along most of its length—is true, and we can only describe it as wounding heartache, as achingly sad to us as the discovery of the physical debilitation of a long-beloved friend. Even though still lined (and in some places densely packed) with Fraser fir, red spruce, sugar maples, shagbark hickory, northern red oak, quaking aspens, tulip poplars, white basswood, yellow buckeyes, black gums, old-growth beech, mountain laurel, and those incomparable dogwoods whose creamy-white bracts light up the woods in early spring, the world along the trail was different. In a span of only 25 years, things had changed—for the worse. How different? What changes? Let us paint you a picture.

Walking various segments of the trail and its arteries in North Carolina, Virginia, and Maryland, we observed the following:

- standing dead Fraser fir and red spruce
- stands of pollution-killed trees, where fallen gray tree trunks crisscrossed one another in a horrible game of giant jackstraws
- standing dead red spruce silhouetted by polluted fog
- understories of brambles looking up at dead sugar maples
- foliage areas bleached by ozone
- trees of all varieties starved to death, the needed soil nutrients leached away by decades of acid deposition, and the trees weakened until they were no longer capable of withstanding the assaults of even ordinary disease and bad weather
- tropospheric ozone damage with chlorophyll bleaching
- branch dieback on northern red oak
- premature leaf drop on quaking aspens
- thinning crowns on sugar maples
- tipped-over tulip poplars with rotted roots
- chemically green ponds in areas where active strip mining occurs
- an orange waterfall next to an abandoned mine
- an overview where 25 years earlier we viewed the surrounding landscape for 50 miles, now veiled in thick, stagnant, polluted fog, with visibility reduced to two or three miles

Our latest sojourn along the Appalachian Trail inspired only a memory of things past, heartache to recollect.

RESPONSE

(a) Choose any *one* of the previously mentioned examples of environmental degradation and respond to each of the following:
   (i)   Describe one specific example of degradation.
   (ii) Describe how the environmental degradation occurred. What are the possible contaminants? What are the possible sources of contaminants?
   (iii) Describe a specific step that can be taken to reduce the threat of this contaminant.
(b) Are Appalachian Trail hikers, thousands each year, contributors to the environmental degradation along the trail? Should backpacking the trail be abolished?

Science and Environmental Science

When you view Figure 1.1, you immediately see that the environmental practitioner, whether a scientist or technologist, is really an interdisciplinarian who must have a wide range of scientific knowledge. The field also demands knowledge beyond the various scientific fields or specialties. The environmentalist must understand and attempt to solve the problems caused by the interaction of natural and cultural systems. A working environmental scientist or technologist can't strictly focus on "pure science." The interdisciplinary nature of the field itself prevents it. But what are the differences between "pure science" and "environmental science?" The best way to differentiate between the two is to compare and contrast them.

In *science*, the scientist uses the scientific method, which is grounded in experimentation. Scientists conduct controlled experimentation, which tends to be reductive (they isolate the problem to a single variable, sometimes missing the big picture). Experimentation takes time. Rushing it can—and often will—invalidate the results. Effective scientists must remain objective, value-free, and bias-free. *Environmental scientists* use problem-solving techniques. They start with a human-caused problem and take into account the human values pertinent to the problem. The environmentalist considers human values, which are not value-free, not objective, and not bias-free (neither is society).

Scientists define natural system structure, function, and behavior that may or may not have direct application to a particular environmental problem. Environmental scientists define a process for solving environmental problems.

Scientists propose hypotheses based on past observations and use the scientific method to continue questioning and testing to establish the validity of hypotheses. Environmental scientists use problem solving to propose future-directed solutions and continually evaluate and monitor situations to improve the solutions.

Scientists are interested in knowledge for its own sake, or in applied sciences, in applications of knowledge found through a precise and thorough process that may or may not solve environmental problems. Environmental scientists are interested in finding the best solution (sometimes before all the facts are in) to "actual" environmental problems within a particular social setting.

Good Science versus Feel-Good Science[4]

When a national or international issue arises that must be dealt with, the problem-solving technique or mitigation process is generally discussed in terms of justice, morality, and/or science. When issues are confronted, several questions arise. For example, Is the national or international problem of the kind or type that can be dealt with by simply doing what is considered the "right" thing to do? That is, could the specific decision-making process involved be accomplished based on ethics, rationality, fairness, or rule of law? Or is the issue and its resolution one that requires judgment based on morality rather than justice? That is, is the proper outcome (i.e., the perceived proper outcome) to be achieved as a moral outcome based on action deemed proper at that particular instant or time? When the question is not best resolved based on justice and morality (is there ever such a question?), then may we turn to science for the answer? If so, then do we not have to be careful that the fork in the road we choose to take is based on good science rather than feel-good science? And if this is the case, what is the difference between "good" science and "feel-good" science?

These are questions that the environmental professional must answer when solutions are sought. In this text, we are concerned almost exclusively with science. It is important to note, however, that in any scientific endeavor, what is or is not accomplished can't be done in a total vacuum, as justice and morality will enter the picture sooner or later (let's hope it is always sooner rather than later). The point is, based on personal experience, whenever a problem arises that must be solved for the common good, the lines between justice, morality, and science may become blurred; that is, (in our opinion) nothing is cut and dry, and the lines of justice, morality, and science can be and are blurred on a daily basis. Many people choose to ignore science, brush it away, or simply detest it because science is not always a straightforward path to a concrete or correct decision; science is not a math problem with an absolute, indisputable outcome, and if there is an indisputable outcome, this does not mean that we will like it.

Good Science versus Feel-Good Science: The Difference

Before we move on to a real-world response question for readers to ponder, there remains one piece of unfinished business for us to clear up: What is the difference between good science and feel-good science? For our purposes in this text, we define good science as scientific research that is independently conducted using the scientific method (the scientist's toolbox) and subjected to peer review. That is, for science to be classified as "good" science, research on whatever issue one is trying to validate must be substantiated.

What about "feel–good" science? For our purposes, feel-good science is nonobjective science. For example, if you think shutting down the smoke-billowing factory next door will solve the world's air pollution problem, that might be an example of "feel-good" science. If you think shutting down the compost factory in your neighborhood will solve an odor-producing problem, the decision to do so might be based on "feel-good" science. If you think that the removal of a hydroelectric dam to allow salmon to return to their native waters to spawn is the right thing to do, this may be an example of "feel-good" science. If you are a researcher hired by a particular funding source and your findings favor the position of the funding source, this may be an example of "feel-good" science (some would call this "feel-good" pocketbook or bank account science, or just plain fraud, thank you very much!). This last example, in our opinion, is an example of science at its worst.

In Response Scenario 1.3, we present facts as we see them. We have attempted to make no definitive statements, but we would be wrong in stating that we have not voiced or interjected our opinion, in one way or another. We are human, and these are touchy, emotion-driven subjects. Thus, we provide the following advice to anyone who reads and responds to Response Scenario 1.3: In making decisions that affect large numbers of living things and the environment, the decision made should take into account the economic, social, health and safety, moral and ethical, as well as scientific, implications of the issue at hand. In attempting to view the big picture, our view should be wide and generalized, not narrow and specialized. In light of this, we offer an outside opinion that is apropos to this discussion, courtesy of Michael Bloch, of Carbonify.com: "We all need to remember . . . that nature doesn't give a tinker's cuss about our opinions. Nature will do what it needs to do, without our consultation, approval or validation. Nature is not a democracy, it is a benevolent dictator."

Response Scenario 1.3
Salmon and the Rachel River[5]

The Rachel River, a hypothetical river system in the northwestern United States, courses its way through an area that includes a Native American reservation. The river system outfalls to the Pacific Ocean, and the headwaters begin deep and high within the Cascade Mountain Range of the state of Washington. For untold centuries, this river system provided a natural spawning area for salmon. The salmon fry thrived in the river, and they eventually grew the characteristic dark blotches on their bodies and transformed from fry into parr. When the time came to make their way to the sea, their bodies now larger and covered with silver pigment, the salmon, now called smolt, inexorably migrated to the ocean, where they flourished until it was time to return to the river and spawn (about four years later). In spawning season, the salmon instinctively homed their way toward the odor generated by the Rachel River (their homing signal) and up the river to their home waters, as their life cycle instincts demanded.

Before non-Native Americans (settlers) arrived in this pristine wilderness region, nature, humans, and salmon lived in harmony and provided for one another. Nature gave the salmon the perfect habitat, and the salmon provided Native Americans with sustenance. Native Americans provided to both their natural world and the salmon the respect they deserved.

After the settlers came to the Rachel River Valley, changes began to take place. The salmon still ran the river, and humans still fed on the salmon, but the circumstances were quickly altered. The settlers wanted more land, and the Native Americans were forced to give way; they were destroyed or forcibly removed to other places, to reservations, where the settlers did all they could to erase Native American beliefs and cultural inheritance. The salmon still ran the streams.

After the settlers drove out the Native Americans, the salmon continued to run, for a while, but more non-Native Americans continued to pour into the area. As the area became more crowded, the salmon still ran, but now their home, their habitat, the Rachel River, started to show the effects of modern civilization's influence. The "civilized" practice and philosophy was, "If I don't want it any more, it's trash. Throw it away," and the river provided a seemingly endless dump—out of the way, out of sight, out of mind. And they threw their trash, all the mountains of trash they could manufacture, into the river. The salmon still ran.

More time passed. More people moved in, and the more people that came to the area, the bigger their demands became. In its natural course, sometimes the river flooded, creating problems for the settler populations. Besides, everyone wanted power to maintain modern lifestyles, and hydropower poured down the Rachel River to the ocean constantly. So they built flood control systems and a dam to convert hydropower to hydroelectric power. (Funny. The Native Americans didn't have a problem with flood control. When the river rose, they broke camp and moved to higher ground. Hydroelectric power? If you don't build your life around things, you don't need electricity to make them work. With the sun, the moon, and the stars and their healthy, vital land at hand, who would want hydroelectric power?) The salmon still ran.

Building dams and flood control systems takes time, but humans, although impatient, have a way of conquering and using time (and anything else that gets in the way) to accomplish their tasks, goals, objectives—and construction projects. As the years passed, the construction moved closer to completion and finally ended. The salmon still ran—but in reduced numbers and size. Soon local inhabitants couldn't catch the quantity and quality of salmon that they had in the past. When the inconvenience finally struck home, they began to ask, "Where are the salmon?"

But no one seemed to know. Obviously, the time had come to call in the scientists, the experts. So the inhabitants' governing officials formed a committee, funded a study, and hired some scientists to tell them what was wrong. "The scientists will know the answer. They'll know what to do," they said, and that was partly true. Notice they didn't try to ask the Native Americans. They also would have known what to do. The salmon had already told them.

The scientists came and studied the situation, conducted testing, tested their tests, and decided that the salmon population needed to increase. They determined increased population could be achieved by building a fish hatchery, which would take the eggs from spawning salmon, raise the eggs to fingerling-sized fish, release them into specially built basins, and, later, release them to restock the river.

A lot of science goes into the operation of a fish hatchery. It can't operate successfully on its own (although Mother Nature never has a serious problem with it when left alone), but it must be run by trained scientists and technicians following a proven protocol based on biological studies of salmon life cycles.

When the time was right, the salmon were released into the river. Meanwhile, other scientists and engineers realized that some mechanism had to be installed in the dam to allow the salmon to swim downstream to the ocean, and the reverse, as well. In the lives of salmon (since they are an anadromous species, they spend their adult lives at sea but return to freshwater to spawn), what goes down must go up (upstream). Those salmon would eventually need some way of getting back up past the dam and into home water, their spawning grounds. So the scientists and engineers devised, designed, built, and installed fish ladders in the dam, so that the salmon could climb the ladders, scale the dam, and return to their native waters to spawn and die.

(continued)

Response Scenario 1.3. (*continued*)

After a few seasons, the salmon again ran strong in the Rachel River. The scientists had temporarily—and at a high financial expenditure—solved the problem. Nothing in life or in nature is static or permanent. All things change. They shift from static to dynamic, in natural cycles that defy human intervention, relatively quickly, without notice—like a dormant volcano, or the Pacific Rim tectonic plates.

After a few more years, local Rachel River residents noticed an alarming trend. Studies over a five-year period showed that no matter how many salmon were released into the river, fewer and fewer returned to spawn each season. So they called in the scientists again. And again they said, "Don't worry. The scientists will know. They'll tell us what to do."

The scientists came in, analyzed the problem, and came up with the following five conclusions:

1. The Rachel River is extremely polluted both from point and nonpoint sources.
2. The Rachel River Dam has radically reduced the number of returning salmon to the spawning grounds.
3. Foreign fishing fleets off the Pacific Coast are depleting the salmon.
4. Native Americans are removing salmon downstream, before they even get close to the fish ladder at the Rachel River Dam.
5. A large percentage of water is withdrawn each year from rivers for cooling machinery in local factories. Large rivers with rapid flow rates can usually dissipate heat rapidly and suffer little ecological damage, unless their flow rates are sharply reduced by seasonal fluctuations. This was not the case, of course, with the Rachel River. The large input of heated water from Rachel River area factories back into the slow-moving Rachel River creates an adverse effect called **thermal pollution**. Thermal pollution and salmon do not mix. First and foremost, increased water temperatures lower the dissolved oxygen (DO) content by decreasing the solubility of oxygen in the river water. Warmer river water also causes aquatic organisms to increase their respiration rates and consume oxygen faster, increasing their susceptibility to disease, parasites, and toxic chemicals. Although salmon can survive in heated water—to a point—many other fish (the salmon's food supply) cannot. Heated discharge water from the factories also disrupts the spawning process and kills the young fry.

The scientists prepared their written findings and presented them to city officials, who read them and were (at first) pleased. "Ah!" they said. "Now we know why we have fewer salmon!" But their pleasure was short-lived. They did indeed have the causal factors defined, but what was the solution? The scientists looked at each other and shrugged. "That's not our job," they said. "Call in the environmental folks." The salmon still ran, but not up the Rachel River to its headwaters.

Within days, city officials had hired an environmental engineering firm to study the salmon depletion problem. The environmentalists came up with the same causal conclusions as the scientists (which they also related to city officials), but they also noted the political, economic, and philosophical implications of the situation. The environmentalists explained that most of the pollution constantly pouring into the Rachel River would be eliminated when the city's new wastewater treatment plant came online, and, that specific **point-source pollution** would be eliminated. They explained that the state agricultural department and its environmental staff were working with farmers along the lower river course to modify their farming practices and pesticide treatment regimens to help control the most destructive types of **nonpoint-source pollution**. The environmentalists explained that the Rachel River dam's present fish ladder was incorrectly configured but could be modified with minor retrofitting.

The environmentalists went on to explain that overfishing by foreign fishing fleets off the Pacific Coast was a problem that the Federal Government was working to resolve with the governments involved. The environmentalists explained that the state of Washington and the Federal Government were also addressing a problem with the Native Americans fishing the downriver locations (before the salmon ever reached the dam). Both governmental entities were negotiating with the local tribes on this problem. Meanwhile, local tribes had litigation pending against the state and Federal Government to determine who actually owned fishing rights to the Rachel River and the salmon.

The final problem was thermal pollution from the factories, which was making the Rachel River unfavorable for spawning, decreasing salmon food supply and/or killing off the young salmon fry. The environmentalists explained that to correct this problem, the outfalls from the factories would have to be changed—relocated. The environmentalists also recommended construction of a channel basin whereby the ready-to-release salmon fry could be released in a favorable environment, at ambient stream temperatures, and where they would have a controlled one-way route to safe downstream locations, where they could thrive until it was time to migrate to the sea.

After many debates and newspaper editorials, city officials put the matter to a vote and voted to fund the projects needed to solve the salmon problem in the Rachel River. Some short-term projects are already showing positive signs of change, long-term projects are under way, and the Rachel River is on its way to recovery.

In short, scientists are professionals who study to find *the* answer to a problem through scientific analysis and study. Their interest is in pure science. The environmentalists (also scientists) can arrive at the same causal conclusions as general scientists, but they are also able to factor in socioeconomic, political, and cultural influences.

But wait! It's not over yet. Concerns over disruption of the wild salmon gene pool by hatchery trout are drawing attention from environmentalists, conservationists, and wildlife biologists. Hatchery- or farm-raised stock of any kind is susceptible to problems caused by, among other things, a lack of free genetic mixing, the spread of disease, infection, and parasites, and reinforcement of negative characteristics. When escaped hatchery salmon breed with wild salmon, the genetic strain is changed and diseases can be transmitted. Many problems can arise.

Yes, many problems arise, and solutions are constantly sought. When nature's natural processes are interrupted, changed, or manipulated in any way, humans need to adjust to the changes, but so does Mother Nature. The question is, Are the human-made changes to natural surroundings a good or bad thing? It depends. It depends on what? It depends on your point of view.

(continued)

Response Scenario 1.3. (*continued*)

RESPONSE

(a) For many, the Rachel River case study probably generates more questions than answers, because there are a number of vignettes within the account, many of which garner separate case studies of their own; however, if we focus on only the dam and its implications, not only for the human inhabitants, but also for the natural resources involved, environmental scientists would study the construction of such a human-made structure based on facts, science, and the pros and cons. Let's consider the pros and cons.

Pros to hydroelectric power (as compared to other power-producing methods) include the following:

- Fuel is not burned, so there is minimal pollution.
- Water to run the power plant is provided free by nature.
- Hydropower plays a major role in reducing greenhouse gas emissions.
- Operations and maintenance costs are relatively low.
- The technology is reliable and has been proven over time.
- It's renewable, since rainfall renews the water in the reservoir, so the fuel is almost always there.

Cons to hydroelectric power (as compared to other power-producing methods) include the following:

- Investment costs are high.
- Hydropower is hydrology dependent (on precipitation).
- In some cases, there is an inundation of a wildlife habitat.
- In some cases, there is a loss or modification of fish habitat.
- Dams can cause fish entrainment or passage restriction.
- In some cases, there can be changes in reservoir and stream water quality
- In some cases, local populations can be displaced. (U. S. Geological Survey, 2009)

(i)   According to the account, the scientists and environmental scientists devised several recommendations to alleviate the downward trend in salmon population. What additional recommendations would you make to mitigate the situation?

(ii)   What is the meaning of the statement, "Notice they didn't try to ask the Native Americans. They also would have known what to do. The salmon had already told them."

(iii) Explain why an increase in water temperature affects the salmon population.

(iv)   When comparing the pros and cons of hydroelectric power it sounds great, so why don't we use it to produce all of our power?

(v)   Does this account and the indicated mitigation procedures indicate to you that science and scientists can solve all problems?

Environmental Science and Technology

As long as capitalism drives most modern economies, people will desire material things, precipitating a high level of consumption. For better or for worse, the human desire to lead the "good life" (which Americans may interpret as a life enriched by material possessions) is a fact of life. Arguing against someone who wants to purchase a new, modern home with all the amenities, who wants to purchase the latest, greatest automobile, is difficult. Arguing against the person wanting to make a better life for his or her children by making sure they have all they need and want to succeed in their chosen pursuit is even harder. How do you argue against such goals with someone who earns his or her own way and spends his or her hard-earned money at will? We should look at the tradeoffs. The tradeoff often affects the environment. That new house purchased with hard-earned money may sit in a field of radon-rich soil or on formerly undeveloped land. That new SUV may get only eight miles to the gallon. The boat used on weekends gets even worse mileage and exudes wastes into the local lake, river, or stream. The weekend retreat on the five wooded acres is part of the watershed of the local community and disturbs breeding and migration habitat for several species.

The environmental tradeoffs never enter the average person's mind. Most of us don't think much about the environment until we damage it, until it becomes unsightly, until it is so fouled that it offends us. People can put up with a lot of environmental abuse, especially with our surroundings—until the surroundings no longer please us. We treat our resources the same way. How often do we think about the air we breathe, the water we drink, the soil our agribusiness conglomerates plant our vegetables in? Not often enough.

Resource utilization and environmental degradation are tied together. While people depend upon resources and must use them, this use impacts the environment. A resource is usually defined as anything obtained from the physical environment that is of use to man. Some resources, such as edible growing plants, water (in many places), and fresh air, are directly available to man, but most resources, like coal, iron, oil, groundwater, game animals, and fish, are not. They become resources only when man uses science and technology to find them, extract them, process them, and convert them, at a reasonable cost, into usable and acceptable forms. Natural gas, found deep below the Earth's surface, was not a resource until the technology for drilling a well and installing pipes to bring it to the surface became available. For centuries, man stumbled across stinky, messy pools of petroleum and had no idea of its potential uses or benefits. When its potential was realized, man exploited petroleum by learning how to extract it and convert (refine) it into heating oil, gasoline, sulfur extract, road tar, and other products.

Earth's natural resources and processes that sustain other species, as well as humans, are known as **Earth's natural capital**. This includes air, water, soil, forests, grasslands, wildlife, minerals, and natural cycles. Societies are the primary engines of resource use, converting materials and energy into wealth, delivering goods and services, and creating waste or pollution. This provision of necessities and luxuries is often conducted in ways that systematically degrade the Earth's natural capital—the ecosystems that support all life.

Excluding **perpetual resources** (solar energy, tides, wind, and flowing water) two different classes (types) of resources are available to us: renewable and nonrenewable (see Figure 1.3). **Renewable resources** (fresh air, fresh water, fertile soil, plants, and animals [via genetic diversity]) can be depleted in the short run if used or contaminated too rapidly, but they are normally replaced through natural processes in the long run. Because renewable resources are relatively plentiful, we often ignore, overlook, destroy, contaminate, and/or mismanage them.

Mismanage? Yes. Classifying anything as "renewable" is a double-edged sword. Renewable resources are renewable only to a point. Timber or grass used for grazing must be managed for **maximum sustainable yield** (the highest rate at which a renewable resource can be used without impairing or damaging its ability to be fully renewed). If timber or grass yield exceeds this rate, the system gives ever-diminishing returns. Recovery is complicated by the time factor, which is dependent on the life cycle. Grass can renew itself in a season or two, but timber takes decades. Any length of time is problematic when people become impatient.

Remember, one of the contributing factors to the plight of the Rachel River salmon was overfishing. When a fishery is pushed past its limit, if the catch is maintained by collecting greater and greater numbers of younger salmon, no increase is possible. If the same practices are used on a wild species, extinction can occur. We no longer have passenger pigeons, heath hens, Carolina parakeets, dodos, solitaires, or great auks—and many other species are at risk.

Exceeding maximum sustainable yield is only the tip of the iceberg, as other environmental, social, and economic problems may develop. Let's look at the **overgrazing** (depleting) of grass on livestock lands. The initial problem occurs when the grass and other grazing cover are depleted, but secondary problems kick in fast. Without grass, the soil erodes quickly. In a short period of time, so much soil is lost that the land is no longer capable of growing grass—or anything else. Productive land converted to nonproductive deserts (**desertification**) is a process of **environmental degradation**, and it impacts social and economic factors. Those who depend on the grasslands must move elsewhere, and moving elsewhere costs time, energy, and money—and puts more land at risk. Should the same level of poor stewardship of land resources continue on more acreage?

Environmental degradation is not limited to salmon and grass. Let's look at a few other examples. Along with overfishing and overgrazing, land can also be overcultivated. Intense overcultivation reduces soil nutrients and increases erosion to the point that agricultural productivity is reduced, leading to overfertilization, which eventually damages the water supply. If irrigation of agricultural lands proceeds without proper drainage, the excessive accumulation of water or salts in the soil decreases productivity. Environmental degradation takes place when trees are removed from large areas without adequate replanting. The result is the destruction of wildlife habitat, increased soil erosion, and flooding. Habitat fragmentation is another problem related to habitat destruction. When habitat is fragmented, species that require distance from human activity, for example, both greater and lesser prairie chickens in Kansas, are affected. Radiotelemetry research demonstrates that prairie chickens are extremely sensitive to human activity. The birds seldom use sandsage within a quarter mile of an inhabited house; a house built on a one-acre site actually eliminates 160 acres of habitat for the birds.

Human habitation isn't the only factor, however. Natural gas compression facilities—and southwest Kansas has a bunch—are noisy, clanging affairs, usually a couple of acres in size. The birds won't use habitat within half a mile of these areas—another 640 acres down the tube. Lesser chickens seldom venture within a mile of a coal-fired power plant, even though the sandsage habitat surrounding it may be the best on the range. A 30-acre power plant chews up 2,500 additional acres of chicken habitat. In addition, lesser chickens rarely nest or raise broods in habitat blocks less than 2,000 to 4,000 acres in size, nor do the birds frequent habitats along well-traveled roads. Do the math, and pretty soon you see the magnitude of the problems associated with preserving or supplying large, open blocks of the necessary habitat for chickens (Taylor, 2002).

Land is often environmentally degraded when a metropolitan area expands. In high-growth areas, productive land is covered with concrete, asphalt, buildings, water, or silt to such an extent that agricultural productivity declines and wildlife habitat is lost.

Nonrenewable resources (copper, coal, tin, and oil, among many others) have built up or evolved during a geological time span. They can't be replaced at will—only over a similar time scale. In this age of advanced technology, we often hear that, for example, when high-grade tin ore runs out (when 80% of its total estimated supply has been removed and used), low-grade tin ore (the other 20%) will become economically workable. This erroneous view neglects the facts of energy resource depletion and increasing pollution with lower-grade burdens. In short, to find, extract, and process the remaining 20% will generally cost more than the result is worth. Even with unlimited supplies of energy (impossible according to the **Laws of Thermodynamics** [discussed later]), what if we could extract that last 20%? When it is gone, nothing is going to bring it back except time measured in centuries and millennia, paired with the elements that produce the resource.

Advances in technology have allowed us to make great strides in creating the "good life." These same technological advances have increased environmental degradation. But not all the news is bad. Technological advances have also allowed us (via recycling and reuse) to conserve finite resources, including aluminum, copper, iron, plastics, and glass. **Recycling** involves collecting household waste items (e.g., aluminum beverage cans) and reprocessing usable portions. **Reuse** involves using a resource over and over in the same form (refillable beverage bottles, water).

We've already discussed the "good life"—modern homes, luxury cars and boats, the second home in the woods. With the continuing depletion of natural resources, prices will be forced upward, until, economically, attaining the "good life," or even gaining a foothold toward it, will become difficult or impossible—and maintaining it will become precarious. Ruthless exploitation of natural resources and the environment—overfishing a diminishing species (e.g., countless marine species populations), intense exploitation of energy and mineral resources, cultivation of marginal land without proper conservation practices, degradation of habitat by unbalanced populations or introduced species, and the problems posed by further technological advances—will result in environmental degradation that will turn the "good life" into something we don't even want to think about.

So, what's the answer? What are we to do? What should we do? Can we do anything? Some people would have us all "return to nature." Those individuals suggest returning to Thoreau's Walden Pond on a large scale, giving up the "good life," to which we have become accustomed. They think that giving up the cars, boats, fancy homes, bulldozers that make construction and farming easier, pesticides that protect our crops, and medicines that improve our health and save our lives—the myriad material improvements that make our lives more comfortable and productive—will solve the problem. Is this approach the answer, or even realistic? To a small minority, it is, although for those who realize how urban Walden Pond was, the idea is amusing.

For the rest of us, it cannot, should not, and will not happen. We can't abandon ship. We must prevent the need for abandoning our society from ever happening. Technological development is a boon to civilization, and it will continue to be. Technological development isn't the problem; improper use of technology is. But we must continue to make advances in technology, we must find further uses for technology, and we must learn to use technology for the benefit of mankind and the environment. Technology and the environment must work hand in hand, not stand opposed to one another. We must also foster respect for, and care for, what we have left.

Just how bad are the problems of technology's influence on the environment? Major advances in technology have provided us with enormous transformation and pollution of the environment. While transformation is generally glaringly obvious (e.g., damming a river system), "polluting" or "pollution" is not always as clear. What do we mean by pollution? To **pollute** means to impair the purity of some substance or the environment. **Air pollution** and **water pollution** refer to alteration of the normal compositions of air and water (their environmental quality) by the addition of foreign matter (e.g., gasoline, sewage).

Ways technology has contributed to environmental transformation and pollution include the following:

- Extraction, production, and processing of raw natural resources, such as minerals, with accompanying environmental disruption.
- Manufacturing enormous quantities of industrial products that consume huge amounts of natural resources and produce large quantities of hazardous waste and water/air pollutants.
- Agricultural practices that result in intensive cultivation of land, irrigation of arid lands, drainage of wetlands, and application of chemicals.
- Energy production and use accompanied by disruption and contamination of soil by strip mining, emission of air pollutants, and pollution of water by the release of contaminants from petroleum production and the effects of acid rain.
- Transportation practices (particularly reliance on the airplane) that cause scarring of land surfaces from airport construction, emission of air pollutants, and greatly increased demands for fuel (energy) resources.
- Transportation practices (particularly reliance on automobiles) that cause loss of land by road and storage construction, emission of air pollutants, and increased demand for fuel (energy) resources.

Throughout this text, we discuss the important aspects of the impact of technology on the environment. When technology is based on a sound foundation of environmental science and common sense, it can be used in solving environmental problems. In short, the goal is to produce manufacturing processes with minimum environmental impact. This procedure has already been aptly demonstrated in the redesign of standard manufacturing processes. In these new, environmentally friendly designs, the production practice focuses on minimizing raw materials, energy consumption, and waste production. In this redesign process, one technique is to construct a manufacturing process to use raw materials and energy sources in ways that minimize environmental impact. When processing chemicals, the process can modify reactions so that the process is much more environmentally friendly. Another key change is in raw material and water usage. An environmentally friendly manufacturing process is designed so that raw materials and water are recycled. State-of-the-art technologies should be employed to minimize air, water, and solid waste emissions. A few of the ways in which technology can be applied to minimize environmental impact include the following:

- Use of waste heat recovery systems to achieve maximum energy use, increase efficiency, and maximum utilization of fuel.
- Implementation of precision machining and processing systems (e.g., lasers) to minimize waste production.
- Application of process optimization operations to increase efficiency.
- Use of materials that minimize pollution.
- Implementation of computerized control systems to achieve maximum energy efficiency, maximum utilization of raw materials, and minimum production of pollutants.
- Application of processes that enable maximum materials recycling and minimum waste production.
- Use of advanced technologies to treat waste products efficiently.

Advancements in technology are evolutionary. Each advancement builds upon its predecessor to produce (to evolve) a technology that improves upon its predecessors. The applications of technology to environmental improvements (the connection) available to us today are addressed throughout this text; however, for environmental improvements to occur, the technologies must be used.

Chapter Summary

When you throw a stone into a pool of quiet water, the ensuing ripples move out in concentric circles from the point of impact. Eventually, those ripples, much dissipated, reach the edge of the pond, where they break, disturbing the shore environment. When we alter our environment, similar repercussions affect the world around us, and some of these actions can—or will—be felt around the world. We use technology to alter our environment to suit our needs. That same technology can be utilized to protect our environment from unrecoverable losses. Environmental scientists must maintain an acute sense of awareness concerning the global repercussions of problems we create for the environment—to extend the boundaries of the problem beyond our own backyards.

Discussion Questions

1. Define science and environmental science. How do they differ? Name and discuss the pertinent aspects of two local, regional, or national environmental problems, as well as two global environmental problems. Explain your answer.
2. Why is finding a solution to an environmental conflict so complex? Explain your answer.
3. What is the quality of life?
4. Discuss extinction as it relates to habitat, maximum sustainable yield, and natural capital.
5. What is the "good life"?
6. What's in store for the future of the Rachel River? Why?
7. In solving local, regional, or national environmental problems, which of these problems can be solved by scientists alone? Explain your answer. If scientists alone cannot solve these issues, what kind of knowledge (from the social and behavioral sciences, arts and humanities, or other sources) is needed to develop culturally acceptable solutions?
8. Do you believe that the society in which you live is on an unsustainable path? Explain your answer.
9. Explain why you agree or disagree with the following proposition: The world will run out of renewable resources because we *cannot* use technology to find substitutes.
10. Do you think that there is a difference between environmentalists and environmental scientists?
11. Can we solve the energy crisis by replacing nonrenewable sources with renewable sources?
12. Are humans a part of or separate from nature?
13. Do you think technology can solve our environmental problems?

Suggested Research Topics and Projects

- Examine the social causes that work to affect the environment and their effectiveness.
- Study the political actions that affect the environment, the history behind the actions, and their results.
- Look at cultural changes in environmental beliefs.
- Assess salmon or related fishery problems.
- Compare the relationships among consumption, capitalism, and environmental science.

- Explore the current research status of replacing nonrenewable resource use with perpetual and renewable resources.
- Survey the effects of the "good life" on the environment.
- Research the natural history and life cycle of an extinct species and how the species' instinctive behaviors and needs fared in encounters with human societies. Examples include the passenger pigeon, heath hen, great auk, Carolina parakeet, dodo, and solitaire.
- Investigate the destruction of a particular habitat (e.g., the tallgrass or short grass prairie), and examine habitat destruction impacts on the various populations affected.
- Examine urban growth versus rural growth.

Notes

1. Adapted from F. R. Spellman & J. Price-Bayer, 2011, *In Defense of Science*. Lanham, MD: Government Institutes.
2. This section is modified from Spellman & Price-Bayer, *In Defense of Science*.
3. Much of the information in this section is from U. S. Department of Agriculture Forest Service, 2004, *Building Models and Cause-Effect*. Washington, DC: U. S. Department of Agriculture Forest Service RMRS-GTR-126.
4. Much of the material in this section is adapted from Spellman & Price-Bayer, *In Defense of Science*.
5. From F. R. Spellman & N. E. Whiting, 2006, *Environmental Science and Technology*, 2nd ed. Rockville, MD: Government Institutes.

References and Recommended Reading

Allaby, A., & Allaby, M. (1991). *The Concise Oxford Dictionary of Earth Sciences*. Oxford, UK: Oxford University Press.

Arms, K. (1994). *Environmental Science*. 2nd ed. Saddle Brook, NJ: HBJ College and School Division.

Associated Press (1997, December 7). "Does Warming Feed El Niño?" *Virginian-Pilot* (Norfolk, VA), A-15.

Associated Press (1998, September 28). "Ozone Hole over Antarctica at Record Size," *Lancaster New Era* (Lancaster, PA), n.p.

Associated Press (1998, September 25). "Tougher Air Pollution Standards Too Costly, Midwestern States Say," *Lancaster New Era* (Lancaster, PA), n.p.

Baden, J., & Stroup, R. C. (eds.). (1981). *Bureaucracy vs. Environment*. Ann Arbor: University of Michigan Press.

Bloch, Michael (2009). *Global Warming: A Hoax?* Carbonify.com. Accessed November 7, 2009, www.carbonify.com/articles/global-warming-hoax.htm.

Botkin, D. B. (1995). *Environmental Science: Earth as a Living Planet*. New York: Wiley.

Box, G., & Draper, N. (1987). *Empirical Model Building and Response Surfaces*. New York: John Wiley & Sons.

Carpi, A., & Egger, A. E. (2009). *The Scientific Method*. VisionLearning.com. Accessed September 3, 2009, www.visionlearing.com/linraary/module_view.php?print=1 &mid=45&mcid=.

Clarke, T., & Clegg, S. (eds.). (2000). *Changing Paradigms*. London: HarperCollins.

Cobb, R. W., & Elder, C. D. (1983). *Participation in American Politics: The Dynamics of Agenda-Building*. 2nd ed. Baltimore, MD: John Hopkins University Press.

Cramer, H. (1946). *Mathematical Methods of Statistics*. Princeton, NJ: Princeton University Press.

Davis, M. L., & Cornwell, D. A. (1991). *Introduction to Environmental Engineering*. New York: McGraw-Hill.

Dawid, P. P. (1983). "Inference, Statistical: I." In Kotz, S., & Johnson, N. L., eds., *Encyclopedia of Statistical Science*, 89–105. New York: John Wiley & Sons.

Diamond, J. (1996). *Guns, Germs, and Steel: The Fates of Human Societies*. New York: W. W. Norton.

Dolan, E. F. (1991). *Our Poisoned Sky*. New York: Cobblehill Books.

Downing, P. B. (1984). *Environmental Economics and Policy*. Boston: Little, Brown.

Easterbrook, G. (1995). *A Moment on the Earth: The Coming Age of Environmental Optimism*. Bergenfield, NJ: Viking Penguin.

Environmental Protection Agency (2005). *Basic Air Pollution Meteorology*. Accessed January 15, 2008, www.epa.gov/apti.

Environmental Protection Agency (2007). *National Ambient Air Quality Standards (NAAQS)*. Accessed January 12, 2008, www.epa.gov/air/criteria/html.

Environmental Protection Agency (2009). *Regulatory Atmospheric Modeling*. Accessed March 2, 2009, www.epa.gov./scram001/.

Environmental Protection Agency (2011). *Sustainability*. Accessed April 11, 2011, http://epa.gov/sustainability/basicinfo.htm.

Euclid (1956). *The Elements*. New York: Dover.

Field, B. C. (1996). *Environmental Economics: An Introduction*. 2nd ed. New York: McGraw-Hill.

Ford, A. (2009). *Modeling the Environment*. 2nd ed. Washington, DC: Island Press.

Franck, I., & Brownstone, D. (1992). *The Green Encyclopedia*. New York: Prentice Hall.

Frazer, D. A. S. (1983). "Inference, Statistical: II." In Kotz, S., & Johnson, N. L., *Encyclopedia of Statistical Science*, 4: 105–14. New York: John Wiley & Sons.

Freese, F. (1967). *Elementary Statistical Methods for Foresters*. Washington, DC: U.S. Department of Agriculture.

Hansen, J. E., Lacis, A. A., & Prather, M. (1989, November). "Greenhouse Effect of Chlorofluorocarbons and Other Trace Gases." *Journal of Geophysical Research* 94: 16, 417–21.

Hansen, J. E., Lacis, A. A., Rind, D. H., & Russell, G. L. (1986). "Climate Sensitivity to Increasing Greenhouse Gases." In Barth M. C., & Titus, J. G., *Greenhouse Effect and Sea Level Rise: A Challenge for This Generation*, 42–62. New York: Van Nostrand Reinhold.

Hegerl, G. C., Zwiers, F. W., Braconnot, P., Gillett, N. P., Luo, Y., Marengo Orsini, J. A., et al. (2007). "Understand and Attributing Climate Change: Section 9.2.2, Spatial and Temporal Patterns of the Response to Different Forcings and Their Uncertainties." In Solomon, S., Qin, D., Manning, M., Chen, Z., Marquis, M., Averyt, K. B., et al., *Climate Change 2007: The Physical Science Basis. Contribution of Working Group I to the Fourth Assessment Report of the Intergovernmental Panel on Climate Change*, 674–77. Cambridge, UK: Cambridge University Press.

Henry, J. G., & Heinke, G. W. (1995). *Environmental Science and Engineering*. 2nd ed. New York: Prentice Hall.

Hestenes, D. (2011). *Modeling Methodology for Physics Teachers*. Proceedings of the International Conference on Undergraduate Physics Education, College Park, MD, August 1996. Accessed April 11, 2011, http://modeling.la.asu.edu/modeling/modmeth.html.

Jackson, A. R., & Jackson, J. M. (1996). *Environmental Science: The Natural Environment and Human Impact.* New York: Longmand.

Kish, L. (1967). *Survey Sampling.* 2nd ed. New York: John Wiley & Sons.

Kuhn, T. S. (1996). *The Structure of Scientific Revolutions.* 3rd ed. Chicago and London: University of Chicago Press.

Ladurie, E. L. (1971). *Times of Feast, Times of Famine: A History of Climate since the Year 1000.* New York: Doubleday.

Lave, L. B. (1981). *The Strategy of Social Regulations: Decision Frameworks for Policy.* Washington, DC: Brookings.

Leopold, A. (1948). *A Sand County Almanac, and Sketches Here and There.* New York: Oxford University Press.

Leopold, A. (1970). *A Sand County Almanac.* New York: Ballantine Books.

McHibben, B. (1995). *Hope, Human, and Wild: True Stories of Living Lightly on the Earth.* Boston: Little Brown and Company.

Miller, G. T. (1997). *Environmental Science: Working with the Earth.* 5th ed. Belmont, CA: Wadsworth Publishing.

Miller, G. T. (2004). *Environmental Science: Working with the Earth.* 10th ed. Pacific Grove, CA: Thomson Brooks/Cole.

Molina, M. J., & Rowland, F. S. (1974, June). "Stratospheric Sink for Chlorofluoromethanes: Chlorine Atom-Catalyzed Destruction of Ozone." *Nature* 249: 810–12.

National Center for Education Statistics. (2011). "National Center for Education Statistics, U.S. Department of Education-Environmental Science: Facts and Discussion Forum." Accessed March 2, 2009, http://nces.ed.gov

Ophuls, W. (1977). *Ecology and the Politics of Scarcity.* New York: W. H. Freeman.

Pepper, I. L., Gerba, C. P., & Brusseau, M. L. (1996). *Pollution Science.* San Diego, CA: Academic Press Textbooks.

Popper, K. (1959). *The Logic of Scientific Discovery.* 2nd ed. New York: Routledge Classics.

Ramanathan, V. (2006). "Atmospheric Brown Clouds: Health, Climate, and Agriculture Impacts." *Pontifical Academy of Sciences Scripta Varia* 106: 47–60.

Rice, Doyle (2009). "Your Eyes Aren't Deceiving You: Skies Are Dimmer. *USA Today.* Accessed March 13, 2009, www.usadtodya.com/tech/science/environment/2009-03-12-global-dimming_N.htm.

Sagan, C. (1996). *The Demon-Haunted World: Science as a Candle in the Dark.* New York: Ballantine Books.

Schreuder, H. T., Ernst, R., & Ramirez-Maldonado, H. (2004). *Statistical Techniques for Sampling and Monitoring Natural Resources.* Washington, DC: U.S. Department of Agriculture.

Shiver, B. D., & Borders, B. E. (1996). "Systematic Sampling with Multiple Random Starts." *For. Sci.* 6: 42–50.

Smith, T. M. F. (1994). "Sample Surveys, 1975–1990: An Age of Reconciliation?" *International Statistical Review* 62: 5–34.

Spellman, F. R. (1996). *Stream Ecology and Self-Purification: An Introduction for Wastewater and Water Specialists.* Lancaster, PA: Technomic.

Spellman, F. R., & Whiting, N. (2006). *Environmental Science and Technology: Concepts and Applications.* Boca Raton, FL: CRC Press.

Stanhill, G., & Moreshet, S. (2004). "Global Radiation Climate Changes in Israel." *Climatic Change* 22: 121–38.

Taylor, J. D. (2002). *The Wild Ones: A Quest for North America's Forest and Prairie Grouse.* Lancaster, PA: Bonasa Press.

Taylor, J. D. (2005). *Gunning the Eastern Uplands.* Lancaster, PA: Bonasa Press.

Time Magazine. (1998, August 24). "Global Warming: It's Here . . . and Almost Certain to Get Worse," n.p.

Tower, E. (1995). *Environmental and Natural Resource Economics.* New York: Eno River Press.

Travis, D. J., Carleton, A. M., & Lauritsen, R. G. (2002). "Climatology: Contrails Reduce Daily Temperature Range." *Nature* 418. Accessed March 2, 2009, www.nature.com/nature/journal/v418/n6898/abs/418601a.html.

Trefil, J. (2008). *Why Science?* New York: Teachers College Press.

Upton, G., & Cook, I. (2008). *Oxford Dictionary of Statistics.* New York: Oxford University Press.

U. S. Department of Agriculture (2011). *Pond Fact Sheet No. 17.* Washington, DC: U.S. Department of Agriculture.

U.S. Geological Survey (2009). *Hydroelectric Power Water Use.* Accessed November 5, 2009, http://ga.water.usgs.gov/edu/wuhy.html.

Vergano, Dan (1997, December 1). "Global Warming: Politics and Economics Further Complicate the Issue." *USA Today*, A-1, 2.

Wadsworth, H. M. (1990). *Handbook of Statistical Methods for Engineers and Scientists.* New York: McGraw-Hill.

Walker, M. (1963). *The Nature of Scientific Thought.* Englewood Cliffs, NJ: Prentice-Hall/Spectrum Books.

Wood, R. A., Randall, D. A., Bony, S., Colman, R., Fichefet, T., Fyfe, J., et al. (2007). "Climate Models and Their Evaluation." In Solomon, S., Qin, D., Manning, M., Chen, Z., Marquis, M., Averyt, K. B., et al., *Climate Change 2007: The Physical Science Basis. Contribution of Working Group I to the Fourth Assessment Report of the Intergovernmental Panel on Climate Change*, 589–662. Cambridge, UK: Cambridge University Press.

World Meteorological Organization (2009). *Manual of Codes.* Accessed March 2, 2009, www.wmo.ch/pages/prog/www/WMOCodes/Manual/WMO306_vol-1-2-PartB.pdf.

Zurer, P. S. (1988, May). "Studies on Ozone Destruction Expand beyond Antarctic." *C & E News*, 18–25.

CHAPTER 2

Environmental Science: The Fundamentals

> When you can measure what you are speaking about, and express it in numbers, you know something about it; but when you cannot measure it, when you cannot express it in numbers, your knowledge is of a meager and unsatisfactory kind; it may be the beginning of knowledge, but you have scarcely . . . advanced to the state of science.
>
> —Lord Kelvin (1891)

Chapter Objectives

After studying this chapter, you should be able to:

- Distinguish between frontier science and consensus science.
- Define and apply the concepts of the various biogeochemical cycles.
- Define, apply, and trace energy flow through ecosystems and the biosphere.
- Define and apply the 1st and 2nd Laws of Thermodynamics as they relate to environmental science concepts and systems.
- Know and understand such basic ecological concepts as food chains, food webs, ecological pyramids, productivity, and population.
- Know, understand, apply, and correctly use the units of measure discussed in this chapter and be able to convert from one measurement system to another as needed.

Chapter Outline

- Definition: frontier science versus consensus science
- Definition: biogeochemical cycles
- Discussion: biogeochemical cycles (gaseous and sedimentary)
- Definitions: carbon cycle, nitrogen cycle, phosphorus cycle, sulfur cycle
- Definition: energy flow
- Definition and discussion: materials balance, 1st and 2nd Laws of Thermodynamics

- Discussion: energy flow through the biosphere, energy flow through an ecosystem, photosynthesis, and primary consumers
- Definition and discussion: ecological pyramids
- Definition and discussion: productivity
- Definition and discussion: population
- Definition and discussion: units of measure
- Definition and applications: units of mass, length, volume, temperature, pressure; commonly used units of measure for environmental science; liquid measure, measurement of gases, and vapors

Key Terms

1st Law of Thermodynamics	law of conservation of mass
2nd Law of Thermodynamics	limiting factor
abiotic	liter
aerobic	mass
anaerobic	mass balance equations/calculations
atmosphere	materials balance
biogeochemical cycles	meter
biotic	nitrification
carbon cycles	nitrogen cycle
conduction	nutrient cycles
consensus science	pascal (Pa)
conservation law	phosphorus cycle
convection	photosynthesis
decomposers	population
density	pressure
energy	primary consumers
entropy	producers
eutrophication	productivity
food chain	radiation
food web	sinks
frontier science	specific gravity
gas laws	succession
gram	sulfur cycle
guano	temperature
hydrological cycle	trophic level
Kelvin	volume
kilogram	weight

Introduction

In this chapter, we discuss fundamental concepts foundational to more complex material that follows in subsequent chapters. Because it is crucial to understand pure science in general, the first area discussed covers a brief description of the difference between **frontier science** and **consensus science**. We then shift to the basics of the circulation of matter through the ecosystem—the **biogeochemical cycles**. Because biogeochemical cycles (and most other processes on Earth) are driven by **energy** from the sun, we next present energy and energy transfer. We also provide a brief discussion of the basics of ecology, including **productivity**, **population**, and **succession**. The final section deals with units and measurement.

FRONTIER SCIENCE VERSUS CONSENSUS SCIENCE

Remember in Response Scenario 1.1 the huckster who was selling his newly discovered rayology treatment, which not only guaranteed to cure every disease and malady known to mankind, but also functioned as a fountain of youth? What if news reports focused on rayology as being a new scientific discovery with proven merit, validity, and positive results? As scientists, we know that rayology (at the present time) is a hoax; it is wishful thinking. (Don't you wish it was true?) However, if we did not know that, we would at least know that news reports not backed up by valid data demonstrating preliminary or tested hypotheses and/or models (by themselves tentative) are fictional, at best. This aspect of science is called *frontier science*, because it has not been tested, widely validated, and accepted. In contrast, *consensus science* would be the verification of rayology using the scientists' toolbox, the scientific method. Unfortunately, it is common practice to use the term *science* to describe both frontier and consensus science, usually without distinction (Miller & Brewer, 2008).

Biogeochemical Cycles

To live, grow, and reproduce, the nutrient atoms, ions, and molecules that organisms need are continuously cycled from the nonliving (**abiotic**) environment to living organisms (**biotic**), then back again. This takes place in what are called biogeochemical cycles (**nutrient cycles**)—literally, life-Earth-chemical cycles. The cycle generally describes the physical state, chemical form, and biogeochemical processes affecting the substance at each point in the cycle in an undisturbed ecosystem. Many of these processes are influenced by microbial populations that are naturally adapted to life in **aerobic**, oxygenated, or **anaerobic**, oxygen free, conditions. Because both of these conditions are readily created by varied and fluctuating water levels, wetlands support a greater variety of these processes than other ecosystems (U.S. Forest Service, 1995).

To understand our physical world, we must understand the natural biogeochemical cycles that take place in our environment. Biogeochemical cycles are categorized into two types, the *gaseous* and the *sedimentary*. Gaseous cycles include the **carbon** and **nitrogen cycles**. The **atmosphere** and the ocean are the main **sinks** (storage sites or reservoirs) of nutrients in the gaseous cycle. The sedimentary cycles include the **sulfur** and **phosphorus cycles**. Soil and the rocks of the Earth's crust are the main **sinks** for sedimentary cycles. These cycles are ultimately powered by the sun and fine-tuned and directed by energy expended by organisms. Another important cycle, the **hydrological**

cycle (discussed later), is also solar-powered and acts as a continuous conveyor system that moves materials essential for life through the ecosystem.

Between 20 and 40 elements of the Earth's 92 naturally occurring elements are ingredients that make up living organisms. The chemical elements carbon, hydrogen, oxygen, nitrogen, and phosphorus are crucial in maintaining life as we know it on Earth. Of the elements needed by living organisms to survive, oxygen, hydrogen, carbon, and nitrogen are needed in larger quantities than some of the others. The point is, no matter what elements are needed to sustain life, these elements exhibit definite biogeochemical cycles. For now, let's cover the life-sustaining elements in greater detail.

The elements needed to sustain life are products of the global environment. The global environment consists of three main subdivisions:

1. Hydrosphere: includes all the components formed of water bodies on the Earth's surface.
2. Lithosphere: comprises the solid components, such as rocks.
3. Atmosphere: the gaseous mantle that envelops the hydrosphere and lithosphere.

To survive, organisms require inorganic metabolites from all three parts of the biosphere. For example, the hydrosphere supplies water as the exclusive source of needed hydrogen. The lithosphere provides essential elements (calcium, sulfur, and phosphorus). Finally, the atmosphere provides oxygen, nitrogen, and carbon dioxide.

Within the biogeochemical cycles, all the essential elements circulate from the environment to organisms and back to the environment. Because these elements are critical for sustaining life, you can easily understand why the biogeochemical cycles are readily and realistically labeled "nutrient cycles." Through these biogeochemical (or nutrient) cycles, nature processes and reprocesses the critical, life-sustaining elements in definite inorganic-organic phases. Some cycles (e.g., the carbon cycle) are more perfect than others—that is, the cycle loses no material in the process for long periods of time. Others are less perfect, but one essential point to keep in mind is that energy flows through an ecosystem (we'll explain how later), but nutrients are cycled and recycled.

Because humans need almost all the elements in our complex culture, we have speeded up the movement of many materials so that the cycles tend to become imperfect, or what Odum (1971) calls "acyclic." One example of a somewhat imperfect (acyclic) cycle is our use of phosphate, which of course affects the phosphorus cycle. Phosphate rock is mined and processed with careless abandon, which leads to severe local pollution near mines and phosphate mills. We also increase the input of phosphate fertilizers in agricultural systems without controlling the inevitable increase in runoff output that severely stresses our waterways and reduces water quality through **eutrophication**, the natural aging of a landlocked body of water.

In agricultural ecosystems, we often supply necessary nutrients in the form of fertilizer to increase plant growth and yield. In natural ecosystems, however, these nutrients are recycled naturally though each **trophic level** (feeding level). Plants take up elemental forms. The consumers ingest these elements in the form of organic plant material. They cycle through the **food chain** from producer to consumer, and eventually the nutrients are degraded back to the inorganic form again.

The following sections present and discuss the nutrient cycles for carbon, nitrogen, phosphorus, and sulfur.

THE CARBON CYCLE

Carbon, an essential ingredient for all living things and the basic building block of the large organic molecules necessary for life (carbohydrates, fats, proteins, DNA, and others), is cycled into **food web**s from the atmosphere (see Figure 2.1). Green plants obtain carbon dioxide (CO_2) from the air (Figure 2.1) and through **photosynthesis**—probably the most important chemical process on Earth—which produces the food and oxygen that enables all organisms to live. Part of the carbon produced remains in living matter; the other part is released as CO_2 in cellular respiration, where it is then returned to the atmosphere.

Some carbon is contained in buried dead animal and plant materials. During the course of eons, much of these buried plant and animal materials was transformed into fossil fuels (coal, oil, and natural gas), which contain large amounts of carbon. When fossil fuels are burned, stored carbon combines with oxygen in the air to form carbon dioxide, which enters the atmosphere.

Did You Know?

Major carbon sinks are the atmosphere (CO_2, actually only a small amount of carbon is stored here), the lithosphere (carbonate rocks and fossil fuels, the largest sink), the hydrosphere (CO_2, carbonate, and bicarbonate molecules in water), and biomass (carbon-based organic molecules) in the ecosphere.

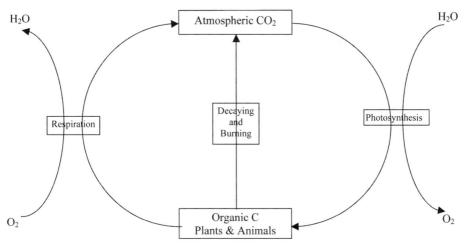

Figure 2.1. Carbon cycle.

In the atmosphere, carbon dioxide acts as a beneficial heat screen: It does not allow the **radiation** of Earth's heat into space. This balance is important. As more carbon dioxide is released into the atmosphere, that balance can be and is altered. Massive increases of carbon dioxide in the atmosphere tend to increase the possibility of global warming. The consequences of global warning might be catastrophic, and the resulting climate change may be irreversible. We'll discuss carbon dioxide and global warming more fully later in the text.

Response Scenario 2.1.
The Carbon Cycle and Deforestation

The carbon cycle is intricate and complex, with several players. Nature is all about balance. Forests take in CO_2 and water, store carbon in wood, and release oxygen. The carbon stored in forests is released back into the atmosphere when trees are burned, such as in forest fires, or when dead trees and leaves decay. Forest management can greatly affect the amount of carbon stored; vigorously growing forests store more carbon than slow-growing ones. When trees are made into lumber or paper, some CO_2 is released, but much continues to be stored in the products or eventually in landfills. Substituting wood for nonrenewable materials can also reduce CO_2 in the atmosphere by reducing fossil fuel energy use (U.S. Forest Service, 2009).

RESPONSE

(i) How does deforestation create imbalances in carbon dioxide levels?

THE NITROGEN CYCLE

The atmosphere contains 78% nitrogen by **volume**. Nitrogen, an essential element for all living matter, constitutes 1% to 3% of the dry **weight** of cells, yet nitrogen is not a common element on Earth. Although it is an essential ingredient for plant growth, nitrogen is chemically very inactive, and before the vast majority of the biomass can incorporate it, it must be fixed.

Although nitrogen gas does make up about 78% of the volume of the Earth's atmosphere, it is useless to most plants and animals in that form. Fortunately, nitrogen gas is converted into compounds containing nitrate ions, which are taken up by plant roots as part of the nitrogen cycle (shown in simplified form in Figure 2.2).

Aerial nitrogen is converted into nitrates mainly by microorganisms, bacteria, and blue-green algae. Lightning also converts some aerial nitrogen gas into forms that return to the Earth as nitrate ions in rainfall and other types of precipitation. Ammonia plays a major role in the nitrogen cycle (Figure 2.2). Excretion by animals and aerobic decomposition of dead organic matter by bacteria produce ammonia. Ammonia is, in turn, converted by **nitrification** bacteria into nitrites and then into nitrates. This pro-

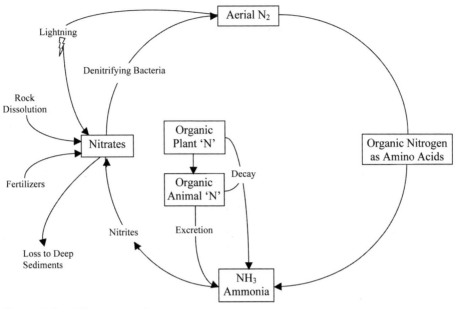

Figure 2.2.   Nitrogen cycle.

cess is known as nitrification. Nitrification bacteria are aerobic. Bacteria that convert ammonia into nitrites are known as nitrite bacteria (*Nitrosococcus* and *Nitrosomonas*); they convert nitrites into nitrates and nitrate bacteria (*Nitrobacter*).

Because nitrogen is often a **limiting factor** in naturally occurring soil, it can inhibit plant growth. Nitrogen is removed from topsoil when we harvest nitrogen-rich crops, irrigate crops, and burn or clear grasslands and forests before planting crops. To increase yields, farmers often provide extra sources of nitrogen by applying inorganic fertilizers or by spreading manure on the field and relying on the soil bacteria to decompose the organic matter and release the nitrogen for plant use.

Did You Know?

Most nitrogen in the atmosphere is in the form of N_2. This gaseous molecule is not reactive and, therefore, needs to be converted to a usable, reactive form. This is accomplished by nitrogen fixation (by lightning and bacteria). In turn, ammonia (NH_3) and ammonium (NH_4) are formed; they are then converted to nitrite (NO_2) and nitrate (NO_3). Nitrate is easily used by plants and then by consumers and returned to the atmosphere in the form of N_2 by ammonification (by decomposers) and then denitrification (by bacteria) processes.

THE PHOSPHORUS CYCLE

Phosphorus (P) is another element common in the structure of living organisms. Phosphorus circulates through water, the Earth's crust, and living organisms in the

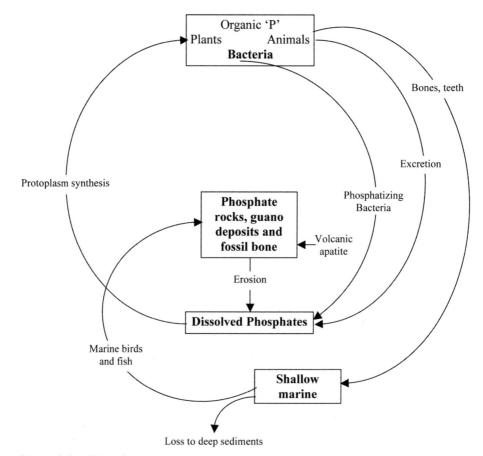

Figure 2.3. Phosphorus cycle.

phosphorus cycle (see Figure 2.3). The ultimate source of phosphorus is rock (Figure 2.3). Phosphorus occurs as phosphate or other minerals formed in past geological ages. It is often stored for long periods of time (millions of years) in phosphate rocks. These massive deposits are gradually eroding, providing phosphorus to various ecosystems. A large amount of eroded phosphorus ends up in deep sediments in the oceans and in lesser amounts in shallow sediments. Some phosphorus reaches land when marine animals are brought out. Birds also play a role in phosphorus recovery. The great **guano** deposit (bird excreta) of the Peruvian coast is one example. Humans have hastened the rate of phosphorus loss through mining and the production of fertilizers, which are washed away and lost.

Phosphorus has become very important in water quality studies, because it is often a limiting factor. Upon entering a stream, phosphates act as fertilizer, which promotes the growth of undesirable algae blooms. As the organic matter decays, dissolved oxygen levels decrease, and fish and other aquatic species die, limiting producer populations in freshwater systems.

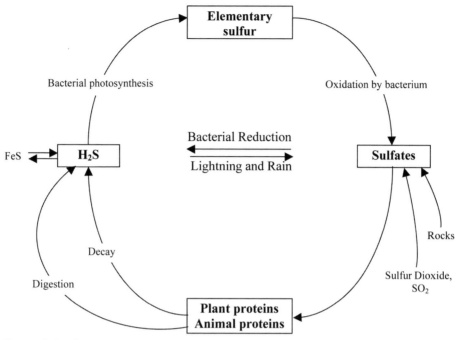

Figure 2.4. Sulfur cycle.

THE SULFUR CYCLE

Sulfur, like nitrogen, is characteristic of organic compounds. Much of it is stored in the lithosphere as sulfide and sulfate minerals. The sulfur cycle (see Figure 2.4) is both sedimentary and gaseous. Bacteria play a major role in the conversion of sulfur from one form to another. In an anaerobic environment, bacteria break down organic matter, thereby producing hydrogen sulfide, with its characteristic rotten-egg odor. Bacteria called *Beggiatoa* convert hydrogen sulfide (H_2S) into elemental sulfur (S). An aerobic sulfur bacterium, *Thiobacillus thiooxidans*, converts sulfur into sulfates. Other sulfates are contributed by the dissolving of rocks and some sulfur dioxide (SO_2) during volcanic eruptions. Sulfur is incorporated by plants into proteins. Some of these plants are then consumed by organisms. Sulfur from proteins is liberated by many heterotrophic anaerobic bacteria, as hydrogen sulfide. In the atmosphere, SO_2 reacts with water to form sulfuric acid (H_2SO_4) and acid rain.

Energy Flow through an Ecosystem and the Biosphere

We often take energy for granted through a deceptive familiarity, because we think of it in so many different ways: atomic energy, food energy, cheap energy, abundant energy, and so forth. This presents a huge double irony, because on the one hand most people know that without it our energy-dependent industrialized society would grind to a halt. On the other hand, energy is more than just the force that powers our machines, our civilization—it powers hurricanes, the movement of the planets, the entire universe. Despite its pervasiveness and its familiarity, energy is a complex and puzzling concept. It cannot be seen, tasted, smelled, or touched. What is it? To answer this question, we must first gain an understanding of **materials balance**.

KEY TERMS DEFINED

- **The Ecological Pyramids**—numbers, productivity, and energy—are based on the fact that due to energy loss, fewer animals can be supported at each additional trophic level (the number of energy transfers an organism is from the rest of the pyramid, which indicates what happens to this energy).
- **Energy** is the ability or capacity to do work. Energy is degraded from a higher to a lower state.
- **The 1st Law of Thermodynamics** states that energy is transformed from one form to another, but is neither created nor destroyed. Given this principle, we should be able to account for all the energy in a system in an energy budget, a diagrammatic representation of the energy flows through an ecosystem.
- **The 2nd Law of Thermodynamics** asserts that energy is only available because of degradation of energy from a concentrated to a dispersed form. This indicates that energy becomes more and more dissipated (randomly arranged) as it is transformed from one form to another or moved from one place to another. It also suggests that any transformation of energy will be less than 100% efficient (i.e., the transfers of energy from one trophic level to another are not perfect); some energy is dissipated during each transfer.
- **Population density** is the number of a particular species in an area. It is affected by natality (birth and reproduction), immigration (moving into), mortality (death), and emigration (moving out of).
- **Ultimate carrying capacity** is the maximum number of a species an area can support; the environmental carrying capacity is the actual maximum capacity a species maintains in an area. Ultimate capacity is always greater than the environmental capacity.

SYSTEMS AND THROUGHPUTS

A *system* is a set of components that operate in a connected and predictable way. It is a defined, physical part of the universe (e.g., the atmosphere, a pond or lake, the human body). Large systems are often made of many smaller systems. All environmental systems have *inputs* (matter, energy, and information), *throughputs* (flows), and *outputs* (wastes; see Figure 2.5). The latter may become inputs for other systems. Consider food and wastewater treatment, for example: We put food in our bodies (input), me-

Inputs   **System throughputs**   **Outputs**

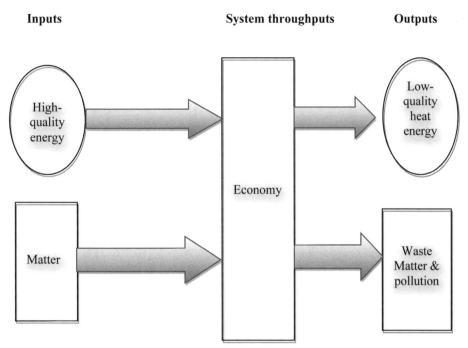

Figure 2.5. Any system requires inputs of energy and matter from the environment. These resources flow through the economy are converted to low quality heat energy, wastes, and pollutants.

tabolize it (throughput), and expel wastes (output). This waste then becomes the input to a wastewater treatment plant or bacteria.

MATERIALS BALANCE[1]

Probably the simplest way to express materials balance, one of the most important and fundamental scientific principles, is to point out that *everything has to go somewhere*. Stated simply, material balance means "what goes in, must come out." According to the **law of conservation of mass or matter**, when chemical reactions take place, matter is neither created nor destroyed (exception: in a nuclear reaction, **mass** can be converted into energy). The importance of this concept in environmental science is that it allows us to track pollutants from one location to another using **mass balance equations**. For example, in a wide variety of air pollution control calculations, material balance equations can be used to evaluate

- formation of combustion products in boilers,
- rates of air infiltration into air pollution control systems,
- material requirements for process operations,
- rate of ash collection in air pollution control systems,
- humidities of exhaust gas streams,

- exhaust gas flow rates from multiple sources controlled by a single air pollution control system, and
- gas flow rates from combustion processes.

Materials balance, or conservation of matter, can be applied in solving problems involving the quantities of matter moving in various parts of a process, as illustrated in Example 2.1.

Example 2.1

Problem: This problem illustrates how a mass balance calculation can be used to check the results of an air emission test.

During an air emission test, the inlet gas stream to a fabric filter is 100,000 actual ft³/min (ACFM), and the particulate loading is 2 grains/actual feet (ACF). The outlet gas stream from the fabric filter is 109,000 ACFM, and the particulate loading is 0.025 grains/ACF (see Figure 2.6). What is the maximum quantity of ash that will have to be removed per hour from the fabric filter hopper, based on these test results?

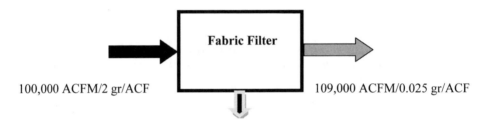

Ash = x lb$_m$/hr

Figure 2.6.   For example 2.1

Solution: Based on particulate mass balance,

$$Mass_{(in)} = Mass_{(out)}$$

Inlet gas stream particulate = Outlet gas steam particulate + Hopper Ash

1. Calculate the inlet and outlet particulate quantities in pounds mass per hour.

$$Inlet\ particulate\ quantity = 100{,}000\ \frac{ACF}{min} \times \left(2\ \frac{gr}{ACF}\right) \times \left(\frac{1\ lb_m}{7{,}000\ gr}\right)$$

$$\times \left(\frac{60\ min}{1\ hr}\right) = 1{,}714.3\ lb_m/hr$$

$$Outlet\ particulate\ quantity = 109{,}000\ ACF/min \times \left(0.025\ \frac{gr}{ACF}\right) \times \left(\frac{1\ lb_m}{7{,}000\ gr}\right)$$

$$\times \left(\frac{60 \text{ min}}{1 \text{ hr}} \right) = 23.4 \text{ lb}_m/\text{hr}$$

2. Calculate the quantity of ash that will have to be removed from the hopper per hour.

Hopper Ash = Inlet gas stream particulate – Outlet gas
Stream particulate
$= 1,714.3 \text{ lb}_m/\text{hr} - 23.4 \text{ lb}_m/\text{hr}$
$= 1,690.9 \text{ lb}_m/\text{hr}$

To perform mass balance analysis, you must first define the particular region to be analyzed. The region you select could include anything—the fabric filter in Example 2.1, a lake, a stretch of river or stream, an air basin above a city or factory, a chemical mixing vat, a coal-fired power plant, or the Earth itself. Whatever region you select for analysis, you must confine the region within an imaginary boundary (see Figure 2.7). From such a region, we can begin to identify the flow of materials across the boundary as well as the accumulation of materials within the region.

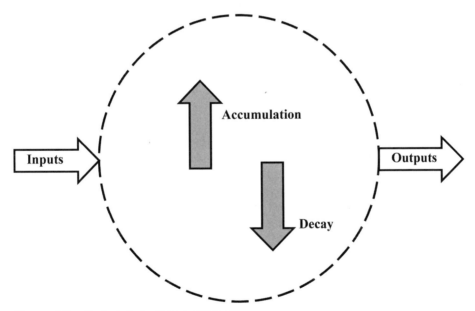

Figure 2.7. Materials balance diagram.

When a material enters the region, it has three possible fates: Some of it may enter and slip through the region unchanged; some of it may accumulate within the boundary; and some of it may be converted—for example, CO to CO_2—to some other material. If we use Figure 2.6 as a guide, a materials balance equation (Equation 2.1) can be written thus:

Input rate = Output rate + Decay rate + Accumulation rate   (2.1)

Note that the decay rate in Equation 2.1 does not imply a violation of the law of conservation of mass. No constraints occur on the change of one substance into another (chemical reactions), but atoms are conserved.

Note: In practice, Equation 2.1 can be (and often is) simplified by assuming steady state of equilibrium conditions (that nothing changes with time), but discussion of this practice is beyond the scope of this text and is generally presented in environmental engineering studies.

Let's get back to our discussion of energy. First of all, what is energy? *Energy* is often defined as the capacity for doing work, and work is often described as the product of force and the displacement of some object caused by that force.

Along with understanding and analyzing the flow of materials through a particular region, we can also determine and analyze the flow of energy. Using the 1st Law of Thermodynamics, we can write *energy balance equations*. The 1st Law states that energy cannot be created or destroyed. In short, energy may change forms in a given process, but we should be able to account for every bit of energy as it takes part in the process. In simplified form, this relationship is shown in Equation 2.2.

$$Energy\ in = Energy\ out \tag{2.2}$$

Equation 2.2 may give you the false impression that the transfer of energy in a process is 100% efficient. This is, of course, not the case. In a coal-fired electrical power generating plant, for example, only a portion of the energy from the burned coal is converted directly into electricity. A large portion of the coal-fired energy ends up as waste heat given off to the environment, because of the 2nd Law of Thermodynamics, which states that every process generates some waste heat; devising a process or machine that can convert heat to work with 100% efficiency is impossible.

Heat can be transferred in three ways: by **conduction**, **convection**, and radiation. When direct contact between two physical objects at different **temperature**s occurs, heat is transferred via conduction from the hotter object to the colder one. When a gas or liquid is placed between two solid objects, heat is transferred by convection. Heat is also transferred when no physical medium exists, by radiation (e.g., radiant energy from the sun).

Did You Know?

The 2nd Law of Thermodynamics holds, I think, the supreme position among laws of nature . . . . [I]f your theory is found to be against the 2nd Law of Thermodynamics, I can give you no hope.—Arthur S. Eddington

---

ENERGY FLOW IN THE BIOSPHERE

Energy flow in the biosphere all starts with the sun. The sun's radiant energy sustains all life on Earth. The sun not only lights and warms the Earth, it provides energy used by green plants to synthesize the compounds that keep them alive. These compounds serve as food for almost all other organisms. The sun's solar energy also powers the biochemical cycles and drives climate systems that distribute heat and fresh water over the Earth's surface.

Figure 2.8 reflects an important point: Not all solar radiant energy reaches the Earth. Approximately 34% of incoming solar radiation is reflected back to space by clouds, dust, and chemicals in the atmosphere and by the Earth's surface. Most of the remaining 66% warms the atmosphere and land, evaporates water and cycles it through the biosphere, and generates winds. Surprisingly, only a small percentage (about 0.022%) is captured by green plants and used to make the glucose essential to life.

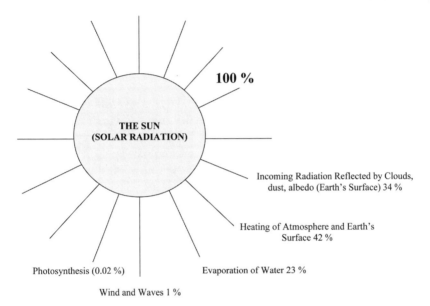

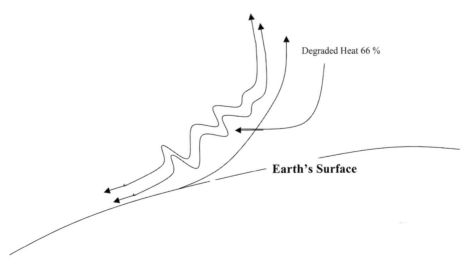

Figure 2.8.   Flow of energy to and from the Earth.

Most of the incoming solar radiation not reflected away is degraded (or wasted) into longer-wavelength heat (in accordance with the 2nd Law of Thermodynamics) and flows into space. The actual amount of energy that returns to space is affected by the presence of molecules of water, methane, carbon dioxide, and ozone, and by various forms of particulate matter in the atmosphere. Many of these barriers are created by man-made activities and might affect global climate patterns by disrupting the rate at which incoming solar energy flows through the biosphere and returns to space. We discuss the possible effects of human activities on climate later.

ENERGY FLOW IN THE ECOSYSTEM

For an ecosystem to exist and to maintain itself, it must have energy. All activities of living organisms involve work—the expending of energy—the degradation of a higher state of energy to a lower state. The flow of energy through an ecosystem is governed by the **1st and 2nd Laws of Thermodynamics**.

Remembering that the 1st law, sometimes called the **conservation law**, states that energy may not be created or destroyed, and that the 2nd law states that no energy transformation is 100% efficient sets the stage for a discussion of energy flow in the ecosystem. Hand in hand with the 2nd law (some energy is always lost, dissipated as heat) is another critical concept—**entropy**. Used as a measure of the nonavailability of energy to a system, entropy increases with an increase in heat dissipation. Because of entropy, input of energy into any system is higher than the output or work done; the resultant efficiency is less than 100%.

Environmental scientists and technicians are primarily concerned with the interaction of energy and materials in the ecosystem. Previously we discussed biogeochemical nutrient cycles and pointed out that the flow of energy drives these cycles. Energy does not cycle as nutrients do in biogeochemical cycles. For example, when food passes from one organism to another, energy contained in the food is reduced step by step, until all the energy in the system is dissipated as heat. This process has been

---

Did You Know?

When an organism loses heat, it represents a one-way flow of energy out of the ecosystem. Plants only absorb a small part of energy from the sun. They store half of the energy and lose the other half. The energy plants lose is metabolic heat. Energy from a primary source will flow in one direction through two different types of food chains. In a grazing food chain, the energy will flow from plants (**producers**) to herbivores, and then through some carnivores. In detritus-based food chains, energy will flow from plants through detrivores and **decomposers**. In terms of the weight (or biomass) of animals in many ecosystems, more of their body mass can be traced back to detritus than to living producers. Most of the time the two food webs will intersect one another. For example, in the Chesapeake Bay, fish in the grazing food web will eat crabs of the detrital food web. (Spellman, 2007)

referred to as a *unidirectional flow* of energy through the system, with no possibility for recycling of energy. When water or nutrients are recycled, energy is required. The energy expended in the recycling is not recyclable. As Odum (1975) points out, this is a "fact not understood by those who think that artificial recycling of man's resources is somehow an instant and free solution to shortages" (p. 61).

The principal source of energy for any ecosystem is sunlight. Producers (green plants—flowers, trees, ferns, mosses, and algae), through the process of photosynthesis, transform the sun's energy into carbohydrates, which are consumed by animals. This transfer of energy, as stated previously, is unidirectional—from producers to consumers. Often the transfer of energy to different organisms is called a *food chain*. Figure 2.9 shows a simple aquatic food chain.

All organisms, alive and dead, are potential sources of food for other organisms. All organisms that share the same general type of food in a food chain are said to be at the same trophic level (feeding level). Because green plants use sunlight to produce

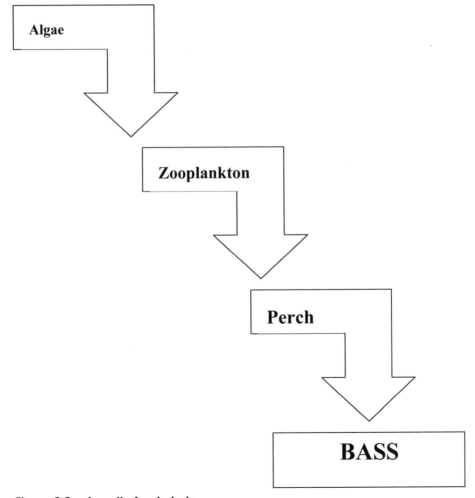

Figure 2.9. Aquatic food chain.

food for animals, they are called producers of the 1st tropic level. The herbivores eat plants directly, and are called the 2nd trophic level, or the **primary consumers**. The carnivores are flesh-eating consumers; they include several trophic levels from the 3rd on up. At each transfer, a large amount of energy (about 80% to 90%) is lost as heat and wastes. Nature normally limits food chains to four or five links. Note, however, that in aquatic food chains, the links are commonly longer than they are on land, because several predatory fish may be feeding on the plant consumers. Even so, the built-in inefficiency of the energy transfer process prevents development of extremely long food chains.

Only a few simple food chains are found in nature, and most are interlocked. This interlocking of food chains forms a *food web*—a map that shows what eats what. An organism in a food web may occupy one or more trophic levels. Food chains and webs help to explain how energy moves through the ecosystem.

Another important trophic level of the food web is comprised of *decomposers*. The decomposers feed on dead plants or animals and play an important role in recycling nutrients in the ecosystem. Healthy ecosystems produce no wastes. All organisms, alive or dead, are potential sources of food (and energy) for other organisms.

Ecological Pyramids

As we proceed in the food chain from the producer to the final consumer, it becomes clear that a particular community in nature often consists of several small organisms associated with a smaller and smaller number of larger organisms. A grassy field, for example, has a larger number of grass and other small plants, a smaller number of herbivores like rabbits, and an even smaller number of carnivores like foxes. The practical significance of this is that we must have many more producers than consumers.

This relationship, which requires more producers than consumers, can be demonstrated graphically by building an *ecological pyramid*. In an ecological pyramid, the number of organisms at various trophic levels in a food chain is represented by separate levels or bars placed one above the other, with the base formed by producers and the apex formed by the final consumer. The pyramid shape is the result of a great amount of energy loss at each trophic level. The same is true if numbers are replaced by the corresponding biomass or energy. Ecologists generally use three types of ecological pyramids: *number*, *biomass*, and *energy*. Obviously, there are differences among them, but some generalizations apply:

1. Energy pyramids must always be larger at the base than at the top (because of the 2nd Law of Thermodynamics, which has to do with dissipation of energy as it moves from one trophic level to another).
2. Likewise, biomass pyramids (in which biomass is used as an indicator of production) are usually pyramid-shaped. This is particularly true of terrestrial systems and aquatic ones dominated by large plants (marshes), in which consumption by heterotroph is low and organic matter accumulates with time. It is important to point out, however, biomass pyramids can sometimes be inverted. This is especially

common in aquatic ecosystems, in which the primary producers are microscopic planktonic organisms that multiply very rapidly, have very short life spans, and are heavily grazed by herbivores. At any single point in time, the amount of biomass in primary producers is less than that in larger, long-lived animals that consume primary producers.

3. Numbers pyramids can have various shapes (and not be pyramids at all, actually) depending on the sizes of the organisms that make up the trophic levels. In forests, the primary producers are large trees and the herbivore level usually consists of insects, so the base of the pyramid is smaller than the herbivore level above it. In grasslands, the number of primary producers (grasses) is much larger than that of the herbivores above (large grazing animals) (Spellman, 2001).

To get a better idea of how an ecological pyramid looks and how it provides information, we need to look at an example. The example to be used here is the energy pyramid. According to Odum (1983), the energy pyramid is a fitting example because among the "three types of ecological pyramids, the energy pyramid gives by far the best overall picture of the functional nature of communities" (p. 154).

In an experiment conducted in Silver Springs, Florida, Odum measured the energy for each trophic level in terms of kilocalories. A kilocalorie is the amount of energy needed to raise 1 cubic centimeter of water 1 degree centigrade. When an energy pyramid is constructed to show Odum's findings, it takes on the typical upright form (as it must because of the 2nd Law of Thermodynamics) shown in Figure 2.10.

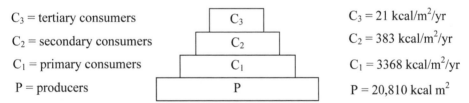

C_3 = tertiary consumers C_3 = 21 kcal/m^2/yr

C_2 = secondary consumers C_2 = 383 kcal/m^2/yr

C_1 = primary consumers C_1 = 3368 kcal/m^2/yr

P = producers   P = 20,810 kcal m^2

Figure 2.10. Energy-flow pyramid. Source: Adapted from Odum, 1971, *Fundamentals of Ecology*, p. 80

In summary, as reflected in Figure 2.10 and according to the 2nd Law, no energy transformation process is 100% efficient. This fact is demonstrated, for example, when a horse eats hay. The horse cannot obtain, for its own body, 100% of the energy available in the hay. For this reason, the energy productivity of the producers must be greater than the energy production of the primary consumers. When human beings are substituted for the horse, it is interesting to note that according to the 2nd Law of Thermodynamics, only a small population could be supported. But this is not the case. Humans also feed on plant matter, which allows a larger population. Therefore, if meat supplies become scarce, we must eat more plant matter. This is the situation we see today in countries where meat is scarce. Consider that if we all ate soybeans, there would be at least enough food for 10 times as many of us as compared to a world in which we all eat beef (or pork, fish, chicken, etc.). Another way of looking at this is that every time we eat meat, we are taking food out of the mouths of nine other people, who could be fed with the plant material that was fed to the animal we are eating (EBE, 1999). It's not quite that simple, of course, but we think you get the general idea.

Productivity[2]

As mentioned previously, the flow of energy through an ecosystem starts with the fixation of sunlight by plants through photosynthesis. In evaluating an ecosystem, the measurement of photosynthesis is important. Ecosystems may be classified into highly productive or less productive. Therefore, the study of ecosystems must involve some measure of their productivity.

Smith (1974) defines production (or more specifically primary production, because it is the basic form of energy storage in an ecosystem) as being "the energy accumulated by plants." Stated differently, primary production is the rate at which the ecosystem's primary producers capture and store a given amount of energy, in a specified time interval. In even simpler terms, primary productivity is a measure of the rate at which photosynthesis occurs; that is, the rate of generation of biomass in an ecosystem via photosynthesis. Odum (1971) lists four successive steps in the production process:

1. *Gross primary productivity*—the total rate of photosynthesis in an ecosystem during a specified interval at a given trophic level.
2. *Net primary productivity*—the rate of energy storage in plant tissues in excess of the rate of aerobic respiration by primary producers.
3. *Net community productivity*—the rate of storage of organic matter not used.
4. *Secondary productivity*—the rate of energy storage at consumer levels.

When attempting to comprehend the significance of productivity as it relates to ecosystems, an example will be useful. Consider the productivity of an agricultural ecosystem such as a wheat field. Often it is expressed as the number of bushels produced per acre. This is an example of the harvest method for measuring productivity. For a natural ecosystem, several one-square-**meter** plots are marked off, and the entire area is harvested and weighed to give an estimate of productivity as **gram**s of biomass per square meter per given time interval. Using this method, net primary production (net yield) can be measured.

Productivity, both in the natural and cultured ecosystems, may vary considerably, not only between type of ecosystems, but also within the same ecosystem. Several factors influence year-to-year productivity within an ecosystem. Such factors as temperature, availability of nutrients, fire, animal grazing, and human cultivation activities are directly or indirectly related to the productivity of a particular ecosystem.

The following study of an aquatic ecosystem is used as an example of productivity. Productivity can be measured in several different ways in the aquatic ecosystem. For example, the production of oxygen may be used to determine productivity. Oxygen content may be measured in several ways. One way is to measure it in the water every few hours for a period of 24 hours. During daylight, when photosynthesis is occurring, the oxygen concentration should rise. At night the oxygen level should drop. The oxygen level can be measured by using a simple x-y graph. It can be plotted on the y-axis, with time plotted on the x-axis, as shown in Figure 2.11.

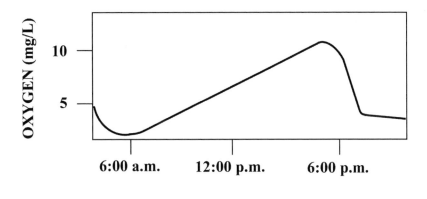

TIME

Figure 2.11. Diurnal oxygen curve for an aquatic ecosystem.

Another method of measuring oxygen production in aquatic ecosystems is to use light and dark bottles. Biochemical oxygen demand (BOD) bottles (300 mL) are filled with water to a particular level. One of the bottles is tested for the initial dissolved oxygen (DO), then the other two bottles (one clear, one dark) are suspended in the water at the depth they were taken from. After a 12-hour period, the bottles are collected, and the DO values for each bottle are recorded. Once the oxygen production is known, the productivity in terms of grams/m/day can be calculated.

Table 2.1 shows representative values for the net productivity of a variety of ecosystems—both natural and managed. Keep in mind that these values are only

Table 2.1. Estimated Net Productivity of Certain Ecosystems

Ecosystem	Kilocalories/m^2/year
Temperate deciduous forest	5,000
Tropical rain forest	15,000
Tall-grass prairie	2,000
Desert	500
Coastal marsh	12,000
Ocean close to shore	2,500
Open ocean	800
Clear (oligotrophic) lake	800
Lake in advanced state of eutrophication	2,400
Silver Springs, Florida	8,800
Field of alfalfa (Lucerne)	15,000
Corn (maize) field, U.S.	4,500
Rice paddies, Japan	5,500
Lawn, Washington, D.C.	6,800
Sugar cane, Hawaii	25,000

approximations derived from Odom's (1971, 1983) work and are subject to marked fluctuations because of variations in temperature, fertility, and availability of water.

In the aquatic (and any other) ecosystem, pollution can have a profound impact on the system's productivity. For example, certain kinds of pollution may increase the turbidity of the water. This increase in turbidity causes a decrease in energy delivered by photosynthesis to the ecosystem. Accordingly, this turbidity and its aggregate effects decrease net community productivity on a large scale (Laws, 1993).

PRODUCTIVITY: THE BOTTOM LINE

The ecological trends paint a clear picture. Wherever we look, ecological productivity is limping behind human consumption. Since 1984, the global fish harvest has been dropping, and so has the per capita yield of grain crops (Brown et al., 1994). Moreover, stratospheric ozone is being depleted, the release of greenhouse gases has changed the atmospheric chemistry and might lead to climate change, erosion and desertification are reducing nature's biological productivity, irrigation water tables are falling, contamination of soil and water is jeopardizing the quality of food, other natural resources are being consumed faster than they can regenerate, and biological diversity is being lost—to reiterate only a small part of a long list. These trends indicate a decline in the quantity and productivity of nature's assets (Wachernagel, 1997).

Population Ecology

Population ecology began with the contributions of Thomas Malthus, an English clergyman, who in 1798 published *Essay on the Principle of Population*. Malthus introduced the concept that at some point in time an expanding population must exceed the supply of prerequisite natural resources—the "struggle for existence" concept. Malthus's theories profoundly influenced Charles Darwin's *On the Origin of Species* in 1859—the "survival of the fittest" concept. Let's begin with the basics.

Population—Defined by the Wordmasters

Webster's *Third New International Dictionary* defines population as:

- "The total number or amount of things especially within a given area."
- "The organisms inhabiting a particular area or biotype."
- "A group of interbreeding biotypes that represents the level of organization at which speciation begins."

Population—Defined by an Ecologist

- A population in an ecological sense is a group of organisms, of the same species, which roughly occupy the same geographical area at the same time.

- Individual members of the same population can either interact directly, or may interact with the dispersing progeny of the other members of the same population (e.g., pollen).
- Population members interact with a similar environment and experience similar environmental limitations (Abedon, 2007).

POPULATION SYSTEM

A population system, or life system (*population system* is definitely better, however), is a population and its effective environment (Clark et al., 1967; Berryman, 1981; Sharov, 1992).

Major Components of a Population System

1. *Population itself:* can be subdivided into groups according to age, stage, sex, and other characteristics.
2. *Resources:* food, shelter, nesting places, space, etc.
3. *Enemies:* predators, parasites, pathogens, etc.
4. *Environment:* air (water, soil) temperature, composition, variability of these characteristics in time and space (Sharov, 1997).

POPULATION ECOLOGY DEFINED

Population ecology is the branch of ecology that studies the structure and dynamics of populations (Sharov, 1996). Population ecology relative to other ecological disciplines is illustrated in Figure 2.12.

The term *population* is interpreted differently in various sciences. For example, in human demography, a population is a set of humans in a given area. In genetics, a population is a group of interbreeding individuals of the same species that is isolated from other groups. In population ecology, a population is a group of individuals of the same species inhabiting the same area.

✓ **Important Point**: Main axiom of population ecology—organisms in a population are ecologically equivalent. Ecological equivalency means that

1. organisms undergo the same life cycle;
2. organisms in a particular stage of the life cycle are involved in the same set of ecological processes; and
3. The rates of these processes (or the probabilities of ecological events) are basically the same if organisms are put into the same environment (however, some individual variation may be allowed) (Sharov, 1996).

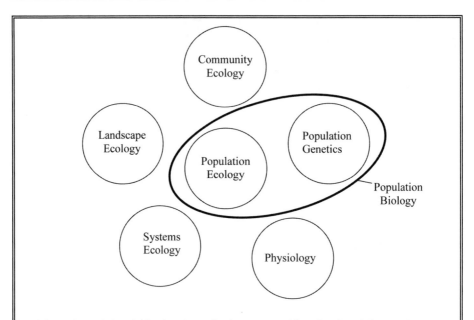

Population ecology – the branch of ecology that studies the structure and dynamics of populations.

Physiology –study of individual characteristics and individual processes. Used as a basis for prediction of processes at the population level.

Community ecology – study of the structure and dynamics of animal and plant communities. Population ecology provides modeling tools that can be used for predicting community structure and dynamics.

Population genetics – the study of gene frequencies and microevolution in populations. Selective advantages depend on the success of organisms in their survival, reproduction and competition. These processes are studied in population ecology. Population ecology and population genetics are often considered together and called 'population biology'. Evolutionary ecology is one of the major topics in population biology.

Systems ecology – a relatively new ecological discipline which studies interaction of human population with environment. One of the major concepts are optimization of ecosystem exploitation and sustainable ecosystem management.

Landscape ecology – another relatively new area in ecology. It studies regional large-scale ecosystems with the aid of computer-based geographic information systems. Population dynamics can be studied at the landscape level, and this is the link between landscape and population ecology

Figure 2.12. Population ecology relative to other ecological disciplines. Adapted from Alexi Sharov, Dept. of Entomology, Virginia Tech, VA, USA, p. 1, 1/1966

Did You Know?

Recent USGS studies have shown that nonnative annual grasses in the genera *Bromus* and *Schismus* now dominate most plant communities in the Mojave Desert. Unlike most native annual plants, these grasses grow in many different situations and can create continuous fuel beds across the landscape by filling in the plant-free space that once separated and protected native perennials from fire.

PROPERTIES OF POPULATIONS

1. Population size (size): Depends on how the population is defined.
2. Population **density** (density): The number of individual organisms per unit area.
3. Patterns of dispersion (dispersion): Individual members of populations may be distributed over a geographical area in a number of different ways, including clumped, uniform, and random distribution.
4. Demographics (demographics): A population's vital statistics, including
   - education,
   - parental status,
   - work environment,
   - geographic location,
   - religious beliefs,
   - marital status,
   - income,
   - sex,
   - race,
   - gender,
   - ethnicity,
   - age,
   - sexual orientation, and
   - physical ability.
5. Population growth (growth): Occurs when there are no limitations on growth within the environment. Two situations result: (1) The population displays its intrinsic rate of increase (i.e., the rate of growth of a population when that population is growing under ideal conditions and without limits); and (2) the population experiences exponential growth (i.e., exponential growth means that a population's size at a given time is equal to the population's size at an earlier time, times some greater-than-one number) (Abedon, 2007).
6. Limits on population growth (limits): Exponential growth cannot go on forever; sooner or later any population will run into limits in the environment.

✓ **Important Point**: Note that all of these properties are not those of individual organisms but instead are properties that exist only if one considers more than one organism at any given time, or over a period of time.

LAWS OF POPULATION ECOLOGY

According to Haemig (2006),[3] the discovery of laws in ecology has lagged behind many of the other sciences (e.g., chemistry, physics, etc.) because ecology is a much younger science. However, as Colyvan and Ginzburg (2003) point out, misunderstandings and unrealistic expectations of what laws are have also hindered the search, as have mistaken beliefs that ecology is just too complex a science to have laws. Nevertheless, over the years, researchers have been able to identify some of the laws that do exist in ecology.

Ginzburg (1986) points out that although much remains to be learned, it now appears that the laws of ecology resemble the laws of physics. Colyvan and Ginsburg (2003) and Ginzburg and Colyvan (2004) point out that the laws of ecology describe idealized situations, have many exceptions, and need not be explanatory or predictive. The laws of population ecology are described below.

- **Malthusian Law** states that when birth and death rates are constant, a population will grow (or decline) at an exponential rate.
- **Allee's Law** states that there is a positive relationship between individual fitness and either the numbers or density of conspecifics (conspecifics are other individuals of the same species).
- **Verhulst's Law** deals with one factor: intraspecific competition (i.e., competition between members of the same species). Because the organisms limiting the population are also members of the population, this law is also called "population self-limitation" (Turchin, 2001).
- **Lotka-Volterra's Law** states that "when populations are involved in negative feedback with other species, or even components of their environments," oscillatory (cyclical) dynamics are likely to be seen (Berryman, 2002, 2003).
- **Liebig's Law** states that of all the biotic or abiotic factors that control a given population, one has to be limiting (i.e., active, controlling the dynamics) (Berryman, 1993, 2003). Time delays produced by this limiting factor are usually one or two generations long (Berryman, 1999). Krebs (2001) defines "a factor as limiting if a change in the factor produces a change in average or equilibrium density."
- **Fenchel's Law** states that species with larger body sizes generally have lower rates of population growth—the maximum rate of reproduction decreases with body size at a power of approximately one-quarter the body mass (Fenchel, 1974). Fenchel's Law is expressed by the following equation:

$$r = aW^{-1/4}$$

where

r = the intrinsic rate of natural increase of the population
a = constant (has three different values)
W = average body weight (mass) of the organism

- **Calder's Law** states that species with larger body sizes generally have longer population cycles—the length of the population cycle increases with increasing body size at a power of approximately one-quarter the body mass (Calder, 1983). Calder's Law is expressed by the following equation:

$$t = aW^{1/4}$$

where

t = average time of the population cycle
a = a constant
W = average body weight (mass) of the organism

- **Damuth's Law** states that species with larger body sizes generally have lower average population densities—the average density of a population decreases with body size at a power of approximately three-quarters the body mass (Damuth, 1981, 1987, 1991). Damuth's Law is expressed by the following equation:

$$d = aW^{-3/4}$$

where

d = the average density of the population
a = a constant
W = average body weight (mass) of the organism

- **Generation-Time Law** states that species with larger body sizes usually have longer generation-times—that the generation-time increases with increasing body size at a power of approximately one-quarter the body mass (Bonner, 1965). **Note:** The body mass used in this law is the body mass of the organism at the time of reproduction. The Generation-Time Law is expressed by the following equation:

$$g = aW^{1/4}$$

where

g = average generation-time of the population
a = a constant
W = average body weight (mass) of the organism

- **Ginzburg's Law** states that the length of a population cycle (oscillation) is the result of the maternal effect and inertial populating growth. According to this law, the periods in the cycles of a population must be either two generations long or six or more generations long (Ginzburg & Colyvan, 2004).

APPLIED POPULATION ECOLOGY

When attempting to explain any concept, it is always best to do so with an illustrative example. In the following discussion, a stream ecosystem is the example used to help explain population ecology.

If environmental scientists wanted to study the organisms in a slow-moving stream or stream pond, they would have two options. They could study each fish, aquatic plant, crustacean, insect, and macroinvertebrate one by one. In that case, they would be studying individuals. It would be easier to do this if the subject were trout, but it would be difficult to separate and study each aquatic plant.

The second option would be to study all of the trout, all of the insects of each specific kind, and all of a certain aquatic plant type in the stream or pond at the time of the study. When stream ecologists study a group of the same kind of individuals in a given location at a given time, they are investigating a population. "Alternately, a population may be defined as a cluster of individuals with a high probability of mating with each other compared to their probability of mating with a member of some other population" (Pianka, 1988). When attempting to determine the population of a particular species, it is important to remember that time is a factor. Whether it is at various times during the day, during the different seasons, or from year to year, time is important because populations change.

When measuring populations, the level of species or density must be determined. Density (D) can be calculated by counting the number of individuals in the population (N) and dividing this number by the total units of space (S) the counted population occupies. Thus, the formula for calculating density is

$$D = N/S \qquad\qquad (2.3)$$

When studying aquatic populations, the occupied space (S) is determined by using length, width, and depth measurements. The volumetric space is then measured in cubic units.

Population density may change dramatically. For example, if a dam is closed off in a river midway through spawning season, with no provision allowed for fish movement upstream (a fish ladder), it would drastically decrease the density of spawning salmon upstream. Along with the swift and sometimes unpredictable consequences of change, it can be difficult to draw exact boundaries between various populations. Pianka (1988) makes this point in his comparison between European starlings that were introduced into Australia and starlings that were introduced into North America. He points out that these starlings are no longer exchanging genes with each other; thus, they are separate and distinct populations.

The population density or level of a species depends on natality, mortality, immigration, and emigration. Changes in population density are the result of both births and deaths. The birth rate of a population is called *natality*, and the death rate, *mortality*. In aquatic populations, two factors besides natality and mortality can affect density. For example, in a run of returning salmon to their spawning grounds, the density could vary as more salmon migrated in or as others left the run for their own spawning grounds. The arrival of new salmon in a population from other places is termed *immigration* (ingress). The departure of salmon from a population is called *emigration* (egress). Thus, natality and immigration increase population density, whereas mortality and emigration decrease it. The net increase in population is the difference between these two sets of factors.

Population regulation is the control of the size of a population. Population is limited by various factors. There are basically two types of population-limiting factors: (1) density-dependent control and (2) density-independent control (Winstead, 2007).

1. **Density-dependent factors** are present when the size of the population depends on the original density or size of the population. Density-dependent factors include the following situations (Abedon, 2007):
    - Density-dependent limits on population growth stem from intraspecific competition.
    - Typically, the organisms best suited to compete with another organism are those from the same species.

- Thus, the actions of conspecifics (again, an organism belonging to the same species as another) can very precisely serve to limit the environment (e.g., eat preferred food, obtain preferred shelter, etc.).
- Actions that serve to limit the environment for conspecifics—e.g., eating, excreting wastes, using up nonfood resources, taking up space, defending territories—are those that determine carrying capacity (K).
- The greater the density of the *population*, the greater their effects.
- They may exert their effect by reducing birth rates, increasing death rates, extending generation times, or forcing the migration of conspecifics to new regions.
- "The impact of disease on a population can be density dependent if the transmission rate of the disease depends on a certain level of crowding the population" (Campbell & Reece, 2004).
- "A death rate that rises as population density rises is said to be density dependent, as in a birth rate that falls with rising density. Density-dependent rates are an example of negative feedback. In contrast, a birth rate or death rate that does not change with population density is said to be density independent. . . . . Negative feedback prevents unlimited population growth" (Campbell & Reece, 2004).
- Predation can also be density dependent, because predators often can switch prey preferences to match whatever prey organisms are more plentiful in a given environment.
- "Many predators, for example, exhibit switching behavior: They begin to concentrate on a particularly common species of prey when it becomes energetically efficient to do so" (Campbell & Reece, 2004).
2. *Density-independent* factors are present

> where the effect of the factor on the size of the population is independent and does not depend upon the original density or size of the population. The effect of weather is an example of a density-independent factor. A severe storm and flood coming through an area can just as easily wipe out a large population as small one. Another example would be a harmful pollutant put into the environment, e.g., a stream. The probability of that harmful substance at some concentration killing an individual would not change depending on the size of the population. For example, populations of small mammals are often regulated more by this type of regulation. (Winstead, 2007)

Density-dependent factors include the following situations:
- Their effects on population sizes (or structures) occur to the same extent regardless of population size.
- They include things like sudden changes in the weather.
- "Over the long term, many populations remain fairly stable in size and are presumably close to a carrying capacity that is determined by density-dependent factors. Superimposed on this general stability, however, are short-term fluctuations due to density-independent factors" (Campbell & Reece, 2004).

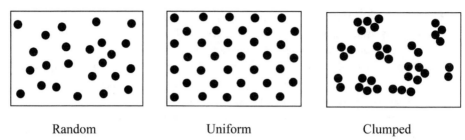

| Random | Uniform | Clumped |

**Figure 2.13.   Basic patterns of distribution. Source: Adapted from Odum, 1971,
Fundamentals of Ecology, p. 205**

DISTRIBUTION OR DISPERSION

Each organism occupies only those areas that can provide for its requirements, resulting in an irregular distribution or dispersion. How a particular population is distributed within a given area has considerable influence on density. As shown in Figure 2.13, organisms in nature may be distributed (dispersed) in three ways, as a result of complex interactions among ecological variables.

In a *random* distribution, there is an equal probability of an organism occupying any point in space, and "each individual is independent of the others" (Smith, 1974). In other words, the position of each individual is not determined or influenced by the other members of the population.

In a *regular* or *uniform* distribution, organisms are spaced more evenly; they are not distributed by chance. Animals compete with each other and effectively defend a specific territory, excluding other individuals of the same species. In regular or uniform distribution, the competition between individuals can be quite severe and antagonistic, to the point where spacing generated is quite even (Odum, 1983). This is seen in forest areas where trees are uniformly distributed so that each receives adequate water and light.

The most common distribution is the *contagious* or *clumped* distribution, in which organisms are found in groups, clumped together; this may reflect the heterogeneity of the habitat. Smith (1974) points out that contagious or clumped distributions "produce aggregations, the result of response by plants and animals to habitat differences."

Organisms that exhibit a contagious or clumped distribution may develop social hierarchies in order to live together more effectively. Animals within the same species have evolved many symbolic aggressive displays that carry meanings that are not only mutually understood but also prevent injury or death within the same species. For example, in some mountainous regions, dominant male bighorn sheep force the juvenile and subordinate males out of the territory during breeding season (Hickman et al., 1990). In this way, the dominant male gains control over the females and need not compete with other males.

As mentioned, distribution patterns are the result of complex interactions among ecological variables. For example, consider a study conducted by Hubbell and Johnson (1977) of five tropical bee colonies (the bees live in colonies in suitable trees) in the tropical dry forests of Costa Rica. The researchers set out to examine relationships between aggressiveness and patterns of colony distribution.

1. The researchers mapped locations of suitable nest trees. They found that the number of suitable trees was greater than the number of colonies—thus nest sites were not a limiting factor. Distribution of suitable trees was random.
2. The researchers next mapped locations of bee colonies. They found that colony sites for one species were dispersed randomly. Members of this species do not exhibit aggression toward one another. The colonies were sometimes quite close to one another. On the other hand, colony sites for the other four species were dispersed in a regular fashion. Members of all four species were aggressive to members of other colonies of the same species. They also marked their colony sites with pheromones and engaged in ritualized battles for colony sites with conspecifics from other colonies.

POPULATION GROWTH

As mentioned previously, the size of animal populations is constantly changing due to natality, mortality, emigration, and immigration. The population size will increase if the natality and immigration rates are high. On the other hand, it will decrease if the mortality and emigration rates are high. Each population has an upper limit on size, often called the *carrying capacity* (K). Carrying capacity can be defined as the "optimum number of species' individuals that can survive in a specific area over time" (Enger et al., 1989). Stated differently, K is the maximum number of species that can be supported in a bioregion. A pond may be able to support only a dozen frogs, depending on the food resources for the frogs in the pond. If there were 30 frogs in the same pond, at least half of them would probably die, because the pond environment wouldn't have enough food for them to live. Carrying capacity is based on the quantity of food supplies, the physical space available, the degree of predation, and several other environmental factors.

Did You Know?

How do we count black and grizzly bear (see Figures 2.14a-b) populations in the wild? The U.S. Geological Survey (2010) has found an apparent answer to this question, launching a 2009 grizzly bear research project in the Northern Continental Divide Ecosystem of northwestern Montana. This work uses hair collection and DNA analysis. This method estimates population growth by collecting hair at natural bear rubs along trails, roads, and fence and power lines. Short pieces of barbed wire were attached to the rubbed surface to facilitate hair collection at most sites; however, barbless wire was used on trees bumped by pack animals. No lures or attractants were used to attract bears to these sites. Using this method, USGS was able to count 258 individual grizzlies that had deposited hair.

Figure 2.14a. Black bear in Sequoia National Park, CA. Photo courtesy of Frank Spellman

Figure 2.14b. Black bear in Sequoia National Park, CA. Photo courtesy of Frank Spellman

There are two types of carrying capacity: ultimate and environmental. *Ultimate* carrying capacity is the theoretical maximum density; that is, the maximum number of individuals of a species in a place that can support itself without rendering the place uninhabitable. The *environmental* carrying capacity is the actual maximum population density that a species maintains in an area. Ultimate is always higher than environmental carrying capacity.

The population for a certain species may exhibit several types of growth. Smith (1974) points out that "the rate at which the population grows can be expressed as a graph of the numbers in the population against time." Figure 2.15 shows one type of growth curve.

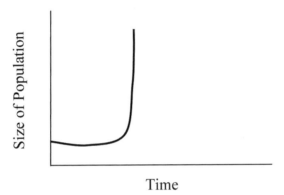

Figure 2.15. J-shaped growth curve.

The J-shaped curve shown in Figure 2.15 shows a rapid increase in size or exponential growth. Eventually, the population reaches an upper limit, at which exponential growth stops. The exponential growth rate is usually exhibited by organisms that are introduced into a new habitat, by organisms with a short life span such as insects, and by annual plants. A classic example of exponential growth by an introduced species is the reindeer transported to Saint Paul Island in the Pribolofs off Alaska in 1911. A total of 25 reindeer were released on the small island, and by 1938 there were over 2,000 animals there. As time went by, however, the reindeer overgrazed their food supply, and the population decreased rapidly. By 1950 only 8 reindeer could be found (Pianka, 1988).

Another example of exponential growth is demonstrated by the "Lily Pond Parable," which provides insight into long-term carrying capacity and population growth.

Lily Pond Parable

1. If a pond lily doubles every day, and it takes 30 days to completely cover a pond, on what day will the pond be one-quarter covered?
2. Half covered?
3. Does the size of the pond make a difference?
4. What kind of environmental, social, and economic developments can be expected as the 30th day approaches?

5. What will begin to happen at one minute past the 30th day?
6. At what point (what day) would preventative action become necessary to prevent unpleasant events?

Answers

1. Day 28. Growth will be barely visible until the final few days. (On the 25th day, the lilies cover 1/32nd of the pond; on the 21st day, the lilies cover 1/512th of the pond.)
2. Day 29.
3. No. The doubling time is still the same. Even if you could magically double the size of the pond on day 30, it would still hold only one day's worth of growth!
4. The pond will become visibly more crowded each day, and this crowding will begin to exhaust the resources of the pond.
5. The pond will be completely covered. Even though the lilies will be reproducing, there will be no more room for additional lilies, and the excess population will die off. In fact, since the resources of the pond have been exhausted, a significant proportion of the original population may die off as well.
6. It depends on how long it takes to implement the action and how full you want the lily pond to be. If it takes two days to complete a project to reduce lily reproductive rates, that action must be started on day 28, when the pond is only 25% full—and that will still produce a completely full pond. Of course, if the action is started earlier, the results will be much more dramatic.

Another type of growth curve is shown in Figure 2.16. This logistic or S-shaped (sigmoidal) curve is used for populations of larger organisms having a longer life span. This type of curve has been successfully used by ecologists and biologists to model populations of several different types of organisms, including water fleas, pond snails, and sheep, to name only a few (Masters, 1991). The curve suggests an early exponential growth phase, while conditions for growth are optimal. As the number of individuals increases, the limits of the environment, or *environmental resistance*, begin to

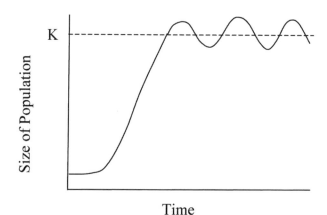

Figure 2.16. S-shaped (sigmoidal) growth curve.

Doubling Time and the Rule of 70

Population growing at a constant rate will have a constant doubling time . . . the time it takes for the population to double in size.

Population growing at a constant rate can be modeled with an exponential growth equation:

$$D_n/d_t = R_n$$

The integral of equation is

$$N_t = N_0 e^{rt}$$

How long will it take for the population to double growing at a constant rate (r)?

$$0.69/R = T$$

THE RULE OF 70

The Rule of 70 is useful for financial as well as demographic analysis. It states that to find the doubling time of a quantity growing at a given annual percentage rate, divide the percentage number into 70 to obtain the approximate number of years required to double. For example, at a 10% annual growth rate, doubling time is 70/10 = 7 years.

Similarly, to get the annual growth rate, divide 70 by the doubling time. For example, 70/14 years doubling time = 5, or a 5% annual growth rate.

The following table shows some common doubling times:

Growth Rate (% per Year)	Doubling Time in Years
0.1	700
0.5	140
1.0	70
2.0	35
3.0	23
4.0	18
5.0	14
6.0	12
7.0	10
10.0	7

decrease the number of individuals, and the population size levels off near the carrying capacity, shown as K in Figure 2.16. Usually there is some oscillation around K before the population reaches a stable size, as indicated on the curve.

As pointed out in the discussion of the Rule of 70 above, the S-shaped curve in Figure 2.16 is derived from the following differential equation:

$$D_n/d_t = R_n(1 - N/K)$$

where N is population size, R is a growth rate, and K is the carrying capacity of the environment. The factor $(1 - N/K)$ is the environmental resistance. As population grows, the resistance to further population growth continuously increases.

It is interesting to note that the S-shaped curve can also be used to find the maximum rate at which organisms can be removed without reducing the population size. This concept in population biology is called the *maximum sustainable yield value* of an ecosystem. For example, imagine fishing for steelheads in a stream. If the stream is at its carrying capacity, theoretically there will be no population growth, so that any steelheads removed will reduce the population. Thus, the maximum sustainable yield will correspond to a population size less than the carrying capacity. If population growth is logistic or S-shaped, the maximum sustainable yield will be obtained when the population is half the carrying capacity. This can be seen in the following:

The slope of the logistic curve is given by

$$D_n/d_t = R_n \, (1 - N/K)$$

Setting the derivative to zero gives

$$d/d_t \, (D_n/d_t = r \, d_n/d_t - r/k \, (2N \, D_n/d_t) = 0$$

yielding

$$1 - 2N/K = 0$$
$$N = K/2$$

The logistic growth curve is said to be density conditioned. As the density of individuals increases, the growth rate of the population declines.

As stated previously, after reaching environmental carrying capacity, a population normally oscillates around the fixed axis due to various factors that work against maintaining the population at the K level due to direct dependence on resource availability. Table 2.2 shows some factors that affect population size.

Table 2.2. Factors Affecting Population Size

Density Independent	Density Dependent
Drought	Food
Fire	Pathogens
Heavy rain	Predators
Pesticides	Space
Human destruction of habit	Psychological disorders/physiological disorders

Density-dependent factors increase in importance as the size of the population increases. For example, as the size of a population grows, food and space may become limited. The population has reached its carrying capacity. When food and space become limited, growth is suppressed by competition. Odum (1983) describes density-dependent factors as acting "like governors on an engine and for this reason [they] are considered one of the chief agents in preventing overpopulation."

Density-independent factors have the same effect on population regardless of size. Typical examples of density-independent factors are devastating forest fires, streambeds drying up, or the destruction of the organism's entire food supply by disease.

Thus, population growth is influenced by multiple factors. Some of these factors are generated within the population, others from without. Usually no single factor can account fully for the curbing of growth in a given population. It should be noted, however, that humans are by far the most important factor; their activities can increase or exterminate whole populations.

POPULATION RESPONSE TO STRESS

When a population reaches its apex of growth (its carrying capacity), various forces work to maintain it at a certain level. On the other hand, populations are exposed to small or moderate environmental stresses. These stresses work to affect the stability or persistence of the population. Ecologists have concluded that a major factor that affects population stability or persistence is species diversity.

Species diversity is a measure of the number of species and their relative abundance. There are several ways to measure species diversity. One is to use the straight ratio, $D = S/N$. In this ratio, D = species diversity, N = number of individuals, and S = number of species. As an example, a community of 1,000 individuals is counted; these individuals are found to belong to 50 different species. The species diversity would be 50/1,000 or 0.050. This calculation does not take into account the distribution of individuals of each species. For this reason, the more commonly used calculation of species diversity is the Shannon-Weiner Index, which measures diversity thus:

$$H = - \sum_{i=1} (pi) (\log pi)$$

where

H = the diversity index
s = the number of species
i = the species number
pi = proportion of individuals of the total sample belonging to the ith species.

The Shannon-Weiner Index is not universally accepted by ecologists as being the best way to measure species diversity, but it is an example of a method that is available.

Species diversity is related to several important ecological principles. For example, under normal conditions, high species diversity, with its large variety of different species, tends to spread risk. That is, ecosystems that are in a fairly constant or stable environment, such as a tropical rain forest, usually have higher species diversity. However, as Odum (1983) points out, "diversity tends to be reduced in stressed biotic communities."

If the stress on an ecosystem is small, it can usually adapt quite easily. Moreover, even when severe stress occurs, ecosystems have a way of adapting. Severe environmental change to an ecosystem can result from such natural occurrences as fires, earthquakes, and floods, and from human-induced changes such as land clearing, surface mining, and pollution.

One of the most important applications of species diversity is in the evaluation of pollution. As stated previously, it has been determined that stress of any kind will reduce the species diversity of an ecosystem to a significant degree. In the case of domestic sewage, for example, the stress is caused by a lack of dissolved oxygen (DO) for aquatic organisms.

Ecological Succession

Ecosystems can and do change. For example, if a forest is devastated by fire, it will grow back, eventually, because of ecological succession. *Ecological succession* is the observed process of change (a normal occurrence in nature) in the species structure of an ecological community over time; that is, a gradual and orderly replacement of plant and animal species takes place in a particular area over time. The result of succession is evident in many places. For example, succession can be seen in an abandoned pasture. It can be seen in any lake and any pond. Succession can even be seen where weeds and grasses grow in the cracks in a tarmac roadway or sidewalk. Other examples of observable succession are the following:

1. Consider a red pine planting area where the growth of hardwood trees (including ash, poplar, and oak) occurs. The consequence of this hardwood tree growth is the increased shading and subsequent mortality of the sun-loving red pines and their replacement by the shade-tolerant hardwood seedlings. The shaded forest floor conditions generated by the pines prohibit the growth of sun-loving pine seedlings and allow the growth of the hardwoods. The consequence of the growth of the hardwoods is the decline and senescence of the pine forest.
2. Consider raspberry thickets growing in the sunlit forest sections beneath the gaps in the canopy generated by wind-thrown trees. Raspberry plants require sunlight to grow and thrive. Beneath the dense shade canopy, particularly of red pines but also dense stands of oak, there is not sufficient sunlight for the raspberry's survival. However, in any place in which there has been a tree fall, the raspberry canes proliferate into dense thickets. Within these raspberry thickets are dense growths of hardwood seedlings. The raspberry plants generate a protected "nursery" for these seedlings and prevent a major browser of tree seedlings (the white-tailed deer) from eating and destroying the trees. By providing these trees a shaded haven in which to grow, the raspberry plants are setting up the future tree canopy, which will extensively shade the future forest floor and consequently prevent the future growth of more raspberry plants!

Succession usually occurs in an orderly, predictable manner. It involves the entire system. The science of ecology has developed to the point that ecologists are now able to predict several years in advance what will occur in a given ecosystem. For example, scientists know that if a burned-out forest region receives light, water, nutrients, and an influx or immigration of animals and seeds, it will eventually develop into another forest through a sequence of steps or stages.

Two types of ecological succession are recognized by ecologists: primary and secondary. The particular type that takes place depends on the conditions at a particular site at the beginning of the process.

Secondary succession is the most common type. It occurs in an area where the natural vegetation has been removed or destroyed, but the soil is not destroyed. For example, succession that occurs in abandoned farm fields, known as *old field succession*, illustrates secondary succession. An example of secondary succession can be seen in the Piedmont region of North Carolina. Early settlers of the area cleared away the native oak-hickory forests and cultivated the land. In the ensuing years, the soil became depleted of nutrients, reducing the soil's fertility. As a result, farming ceased in the region a few generations later, and the fields were abandoned. Some 150 to 200 years after abandonment, the climax oak-hickory forest was restored.

PROCESS OF SUCCESSION

Five factors are involved in the process of succession:

1. *Inertia*—the tendency of an ecosystem to maintain its overall structure.
2. *Disturbance*—an event that will instigate the process of succession.
3. *Primary succession*—when a community starts from bare rock.
4. *Secondary succession*—when succession starts from an area where humans once farmed.
5. *Tolerance*—when late succession plants are not disturbed by early succession plants.

Units of Measurement

A basic knowledge of units of measurement and how to use them is essential for students of environmental science. Environmental science students and practitioners should be familiar with both the *U.S. Customary System (USCS)* or *English System* and the *International System of Units (SI)*. We summarize some of the important units here to enable better understanding of material covered later in the text. Table 2.3 provides conversion factors between the SI and USCS systems for some of the most basic units encountered.

In the study of environmental science, you will commonly encounter both extremely large quantities and extremely small ones. The concentration of some toxic substance may be measured in parts per million or billion (ppm or ppb), for example. *ppm* may be roughly described as the volume of liquid contained in a shot glass compared to the volume of water contained in a swimming pool. To describe quantities that may take on such large or small values, a system of prefixes that accompany the units is useful. We present some of the more important prefixes in Table 2.4.

Table 2.3. Commonly Used Units and Conversion Factors

Quantity	SI Units	SI Symbol	Conversion Factor	USCS Units
Length	Meter	m	3.2808	Ft
Mass	Kilogram	kg	2.2046	lb.
Temperature	Celsius	C	1.8 (C) + 32	F
Area	Square meter	m^2	10.7639	ft^2
Volume	Cubic meter	m^3	35.3147	ft^3
Energy	Kilojoule	Kj	0.9478	Btu
Power	Watt	W	3.4121	Btu/hr
Velocity	Meter/second	m/s	2.2369	mi/hr

UNITS OF MASS

Simply defined, mass is a quantity of matter and measurement of the amount of inertia that a body possesses. Mass expresses the degree to which an object resists a change in its state of rest or motion and is proportional to the amount of matter in the object. Another, simpler way to understand mass is to think of it as the quantity of matter an object contains.

Beginning science students often confuse mass with weight. Weight is the gravitational force acting upon an object and is proportional to mass. In the SI system (a modernized metric system), the fundamental unit of mass is the gram (g). How does this stack up against weight?

To show the relationship between mass and weight, consider that a pound contains 452.6 grams. In laboratory-scale operations, the gram is a convenient unit of measurement. However, in real-world applications the gram is usually prefixed with one of the prefixes shown in Table 2.4. For example, human body mass is expressed in **kilograms** (1 kg = 2.2 pounds). In everyday terms, a kilogram is the mass of one **liter** of water. When dealing with units of measurement pertaining to environmental conditions such as air pollutants and toxic water pollutants, they may be measured in teragrams (1 × 10^{12} grams) and micrograms (1 × 10^{-6} grams), respectively. When dealing with large-scale industrial commodities, the mass units may be measured in units of megagrams (Mg), also known as a metric ton.

Often mass and density are mistaken as signifying the same thing—they do not. Where mass is the quantity of matter and measurement of the amount of inertia that

Table 2.4.   Common Prefixes

Quantity	Prefix	Symbol
10^{-12}	Pico	P
10^{-9}	Nano	N
10^{-6}	Micro	M
10^{-3}	Milli	M
10^{-2}	centi	C
10^{-1}	Deci	D
10	Deca	Da
10^2	Hecto	H
10^3	Kilo	K
10^6	Mega	M

a body contains, density refers to how compacted a substance is with matter; density is the mass per unit volume of an object, and its formula can be written as:

$$Density = \frac{mass}{volume}$$

Something with a mass of 25 kg that occupies a volume of 5 m^3 would have a density of 25 kg/5m^3 = 5 kg/m^3. In this example the mass was measured in kilograms and the volume in cubic meters.

UNITS OF LENGTH

In measuring locations and sizes, we use the fundamental property of length, defined as the measurement of space in any direction. Space has three dimensions, each of which can be measured by length. This can be easily seen by considering the rectangular object shown in Figure 2.17. It has length, width, and height, but each of these dimensions is a length.

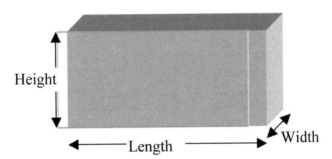

Figure 2.17. Length.

In the metric system, length is expressed in units based on the meter (m), which is 39.37 inches long. A kilometer (km) is equal to 1,000 m and is used to measure relatively great distances. In practical laboratory applications, the centimeter (cm = 0.01 m) is often used. There are 2.540 cm per inch, and the cm is employed to express lengths that would be given in inches in the English system. The micrometer (μm) is also commonly used to express measurements of bacterial cells and wavelengths of infrared radiation by which Earth re-radiates solar energy back to outer space. For measuring visible light (400 to 800 nm), the nanometer (nm) (10^{-9}) is often used.

UNITS OF VOLUME

The easiest way to approach measurements involving volume is to remember that volume is surface area multiplied by a third dimension. The liter is the basic metric unit of volume and is the volume of a decimeter cubed (1 L = 1 dm^3). A milliliter (mL) is the same volume as a cubic centimeter, cm^3.

UNITS OF TEMPERATURE

Temperature is a measure of how "hot" something is—how much thermal energy it contains. Temperature is a fundamental measurement in environmental science, especially in most pollution work. The temperature of a stack gas plume, for example, determines its buoyancy and how far the plume of effluent will rise before attaining the temperature of its surroundings. This in turn determines how much it will be diluted before traces of the pollutant reach ground level.

Temperature is measured on several scales; for example, the centigrade or Celsius and Fahrenheit scales are both measured from a reference point—the freezing point of water—which is taken as 0°C or 32°F, respectively. The boiling point of water is taken as 100°C or 212°F, respectively. Thermodynamic devices usually work in terms of absolute or "thermodynamic temperature," where the reference point is absolute 0, the lowest possible temperature attainable. For absolute temperature measurement, the thermodynamic unit or **Kelvin** (K) scale—which uses centigrade divisions, for which zero is the lowest attainable measurement—is used. A unit of temperature on this scale is equal to a Celsius degree, but is not called a degree. It is called a Kelvin and designated as K, not °K. The value of absolute zero on the Kelvin scale is −273.15°C, so the Kelvin temperature is always a 273 (rounded) higher than the Celsius temperature. Thus, water boils at 373 K and freezes at 273 K.

To convert from the Celsius scale to the Kelvin scale, simply add 273 to the Celsius temperature. Mathematically,

$$K = {}^\circ C + 273 \qquad (2.5)$$

where

K = temperature on the Kelvin scale
$^\circ C$ = temperature on the Celsius scale

Converting from Fahrenheit to Celsius or vice versa is not so easy. The equations used are

$$^\circ C = 5/9(^\circ F - 32) \qquad (2.6)$$

and

$$^\circ F = 9/5\,^\circ C + 32 \qquad (2.7)$$

where

$^\circ C$ = temperature on the Celsius scale
$^\circ F$ = temperature on the Fahrenheit scale

As examples, 15°C = 59°F and 68°F = 20°C. Either, of course, can be a negative number.

UNITS OF PRESSURE

Pressure is force per unit area and can be expressed in a number of different units, including the atmosphere (atm), the average pressure exerted by air at sea level, or the **pascal** (Pa), usually expressed in kilopascal (1 kPa = 1,000 Pa, and 101.3 kPa = 1 atm). Pressure can also be given as millimeters of mercury (mm Hg), based on the amount of pressure required to hold up a column of mercury in a mercury barometer. One mm of mercury is a unit called the *torr*, and 760 torr equal 1 atm.

UNITS OFTEN USED IN ENVIRONMENTAL STUDIES

In environmental studies, often the concentration of some substance (foreign or otherwise) in air or water is of interest. In either medium, concentrations may be based on volume or weight, or a combination of the two (which may lead to some confusion). Following are explanations of how weight and volume are used to determine concentrations when studying liquids or gases/vapors.

Liquids

Concentrations of substances dissolved in water are usually expressed in terms of weight of substance per unit volume of mixture. In environmental science, a good practical example of this weight per unit volume is best observed whenever a contaminant is dispersed in the atmosphere in solid or liquid form as a mist, dust, or fume. When this occurs, its concentration is usually expressed on a weight-per-volume basis. Outdoor air contaminants and stack effluents are frequently expressed as grams, milligrams, or micrograms per cubic meter; ounces per thousand cubic feet; pounds per thousand pounds of air; and grains per cubic foot. Most measurements are expressed in metric units. However, the use of standard U.S. units is justified for purposes of comparison with existing data, especially those relative to the specifications for air-moving equipment.

Alternatively, concentrations in liquids are expressed as weight of substance per weight of mixture, with the most common units being parts per million (ppm) or parts per billion (ppb).

Since most concentrations of pollutants are very small, one liter of mixture weighs essentially 1,000 g, so that for all practical purposes we can write:

$$1 \text{ mg/L} = 1 \text{ g/m}^3 = 1 \text{ ppm (by weight)} \tag{2.8}$$

$$1 \text{ μg/L} = 1 \text{ mg/m}^3 = 1 \text{ ppb (by weight)} \tag{2.9}$$

The environmental science practitioner may also be involved with concentrations of liquid wastes that may be so high that the **specific gravity** (the ratio of an object's or substance's weight to that of an equal volume of water) of the mixture is affected, in which case a correction to equations 2.8 and 2.9 may be required:

$$\text{mg/L} = \text{ppm by weight} \times \text{specific gravity} \tag{2.10}$$

Gases/Vapors

For most air pollution work, by custom, we express pollutant concentrations in volumetric terms. For example, the concentration of a gaseous pollutant in parts per million (ppm) is the volume of pollutant per million volumes of the air mixture. That is:

$$ppm = \frac{parts\ of\ contaminant}{million\ parts\ of\ air} \qquad (2.11)$$

Calculations for gas and vapor concentrations are based on the **gas laws**:

- The volume of a gas under constant temperature is inversely proportional to the pressure.
- The volume of a gas under constant pressure is directly proportional to the Kelvin temperature. The Kelvin temperature scale is based on absolute zero (0°C = 273K).
- The pressure of a gas of a constant volume is directly proportional to the Kelvin temperature.

When measuring contaminant concentrations, you must know the atmospheric temperature and pressure under which the samples were taken. At standard temperatures and pressure (STP), 1 gm-mol of an ideal gas occupies 22.4 liters (L). The STP is 0°C and 760 mm Hg. If the temperature is increased to 25°C (room temperature), and the pressure remains the same, 1 g-mol of gas occupies 24.45 liters.

Sometimes you'll need to convert milligrams per cubic meter (mg/m³) (weight-per-volume ratio) into a volume-per-unit-volume ratio. If one gram-mole of an ideal gas at 25°C occupies 24.45 L, the following relationships can be calculated.

$$ppm = \frac{24.45\ mg/m^3}{molecular\ wt} \qquad (2.12)$$

$$mg/m^3 = \frac{molecular\ wt}{24.45}\ ppm \qquad (2.13)$$

Chapter Summary

Environmental science, like any other true science, has a foundation in observation and numerical analysis. The biogeochemical cycles that allow and sustain life on our planet operate on levels beyond ordinary observation, a common enough problem in scientific analysis. Without fundamental knowledge of the foundational biogeochemical cycles, energy's position and importance in all life cycles, basic principles of ecology, and the basics of how to quantify information gathered from the environments studied, you have not "advanced to the state of science" (Lord Kelvin, 1891).

Discussion Questions and Problems

1. Distinguish between work and energy.
2. How can we best conserve our energy resources?
3. Define environment.
4. What is a biogeochemical cycle? How do such cycles connect past, present, and future forms of life?
5. Describe several advantages for an animal that can occupy more than one trophic level.
6. Trace the route carbon might follow as it cycles through a terrestrial ecosystem. Include at least four organisms in the cycle.
7. How does biological fixation of nitrogen differ from atmospheric fixation?
8. Using the 2nd Law of Thermodynamics, explain why such a sharp decrease in high-quality energy occurs along each step of the food chain. Doesn't energy loss at each step violate the 1st Law of Thermodynamics? Explain.
9. Suggest ways in which the transportation systems can be modified to result in environmental improvement compared to present practices.
10. Explain the differences among ecosystem, niche, and habitat. Give examples of each.
11. The vapor pressure of a solvent (molecular weight = 100) at 25°C and 1 atm pressure is 400 mm Hg. Calculate the concentration resulting from a substantial spill in a small space that is left uncleaned. Express the answer in both ppm and mg/m^3.
12. How many mL of liquid CCl_4 must be evaporated into a 5-L bag at 25°C and 1 atm pressure if a final concentration of 25-ppm (v/v) is desired?
13. The air quality standard for ozone (O_3) is 0.08 ppm. Express that standard in $\mu g/m^3$ at 1 atm pressure and 25°C.
14. The exhaust gas from an automobile contains 1.0% by volume of carbon monoxide. Express the concentration in mg/m^3 at 20°C and 1 atm.
15. The federal air quality standard for carbon monoxide (based on an 8-hour measurement) is 9.0 ppm. Express this standard as a percentage by volume as well as in mg/m^3 at 1 atm and 20°C.
16. Explain why the level of phosphorus in soil often limits plant growth on land and why phosphorus also limits the growth of producers in many freshwater streams and lakes.

Suggested Research Topics and Projects

- Research human activities that affect biogeochemical cycles.
- Research how phosphorus affects water bodies.
- Perform a mass balance analysis for a region.
- Extended definition: 1st and 2nd Laws of Thermodynamics.
- Research human activities that affect global weather patterns.

- Trace how energy moves through an ecosystem.
- Research possible energy resource conservation techniques.
- Visit a nearby stream and try to determine the major producers, consumers, detritivores, and decomposers.

Notes

1. From U.S. Environmental Protection Agency, 2010, "Material Balance—Air Pollution Control Module 1." Accessed April 16, 2011, www.epa.gov/apti/bces/module1/material/material.htm.

2. This section is from F. R. Spellman, 2007, *Ecology for Non-Ecologists*. Lanham, MD: Government Institutes Press.

3. The information in this section is based on and adapted from P. D. Haemig, 2006, "Laws of Population Ecology," *ECOLOGY.INFO* 23.

References and Recommended Reading

Abedon, S. T. (2007). *Population Ecology*. Accessed February 27, 2007, abdeon.1@osu.edu.

Allee, W. C. (1932). *Animal Aggregations: A Study in General Sociology*. Chicago: University of Chicago Press.

Berryman, A. A. (1981). *Population Systems: A General Introduction*. New York: Plenum Press.

Berryman, A. A. (1993). "Food Web Connectance and Feedback Dominance, Or Does Everything Really Depend on Everything Else?" *Oikos* 68: 13–185.

Berryman, A. A. (1999). *Principles of Population Dynamics and Their Application*. Cheltenham, UK: Stanley Thornes.

Berryman, A. A. (2002). *Population Cycles: The Case for Trophic Interactions*. New York: Oxford University Press.

Berryman, A. A. (2003). "On Principles, Laws, and Theory in Population Ecology." *Oikos* 103: 695–701.

Bolin, B., & Cook, R. B. (1983). *The Major Biogeochemical Cycles and Their Interactions*. New York: Wiley.

Bonner, J. T. (1965). *Size and Cycle*. Princeton, NJ: Princeton University Press.

Brown, L. R., Durning, A., Flavin, C., French, H., Lenssen, N., Lowe, M., et al. (1994). "Facing Food Insecurity." In Brown L. R., et al. (eds.), *State of the World, 1994*, 177–97. New York: W. W. Norton.

Calder, W. A. (1983). "An Allometric Approach to Population Cycles of Mammals." *Journal of Theoretical Biology* 100: 275–82.

Calder, W. A. (1996). *Size, Function, and Life History*. Mineola, NY: Dover Publications.

Campbell, N. A., & Reece, J. B. (2004). *Biology*. 7th ed. Menlo Park, CA: Benjamin Cummings.

Clark, L. R., Gerier, P. W., Hughes, R. D., & Harris, R.F. (1967). *The Ecology of Insect Populations*. London: Methuen.

Colinvaux, P. (1986). *Ecology*. New York: John Wiley & Sons.

Colyvan, M., & Ginzburg, L. R. (2003). "Laws of Nature and Laws of Ecology." *Oikos* 101: 649–53.

Damuth, J. (1981). "Population Density and Body Size in Mammals." *Nature* 290: 699–700.

Damuth, J. (1987). "Interspecific Allometry of Population Density in Mammals and Other Animals: The Independence of Body Mass and Population Energy Use." *Biological Journal of the Linnean Society* 31: 193–246.

Damuth, J. (1991). "Of Size and Abundance." *Nature* 351: 268–69.

Dasmann, R. F. (1984). *Environmental Conservation*. New York: John Wiley & Sons.

Ehrlich, P. R., Ehrlich, A. H., & Holdren, J. P. (1977). *Ecoscience: Population, Resources, and Environment*. San Francisco: W. H. Freeman.

Enger, E., Kormelink, J. R., Smith, B. F., & Smith, R. J. (1989). *Environmental Science: The Study of Interrelationships*. Dubuque, IA: William C. Brown Publishers.

Fenchel, T. (1974). "Intrinsic Rate of Natural Increase: The Relationship with Body Size." *Oecologia* 14: 317–26.

Ginzburg, L. R. (1986). "The Theory of Population Dynamics: 1. Back to First Principles." *Journal of Theoretical Biology* 122: 385–99.

Ginzburg, L. R., & Colyvan, M. (2004). *Ecological Orbits: How Planets Move and Populations Grow*. New York: Oxford University Press.

Ginzburg, L. R., & Jensen C. X. J. (2004). "Rules of Thumb for Judging Ecological Theories." *Trends in Ecology and Evolution* 19: 121–26.

Haemig, P. D. (2006). "Laws of Population Ecology." *ECOLOGY.INFO* 23.

Hickman, C. P., Roberts, L. S., & Hickman, F. M. (1990). *Biology of Animals*. St. Louis, MO: Time Mirror/Mosby College Publishing.

Hubbell, S. P., & Johnson, L. K. (1977). "Competition and Next Spacing in a Tropical Stingless Bee Community." *Ecology* 58: 949–63.

Kormondy, E. J. (1984). *Concepts of Ecology*, 3rd ed. Englewood Cliffs, NJ: Prentice-Hall.

Krebs, R. E. (2001). "Scientific Laws, Principles, and Theories." Westport, CT: Greenwood Press.

Laws, E. A. (1993). *Environmental Science: An Introductory Text*. New York: John Wiley & Sons.

Liebig, J. (1840). *Chemistry and Its Application to Agriculture and Physiology*. London: Taylor Walton.

Lotka, A. J. (1925). *Elements of Physical Biology*. Baltimore: Williams & Wilkins.

Malthus, T. R. (1798). *An Essay on the Principle of Population*. London: J. Johnson.

Manahan, S. E. (1997). *Environmental Science and Technology*. Boca Raton, FL: Lewis Publishers.

Masters, G. M. (1991). *Introduction to Environmental Engineering and Science*. Englewood Cliffs, NJ: Prentice-Hall.

McShaffrey, D. (1999). "Environmental Biology: Ecosystems." Accessed February 27, 2007, www.marietta.edu.biol.102/ecosystem.html.

Miller, G. T. (1988). *Environmental Science: An Introduction*. Belmont, CA: Wadsworth.

Miller, T., Jr., & Brewer, R. (2008). *Living in the Environment*. Belmont, CA: Brooks/Cole.

Moran, J. M., Morgan, M. D., & Wiersma, H. H. (1986). *Introduction to Environmental Science*. New York: W. H. Freeman and Company.

Odum, E. P. (1971). *Fundamentals of Ecology*. Philadelphia, PA: Saunders College Publishing.

Odum, E. P. (1975). *Ecology: The Link Between the Natural and the Social Sciences*. New York: Hold, Rinehart, and Winston.

Odum, E. P. (1983). *Basic Ecology*. Philadelphia, PA: Saunders College Publishing.

Pianka, E. R. (1988). *Evolutionary Ecology*. New York: HarperCollins.

Porteous, A. (1992). *Dictionary of Environmental Science and Technology*. New York: John Wiley.

Price, P. W. (1984). *Insect Ecology*. New York: John Wiley & Sons.

Ramade, F. (1984). *Ecology of Natural Resources*. New York: John Wiley.

Sharov, A. (1992). "Life-System Approach: A System Paradigm in Population Ecology." *Oikos* 63: 485–94.

Sharov, A. (1996). *What Is Population Ecology?* Blacksburg, VA: Department of Entomology, Virginia Tech University.

Sharov, A. (1997). *Population Ecology.* Accessed February 28, 2007, www.gypsymoth.ent.ut.edu/sharov/population/welcome.

Smith, R. L. (1974). *Ecology and Field Biology.* New York: Harper & Row.

Spellman, F. R. (1996). *Stream Ecology and Self-Purification.* Boca Raton, FL: CRC Press.

Spellman, F. R. (2007). *Ecology for Nonecologists.* Lanham, MD: Government Institutes.

Tomera, A. N. (1989). *Understanding Basic Ecological Concepts.* Portland, ME: J. Weston Walch, Publisher.

Townsend, C. R., Harper, J. L., & Begon, M. (2000). *Essentials of Ecology.* Malden, MA: Blackwell Science.

Turchin, P. (2001). "Does Population Ecology Have General Laws?" *Oikos* 94: 17–26.

Turchin, P. (2003). *Complex Population Dynamics: A Theoretical/Empirical Synthesis.* Princeton, NJ: Princeton University Press.

U.S. Forest Service (1995). *Forested Wetlands.* NA-PR-01-95. Washington, DC: U.S. Department of Agriculture.

U.S. Forest Service (2009). *U.S. Forest Resource Facts and Historical Trends.* Accessed March 26, 2011, http://fia.fs.fed.us/library/briefings-summaries-overviews/docs/2002_ForestStats_%20FS801.pdf.

U.S. Geological Survey (1999). "Hawaiian Volcano Observatory." Accessed March 1, 2007, http://hvo.wr.usgs.gov /volcano-watch/1999/99_04_01.html.

Verhulst, P. F. (1838). "Notice sur la loi que la population suit dans son accrossement." *Corr. Math. Phys.* 10: 113–21.

Volterra, V. (1926). "Variazioni e fluttuazioni del numero d'indivudui in specie animali conviventi. " *Mem. R. Accad. Naz. die Lincei Ser. VI* 2.

Wachernagel, M. (1997). "Framing the Sustainability Crisis: Getting from Concerns to Action." Accessed February 26, 2007, www.sdri.ubc.ca/publications/wacherna.html.

Wanielista, M. P., Yousef, Y. A., Taylor, J. S., & Cooper, C. D. (1984). *Engineering and the Environment.* Monterey, CA: Brooks/Cole Engineering Division.

Wessells, N. K., & Hopson, J. L. (1988). *Biology.* New York: Random House.

Winstead, R. L. (2007). *Population Regulation.* Accessed February 28, 2007, http://nsm1.nsm.iup.edu/

World Commission on Environment and Development. (1987). *Our Common Future.* New York: Oxford University Press.

CHAPTER 3

Environmental Chemistry

Once I was let down into a deep well into which choke-damp had settled, and nearly lost my life. The deeper I was immersed into the invisible poison, the less capable I became of willing measures to escape from it. And in just this condition are those who toil or dawdle or dissipate in crowded towns, in the sinks of commerce or pleasure.—John Muir (1874)

Chapter Objectives

After studying this chapter, you should be able to:

- Discuss and define the three states of matter, its components, their physical/chemical properties, and controlling laws.
- Define and discuss elements and compounds, the nomenclature, and naming processes.
- Define, apply, and correctly use the information contained in the periodic table: classification, atomic structure, and periodic structure.
- Calculate atomic weights and formulae.
- Define and discuss the similarities and differences between ionic and covalent bonds and compounds.
- Apply and discuss how thermal properties affect/effect changes in particular substances.
- Apply and discuss the properties of pH and acids, bases, and salts
- Define, describe, and discuss the similarities and differences between organic chemistry and chemistry.

Chapter Outline

- Discussion: chemistry and environmental science
- Definition and discussion: chemistry and matter

- Definition and discussion: elements and compounds
- Definition and discussion: element classification
- Definition and discussion: physical and chemical changes and chemical bonds
- Definition and discussion: atomic structure, weight, and number
- Definition and discussion: periodic classification and periodic law
- Definition and discussion: atoms, compounds, molecules, and ions
- Definition and discussion: chemical bonds, ionic and covalent bonds, and how they form compounds
- Definition and discussion: notation of chemical formula and equations
- Definition and discussion: calculation of molecular weights and formula
- Definition and discussion: characteristics of the two types of properties of matter
- Definition and discussion: solid, liquid, and gaseous states and how temperature effects change between them
- Definition and discussion: gaseous state, pressure, volume, and temperature
- Definition and discussion: liquids and solutions, solvents, concentrates, and saturation
- Definition and discussion: thermal properties of chemicals, units of measure, and caloric calculations
- Definition and discussion: acid and base neutralization and pH scale
- Definition and discussion: organic chemistry, organic compounds, molecular structure, and hydrocarbons
- Definition and discussion: soil pollution
- Definition and discussion: chemistry as it relates to environmental science

Key Terms

absorption
acid
adsorption
aggregate
alkalinity
anaerobic
aliphatic hydrocarbon
alkanes
alkenes
alkynes
analysis
aqueous solution
aromatic hydrocarbons
atomic number
atomic orbital/electron shell
atomic weight
atoms
Avogadro's number

base
boiling point
Btu
calorie
chemical bonds
chemical change
chemical equation
chemical formula
chemical reaction
color
colloidal
compound
concentrated solution
covalent bonds
density
dilute solutions
electron
elements

formula weight
gas
greenhouse effect
heat
hydrocarbon
ideal gas law
inorganic substance
ionic bonds
latent heat of fusion
latent heat of vaporization
leaching
liquid
melting point
metalloids
metals
mixture
mole
molar concentration (molarity)
molecular weight
molecule
neutron
nonmetals
nutrient

organic chemistry
organic substance
parent material
particulate matter
periodic law
periodic table
period
pH
photochemical smog
physical change
pressure
proton
precipitate
saturated solution
sewage
solid
solubility
solute
solvent
specific heat
standard temperature and pressure (STP)
synthesis
valence

Introduction

Why do we need to study chemistry for environmental science? In a general sense, consider that on foundational levels, chemistry affects everything we do. Not a single moment goes by during which we are not affected in some way by a chemical substance, process, or reaction. Chemistry affects every aspect of our daily lives.

In a specific sense, consider that almost every environmental and pollution problem we face today (and probably tomorrow) has a chemical basis. In short, in environmental studies, to examine critical environmental problems, including the **greenhouse effect**, ozone depletion, groundwater contamination, toxic wastes, air pollution, stream pollution, and **acid rain**, without some fundamental understanding of basic chemical concepts would be difficult, if not impossible. An environmental practitioner who must solve environmental problems and understand remediation clean-up processes, such as emission control systems or waste treatment facilities, must be well grounded in chemical principles and the techniques of chemistry in general, because many of these techniques are used to solve environmental problems.

The environmental science practitioner, student, or interested reader who uses this text may or may not have some fundamental knowledge of chemistry. This chapter's topics were selected with the goal of reviewing only the essential chemical principles required to understand the nature of the environmental problems we face and the chemistry involved in scientific and technological approaches to their solutions.

Case Study 3.1. Toxic Sulfuric Acid

At 6:30 p.m. on Monday, October 5, 1998, 16 railroad cars derailed on the Buffalo and Pittsburgh Railroad at the edge of the Allegheny National Forest near the Clarion River, not far from Erie, Pennsylvania. One of the derailed cars spilled its load of toxic sulfuric acid.

Emergency workers contained the spill about eight hours after the accident occurred, and the leaking tank car was sealed about three hours later. Once the tank was sealed, the acid, which hung in the air in a light mist, dissipated.

No injuries were reported, although 100 people were evacuated from their homes in nearby Portland Mills overnight. Route 949 was closed while workers from a remediation company finished cleaning up the spill.

Emergency workers had been concerned about acid contamination of the Clarion River, but the spill's flow had been contained in a ditch between the tracks and the road. None of the sulfuric acid reached the river (Associated Press, 1998).

In this particular hazardous materials emergency, proper planning and emergency procedures prevented both human health and environmental damage.

The environmental problems we face are too numerous to list in one book. However, consider the incident detailed in Case Study 3.1 as a representative sample of the kinds of issues the environmental practitioner may be called upon to mitigate. In this particular case, an understanding of basic chemistry and the dangers associated with the spilling of sulfuric acid is important.

What Is Chemistry?

Science is about asking questions. Chemistry is the science that asks questions about the composition of matter (**gas**, liquid, or solid), the differences between these three forms, how they react with one another, how heat and other forms of energy affect them, and the changes that take place in all three forms under certain conditions.

Every substance, material, and object in the environment is either a chemical substance or a mixture of chemical substances. Your body is made up of literally thousands of chemicals. The food we eat, the clothes we wear, the fuel we burn, and the vitamins we take in from natural or synthetic sources are all products of chemistry, wrought either by the forces of nature or the hand of man. Again, chemistry is about matter; its actual makeup, constituents, and consistency. It is about measuring and quantifying matter.

What is matter? All matter can exist in three states: **gas**, **liquid**, or **solid**. It is composed of minute particles termed **molecules**, which are constantly moving, and may be further divided into **atoms**. Molecules that contain atoms of one kind only are known as **elements**; those that contain atoms of different kinds are called **compounds**.

Chemical compounds are produced by a chemical action that alters the arrangements of the atoms in the reacting molecules. Heat, light, vibration, catalytic action, radiation or pressure, as well as moisture (for ionization) may be necessary to produce a chemical change. Examination and possible breakdown of compounds to determine their components is **analysis**, and the building up of compounds from their components is **synthesis**. When substances are brought together without changing their molecular structures, they are said to be **mixtures**.

Organic substances consist of virtually all compounds that contain carbon. All other substances are **inorganic substances**.

Elements and Compounds

A **pure substance** is a material from which all other materials have been separated. Pure substances (samples of pure substances are indistinguishable from each other, no matter what procedures are used to purify them or their origins) include copper metal, aluminum metal, distilled water, table sugar, and oxygen. All samples of table sugar are alike and indistinguishable from all other table sugar samples.

Usually expressed in terms of percentage by mass, a *substance* is characterized as a material having a fixed composition. Distilled water, for example, is a pure substance consisting of approximately 11% hydrogen and 89% oxygen by mass. By contrast, a lump of coal is not a pure substance, because its carbon content may vary from 35 to 90% by mass. Materials (like coal) that are not pure substances are mixtures. When substances can be broken down into two or more simpler substances, they are called compounds.

When substances cannot be broken down or decomposed into simpler forms of matter, they are called elements. The elements are the basic substances of which all matter is composed. At the present time there are only roughly 100 known elements, but there are well over a million known compounds. Of the more than 100 elements, only 88 are present in detectable amounts on Earth, and many of them are rare. Ten elements make up approximately 99% by mass of the Earth's crust, including the surface layer, the atmosphere, and the bodies of water. Table 3.1 shows that the most abundant element on Earth is oxygen, which is found in the free state in the atmosphere, as well as in combined form with other elements in numerous minerals and ores.

Table 3.1 also lists the symbols and **atomic number** of the ten chemicals listed. The symbols consist of either one or two letters, with the first letter capitalized. The atomic number of an element is the number of protons in the nucleus.

Classification of Elements

Every element may be classified as a metal, nonmetal, or metalloid. **Metals**, elements that are typically lustrous solids, are good conductors of heat and electricity, melt and boil at high temperatures, possess relatively high densities, and are normally malleable (can be hammered into sheets) and ductile (can be drawn into a wire). Examples of metals are copper, iron, silver, and platinum. Almost all metals are solids (none is gaseous) at room temperature (mercury being the only exception).

Table 3.1.   Elements That Make up 99% of Earth's Crust, Oceans, and Atmosphere

Element	Symbol	% of Composition	Atomic Number
Oxygen	O	49.5	8
Silicon	Si	25.7	14
Aluminum	Al	7.5	13
Iron	Fe	4.7	26
Calcium	Ca	3.4	20
Sodium	Na	2.6	11
Potassium	K	2.4	19
Magnesium	Mg	1.9	12
Hydrogen	H	1.9	1
Titanium	Ti	0.58	22

Elements that do not possess these general physical properties (i.e., are poor conductors of heat and electricity, boil at relatively low temperatures, do not possess a luster, and are less dense than metals) are called **nonmetals**. At room temperature, most nonmetals are either solids or gases (the exception is bromine, a liquid). Nitrogen, oxygen, and fluorine are examples of gaseous nonmetals; sulfur, carbon, and phosphorus are examples of solid nonmetals.

Several elements have properties resembling both metals and nonmetals. They are called **metalloids** (semimetals). The metalloids are boron, silicon, germanium, arsenic, tellurium, antimony, and polonium.

Physical and Chemical Changes

Internal linkages among a substance's units (between one atom and another) maintain its constant composition. These linkages are called **chemical bonds**. When a particular process occurs that involves the making and breaking of these bonds, we say that a **chemical change** or **chemical reaction** has occurred; that is, chemical changes are those that result in the production of another substance. Combustion, photosynthesis, decomposition, and corrosion are common examples of chemical changes that impact our environment.

Let's briefly consider some examples of chemical change. When a flame is brought into contact with a mixture of hydrogen and oxygen gases, a violent reaction takes place. The **covalent bonds** in the hydrogen (H_2) molecules and of the oxygen (O_2) molecules are broken, and new bonds are formed to produce molecules of water, H_2O.

The key point to remember is that *whenever chemical bonds are broken, or formed, or both, a chemical change takes place*. The hydrogen and oxygen undergo a chemical change to produce water, a substance with new properties.

When mercuric oxide, a red powder, is heated, small globules of mercury are formed, and oxygen gas is released. This mercuric oxide is changed chemically to form molecules of mercury and molecules of water.

By contrast, a **physical change** (nonmolecular change) is one in which the molecular structure of a substance is not altered. When a substance freezes, melts, or changes to vapor, the composition of each molecule does not change. For example, ice, steam, and liquid water are all made up of molecules containing two atoms of hydrogen and one atom of oxygen. Painting a piece of wood will not make it stop being wood. A substance can be ripped or sawed into small pieces, ground into powder, or molded into a different shape without changing the molecules in any way.

The types of behavior that a substance exhibits when undergoing chemical changes are called its **chemical properties**. The characteristics that do not involve changes in the chemical identity of a substance are called its **physical properties**. All substances may be distinguished from one another by these properties, in much the same way as certain features (DNA, for example) distinguish one human being from another.

STRUCTURE OF THE ATOM

If a small piece of an element, say copper, were hypothetically divided and subdivided and subdivided into the smallest pieces possible, the result would be one particle of copper. This smallest unit of the element that is still representative of the element is called an atom.

Although infinitesimally small, the atom is composed of particles, principally electrons, protons, and neutrons. The simplest atom possible consists of a **nucleus** having a single **proton** (positively charged particle) with a single **electron** (negatively charged particle) traveling around it—an atom of hydrogen, which has an atomic weight of 1 because of the single proton. The **atomic weight** of an element is equal to the total number of protons and **neutrons** (neutral particles) in the nucleus of an atom of that element. Electrons and protons bear the same magnitude of charge, but have opposite polarity.

The hydrogen atom also has an atomic number of 1 because of its one proton. The atomic number of an element is equal to the number of protons in its nucleus. A neutral atom has the same number of protons and electrons, so the atomic number is also equal to the number of electrons in the atom. The number of neutrons in an atom is always equal to or greater than the number of protons, except in the atom of hydrogen.

The protons and neutrons of an atom reside in the nucleus. Electrons reside primarily in designated regions of space surrounding the nucleus, called **atomic orbitals** or **electron shells**. Only a prescribed number of electrons may reside in a given type of electron shell. With the exception of hydrogen (with only one electron), two electrons are always close to the nucleus, in an atom's innermost electron shell. In most atoms, other electrons are located in electron shells some distance from the nucleus.

Although neutral atoms of the same element have an identical number of electrons and protons, they may differ in the number of neutrons in their nuclei. Atoms of the same element having different numbers of neutrons are called **isotopes** of that element.

Periodic Classification of the Elements

Through experience, scientists discovered that the chemical properties of the elements repeat themselves. Chemists summarize all such observations in the **periodic law**: The properties of the elements vary periodically with their atomic numbers.

In 1869 Dimitri Mendeleev, using relative atomic masses, developed the original form of what today is known as the **periodic table**, a chart of elements arranged in order of increasing proton number to show the similarities between chemical elements with related electron configurations. The elements fall into vertical columns known as **groups**. Going down a group, the atoms of the elements all have the same outer shell structure, but an increasing number of inner shells. Traditionally, the alkali metals were shown on the left of the table, and the groups were numbered IA to VIIA, IB to VIIB, and 0 (for noble gases). Now we more commonly classify all the elements in the middle of the table as transition elements and regard the nontransition elements as **main-group** elements, numbered from I to VII, with the noble gases in group 0. Horizontal rows in the table are **periods**. The first three are called *short periods*; the next four (which include transition elements) are *long periods*. Within a period, the atoms of all the elements have the same number of shells, but with a steadily increasing number of electrons in the outer shell.

The periodic table is an important tool for learning chemistry because it organizes, tabulates, and presents a variety of information in one spot. For example, we can immediately determine the atomic number of the elements because they are tabulated on the periodic table (see Figure 3.1). We can also readily identify which elements are metals, nonmetals, and metalloids. Usually a bold zigzag line separates metals from nonmetals, while those elements lying to each immediate side of the line are metalloids. Metals fall to the left of the line, and nonmetals fall to the right of it.

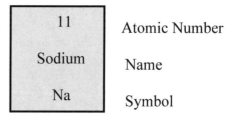

Figure 3.1. The element sodium as it is commonly shown in one of the horizontal boxes in the periodic table.

Response Scenario 3.1.
The Amish and Lancaster County, Pennsylvania[1]

Read the following account and choose and comment on one of the apparent results.

Lancaster County, Pennsylvania, is fortunate to encompass some of the best nonirrigated farmland in the country. Lancaster also has a higher than average dewfall, and in years when counties around it are in drought, Lancaster can still bring in a reasonable crop. For many years, farming was the primary industry in the region, primarily accomplished by Amish farmers, working with minimum technology, teams of mules, and their neighbors and families. Lancaster County still has a high Amish farmer population, which is steadily expanding. Those who farm typically raise high-profit, labor-intensive crops, as well as garden produce for their own use. But farming is no longer their primary local industry. More than 50% of the Amish work (not by choice) at something other than farming. Why? In the last 20 years, property values around Lancaster County have risen steeply. Per acre costs of good farmland mean that a small farm that goes on the market will now sell for astronomical prices. Why? Lancaster is a popular tourist area. Developers, seeing the tourist trade increase, wish to increase the number of attractions the tourists can visit. Most tourists come to Lancaster County to do two things: see the Amish or shop the outlets.

This problem is compounded by local growth. Industrial growth and a heavy influx of population over the last 20 years have made the county expand quickly, especially in and around Lancaster City itself. With Philadelphia, Baltimore, and the DC area within easy reach, Lancaster is expanding in population rapidly, and residential and commercial building is keeping pace. Many new residents don't want to live in the city in row houses, though hundreds of homes in the city are for sale. They want new houses with big yards and suburban schools. They don't want to shop downtown, where business is struggling and storefronts are empty or business success transient. They want to shop at the outlet malls, at Park City, or at the strip malls in their own neighborhoods.

"What's the problem with that?" you ask. Take your pick.

RESPONSE

Comment on any one of the following apparent results.

- The Amish can't afford to buy land for their sons to farm. They now often band together and purchase what land they can cooperatively, but even though their methods allow them to farm incredibly profitably, they can't compete with the developers for the per acre prices.
- Every year more acres of prime farm land are bulldozed for health campuses, outlet stores, entertainment complexes, and subdevelopments, while the tax base of Lancaster City moves to the suburbs and the city dies a slow death, and local farmlands and wildlife habitats dwindle.
- Lancaster's urban sprawl encompasses what only a few years ago were separate towns, five or six miles away. Now developments full of houses, strip malls, and car dealerships fill in those spaces, and the farmland they cover is destroyed.
- All this growth is springing up on what used to be corn and tobacco fields—farmland. once a strip mall is put on farmland, the land isn't much good for growing anything. Asphalt parking lots are hard to plow.
- The farmers who remain must use every available inch of cropland. They plow and plant to the edges of the roads and remove remaining copses and fencerows, destroying valuable agricultural edge habitat that formerly supported songbirds, pheasants, quail, and small mammals.
- Those people who move out into the developments built on former farms realize quickly that they don't like the smells associated with the farms still in their neighborhoods. They sometimes go so far as to take their neighbors to court.

(continued)

Response Scenario 3.1. *(continued)*

- Low-lying areas suffer from flooding. When uphill land that used to be open to the rain is covered with asphalt, runoff quickly overwhelms the creeks below, creating new flood plains in areas that weren't at risk before.
- Construction fouls local creeks, releasing quantities of silt and dirt into the streams, altering habitat, and reducing habitat quality.
- The system of roads designed for the lower rates of growth predicted when the roads were built 40 or so years ago are clogged and congested with traffic. Route 30 from Gap to Lancaster (15 miles) can take two hours to drive in tourist season, in bumper-to-bumper traffic.
- Exhaust fumes build up until the air is gray, and people keep their car windows closed and air conditioners going so they don't have to breathe it, while they sit in traffic with their engines running. Air pollution alert days are common, especially in the hot summer months.

Molecules and Ions

When elements other than noble gases (which exist as single atoms) exist in either the gaseous or liquid state of matter at room conditions, they consist of units containing pairs of like atoms. These units are called **molecules**. For example, we generally encounter oxygen, hydrogen, chlorine, and nitrogen as gases. Each exists as a molecule having two atoms. These molecules are symbolized by the notations O_2, H_2, Cl_2, and N_2, respectively.

The smallest particle of many compounds is also the molecule. Molecules of compounds contain atoms of two or more elements. The water molecule, for example, consists of two atoms of hydrogen and one atom of oxygen (H_2O). The methane molecule consists of one carbon atom and four hydrogen atoms (CH_4).

Not all compounds occur naturally as molecules. Many occur as aggregates of oppositely charged atoms or groups of atoms called **ions**. Gaining or losing some of their electrons charges atoms. Atoms of metals that lose their electrons become positively charged, and atoms of nonmetals that gain electrons become negatively charged.

Chemical Bonding

When compounds form, the atoms of one element become attached to, or associated with, atoms of other elements by forces called **chemical bonds**. Chemical bonding is a strong force of attraction holding atoms together in a molecule. Various types of chemical bonds occur. *Transfer of electrons can form **ionic bonds**.* For instance, the calcium atom has an electron configuration of two electrons in its outer shell. The chlorine atom has seven outer electrons. If the calcium atom transfers two electrons, one to each chlorine atom, it becomes a calcium ion with the stable configuration of an inert gas. At the same time, each chlorine atom, having gained one electron, becomes a chlorine ion, also with an inert-gas configuration. The bonding in calcium chloride is the electrostatic attraction between the ions.

Covalent bonds are formed by sharing of **valence** (the number of electrons an atom can give up or acquire to achieve a filled outer shell) electrons. Hydrogen atoms, for instance, have one outer electron. In the hydrogen molecule, H_2, each atom contributes one electron to the bond. Consequently, each hydrogen atom has control of two electrons—one of its own and the second from the other atom—giving it the electron configuration of an inert gas. In the water molecule, H_2O, the oxygen atom, with six outer electrons, gains control of two extra electrons supplied by the two hydrogen atoms. Similarly, each hydrogen atom gains control of an extra electron from the oxygen.

Chemical compounds are often classified into one of two groups based on the nature of the bonding between their atoms. Chemical compounds consisting of atoms bonded together by means of ionic bonds are called *ionic compounds*. Compounds whose atoms are bonded together by covalent bonds are called *covalent compounds*.

There are some interesting contrasts between most ionic and covalent compounds. For example, ionic compounds have higher melting points, boiling points, and solubility in water than covalent compounds. Ionic compounds are nonflammable; covalent compounds are flammable. Ionic compounds that are molten in water solutions conduct electricity. Molten covalent compounds do not conduct electricity. Ionic compounds generally exist as solids at room temperature, whereas covalent compounds exist as gases, liquids, and solids at room temperature.

Box 3.1 Did You Know?

Scientists have determined how much energy it takes to break the bonds in molecules. This is called the bond energy. It is given in kilojoules (kJ). Look at the bond energies below. 436 kJ must be supplied to break the bonds in hydrogen molecules. But if the atoms join again to form molecules, 436 kJ of energy are given out again. Thus, bond energy is the energy needed to break bonds or the energy released when bonds form.

Bond energy/kJ	
H—H	436
H—Cl	431
Cl—Cl	242
C—C	346
C—O	358

Chemical Formulas and Equations

Chemists have developed a shorthand method of writing **chemical formulas**. Elements are represented by groups of symbols called *formulas*. A common compound is sulfuric acid; its formula is H_2SO_4. The formula indicates that the acid is composed of two atoms of hydrogen, one atom of sulfur, and four atoms of oxygen. However, this is not a recipe for making the acid. The formula does not tell us how to prepare the acid, only what is in it.

A **chemical equation** shows what elements and compounds are present before and after a chemical reaction. Sulfuric acid poured over zinc will cause the release of hydrogen and the formation of zinc sulfate, shown by the following equation:

$$\underset{\text{(Zinc)}}{\text{Zn}} \quad + \quad \underset{\text{(sulfuric acid)}}{\text{H}_2\text{SO}_4} \quad \Rightarrow \quad \underset{\text{(zinc sulfate}}{\text{ZnSO}_4} \quad + \quad \underset{\text{(hydrogen}}{\text{H}_2} \tag{3.1}$$

One atom (also one molecule) of zinc unites with one molecule of sulfuric acid, producing one molecule of zinc sulfate and one molecule (two atoms) of hydrogen. Notice that the same number of atoms of each element still exists on each side of the arrow. However, the atoms are combined differently.

Molecular Weights, Formulas, and the Mole

The relative weight of a compound that occurs as molecules is called its **molecular weight**, the sum of the atomic weights of each atom that comprises the molecule. Consider the water molecule. Its molecular weight is determined as:

$$\begin{array}{r} 2\text{ hydrogen atoms} = 2 \times 1.008 = 2.016 \\ \underline{1\text{ oxygen atom} = 1 \times 15.999 = 15.999} \\ \text{Molecular weight of } \text{H}_2\text{O} = 18.015 \end{array} \tag{3.2}$$

Thus, the molecular weight of a molecule is simply the sum of the atomic weights of all the constituent atoms. If we divide the mass of a substance by its molecular weight, the result is the mass expressed in **moles** (mol). Usually the mass is expressed in grams, in which case the moles are written as *g-moles*; in a like fashion, if mass is expressed in pounds, the result would be *lb-moles*. One g-mole contains 6.022×10^{23} molecules (**Avogadro's number**, in honor of the scientist who first suggested its existence) and one lb-mole, about 2.7×10^{26} molecules:

$$\text{Moles} = \frac{\text{Mass}}{\text{Molecular Weight}} \tag{3.3}$$

The relative weight of a compound that occurs as formula units is called the **formula weight**, the sum of the atomic weights of all atoms that comprise one formula unit. Sodium fluoride's formula weight is determined as:

$$\begin{array}{r} 1\text{ sodium ion} = 22.990 \\ \underline{1\text{ fluoride ion} = 18.998} \\ \text{Formula weight of NaF} = 41.988 \end{array} \tag{3.4}$$

Density

The physical properties most commonly used in describing and identifying particular kinds of matter are density, color, and solubility. **Density** (d) is mass per unit volume and is expressed by this equation:

$$d = \frac{mass}{volume} \qquad (3.5)$$

All matter has weight and takes up space; it also has density, which depends on weight and space. We commonly say that a certain material will not float in water because it is *heavier* than water. What we really mean is that a particular material is *denser* than water. The density of an element differs from the density of any other element. The densities of liquids and solids are normally given in units of grams per cubic centimeter (g/cm³), which is the same as grams per milliliter (g/mL). The advantage of using the physical property **color** is that no chemical or physical tests are required. **Solubility** refers to the degree to which a substance dissolves in a liquid, such as water. In environmental science, the density, color, and solubility of a substance are important physical properties that aid in the determination of various pollutants, stages of pollution or treatment, and determining the remedial actions required to clean up toxic/hazardous waste spills or other environmental problems.

The properties involved in the transformation of one substance into another are known as **chemical properties**. For example, when a piece of wood burns, oxygen in the air unites with the substances in the wood to form new substances. When iron corrodes during the corrosion process, oxygen combines with the iron and water to form a new substance, commonly known as rust. Changes that result in the formation of new substances are known as chemical changes.

States of Matter

The three common states (or phases) of matter (solid, liquid, gaseous) have unique characteristics. In the **solid** state, the molecules or atoms are in a relatively fixed position. The molecules are vibrating rapidly, but about a fixed point. Because of this definite position of the molecules, a solid holds its shape. *A solid occupies a definite amount of space and has a fixed shape.*

When the temperature of a gas is lowered, the molecules of the gas slow down. If the gas is cooled sufficiently, the molecules slow down so much that they lose the energy needed to move rapidly throughout their container. The gas may turn into **liquid**. Common liquids are water, oil, and gasoline. *A liquid is a material that occupies a definite amount of space, but takes the shape of the container.*

In some materials, the atoms or molecules have no special arrangement at all. Such materials are called gases. Oxygen, carbon dioxide, and nitrogen are common gases. *A gas is a material that takes the exact volume and shape of its container.*

Although the three states of matter discussed here are familiar to most people, the change from one state to another is of primary interest to environmentalists. Changes in matter, including water vapor changing from the gaseous state to liquid precipitation or a spilled liquid chemical changing to a semisolid substance (by addition of chemicals, which aids in the cleanup effort), are examples of how changing from one state to another has an impact on environmental concerns.

Gas Laws

The atmosphere is composed of a mixture of gases, the most abundant of which are nitrogen, oxygen, argon, carbon dioxide, and water vapor (gases and the atmosphere are addressed in greater detail later). The **pressure** of a gas is the force that the moving gas molecules exert on a unit area. A common unit of pressure is newton per square meter, N/m_2, called a pascal (Pa). An important relationship exists among the pressure, volume, and temperature of a gas. This relation is known as the **ideal gas law** and can be stated as:

$$\frac{P_1 V_1}{T_1} = \frac{P_2 V_2}{T_2} \tag{3.6}$$

where P_1, V_1, T_1 are pressure, volume, and absolute temperature at time 1, and P_2, V_2, T_2, are pressure, volume, and absolute temperature at time 2. A gas is called perfect, or ideal, when it obeys this law.

A temperature of 0°C (273 K) and a pressure of 1 atmosphere (atm) have been chosen as **standard temperature and pressure (STP)**. At STP the volume of 1 mole of ideal gas is 22.4 L.

Liquids and Solutions

The most common solutions are liquids. However, solutions, which are homogenous mixtures, can be solid, gaseous, or liquid. The substance in excess in a solution is called the **solvent.** The substance dissolved is the **solute**. Solutions in which water is the solvent are called **aqueous solutions**. A solution in which the solute is present in only a small amount is called a **dilute solution**. If the solute is present in large amounts, the solution is a **concentrated solution**. When the maximum amount of solute possible is dissolved in the solvent, the solution is called a **saturated solution**.

The concentration (the amount of solute dissolved) is frequently expressed in terms of the **molar concentration**, or **molarity**, which is the number of moles of solute per liter of solution. Thus, a one-molar solution, written 1.0M, has one-gram formula weight of solute dissolved in one liter of solution. In general:

$$\text{Molarity} = \frac{\text{moles of solute}}{\text{number of liters of solution}} \tag{3.7}$$

Note that the *number of liters of solution*, not the number of liters of solvent, is used.

Example: Exactly 40 g of sodium chloride (NaCl), or table salt, were dissolved in water, and the solution was made up to a volume of 0.80 liter of solution. What was the molar concentration, M, of sodium chloride in the resulting solution?

Answer: First find the number of moles of salt:

$$\text{Number of moles} = \frac{40\,\text{g}}{58.5\,\text{g/mole}} = 0.68\,\text{mole} \qquad (3.8)$$

$$\text{Molarity} = \frac{0.68\,\text{mole}}{0.80\,\text{liter}} = 0.85\text{M} \qquad (3.9)$$

Did You Know?

We know a substance can change from solid to liquid to gas. The individual particles of the substance are the same in each state. It is their arrangement that is different.

Thermal Properties

Thermal properties of chemicals and other substances are important to the environmental practitioner. Such knowledge is used in hazardous materials spill mitigation and in solving many other complex environmental problems. **Heat** is a form of energy. Whenever work is performed, usually a substantial amount of heat is caused by friction. The conservation of energy law tells us that the work done plus the heat energy produced must equal the original amount of energy available. That is:

$$Total\ energy = work\ done + heat\ produced \qquad (3.10)$$

As environmental scientists, technicians, and practitioners, we are concerned with several properties related to heat for particular substances. Thermal properties we should be familiar with are discussed in the following sections.

A traditional unit for measuring heat energy is the calorie. A **calorie** (cal) is defined as the amount of heat necessary to raise one gram of pure liquid water by one degree Celsius at normal atmospheric pressure. In SI units:

$$1\ \text{cal} = 4.186\ \text{J (Joule)} \qquad (3.11)$$

The calorie we have defined should not be confused with the one used when discussing diets and nutrition. **A kilocalorie** is 1,000 calories as we have defined it—the amount of heat necessary to raise the temperature of one kilogram of water by 1°C.

In the British system of units, the unit of heat is the British thermal unit, or Btu. One **Btu** is the amount of heat required to raise one pound of water 1°F at normal atmospheric pressure (1 atm).

SPECIFIC HEAT

As mentioned previously, one kilocalorie of heat is necessary to raise the temperature of one kilogram of water 1°C. Other substances require different amounts of heat to raise the temperature of one kilogram one degree. The **specific heat** of a substance is the amount of heat in kilocalories necessary to raise the temperature of one kilogram of the substance 1°C. The units of specific heat are Kcal/kg°C, or, in SI units, J/kg°C. The specific heat of pure water, for example, is 1.000 kcal/kg°C, or 4186 J/kg°C. The greater the specific heat of a material, the more heat is required. Also, the greater the mass of the material or the greater the temperature change desired, the more heat is required.

The amount of heat necessary to change one kilogram of a solid into a liquid at the same temperature is called the **latent heat of fusion** of the substance. The temperature of the substance at which this change from solid to liquid takes place is known as the **melting point**. The amount of heat necessary to change one kilogram of a liquid into a gas is called the **latent heat of vaporization**. When this point is reached, the entire mass of the substance is in the gaseous state. The temperature of the substance at which this change from liquid to gas occurs is known as the **boiling point**.

HEAT CAPACITY

The *heat capacity* of a gas is the amount of heat required to change the temperature of a unit-mass of gas one degree. Common units of heat capacity are provided in Table 3.2.

Table 3.2. Common Units of Heat Capacity

	American Engineering Units	Cgs Units
Specific heat	$\dfrac{Btu}{(lb_m)(°F)}$	$\dfrac{cal}{(gm)(°C)}$
Molar heat capacity	$\dfrac{Btu}{(lb\ mole)(°F)}$	$\dfrac{cal}{(gm\ mole)(°C)}$

Actually, the numerical values for specific heat are the same regardless of which system of units is used. The same is true for molar heat capacity. For example, the molar heat capacity expressed in Btus per pound mole degree Fahrenheit is identical to the heat capacity expressed in calories per gram mole degree Celsius. This can be demonstrated by substituting the appropriate correction factors and deriving one set of dimensional units from another.

ENTHALPY

Enthalpy represents the total quantity of internal energy, such as heat, measured for a specific quantity of a material at a given temperature. Enthalpy data are often represented in units of energy (e.g., Btu, kcal, joule, etc.). The enthalpy content change is often expressed in Btu/unit mass (Btu/lb_m) or Btu/unit gas volume (Btu/SCF). The change in enthalpy of the total quantity of material present in a system is expressed in units of Btu/unit time (Btu/min). The symbols H and ΔH denote enthalpy and the change in enthalpy, respectively.

Acids + Bases $\Rightarrow$ Salts

When acids and bases are combined in the proper proportions, they neutralize each other, each losing its characteristic properties and forming a salt and water:

$$NaOH + HCl \Rightarrow NaCl + H_2O \qquad (3.12)$$

which is

> sodium hydroxide + hydrochloric acid E sodium chloride + water

The acid-base-salt concept originated with the beginning of chemistry and is very important in the environment, life processes, and industrial chemicals.

The word *acid* is derived from the Latin *acidus*, which means sour. Sour taste is one of the properties of acids (however, you should never actually taste an acid in the laboratory or anywhere else). An **acid** is a substance that, in water, produces hydrogen ions, H+, and has the following properties. It

1. conducts electricity,
2. tastes sour,
3. changes the color of blue litmus paper to red,
4. reacts with a base to neutralize its properties, and
5. reacts with metals to liberate hydrogen gas.

Typical acid reactions

> Acid + metal hydroxide $\rightarrow$ metal salt + water
> Acid + metal $\rightarrow$ metal salt + hydrogen
> Acid + metal carbonate $\rightarrow$ metal salt + water + carbon dioxide
> Acid + metal oxide $\rightarrow$ metal salt + water

A **base** is a substance that produces hydroxide ions, OH-, and/or accepts H+, and when dissolved in water, has the following properties. It

1. conducts electricity,
2. changes the color of red litmus paper to blue,
3. tastes bitter and feels slippery, and

4. reacts with an acid to neutralize the acid's properties, such as alkalis, insoluble metal oxides and hydroxides, metal carbonates and hydrogen carbonates, and ammonia solution.

pH Scale

A common way to determine whether a solution is an acid or a base is to measure the concentration of hydrogen ions (H+) in the solution. The concentration can be expressed in powers of 10, but is more conveniently expressed as **pH**. For example, pure water has 1×10^{-7} grams of hydrogen ions per liter. The negative exponent of the hydrogen ion concentration is called the pH of the solution. The pH of water is 7; a neutral solution. A concentration of 1×10^{-12} has a pH of 12. A pH less than 7 indicates an acid solution; a pH greater than 7 indicates a basic solution (see Table 3.3).

Table 3.3. Standard pH Scale*

pH Scale pH	Concentration of H Ions	Acidic/Basic
1	1.0×10^{-1} mole/liter	Very Acidic
2	1.0×10^{-2} mole/liter	
3	1.0×10^{-3} mole/liter	
4	1.0×10^{-4} mole/liter	
5	1.0×10^{-5} mole/liter	
6	1.0×10^{-6} mole/liter	Acidic
7	**1.0×10^{-7} mole/liter**	**Neutral**
8	1.0×10^{-8} mole/liter	Basic
9	1.0×10^{-9} mole/liter	
10	1.0×10^{-10} mole/liter	
11	1.0×10^{-11} mole/liter	
12	1.0×10^{-12} mole/liter	
13	1.0×10^{-13} mole/liter	
14	1.0×10^{-14} mole/liter	Very Basic

*The "p" is for the German word *Potenz* ("power"); the H stands for *hydrogen*.

The pH of substances found in our environment varies in value. Acid-base reactions are among the most important in environmental science. In diagnosing various environmental problems (acid rain problems, hazardous materials spills into lakes and ponds), pH value is critical. Remediation or prevention is also important. To protect local ecosystems, wastes often require neutralization before being released into the environment. Another important aspect of pH control is seen in waste treatment (wastewater treatment), where removing nitrogen is essential. If not removed, nitrogen stimulates growth of algae in the receiving body of water. (Table 3.4 lists the approximate pH of some common substances.)

Table 3.4. pH of Various Substances

Substance	pH
Battery acid	0.0
Gastric juice	1.2
Lemons	2.3
Vinegar	2.8
Soft drinks	3.0
Apples	3.1
Grapefruit	3.1
Wines	3.2
Oranges	3.5
Tomatoes	4.2
Beer	4.5
Bananas	4.6
Carrots	5.0
Potatoes	5.8
Coffee	6.0
Milk (cow)	6.5
Pure Water ————NEUTRAL————	**7.0**
Blood (human)	7.4
Eggs	7.8
Sea water	8.5
Milk of magnesia	10.5
Oven cleaner	13.0

Organic Chemistry

Organic chemistry is the branch of chemistry concerned with compounds of carbon. The science of organic chemistry is incredibly complex and varied. Millions of organic compounds are known today, and more than 100,000 of these are products of synthesis, unknown in nature. This text can only provide a very basic introduction to some of the most common organic substances important to environmental science (because of their toxicities as pollutants and other hazards) so that they will be more familiar when we encounter them elsewhere in the text.

Before 1828, scientists thought that plants and animals (living things) could only make organic compounds. In that year, Friedrich Wohler made urea from ammonium cyanate. Wohler's discovery disproved the theory that stated urea (and thus all organic compounds) could only be made by living things. With his discovery, the science of organic chemistry was born.

Organic compounds are components of all the familiar commodities that our technological world requires—motor and heating fuels, adhesives, cleaning solvents, paints, varnishes, plastics, refrigerants, aerosols, textiles, fibers, and resins, among many others.

From an environmental science perspective, the principal concern about organic compounds is that they are pollutants of water, air, and soil environments. As such, they are safety and health hazards. They are also combustible or flammable substances, with few exceptions. From a health standpoint, they can cause a wide range of detrimental health effects. In humans, some of these compounds damage the kidneys, liver, and heart; others depress the central nervous system; and several are suspected to cause cancer. If human beings are subject to such health hazards from these compounds, for the environmental scientist, the logical question is: What about their impact on delicate ecosystems?

ORGANIC COMPOUNDS

The molecules of organic compounds have one common feature: one or more carbon atoms that covalently bond to other atoms. That is, pairs of electrons are shared between atoms. A carbon atom may share electrons with other nonmetallic atoms and also with other carbon atoms. As Figure 3.2 shows, methane, carbon tetrachloride, and carbon monoxide are compounds having moles in which the carbon atom is bonded to other nonmetallic atoms.

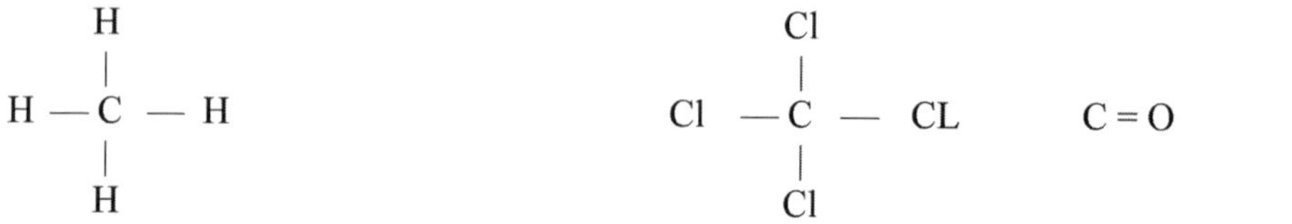

Methane   Carbon tetrachloride   Carbon monoxide

Figure 3.2. Shows carbon atoms sharing their electrons with the electrons of other nonmetallic atoms, like hydrogen, chlorine, and oxygen. The compounds that result from such electron sharing are methane, carbon tetrachloride, and carbon monoxide, respectively.

When carbon atoms share electrons with other carbon atoms, two carbon atoms may share electrons in such a manner that they form any of the following: carbon-carbon single bonds (C–), carbon-carbon double bonds (C =), or carbon-carbon triple bonds (C ≡). Each bond written here as a dash (—) is a shared pair of electrons. Figure 3.3 illustrates the bonding of molecules of ethane, ethylene, and acetylene, compounds

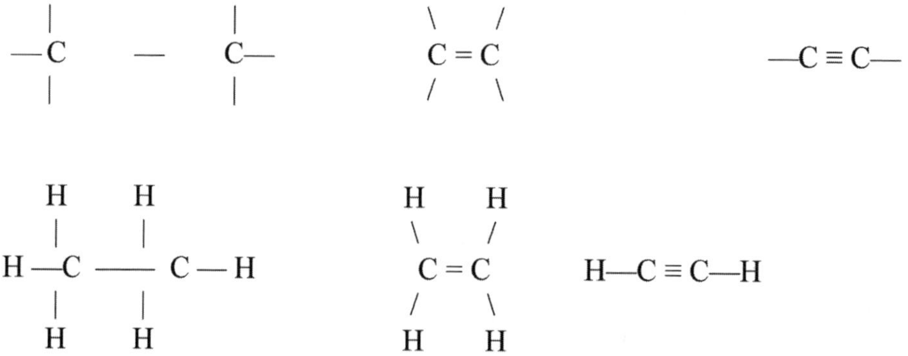

Figure 3.3. Illustrates that two carbon atoms may share their own electrons in any of the three ways noted. When these carbon atoms further bond to hydrogen atoms, the resulting compounds are ethane, ethylene, and acetylene, respectively.

having molecules with only two carbon atoms. Molecules of ethane have carbon-carbon single bonds, molecules of ethylene possess carbon-carbon double bonds, and molecules of acetylene have carbon-carbon triple bonds.

Covalent bonds between carbon atoms in molecules of more complex organic compounds may be linked in chains, including branched chains, or in rings.

HYDROCARBONS

The simplest organic compounds are the **hydrocarbons**, whose molecules are composed only of carbon and hydrogen atoms. All hydrocarbons are broadly divided into two groups: aliphatic and aromatic hydrocarbons.

Aliphatic Hydrocarbons

Aliphatic hydrocarbons can be characterized by the chain arrangements of their constituent carbon atoms. They are divided into the alkanes, alkenes, and alkynes.

The **alkanes**, also called **paraffins** or aliphatic hydrocarbons, are saturated hydrocarbons (hydrogen content is at maximum) with the general formula C_nH_{2n+2}. In systematic chemical nomenclature, alkane names end in the suffix -ane. They form the alkane series methane (CH_4), ethane (C_2H_6), propane (C_3H_8), butane (C_4H_{10}), etc. The lower members of the series are gases; the high-molecular-weight alkanes are waxy solids. Alkanes are present in natural gas and petroleum.

Alkenes (olefins) are unsaturated hydrocarbons (can take on hydrogen atoms to form saturated hydrocarbons) that contain one or more double carbon-carbon bonds in their molecules. In systematic chemical nomenclature, alkene names end in the suffix-ene. Alkenes with only one double bond form the alkene series starting with ethene—the gas that is liberated when food rots—(ethylene), $CH_2:CH_2$; propene, $CH_3CH: CH_2$, etc.

Alkynes (acetylenes) are unsaturated hydrocarbons that contain one or more triple carbon-carbon bonds in their molecules. In systematic chemical nomenclature, alkyne names end in the suffix –yne: acetylene, $H—C \equiv C—H$.

Aromatic Hydrocarbons

Aromatic hydrocarbons are unsaturated organic compounds that contain a benzene ring in their molecules or that have chemical properties similar to benzene, a clear, colorless, water-insoluble liquid that rapidly vaporizes at room temperature, whose molecular formula is C_6H_6. The molecular structure of benzene is commonly represented by a hexagon with a circle inside, as shown in Figure 3.4.

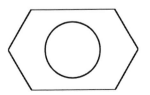

Figure 3.4. Symbol for benzene

Environmental Chemistry: Environmental Media

Environmental chemistry is a blend of aquatic, atmospheric, and soil chemistry, and the "chemistry" generated by human activities. As stated previously, the focus of this text is the three major environmental media, air, water, and soil, and that a loss of or total damage to any of these three would mean there could be no life as we know it on Earth. The environmental effects brought about by humans will not be ignored here.

Understanding that the three environmental media are what they are because of many interwoven scientific principles (including chemistry) is most important. We are interested in the chemistry that makes up these media as well as the chemical reactions that take place to preserve or destroy them. As we proceed in this text, we are concerned with the environmental impact of human activities—mining; acid rain; erosion from poor cultivation practices; disposal of hazardous wastes; photochemical reactions (smog); air pollutants from particulate matter to the greenhouse effect; ozone; and water degradation problems related to organic, inorganic, and biological pollutants. All of these activities and problems have something to do with chemistry. The remediation and/or mitigation processes to repair them are also tied to chemistry.

To say that environmental science, studies, and engineering are built on a strong foundation of chemistry is more than a mild understatement of chemistry's real importance and relevance in the field.

WATER CHEMISTRY FUNDAMENTALS

Whenever we add a chemical substance to another chemical substance, such as adding sugar to tea or adding chlorine to water to make it safe to drink, we are performing the work of chemists, because we are dealing with a chemical substance for a specific result. Chemicals and chemical compounds, along with their common applications in water treatment, are listed in Table 3.5.

The Water Molecule

Just about everyone knows that water is a chemical compound of two simple and abundant elements—hydrogen and oxygen (H_2O). Yet scientists continue to argue the merits of rival theories about the structure of water. The fact is, we still know little about water. For example, we don't know how water works.

Water is very complex. It has many unique properties that are essential to life and determine its environmental chemical behavior. The water molecule is different. The two hydrogen atoms (the two in the H_2 part of the water formula) always come to rest at an angle of approximately 105 degrees from each other. The hydrogens tend to be positively charged, and the oxygen tends to be negatively charged. This arrangement gives the water molecule an electrical polarity; that is, one end is positively charged and the other is negatively charged. This 105 degree relationship makes water lopsided, peculiar, and eccentric—it breaks all the rules.

Table 3.5. Chemicals/Chemical Compounds Used in Water Treatment

Name	Common Application
Activated carbon	Taste & odor control
Aluminum sulfate	Coagulation
Ammonia	Chloramine disinfection
Ammonium sulfate	Coagulation
Calcium hydroxide	Softening
Calcium hypochlorite	Disinfection
Calcium oxide	Softening
Carbon dioxide	Recarbonation
Copper sulfate	Algae control
Ferric chloride	Coagulation
Ferric sulfate	Coagulation
Magnesium hydroxide	Defluoridation
Oxygen	Aeration
Potassium permanganate	Oxidation
Sodium aluminate	Coagulation
Sodium bicarbonate	pH adjustment
Sodium carbonate	Softening
Sodium chloride	Ion exchanger regeneration
Sodium fluoride	Fluoridation
Sodium fluosilicate	Fluoridation
Sodium hexametaphosphate	Corrosion control
Sodium hydroxide	pH adjustment
Sodium hypochlorite	Disinfection
Sodium silicate	Coagulation aid
Sodium thiosulfate	Dechlorination
Sulfur dioxide	Dechlorination
Sulfuric acid	pH adjustment

In the laboratory, pure water contains no impurities, but in nature water contains a lot of materials besides water, an important consideration for the environmental specialist who is tasked with maintaining the purest, cleanest water possible.

Water is often called the universal solvent, and this is fitting when we consider that given enough time, water will dissolve anything and everything on Earth.

Water Solutions

A *solution* is a homogenous mixture of two or more substances, in a condition in which the substances are uniformly and evenly mixed or dissolved. Solutions can be solids, liquids, or gases. We focus here primarily on liquid solutions.

A solution has two components: a **solvent** and a **solute**. The solvent is the component that does the dissolving. Typically the solvent is the substance present in the greater quantity. The solute is the component that is dissolved. When water dissolves substances, it creates solutions with many impurities.

A solution is usually transparent, not cloudy, and visible to longer wavelength ultraviolet light. Because water is colorless, the light necessary for photosynthesis can travel to considerable depths. However, a solution may be colored when the solute remains uniformly distributed throughout the solution and does not settle with time.

When molecules dissolve in water, the atoms making up the molecules come apart (dissociate) in the water. This dissociation in water is called **ionization**. When the atoms in the molecules come apart, they do so as charged atoms (both negatively and positively charged) called ions. The positively charged ions are **cations** and the negatively charged ions are **anions**.

Following are examples of ionization:

$$\underset{\text{calcium carbonate}}{CaCO_3} \leftrightarrow \underset{\underset{\text{(cation)}}{\text{calcium ion}}}{Ca^{++}} + \underset{\underset{\text{(anion)}}{\text{carbonate ion}}}{CO_3^{-2}}$$

$$\underset{\text{sodium chloride}}{NaCl} \leftrightarrow \underset{\underset{\text{(cation)}}{\text{sodium ion}}}{Na^{+}} + \underset{\underset{\text{(anion)}}{\text{chloride ion}}}{CO_3^{-2}}$$

(3.12a)

Some of the common ions found in water are shown in Table 3.6:

Table 3.6. Ions Found in Water

Ion	Symbol
Hydrogen	H^+
Sodium	Na^+
Potassium	K^+
Chloride	Cl^-
Bromide	Br^-
Iodide	I^-
Bicarbonate	HCO_3^-

Solutions serve as a vehicle to (1) allow chemical species to come into close proximity so that they can react; (2) provide a uniform matrix for solid materials (e.g., paints, inks, and other coatings) so that they can be applied to surfaces; and (3) dissolve oil and grease so that they can be rinsed away.

Water dissolves polar substances better than nonpolar substances. For example, **polar substances** (e.g., mineral acids, bases, and salts) are easily dissolved in water. **Nonpolar substances** (e.g., oils and fats and many organic compounds) *do not* dissolve as easily in water.

Concentrations

Because the properties of a solution depend largely on the relative amounts of solvent and solute, the **concentrations** of each must be specified.

✔ **Key Point:** Chemists use both relative terms (e.g., saturated and unsaturated), as well as more exact concentration terms (weight percentages, molarity, and normality) to discuss, define, and describe solutions and substances.

Though polar substances dissolve better than nonpolar substances in water, polar substances dissolve in water only to a point; that is, only so much solute will dissolve at a given temperature. When that limit is reached, the resulting solution is **saturated**; when a solution becomes saturated, the solution is in equilibrium, and no more solute can be dissolved. A liquid/solids solution is **supersaturated** when the solvent actually dissolves more than an equilibrium concentration of solute (usually when heated).

The exact concentrations of solutions are usually given by specifying the relative amounts of solvent and solute or the amount of one component relative to the whole. Solution concentrations are sometimes specified as **weight percentages**.

$$\% \text{ of Solute} = \frac{\text{Mass of solute}}{\text{Total mass of solution}} \times 100$$

To understand the concepts of **molarity**, **molality**, and **normality**, we must first understand the concept of a **mole**. The *mole* is defined as the amount of a substance that contains exactly *the same number of items* (atoms, molecules, or ions) as 12 grams of carbon-12. Through experimentation, Avagodro determined this number to be 6.02×10^{23} (to three significant figures).

If one mole of C atoms equals 12 g, how much is the mass of one mole of H atoms?

1. Note that carbon is 12 times as heavy as hydrogen.
2. Therefore we need only 1/12 the weight of H to equal the same number of atoms of C.

✓ **Key Point:** One mole of H equals 1 g.

By the same principle:

- 1 mole of CO_2 = 12 + 2(16) = 44 g
- 1 mole of Cl^- = 35.5 g
- 1 mole of Ra = 226 g

In other words, we can calculate the mass of a mole if we know the formula of the "item."

Molarity (M) is defined as the number of moles of solute per liter of solution. The *volume* of a solution is easier to measure in the lab than its *mass*:

$$M = \frac{\text{No. of moles of solute}}{\text{No. of liters of solute}}$$

Molality (m) is defined as the number of moles of solute per *kilogram* of *solvent*:

$$m = \frac{\text{No. of moles of solute}}{\text{No. of kilograms of solution}}$$

✓ **Key Point:** Molality is not as frequently used as molarity, except in theoretical calculations.

Especially for acids and bases, the *normality* (N) rather than the molarity of a solution is often reported:

$$N = \frac{No. \text{ of equivalents of solute}}{No. \text{ of liters of solution}}$$

In acid/base terms, an **equivalent** (or gram equivalent weight) is the amount that will react with one mole of H^+ or OH^-. For example:

1 mole of HCl will generate one mole of H^+
    Therefore 1 mole HCl = 1 equivalent

1 mole of $Mg(OH)_2$ will generate two moles of OH^-
    Therefore 1 mole of $Mg(OH)_2$ = 2 equivalents

$$HCl \Rightarrow H^+ + Cl^- \qquad\qquad Mg(OH)^{+2} \Rightarrow Mg^{+2} + 2OH^-$$

By the same principle:

A 1 M solution of H_3PO_4 is 3 N
A 2 N solution of H_2SO_4 is 1M
A 0.5 N solution of NaOH is 0.5 M
A 2 M solution of HNO_3 is 2 N

Chemists **titrate** acid/base solutions to determine their normality. An **endpoint indicator** is used to identify the point at which the titrated solution is neutralized.

✓ **Key Point:** If it takes 100 mL of 1N HCl to neutralize 100 mL of NaOH, then the NaOH solution must also be 1N.

Predicting Solubility

Predicting solubility is difficult, but a few general rules of thumb are useful:

Like dissolves like.

Liquid-Liquid Solubility

Liquids with similar structure and hence similar **intermolecular** forces are completely **miscible.** For example, we would correctly predict that methanol and water are completely soluble in any proportion.

Liquid-Solid Solubility

Solids *always* have limited solubilities in liquids, in general because of the difference in magnitude of their intermolecular forces. Therefore, the closer the temperature is to its melting point, the better the match between a solid and a liquid.

✓ **Key Point:** At a given temperature, lower melting solids are more soluble than higher melting solids.

Structure is also important; for example, nonpolar solids are more soluble in nonpolar solvents.

Liquid-Gas Solubility

As with solids, the more similar the intermolecular forces, the higher the solubility. Therefore, the closer the match between the temperature of the solvent and the boiling point of the gas, the higher the solubility.

When water is the solvent, an additional *hydration* factor promotes solubility of charged species.

Other factors that can significantly affect solubility are **temperature** and pressure. In general, *raising the temperature* typically *increases* the solubility of *solids* in liquids.

✓ **Key Point:** Dissolving a solid in a liquid is usually an **endothermic** process (heat is absorbed), so raising the temperature "fuels" this process.

In contrast, dissolving a gas in a liquid is usually an **exothermic** process (it evolves heat). Therefore, *lowering the temperature* generally *increases* the solubility of *gases* in liquids.

✓ **Interesting Point:** "Thermal" pollution is a problem because of the decreased solubility of O_2 in water at higher temperatures.

Pressure has an appreciable effect on the solubility of *gases* in liquids. For example, carbonated beverages such as soda water are typically bottled at significantly higher atmospheres. When the beverage is opened, the decrease in the pressure above the liquid causes the gas to bubble out of solution. When shaving cream is used, dissolved gas comes out of solution, bringing the liquid with it as foam.

Colligative Properties

Some properties of a solution depend on the concentrations of the solute species rather than their identity:

- Lowering vapor pressure
- Raising the boiling point
- Decreasing the freezing point
- Osmotic pressure

True colligative properties are directly *proportional to the concentration* of the solute, but entirely *independent of its identity*.

Lowering Vapor Pressure

With all other conditions identical, the vapor pressure of water above the pure liquid is higher than that above sugar water. The vapor pressure above a 0.2 m sugar solution is the same as that above a 0.2 m urea solution. The lowering of vapor pressure above a 0.4 m sugar solution is twice as great as that above a 0.2 m sugar solution.

Solutes lower vapor pressure because they *lower the concentration of solvent* molecules. To remain in equilibrium, the solvent vapor concentration must decrease (hence the vapor pressure decreases).

Raising the Boiling Point

A solution containing a *nonvolatile* solute boils at a **higher temperature** than the pure solvent. The increase in boiling point is directly proportional to the increase in solute concentration in dilute solutions. This phenomenon is explained by the lowering of vapor pressure already described.

Decreasing the Freezing Point

At low solute concentrations, solutions generally freeze or melt at lower temperatures than the pure solvent.

✓ **Key Point:** The presence of dissolved "foreign bodies" tends to interfere with freezing. Therefore, solutions can only be frozen at temperatures below that of the pure solvent.

✓ **Key Point:** We add antifreeze to the water in our radiators to both lower its freezing point and increase its boiling point.

Osmotic Pressure

Water moves spontaneously from an area of high vapor pressure to an area of low vapor pressure. If such an experiment were allowed to continue, in the end all of the water would move to the solution.

A similar process will occur when *pure* water is separated from a *concentrated* solution by a semipermeable membrane (only allows the passage of water molecules).

The *osmotic pressure* is the pressure that is just adequate to prevent osmosis. In dilute solutions, the osmotic pressure is directly proportional to the solute concentration and is *independent* of its identity.

The properties of electrolyte solutions follow the same trends as nonelectrolyte solutions, but are also dependent on both the *nature* of the electrolyte as well as its *concentration*.

Colloids/Emulsions

As previously mentioned, a solution is a *homogenous* mixture of two or more substances (e.g., seawater). A *suspension* is a brief comingling of solvent and undissolved particles (e.g., sand and water). A *colloidal suspension* is a comingling of particles not visible to the naked eye but larger than individual molecules.

✓ **Key Point:** Colloidal particles do not settle out by gravity alone.

Colloidal suspensions can consist of the following:

- **Hydrophilic** "solutions" of **macromolecules** such as proteins that spontaneously form in water.
- **Hydrophobic suspensions** that gain stability from their repulsive electrical charges.
- **Micelles**, which are special colloids having charged hydrophilic "heads" and long hydrophobic "tails."

Colloids are usually classified according to the original states of their constituent parts (see Table 3.7).

The stability of colloids can be primarily attributed to *hydration* and *surface charge*, both of which help to prevent contact and subsequent coagulation.

Table 3.7. Types of Colloids

Name	Dispersing Medium	Dispersed Phase
Solid sol	Solid	Solid
Gel	Solid	Liquid
Solid form	Solid	Gas
Solid	Liquid	Solid
Emulsion	Liquid	Liquid
Foam	Liquid	Gas
Solid aerosol	Gas	Solid
Aerosol	Liquid	Aerosol

Source: Adapted from "Types of Colloids," accessed December 18, 2002, http://www.chm.bris.ac.uk/webprojects2002/pdavies/types.html.

✓ **Key Point:** In many cases, water-based **emulsions** have been used to replace organic solvents (paints, inks, and so forth), even though the compounds are not readily soluble in water.

In wastewater treatment, the *elimination* of colloidal species and emulsions is achieved by various means, including the following:

- agitation
- heat
- acidification
- coagulation (adding ions)
- flocculation (adding bridging groups)

Water Constituents

Natural water can contain a number of substances, or what we call impurities or **constituents**. When a particular constituent can affect the health of the water user, it is called a **contaminant** or **pollutant**. The environmental specialist works to prevent these contaminants from entering the water supply and to remove them from the water supply.

Solids

Other than gases, all contaminants of water contribute to the **solids** content. Natural waters carry quantities of both dissolved and not-dissolved solids. The **not-dissolved solids** are nonpolar substances and relatively large particles of materials, such as **silt**, that won't dissolve. Classified by their size and state, chemical characteristics, and size distribution, solids can be dispersed in water in both suspended and dissolved forms.

Solids in water can be classified by size as

- suspended
- settleable
- colloidal
- dissolved

Total solids are those solids, both suspended and dissolved, that remain behind when the water is removed by evaporation. Solids are also characterized as being *volatile* or *nonvolatile*.

✓ **Important Point:** Though not technically accurate from a chemical point of view because some finely suspended material can actually pass through the filter, **suspended solids** are defined as those that can be filtered out in the suspended solids laboratory test. The material that passes through the filter is defined as **dissolved solids**.

Colloidal solids are extremely fine suspended solids (particles) of less than one micron in diameter; they are so small (but still make water cloudy) that they will not settle even if allowed to sit quietly for days or weeks.

Turbidity

One of the first characteristics people notice about water is its **clarity**. *Turbidity* is a condition in water caused by the presence of suspended matter, resulting in the scattering and **absorption** of light rays. In plain English, turbidity is a measure of the light-transmitting properties of water. Natural water that is very clear (low turbidity) allows visibility to considerable depths. High turbidity water appears cloudy. Even water with low turbidity, however, can still contain dissolved solids, which do not cause light to be scattered or absorbed; thus, the water looks clear. High turbidity causes problems for the waterworks operator because the components that cause high turbidity can cause taste and odor problems and will reduce the effectiveness of disinfection.

Color

Water can be colored, but often the *color* of water can be deceiving. For example, color is considered an aesthetic quality of water, with no direct health impact. Many of the colors associated with water are not "true" colors, but the result of colloidal suspension (apparent color). This **apparent color** can be attributed to dissolved tannin extracted from decaying plant material. **True color** is the result of dissolved chemicals, most often organics that cannot be seen.

Dissolved Oxygen (DO)

Gases can be dissolved in water. For example, gases (including oxygen, carbon dioxide, hydrogen sulfide, and nitrogen) dissolve in water. Gases dissolved in water are important for environmental health. For example, carbon dioxide plays a critical role in pH and alkalinity. It is released into the water by microorganisms and consumed by aquatic plants. **Dissolved oxygen** (DO) in water is of most importance to waterworks operators as an indicator of water quality.

We stated previously that solutions could become saturated with solute. This is also the case with water and oxygen. The amount of oxygen that can be dissolved at saturation depends on the temperature of the water. In this case, however, the effect is just the opposite of what occurs with other solutes. The higher the temperature, the lower the saturation level; the lower the temperature, the higher the saturation level.

Metals

One of the constituents or impurities often carried by water is *metal*. At normal levels, most metals are not harmful; however, a few can cause taste and odor problems in drinking water. Some metals may be toxic to humans, animals, and microorganisms. Most metals enter water as part of compounds that ionize to release the metal as positive ions. Table 3.8 lists some metals commonly found in water and their potential health hazards.

Table 3.8. Common Metals Found in Water

Metal	Health Hazard
Barium	Circulatory system effects and increased blood pressure
Cadmium	Concentration in the liver, kidneys, pancreas, and thyroid
Copper	Nervous system damage and kidney effects, toxic to humans
Lead	Same as copper
Mercury	Central nervous system disorders
Nickel	Central nervous system disorders
Selenium	Central nervous system disorders
Silver	Turns skin gray
Zinc	Causes taste problems; not a health hazard

Organic Matter

Organic matter or *organic compounds* are those that contain the element **carbon** and are derived from material that was once alive (i.e., plants and animals). They include, among other things, the following:

- fats
- dyes
- soaps
- rubber product
- wood
- fuels
- cotton
- proteins
- carbohydrates.

Organic compounds in water are usually large, nonpolar molecules that do not dissolve well in water. They often provide large amounts of energy to animals and microorganisms.

Inorganic Matter

Inorganic matter or *inorganic compounds* are carbon-free, not derived from living matter, and easily dissolved in water; they are of mineral origin. The inorganics include acids, bases, oxides, salts, etc. Several inorganic components are important in establishing and controlling water quality.

Acids

An *acid* is a substance that produces hydrogen ions (H^+) when dissolved in water. Hydrogen ions are hydrogen atoms stripped of their electrons. A single hydrogen ion is nothing more than the nucleus of a hydrogen atom. Lemon juice, vinegar, and sour milk are acidic or contain acid. The common acids used in treating water are hydrochloric acid (HCl), sulfuric acid (H_2SO_4), nitric acid (HNO_3), and carbonic acid (H_2CO_3). Note that in each of these acids, hydrogen (H) is one of the elements. The relative strengths of acids in water, listed in descending order, are classified in Table 3.9.

Bases

A *base* is a substance that produces hydroxide ions (OH^-) when dissolved in water. For example, lye and common soap (bitter things) contain bases. Bases used in waterworks operations are calcium hydroxide ($Ca(OH)_2$), sodium hydroxide ($NaOH$), and potassium hydroxide (KOH). Note that the hydroxyl group (OH) is found in all bases. Certain bases also contain metallic substances, such as sodium (Na), calcium (Ca), magnesium (Mg), and potassium (K). These bases contain the elements that produce the **alkalinity** in water.

Table 3.9. Relative Strengths of Acids in Water

Acid	Chemical Symbol
Perchloric acid	$HClO_4$
Sulfuric acid	H_2SO_2
Hydrochloric acid	HCl
Nitric acid	HNO_3
Phosphoric acid	H_3PO_4
Nitrous acid	HNO_2
Hydrofluoric acid	HF
Acid	CH_3COOH
Carbonic acid	H_2CO_3
Hydrocyanic acid	HCN
Boric acid	H_3BO_3

Salts

When acids and bases chemically interact, they neutralize each other. The compound other than water that forms from the neutralization of acids and bases is called a *salt*. Salts constitute by far the largest groups of inorganic compounds. A common salt used in waterworks operations, **copper sulfate**, is used to kill algae in water.

pH

pH is a measure of the hydrogen ion (H^+) concentration. Solutions range from very acidic (having a high concentration of H^+ ions) to very basic (having a high concentration of OH^- ions). The pH scale ranges from 0 to 14, with 7 being the neutral value.

The pH of water is important to the chemical reactions that take place in it, and pH values that are too high or low can inhibit growth of microorganisms.

High pH values are considered basic and low pH values are considered acidic. Stated another way, low pH values indicate a high level of H^+ concentration, whereas high pH values indicate a low H^+ concentration. Because of this inverse **logarithmic** relationship, there is a tenfold difference in H^+ concentration.

Natural water varies in pH depending on its source. Pure water has a neutral pH, with an equal number of H^+ and OH^-. Adding an acid to water causes additional $^+$ ions to be released so that the H^+ ion concentration goes up and the pH value goes down:

$$HCl \rightarrow H^+ + Cl$$

Changing the hydrogen ion activity in solution can shift the chemical equilibrium of water. Thus pH adjustment is used to optimize coagulation, softening, and disinfection reactions, and for corrosion control. To control water coagulation and corrosion, waterworks operators must test for the hydrogen ion concentration of the water to get pH. In coagulation tests, as more alum (acid) is added, the pH value is lowered. If more lime (alkali—base) is added, the pH value is raised. This relationship is important—and if good floc is formed, the pH should then be determined and maintained at that pH value until a change in incoming waters.

Alkalinity

Alkalinity is defined as the capacity of water to accept protons (positively charged particles); it can also be defined as a measure of water's ability to neutralize an acid. Stated in simpler terms, alkalinity is a measure of water's capacity to absorb hydrogen ions without significant pH change (to neutralize acids).

Bicarbonates, carbonates, and hydrogen cause alkaline compounds in a raw or treated water supply. Bicarbonates are the major components because of carbon dioxide action on "basic" materials of soil; borates, silicates, and phosphates may be minor components. Alkalinity of raw water may also contain salts formed from organic acids, such as humic acid. Alkalinity in water acts as a **buffer** that tends to stabilize and prevent fluctuations in pH. Having significant alkalinity in water is usually beneficial, because it tends to prevent quick changes in pH, which interfere with the effectiveness of common water treatment processes. Low alkalinity also contributes to corrosive tendencies of water. When alkalinity is below 80 mg/L, it is considered *low*.

Hardness

Hardness may be considered a physical or chemical parameter of water. It represents the total concentration of calcium and magnesium ions, reported as calcium carbonate. Hardness causes soaps and detergents to be less effective and contributes to scale formation in pipes and boilers. It is not considered a health hazard. However, lime precipitation or ion exchange must often be used to soften hard water. Low hardness contributes to the corrosive tendencies of water. Hardness and alkalinity often occur together because some compounds can contribute both alkalinity and hardness ions. Hardness is generally classified as shown in Table 3.10.

Table 3.10. Water Hardness

Classification	mg/L $CaCo_3$
Soft	0–75
Moderately Hard	75–150
Hard	150–300
Very Hard	Over 300

Important Properties of Water

Solubility

Compounds that can form hydrogen bonds with water *tend to be far more soluble* in water than compounds that cannot form H-bonds.

Surface Tension

Water has a high **surface tension**, which governs surface phenomena and is an important factor in physiology. Water's surface tension allows certain organisms to walk on water (see Sidebar 3.1).

Sidebar 3.1. Water Strider ("Jesus Bugs"; Order: Hemiptera)

It is fascinating to sit on a log at the edge of a stream pool and watch the drama that unfolds among the small water animals. Among the star performers in small streams are the water bugs. These are aquatic members of that large group of insects called the "true bugs," most of which live on land. Moreover, unlike many other types of water insects, they do not have gills but get their oxygen directly from the air.

Most conspicuous and commonly known are the water striders or water skaters. They ride the top of the water, with only their feet making dimples in the surface film. Like all insects, the water strider has a three-part body (head, thorax, and abdomen), six jointed legs, and two antennae. It has a long, dark, narrow body (see Figure 3.5). The underside of the body is covered with water-repellent hair. Some water striders have wings; others do not. Most water striders are over 0.2 inch (5 mm) long.

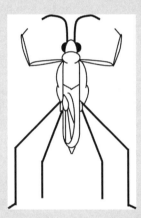

Figure 3.5.   Water strider. Source: Adapted from Standard Methods, 15th Edition. Copyright © 1981 by the American Public Health Association, the American Water Works Association, and the Water Pollution Control Federation

Water striders eat larvae and small insects that fall on the water's surface. The water strider is very sensitive to motion and vibrations on the water's surface. It uses this ability to locate prey. It pushes it mouth into its prey, paralyzes it, and sucks the insect dry. Predators of the water strider, like birds, fish, water beetles, backswimmers, dragonflies, and spiders, take advantage of the fact that water striders cannot detect motion above or below the water's surface (Spellman, 2003).

Density

Water reaches its maximum liquid **density** at 4°C. Recall that density is mass per unit volume. When water freezes, ice floats.

Boiling Point

In general, boiling point increases with molecular weight, but **hydrogen bonding** increases the boiling point of water above that predicted based on molecular weight alone.

Heat Capacity

Water has a higher **heat capacity** than any liquid other than ammonia. Heat capacity is the amount of energy it takes to raise the temperature of a substance one degree. This allows organisms and geographical regions to stabilize temperature more easily.

Heat of Vaporization

Water has a higher **heat of vaporization** than any other material. Heat of vaporization is the energy required to change a liquid into a vapor. It affects the transfer of water molecules between surface water and the atmosphere.

Latent Heat of Fusion

Water has a higher latent heat of fusion than any other liquid except ammonia. The **heat of fusion** is the energy released when a liquid condenses into a solid. Temperature is thus stabilized at the freezing point.

Phase Transitions

A *phase transition* is the spontaneous conversion of one phase to another that occurs at a characteristic temperature for a given pressure. For example, at 1 atm, ice is the stable phase of water below 0 degrees C, but above this temperature the liquid is more stable. A phase diagram of water, for example, is a map of the ranges of pressure and temperature at which each phase of the water is the most stable.

Chemistry of Water Pollution

What Is Water Pollution?

People's opinions differ in what they consider to be a pollutant on the basis of their assessment of benefits and risk to their health and economic well-being. For example, visible and invisible chemicals spewed into water by an industrial facility might be harmful to people and other forms of life living nearby and in the water body itself. However, if the facility is required to install expensive pollution control equipment, forcing the industrial facility to shut down or to move away, workers who would lose their jobs and merchants who would lose their livelihoods might feel that the risks from polluted air and water are minor weighed against the benefits of profitable employment. The same level of pollution can also affect two people quite differently. Some forms of water pollution, for example, might cause only a slight irritation to a healthy person but cause life-threatening problems to someone with autoimmune deficiency problems. Differing priorities lead to differing perceptions of pollution (concern about the level of pesticides in foodstuffs prompting the need for wholesale banning of insecticides is unlikely to help the starving). Public perception lags behind reality because the reality is sometimes unbearable. Pollution is a judgement, and pollution demands continuous judgment. (Spellman, 2003)

Acidity, Alkalinity, and Salinity

The acidity of a natural water system is defined as its capacity to neutralize OH⁻. Acidity is more difficult to measure than alkalinity because volatile gases (CO_2 and H_2S, for example) affect acidity.

✓ **Key Point:** Common sources of "natural" acidity include weak acids, such as $H_2PO_4^-$, CO_2, H_2S, proteins, fatty acids, and acidic metal ions.

Recall that alkalinity is defined as the *capacity* of water to accept H^+. In contrast to pH, which is an *intensity factor*, alkalinity is a *capacity factor*.

Chemists usually express alkalinity in terms of *equivalents per liter*.

$$CaCO_3 + 2H^+ \Rightarrow Ca^{+2} + CO_2 + H_2O$$

The **salinity** of water is its salt load (i.e., concentration of dissolved salts). Increased salt concentrations can arise from numerous human activities, including the following:

• Municipal water treatment
• Leaching from waste piles
• Irrigation and agriculture

Note: 1 liter of 0.001M NaOH has a pH of 11 but can only neutralize 0.001 mole of acid. 1 mole of $CaCO_3$ neutralizes 2 moles of H⁻, or 0.5 mole of $CaCO_3$ neutralizes 1 mole of H^+, therefore a 0.5 M solution of $CaCO_3$ equals 1 equivalent/L alkalinity. 1 liter of 0.1 M HCO_3^- has a pH of 8.34 but can neutralize 0.1 mole of acid.

Water Hardness

Water hardness is attributed to the concentration of Ca^{+2} (plus Mg^{+2} and sometimes Fe^{+2}). The degree of water hardness relates to the amount of dissolved minerals, especially calcium and magnesium, in the water. It is generally expressed in the amount of calcium carbonate ($CaCO^3$). Water hardness is measured in ppm, kH (carbonate hardness), and dH (degrees of hardness) or gH (general hardness). Water is descibed as "soft" (having few dissolved minerals) or "hard" (having many dissolved minerals). General levels of water hardness are shown in Table 3.11 (1 dH is equivalent to about 17 ppm).

High concentrations of dissolved CO_2 enhance the solubility of Ca^{+2}. Heating the water, which drives out CO_2, can decrease the solubility of Ca^{+2}. This causes problems in hot water systems, which can become choked or clogged with insolubles.

$$Ca^{+2} + 2HCO_{3-} \Rightarrow CaCO_3(s) + H_2O$$

Table 3.11. Oxygen: Physical Properties

Chemical formula	O_2
Molecular weight	31.9988
Freezing point	-361.12°F
Boiling point	-297.33°F
Heat of fusion	5.96 Btu/lb
Heat of vaporization	91.70 Btu/lb
Density of gas @ boiling point	0.268 lb/ft³
Density of gas @ room temperature	0.081 lb/ft³
Vapor density (air = 1)	1.105
Liquid-to-gas expansion ratio	8.75

In the presence of soap, hard water forms a "curdlike" **precipitate**.

$$2C_{17}H_{35}COO^-Na^+ + Ca^{+2} \Rightarrow Ca(C_{17}H_{35}CO_2)_2(s) + 2Na^+$$

Although Ca^{+2} does not form insoluble precipitates with detergents, it does adversely affect their performance.

Industrial scale water softening techniques (the removal of Ca^{+2} and Mg^{+2}) include the following:

• The addition of **lime** $(CA)OH)_2$ when only "bicarbonate hardness" is of significant concern.

$$Ca^{+2} + 2HCO_{3.} + Ca(OH)_2 \Rightarrow 2CaCO_3(s) + 2H_2O$$

• The addition of lime and **soda ash** (Na_2CO_3) when bicarbonate is not a factor.

$$Ca^{+2} + 2Cl^- + 2Na^+CO_{3.} \Rightarrow CaCO_3(s) + 2Cl^- + 2Na^+$$

• Converting the precipitated $CaCO_3$ into lime $(Ca(OH)_2$ with heat:

$$CaCO_3 \text{ heat} \Rightarrow CaO + CO_2(g)$$

$$CaO + H_2O \Rightarrow CA(OH)_2$$

• Various problems with water "softened" by this process include residual concentrations of $CaCO_3$ and $Mg(OH)_2$ and extremely high pH.

✓ **Key Point:** Recarbonation generally lowers the pH to an acceptable range.

Additional water softening techniques include the following:

• **ion exchange**
• addition of **orthophosphate** (precipitation)

$$5Ca^{+2} + 3PO_4^{-3} + OH^- \Rightarrow Ca_5OH(PO_4)_3(s)$$

• **chelation** (sequestration)

$$Ca^{+2} + Y^{-4} \Rightarrow CaY^{-2}$$

METAL CONTAMINATION AND CHELATING AGENTS

Common aqueous metal contaminants include the following:

- common metals (Fe, Mn)
- heavy metals (Cd, Pb, Hg)
- metalloids (As, Se, Sb)
- organometallics
- radionuclides

Metal ions in water occur as hydrated ions $M(H_2O)_x^{n+}$ or **complexes**.

Heavy metals like lead and cadmium are released into the atmosphere by vehicle and power station emissions. These dissolve with water vapor and sulfuric and nitric acids in the atmosphere, returning to the Earth as acid rain to pollute water supplies. This problem is compounded by the corrosive effect acids have on metal water pipes, further contaminating water supplies. *Common metal contaminants* such as iron and manganese are removed by oxidation to insoluble forms (e.g., Fe(III) and MnO_2). *Colloidal suspensions* or Fe(III) and Mn(IV) and naturally occurring organic substances are difficult to remove. Water contamination by *heavy metals* (those found in the lower right-hand portion of the periodic table) can be very harmful because these elements:

- Attack S bonds, carboxylic acids, and amino groups.
- Bind to cell membranes.
- Precipitate and/or destroy biologically important phosphates.

Cadmium pollution, arising from industrial and mining activities, is thought to replace biological zinc, resulting in serious adverse health effects such as high blood pressure, damage to the kidneys, and destruction of red blood cells.

Lead from food, drink, and drinking water contamination, as well as industrial and natural sources, can lead to kidney, brain, and central nervous system disorders, among other serious adverse health effects.

Mercury enters the environment from numerous minor sources, which cumulatively add up to substantial toxic effects:

- Sewage can contain 10 × higher concentration of mercury than natural waters.
- The high levels of mercury found in fish in the early 1970s were traced to the production of soluble CH_3Hg^+ and volatile $(CH_3)_2Hg$, which biomagnified in fish tissue >1,000 ×.

Various methods are used to remove heavy metals. For example, lime treatment removes heavy metals. Other heavy metal removal techniques include the following:

- Electrodeposition
- Reverse osmosis
- Ion exchange
- Cementation

$$Cu^{+2} + Fe \text{ (iron scrap)} \Rightarrow Fe^{+2} + Cu$$

- Sorption on activated carbon (+ chelation)
- Ferric chloride flocculation (Cl^3Fe)
- Alum ($Al_2(SO_4)_3 \cdot 18H_2O$) coagulation

$$Al(H_2O)_6{}^{+3} + 3OH^- \Rightarrow Al(OH)_3(s) + 6H_2O$$

✓ **Important Point:** Caution must be used in the disposal of sludges because of the accumulation of heavy metals and other contaminants removed by precipitation or other methods.

Arsenic, which is the primary aqueous **metalloid** contaminant of concern, is released into the atmosphere in significant amounts from the burning of fossil fuels. It is a by-product of lead, copper, and gold refining. Bacteria have been implicated in the transformation of arsenic into more mobile, toxic forms such as $(CH_3)_2AsH$.

Organometallics, including the large class of organotin biocides currently in use, are potentially dangerous water pollutants because of their toxicity and widespread use. Approximately 40,000 metric tons/year of organotin compounds are produced as bactericides, fungicides (antifouling), insecticides, and preservatives.

Radionuclides can enter water systems through human and natural sources. Naturally occurring are C-14, Si-32, L-40, Ra-226, Pb-210, Th-230, and Th-234. Significant Ra contamination has been detected in western mining areas, and in Iowa, Illinois, Wisconsin, Mississippi, Minnesota, Florida, North Carolina, Virginia, and New England. Dangerous radionuclides resulting from human activities include some with man-made origins: Sr-90, I-131, Cs-137, Ba-140, Zr-95, Ce-141, Sr-89, Ru-103, Kr-85, Co-60, Mn-54, Fe-55, and Pu-239.

Chelating Agents

If the species complexing with the metal has only one bonding site, it is called a *ligand.* If the species complexing with the metal has multiple bonding sites, it is called a **chelating agent**.

Metals complex with both natural and human-made chelating agents. Natural chelating agents are called **humic substances**, the residuals from the biodegradation of vegetation. The molecular weights of these substances range from a few 100 to >10,000.

- *Soluble* humic substances will:
  - Add a yellow tint to water.
  - Solubilize biologically important metals.
  - Generate trihalomethanes (carcinogens) during municipal chlorination processes.
- *Insoluble* humic substances will:
  - Exchange cations with water.
  - Accumulate metals.
- *Man-made* chelating agents, such as EDTA, are used as cleaning agents (decontamination) that solubilize metals. This increased metal solubility also increases the mobility of chelated species released into the environment.

- Antibiotics such as streptomycin, aspergillic acid, and tetracyclines and others are known to have chelating properties.

Other Inorganic Water Pollutants

NH_3 (from nitrogenous organic wastes)
H_2S (**anaerobic** digestion, geothermal emissions, industrial wastes)
CO_2 (organic decay, recarbonation)
NO_2^- (corrosion inhibitor)
SO_3^{-2} (boiler feedwater)
asbestos (industrial mining wastes)

The removal of dissolved inorganics is an essential part of wastewater treatment, even if the treated water is not destined for drinking. Distillation is too costly and does not remove inorganic volatiles (e.g., NH_3). Freezing is also not cost effective.

Common techniques for the removal of dissolved inorganics include the following:

- Electrodialysis and reverse osmosis
- Ion exchange
- Air stripping at high pH (NH_3)
- Precipitation (phosphate)

$$5Ca(OH)_2 + 3HPO_4^{-2} \Rightarrow Ca_5OH(PO_4)_3(s) + 3H_2O + 6OH^-$$

Organic Water Pollutants

Domestic and industrial **sewage** contains a wide variety of organic pollutants, including viruses, detergents, phosphates, grease, oil, salts, heavy metals, chelating agents, solids, and **biorefractory** (for example, biodegradation resistant) organics. Soaps, detergents, surfactants, and detergent builders are also released into domestic and industrial wastewaters in large quantities.

✓ **Key Point:** If not properly treated, the resulting treated water, as well as sludge, can still contain all or many of these pollutants.

Many human-made organic compounds cannot be easily biodegraded by microorganisms. These low molecular weight, relatively nonvolatile biorefractory compounds persist in the environment, with unknown consequences. The list of these compounds is filled with aromatic and chlorinated hydrocarbons or both. Biological treatment of biorefractory compounds must be accompanied by other processes, including air stripping, solvent extraction, ozonation, and carbon absorption, to remove them. Many also cause taste and odor problems in drinking water.

Pesticides and herbicides are manufactured and used in large quantities and often find their way unintentionally into environmental media; for example, Kepone contamination has occurred in the James River in Virginia. In addition, biorefractory-starting materials for pesticide production, such as hexachlorobenzene, have been found in drinking water. Another example is dioxin, a potentially toxic by-product of pesticide and herbicide manufacture.

PCBs also find their way into water bodies. They contain between 1 and 10 CL substitutions of biphenyl, making a total of 209 possible **congeners**. PCBs have been detected in sediments, animal, and bird tissues throughout the world. The Environmental Protection Agency (EPA) has estimated that 91% of all Americans have detectable levels of PCBs in their tissues.

Removal of dissolved organics before chlorination is necessary to avoid the formation of trihalomethanes. Organics that typically survive through (or are produced by) secondary waste treatment processes include humic substances (~59%), carbohydrates, detergents, and tannins.

The primary method for the removal of dissolved organics is sorption by activated carbon. The "activation process" creates greater porosity, surface area, and affinity for organics. Activated carbon must be periodically flushed to remove particulates and can be regenerated by heating in steam/air to 950°C. Other techniques for the removal of dissolved organics include adsorption by synthetic polymers (amberlite resins) and oxidation.

The disposal of sludge from wastewater treatment plants is a major problem around the world. Ocean dumping was completely banned in the United States in 1992. Before acceptable disposal, these sludges are typically reduced in volume by anaerobic digestion, followed by conditioning, thickening, and dewatering.

These nutrient-rich sludges (5% N, 3% P, 0.5% K) can be used to fertilize and condition soil. Problems include contaminated runoff, high concentrations of heavy metals and chemical "precipitating" agents, crop contamination, and pathogens. Sludge samples have been found to contain 9,000 ppm Zn, 6,000 ppm Cu, 600 ppm Ni, and 800 ppm Cd.

TMDLs

The **TMDLs** (total maximum daily load) is the amount of a pollutant that can be discharged into a water body and still attain water quality goals. TMDLs are required for impaired or polluted waters and are used to set priorities for developing watershed plans and to calculate individual load allocations. Load allocations assign responsibility for water quality to those discharging into the water body (Spellman & Drinan, 2001).

On July 11, 2000, the EPA administrator signed a rule that revised the TMDL program and made related changes to the National Pollutant Discharge Elimination System (NPDES) and Water Quality Standards programs (65 FR 43585, July 13). According to former president Clinton, the EPA's move was a "critical, common-sense step" to clean up the nation's waterways.

Why was a new TMDL rule needed? The EPA points out that over 20,000 water bodies across America have been identified as polluted by states, territories, and authorized tribes. These waters include over 300,000 stream/river and shoreline miles and 5 million acres of lakes. The overwhelming majority of people in the United States live within 10 miles of these polluted waters.

The Clean Water Act (CWA) provides special authority for restoring polluted waters. The act calls on states to work with interested parties to develop TMDLs for polluted waters. A TMDL is essentially a "pollution budget" designed to restore the health of the polluted body of water.

The goal of the TMDL rule is to make thousands more streams/rivers, lakes, and coastal waters safe for swimming, fishing, and healthy population of fish and shellfish. Its key provisions include the following:

- It requires states to develop more detailed listing methods and comprehensive lists of polluted water bodies, which must be submitted to the EPA every four years. The lists also may include threatened waters.
- It requires states to prioritize water bodies and develop TMDLs first for those that are drinking water sources or support endangered species. Once a TMDL is developed, the rule requires states to establish a cleanup schedule that would enable polluted water bodies to achieve water quality standards within 10 years (15 years if the state requests, and EPA grants, an extension).
- It requires that TMDL development include an implementation plan that identifies specific actions and schedules for meeting water quality goals and addresses both point and nonpoint pollution sources. Runoff controls must also be installed five years after this plan is developed, if practicable, and TMDL allocations for nonpoint sources must be
  - pollution specific,
  - implemented expeditiously,
  - met through effective programs, and
  - supported by adequate water quality funding.
- It does not require new permits for forestry, livestock, or aquaculture operations. It also does not require "offsets" for new pollution discharges to impaired waters prior to TMDL development.

DDT and Biomagnification

Figure 3.6 shows how DDT becomes concentrated in the tissues of organisms representing four successive trophic levels in a food chain.

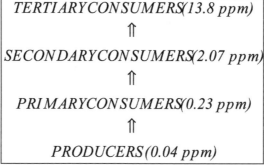

Figure 3.6. The numbers are representative values of the concentration of DDT and its derivatives in tissues (in parts per million, ppm).

The concentration effect occurs because DDT is metabolized and excreted much more slowly than the nutrients that are passed from one trophic (feeding) level to the next. Therefore, DDT accumulates in the body (especially in fat). Most of the DDT ingested as part of gross production is still present in the net production that remains at that trophic level.

✓ **Key Point:** This is why the hazard of DDT to nontarget animals is particularly acute for those species living at the top of food chains.

Summary of Chemical Properties of Water

Important chemical properties of water include the following:

- Water is essential to life.
- Water is transparent.
- Water is an excellent solvent.
- Water is a polar solvent.
- Water has high surface tension.
- Water's maximum liquid density is at 4°C.
- Hydrogen bonding increases the boiling point of water above that predicted based on molecular weight.
- Water has a higher heat capacity than any other liquid other than ammonia.
- Water has a higher heat of vaporization than any other material.
- Water has a higher latent heat of fusion than any other liquid other than ammonia.
- A solution is a homogeneous mixture of a solute in a solvent.
- The solvent can be separated from its solution by distillation.
- Polar solutes dissolve in polar solvents.
- Nonpolar solutes dissolve in nonpolar solvents.
- A concentrated solution has a large amount of solute dissolved in the solution.
- A dilute solution has a small amount of solute dissolved in its solution.
- The acidity of a natural water system is defined as its capacity to neutralize OH^-.
- Alkalinity is defined as the capacity of water to accept H^+.
- Alkalinity is usually expressed by chemists in terms of equivalents per liter.
- The salinity of water is its salt load.
- Water hardness is attributed to the concentration of Ca^{+2}.
- Common aqueous metal contaminants include common metals, heavy metals, met-alloids, organometallics, and radionuclides.
- Organic and inorganic substances contribute to water pollution.
- TMDLs are the amount of a pollutant that can be discharged into a water body and still attain water quality goals.
- Biomagnification is demonstrated when DDT becomes concentrated as it passes through a food chain.
- Primary treatment is the first step in the wastewater treatment process.
- Secondary wastewater treatment uses biochemical processes to digest organic wastes.

- Secondary treatment uses trickling filters, rotating biological contactors, and activated sludge.
- Tertiary treatment involves one or more physical, chemical, and/or biochemical processes used to remove nutrients.

Important Points!

Bioaccumulation and biomagnification are two of the most important processes environmental scientists need to know about and be intimately familiar with. In bioaccumulation, fat-soluble molecules accumulate and stay in the fatty tissues of animals because they can't dissolve in water. Biomagnification occurs when compounds are passed from prey to predator. The more the predator eats, the more of the compound is accumulated, and the concentration becomes much higher than one would expect to find in the environment.

EARTH'S ATMOSPHERE: "A FLASK WITHOUT WALLS"

Note: In the following discussion of the chemistry of Earth's atmosphere, note that we refer to the atmosphere as it is at present (during the age of humans). The atmosphere previous to this period was chemically quite different. Note also that "atmospheric chemistry" is a scientific discipline of its own. An in-depth presentation of atmospheric chemistry is beyond the scope of this book. Here, certain important atmospheric chemistry phenomena are highlighted, especially those problems caused by organic and inorganic air pollutants.

The full range of chemistry occurs in the atmosphere—the atmosphere is a "flask without walls" (Graedel & Crutzen, 1995). Excluding highly variable amounts of water vapor, more than 99% of the molecules constituting the Earth's atmosphere are nitrogen, oxygen, and chemically inert gases (noble gases such as argon, etc.).

The chemistry (and thus the reactivity) of these natural gases (nitrogen, oxygen, carbon dioxide, argon, and others) is well known. The other reactive chemicals (anthropogenically [human] produced) that are part of Earth's atmosphere are also known, but opinions still differ about their "exact" total effect on our environment. For example, methane is by far the most abundant reactive compound in the atmosphere, and it currently is at a ground-level concentration (in the northern hemisphere) of about 1.7 ppmv. We have significant amounts of information about methane (its generation and fate when discharged) and its influence on the atmosphere; however, we are still conducting research to find out more, as we should.

Many reactive molecules other than methane exist in the atmosphere. We may not be familiar with each of these reactants, but many of us certainly are familiar with their consequences: the ozone hole, the greenhouse effect and global warming, smog, acid rain, the rising tide, and so on. It may surprise you to know, however, that the total amount of all these reactants in the atmosphere is seldom more than 10 ppmv anywhere in the world at any given time. The significance should be obvious: The atmospheric problems currently occurring on Earth are the result of less than one thousandth of 1% of all the molecules in the atmosphere. This indicates that environmental damage (causing global atmospheric problems) can result from far less than the tremendous amounts of reactive substances we might imagine are dangerous.

Various contaminants released into the atmosphere manifest a variety of environmental problems. Consider, for example, the following airborne contaminants and their implications in global warming, acid rain, distortion of visibility, increased respiratory problems, and/or plant necrosis (yellowing):

- Particulates distort visibility and increase respiratory problems.
- CO is a greenhouse contributor because it slowly breaks down into CO_2.
- CH_4 is a greenhouse gas.
- Fly ash distorts visibility and increases respiratory problems.
- CFCs are a greenhouse gas.
- N_2O is a greenhouse gas, contributes to acid rain, increases respiratory problems, and causes plant necrosis.
- CO_2 is a greenhouse gas.
- SO_2 contributes to acid rain, increases respiratory problems, and causes plant necrosis.
- NO_x is a greenhouse gas, contributes to acid rain, increases respiratory problems, and causes plant necrosis.
- Coal dust distorts visibility and increases respiratory problems.

More specifically, various chemical activities contribute to environmental pollution. In addition to the isuues listed above, the types of environmental pollution from the chemical industry include sulfur dioxide, toxic gas emissions, foul-smelling gases, dust, smoke, sprays, and radioactivity.

The quality of the air we breathe, visibility and atmospheric esthetics, and our climate are important to our health and quality of life—all depend on chemical phenomena that occur in the atmosphere. Global atmospheric problems, such as the nature and level of air pollutants, concern the environmental scientist the most because they affect health, quality of life, and the environment.

Functions of the Atmosphere

The Earth's **atmosphere** has many functions:

- It serves as a reservoir of gases of use to the biosphere, including carbon dioxide (photosynthesis), oxygen (respiration), and nitrogen (nitrogen fixation), as well as water.
- It is a protective shield for the biosphere (role of ozone).
- It is a transport medium for energy and water.
- It is a medium for waste disposal.
- It moderates temperature (transports heat).

✓ **Important Point:** The atmosphere has a large capacity to absorb, dilute, and remove pollutants. Its capacity to dilute and disperse varies by a factor of ~ 10,000, depending on aspects such as atmospheric stability, but is *not limitless*.

Chemical Reactions in the Atmosphere

Atmospheric reactions generally occur at very *low pressures* (e.g., low concentrations) in the presence of large amounts of *energy* (e.g., sunlight).

✓ **Interesting Point:** Manahan (1997) points out that the "study of atmospheric chemical reactions is difficult." Why? "Because the chemist must deal with incredibly low concentrations, so that detection and analysis of reaction products is quite difficult. It is difficult to simulate these reactions in the laboratory because even the walls of the container can act as a 'third body' to absorb energy or act as a catalyst."

Because of *low concentrations* of atoms and molecules, chemically reactive species tend to persist in the upper atmosphere. The most important reactive species are

- photochemically excited species X*,
- ions and electrons (charges species), and
- free radicals.

An asterisk (*) designates an electronically excited molecule.

Not surprisingly, **photochemical reactions,** which occur in the presence of *light*, play a significant role in atmospheric chemistry.

✓ **Key Point:** Many of these reactions would not occur in the absence of light, especially under the conditions (e.g., the temperatures) found in the upper atmosphere.

Excited State X: Chemicals in the atmosphere can absorb light to form an **excited state X***. These excited molecules primarily lose energy through the following activities:

- Dissociation—bond broken by absorption of a photon (light)

$$O_2^* \Rightarrow O + O$$

- Photoionization—removal of an outer (valence) electron from a molecule by absorption of a photon

$$N_2^* \Rightarrow N_2^* + e^-$$

- Direct reaction

$$O_2^* + O_3 \Rightarrow 2O_2 + O$$

Ions and Electrons: Ions and electrons (charged atoms or molecular fragments) are present in such high quantities in the upper atmosphere (>50 km; because solar radiation is very intense) that this region is called the **ionosphere**. Radio transmission around the curvature of the Earth is possible because radio waves bounce off the ionosphere.

✓ **Interesting Point:** At night, the formation of ions ceases and the lower limit of the ionosphere "lifts" due to recombination, allowing radio wave transmissions over greater distances.

Free Radicals: **Free radicals** are composed of atoms or molecular fragments with unshared electrons. They are formed by the action of high-energy radiation. These radicals can react with other species to form new radicals or can be "quenched" by another radical.

The **hydroxyl radical,** an extremely important chemical species in atmospheric chemistry, is produced by many reactions, including:

$$H_2 \Rightarrow +hv \quad HO^* + H$$
$$O_3 \Rightarrow +hv \quad O^* + O2$$
$$O^* + H_2O \Rightarrow hv \quad 2HO^*$$

Reactions of Atmospheric Oxygen

Oxygen (O_2: Greek *oxys*, "acid" and *genes*, "forming") constitutes approximately one-fifth (21% by volume and 23.2% by weight) of the air in Earth's atmosphere. Gaseous oxygen (O_2) is vital to life as we know it. On Earth, oxygen is the most abundant element. Most oxygen on Earth is not found in the free state, however, but rather in combination with other elements as chemical compounds. Water and carbon dioxide are common examples of compounds that contain oxygen, but there are countless others.

Photosynthetic organisms are thought to generate all the *molecular* oxygen (O_2) in the atmosphere. In the upper atmosphere, *elemental* oxygen and other forms also exist: O, O^*, O_2^*, and ozone (O_3). The physical properties of oxygen (O_3) are noted in Table 3.11.

✓ **Key Point:** Less than 10% of the oxygen at altitudes >400 km exists in the form of O_2.

Atomic oxygen (O) is produced by the photochemical decomposition of molecular oxygen. It is found in the rarified *thermosphere.*

$$O_2 + hv \Rightarrow O + O$$

O^+ is the principal cation in parts of the ionosphere.

$$O + hv \Rightarrow O^+ + e^-$$

Ozone (O_3)—another form of oxygen—is a highly reactive pale-blue gas with a penetrating odor. Ozone is an allotropic modification of oxygen. An *allotrope* is a variation of an element that possesses a set of physical and chemical properties significantly different from the normal form of the element. Only a few elements have allotropic forms: oxygen, phosphorus, and sulfur are some of them. Formed when ultraviolet (UV) radiation or electrical discharge splits the molecule of the stable form of oxygen (O_2), it has three, instead of two, atoms of oxygen per molecule. Thus, its chemical formula is represented by O_3.

Ozone forms a thin layer (concentrations as high as 10%) in the upper atmosphere and serves as a radiation shield (230–330 nm) that protects life on Earth from ultraviolet rays (a cause of skin cancer). At lower atmospheric levels, it is an air pollutant and contributes to the greenhouse effect. At ground level, ozone, when inhaled, can cause asthma attacks, stunted growth in plants, and corrosion of certain materials. Produced by the action of sunlight on air pollutants (including car exhaust fumes), ozone is a major air pollutant especially noticeable in hot summers.

$$O_2 + hv \Rightarrow O + O \, (< 242.4 \, nm)$$

$$O + O_2 + M \rightarrow O_3 \, M \, (\text{increased energy})$$

✓ **Key Point:** The radiation absorbed by O_3 is transformed into heat.

✓ **Key Point:** Ozone is a toxic pollutant in the **troposphere.**

Reactions of Atmospheric Nitrogen

Nitrogen (N_2) makes up the major portion of the atmosphere (78.03% by volume, 75.5% by weight). A colorless, odorless, tasteless, nontoxic, and almost totally inert gas, nitrogen is nonflammable, will not support combustion, and is not life supporting.

Nitrogen is part of the Earth's atmosphere primarily because, over time, it has simply accumulated there and remained in place and in balance. This nitrogen accumulation process has occurred because, chemically, nitrogen is not very reactive. When released by any process, it tends not to recombine with other elements and accumulates in the atmosphere.

✓ **Key Point:** We need nitrogen not for breathing, but for other life-sustaining processes.

Although nitrogen in its gaseous form is of little use to us, after oxygen, carbon, and hydrogen, it is the most common element in living tissues. As a chief constituent of chlorophyll and amino acids and nucleic acids—the "building blocks" of proteins (used as structural component in cells)—nitrogen is essential to life. Animals cannot use nitrogen directly, only when they obtain it by eating plant or animal tissues. Plants obtain the nitrogen they need in the form of inorganic compounds, principally nitrate and ammonium.

Gaseous nitrogen is converted to a form usable by plants (nitrate ions) chiefly through the process of nitrogen fixation via the nitrogen cycle.

$$N_2 + hv \Rightarrow N + N$$

✓ **Key Point:** UV light at altitudes below 100 km does not readily dissociate diatomic nitrogen.

The physical properties of nitrogen are noted in Table 3.12.

Table 3.12.   Nitrogen: Physical Properties

Chemical formula	N_2
Molecular weight	28.01
Density of gas @ 70°F	0.072 lb/ft³
Specific gravity of gas @ 70°F and 1 atm (air = 1)	0.967
Specific volume of gas @ 70°F and 1 atm	13.89 ft³/lb
Boiling point @ 1 atm	–320.4°F
Melting point @ 1 atm	–345.8°F
Critical temperature	–232.4°F
Critical pressure	493 psia
Critical density	19.60 lb/ft³
Latent heat of vaporization @ boiling point	85.6 Btu/lb
Latent heat of fusion @ melting point	11.1 Btu/lb

Nitrogen oxides—usually collectively symbolized by the formula NO_x—include nitrous oxide (N_2O), nitric oxide (NO), dinitrogen trioxide (N_2O_3), nitrogen dioxide (NO_2), dinitrogen tetroxide (N_2O_4), and dinitrogen pentoxide (N_2O_5).

Nitric oxide, nitrogen dioxide, and nitrogen tetroxide are fire gases. One or more of them is generated when certain nitrogenous organic compounds (polyurethanes) burn. Nitric oxide is the product of incomplete combustion, and a mixture of nitrogen dioxide and nitrogen tetroxide is the product of complete combustion.

NO is thought to be the primary mechanism by which O_3 is removed from the stratosphere.

$$O_3 + NO \Rightarrow NO_2 + O_2$$

$$NO_2 + O \Rightarrow NO + O_2 \text{ (regeneration of NO)}$$

✓ **Key Point:** NO_2 is a primary cause of **photochemical smog**.

$$NO_2 + hv \Rightarrow NO + O$$

Atmospheric Carbon Dioxide

Carbon dioxide (CO_2) is a colorless, odorless gas (although some people feel it has a slight pungent odor and biting taste), slightly soluble in water, more dense than air (one and a half times heavier than air), and slightly acidic. Carbon dioxide gas is relatively nonreactive and nontoxic. It will not burn, and it will not support combustion or life.

CO_2 is normally present in atmospheric air at about 0.035% by volume and cycles through the biosphere (carbon cycle). Carbon dioxide, along with water vapor, is primarily responsible for the absorption of infrared energy re-emitted by the Earth. In turn, some of this energy is reradiated back to the Earth's surface. It is also a normal end product of human and animal metabolism. Our exhaled breath contains up to 5.6% carbon dioxide. Burning carbon-laden fossil fuels also releases carbon dioxide into the atmosphere. Much of this carbon dioxide is absorbed by ocean water; some of it is taken up by vegetation through photosynthesis in the carbon cycle, and some remains in the atmosphere.

✓ **Interesting Point:** Today, scientists estimate that the concentration of carbon dioxide in the atmosphere is approximately 350 ppm and increasing at a rate of approximately 20 ppm every decade. The increasing rate of combustion of coal and oil has been primarily responsible for this occurrence, which may eventually have an impact on global climate.

The physical properties of carbon dioxide are noted in Table 3.13.

Table 3.13.   Carbon Dioxide: Physical Properties

Chemical formula	CO_2
Molecular weight	44.01
Vapor pressure @ 70°F	838 psig
Density of gas @ 70°F and 1 atm	0.1144 lb/ft³
Specific gravity of gas @ 70°F and 1 atm (air = 1)	1.522
Specific volume of gas @ 70°F and 1 atm	8.741 ft³/lb
Critical temperature	–109.3°F
Critical pressure	1070.6 psia
Critical density	29.2 lb/ft³
Latent heat of vaporization @ boiling point	100.8 Btu/lb
Latent heat of fusion @ –69.9°	85.6 Btu/lb

Air Pollutants

Traditionally, it has been convenient to categorize air pollutants as either organic (particulate, carbon oxides, sulfur dioxide, and nitrogen oxides) or inorganic (direct pollutants that cause cancer, etc., and secondary pollutants that contribute to photochemical smog). Even though Manahan (1997) points out that "there is a strong connection between inorganic and organic substances in the atmosphere," here we choose to stick to tradition, discussing various air pollutants separately, as inorganic and organic.

Before discussing various air pollutants, however, we point out that strictly speaking, too much of any substance in the wrong place or at the wrong time is a pollutant. More to the point, atmospheric pollution may be defined as "the presence of substances in the atmosphere, resulting from human-made activities or from natural processes, causing adverse effects to man and the environment. [Simply], air pollution is a term used to describe any unwanted chemicals or other materials that contaminate the air that we breathe resulting in the degradation of air quality" ("Air Pollutants," 2002).

✓ **Key Point:** The inorganic air pollutants discussed in this section are all typical urban air pollutants from human activities. They include nitrogen oxides, carbon monoxide, sulfur dioxide, hydrocarbons, and particulates. All these pollutants are called **primary pollutants** because they are emitted directly into the atmosphere.

Inorganic Air Pollutants

Particulate Matter   Hastie (2002) points out that **atmospheric particulate matter** (PM, or aerosols) is important in the atmosphere for at least four reasons. It provides a sink for reactive gases; for example, particulate matter contains sulphate and nitrate from oxidation of SO_2 and NO_2. It also provides a surface for chemical reactions; the chemistry of antarctic ozone depletion attests to that. Particles can carry toxic chemicals such as PAHs and metals to remote areas; many of the toxic chemicals found in the arctic get there this way. Particles can also penetrate into the bronchial tract and the lungs, causing human health problems such as bronchitis and pneumonia. There is now overwhelming evidence relating mortality to particulate levels.

Atmospheric particulate matter is defined as any dispersed matter, solid or liquid, in which the individual aggregates are larger than single small molecules (about 0.0002 μm in diameter), but smaller than about 500 μm (Masters, 1991). In practice, particulate matter is a collective term used to describe small solid and liquid particles present in the atmosphere over relatively brief (minutes) to extended (days to weeks) periods of time. Individual particles vary in size, geometry, mass, concentration, chemical composition, and physical properties. They may be produced naturally or as a direct or indirect result of human activities.

Significant amounts of particulate matter are suspended in the atmosphere, particularly in the troposphere. These particles originate in nature from smoke, sea spray, dust, and the evaporation of organic materials from vegetation. A wide variety of nature's living or semiliving particles are also present—spores and pollen grains, mites and other tiny insects, and diatoms. The atmosphere also contains a bewildering variety of anthropogenic (human-made) particles produced by automobiles, refineries, production mills, and many other human activities.

Elements in particulate matter include:

- Al, Fe, Ca, Si from soil, rocks, or coal combustion;
- C as a result of incomplete combustion;
- Na, Cl from marine aerosols, incineration of organohalide polymers;
- Sb, Se from combustion of oil, coal, or refuse;
- V, Zn, Pb resulting from combustion; and
- Be, Ca, Cr, Ni, As, Hg from various sources.

Atmospheric particulate matter varies greatly in size, ranging over many orders of magnitude from molecular clusters to those that are visible with the unaided eye.

Colloidal-sized particles in the atmosphere are called *aerosols*—usually less than 0.1 mm in diameter; the smallest are gaseous clusters, ions and submicroscopic liquids and solids. Somewhat larger ones produce the beautiful blue haze in distant vistas; those two to three times larger are highly effective in scattering light; and the largest consist of such things as rock fragments, salt crystals, and ashy residues form volcanoes, forest fires, or incineration.

The largest number of airborne particulates is always in the invisible range. These numbers vary from less than one per liter, to more than a half million per cubic centimeter in heavily polluted air, to at least 10 times more than that when a gas-to-particle reaction is occurring (Schaefer & Day, 1981).

Based on particulate level, we can define two distinct regions in the atmosphere: very clean and dirty. The clean parts hold so few particulates that they are almost invisible, making them difficult to collect or measure. In the dirty parts of the atmosphere—for example, the air of a large metropolitan area—the concentration of particles includes an incredible quantity and variety of particulates from a wide variety of sources.

Atmospheric particulate matter performs a number of functions, undergoes several processes, and is involved in many chemical reactions in the atmosphere. Probably the most important function of particulate matter in the atmosphere is its action as nuclei for the formation of water droplets and ice crystals. Much of the work of Vincent J. Schaefer (inventor of cloud seeding) involved using dry ice in early attempts, but it later evolved around the addition of condensing particles to atmospheres supersaturated with water vapor and the use of silver iodide, which forms huge numbers of very small particles. Another important function of atmospheric particulate matter is that it helps determine the heat balance of the Earth's atmosphere by reflecting light. Particulate matter is also involved in many chemical reactions in the atmosphere: neutralization, catalytic effects, and oxidation reactions.

Carbon Oxides   Carbon monoxide (CO) is a colorless, odorless, tasteless gas that is by far the most abundant of the primary pollutants, as Table 3.14 indicates. It has little direct effect on ecosystems, but has an indirect environmental impact by contributing to the greenhouse effect and depletion of the Earth's protective ozone layer.

Table 3.14.   U.S. Emission Estimates, 1986 (10^{12} g/yr)

Source	SO_x	NO_x	VOC	CO	Lead	PM
Transportation	0.9	8.5	6.5	42.6	0.0035	1.4
Stationary source fuel	17.2	10.0	2.3	7.2	0.0005	1.8
Industrial processes	3.1	0.6	7.9	4.5	0.0019	2.5
Solid waste disposal	0.0	0.1	0.6	1.7	0.0027	0.3
Miscellaneous	0.0	0.1	2.2	5.0	0.0000	0.8
Total	**21.2**	**19.3**	**19.5**	**61.0**	**0.0086**	**6.8**

Source: U.S. EPA, 1988.

✓ **Important Point:** The residence time of CO in the atmosphere is approximately four months.

The most important natural source of atmospheric carbon monoxide is the combination of oxygen with methane (CH_4), a product of the anaerobic decay of vegetation. (Anaerobic decay takes place in the absence of oxygen.) At the same time, however, carbon monoxide is removed from the atmosphere by the activities of certain soil microorganisms, so the net result is a harmless average concentration that is less than 0.12–15 ppm in the Northern Hemisphere. Because stationary source combustion facilities are under much tighter environmental control than are mobile sources, the principal source of carbon monoxide from human activities is motor vehicle exhaust, which contributes about 70% of all CO emissions in the United States.

✓ **Key Point:** Soil microorganisms act as a CO sink.

CO also slowly breaks down in the atmosphere to produce carbon dioxide (CO_2). Carbon dioxide and other infrared absorbing gases in the atmosphere contribute to global warming (the *greenhouse effect*).

✓ **Key Point:** Methane (CH_4), chlorofluorocarbons (CFCs), water vapor, and nitrous oxide (N_2O) are also greenhouse gases.

Greenhouse Gases and Global Warming

Most gardeners understand the operation and importance of a garden greenhouse. The typical garden greenhouse is composed of glass walls and ceilings. These glass partitions are transparent, of course, to short-wave radiation from the sun, which is absorbed by the surfaces and objects inside the greenhouse. Once absorbed, the radiation is transformed into long-wave (infrared) radiation (heat), which is radiated back from the interior of the greenhouse. But the glass does not allow the long-wave radiation to escape; instead, it absorbs the warm rays. With the heat trapped inside, the interior of the greenhouse becomes and remains much warmer than the air outside.

The Earth's atmosphere allows much the same greenhouse effect to take place. The short wave and visible radiation that reaches Earth is absorbed by the surface as heat. The long heat waves are then radiated back out toward space, but the atmosphere instead absorbs many of them. This natural and balanced process is essential to life as we know it on Earth. A problem arises when changes in the atmosphere radically change the amount of absorption and therefore the amount retained. Scientists in recent decades have speculated that this may have been happening as various air pollutants caused the atmosphere to absorb more heat. This phenomenon takes place at the local level with air pollution, causing heat islands in and around urban centers.

As mentioned, the main contributors to this effect are the so-called greenhouse gases: water vapor, carbon dioxide, carbon monoxide, methane, volatile organic compounds (VOCs), nitrogen oxides, chlorofluorocarbons (CFCs), and surface ozone. These gases delay the escape of infrared radiation from the Earth into space, causing a general climatic warming. Note that scientists stress that this is a natural process. Indeed, the Earth would be 33°C cooler than it is presently if the "normal" greenhouse effect did not exist (Hansen et al., 1986).

The problem with Earth's greenhouse effect is that human activities are now rapidly intensifying this natural phenomenon, which may lead to global warming.

Debate, confusion, and speculation about this potential consequence are rampant. Scientists are not entirely sure whether the recently perceived worldwide warming trend is because of greenhouse gases or some other cause, or whether it is simply a wider variation in the normal heating and cooling trends they have been studying. If it continues unchecked, however, the process may lead to significant global warming, with profound effects. Human impact on the greenhouse effect is real; it has been detected and measured. The levels of "greenhouse gases" have rapidly increased in recent decades, and this trend is continuing. The rate at which the greenhouse effect is intensifying is now more than five times what it was during the 1800s.

✓ **Key Point:** Most computer models predict global warming of 1.5° to 5°C, which would have a profound effect on rainfall, plant growth, and sea levels (which would rise as much as 1.5 meters).

At the present time, scientists are able to point to six factors that could be involved in long-term global warming and cooling:

1. Long-term global warming and cooling could result if changes in the Earth's position relative to the sun occur, with higher temperatures when the two are closer together and lower ones when they are farther apart.
2. Long-term global warming and cooling could result if major catastrophes occur (meteor impacts or massive volcanic eruptions) and throw pollutants into the atmosphere, blocking out solar radiation.
3. Long-term global warming and cooling could result if changes in albedo (the reflectivity of Earth's surface) occur. If the Earth's surface were more reflective, for example, the amount of solar radiation radiated back toward space instead of being absorbed would increase, lowering temperatures on Earth.
4. Long-term global warming and cooling could result if the amount of radiation emitted by the sun changes.
5. Long-term global warming and cooling could result if the shape and relationship of the land and oceans change.
6. Long-term global warming and cooling could result if the composition of the atmosphere changes.

The true effect of increased greenhouse gases is difficult to predict because of the role of the oceans, the influence of clouds, and biofeedback mechanisms.

Sulfur Dioxide   Sulfur dioxide (SO_2) is a colorless gas possessing the sharp, irritating, pungent odor of burning rubber. On a global basis, nature and anthropogenic activities produce sulfur dioxide in roughly equivalent amounts. Natural sources include volcanos, decaying organic matter, and sea spray; anthropogenic sources include combustion of sulfur-containing coal and petroleum products and smelting of nonferrous ores.

✓ **Key Point:** Background levels of SO_2 are very low, with typical concentrations ranging from 24 to 90 pptv. In remote areas relatively unaffected by pollutant sources, concentrations are typically < 5 ppbv.

According to the World Resources Institute and Internal Institute for Environment and Development (WRI & IIED), in industrial areas, much more sulfur dioxide comes from human activities than from natural sources (WRI & IIED, 1988). Sulfur-containing substances are often present in fossil fuels; SO_2 is a product of combustion that results from the burning of sulfur-containing materials. The largest single source of sulfur dioxide is the burning of fossil fuels to generate electricity. Thus, near major industrialized areas, it is often encountered as an air pollutant.

✓ **Key Point:** Approximately 100 million metric tons of sulfur per year enter the global atmosphere because of human activity, primarily the burning of coal and fuel oil.

In the atmosphere, sulfur dioxide converts to sulfur trioxide (SO_3) and sulfate particles (SO_4). Sulfate particles restrict visibility, and in the presence of water they form sulfuric acid (H_2SO_4), a highly corrosive substance that also lowers visibility.

Global output of sulfur dioxide has increased sixfold since 1900. Most industrial nations, however, since 1975–1985, have lowered sulfur dioxide levels by 20 to 60% by shifting away from heavy industry and imposing stricter emission standards. Major sulfur dioxide reductions have come from burning coal with a lower sulfur content and using less coal to generate electricity (MacKenzie & El-Ashry, 1988).

Two major environmental problems have developed in highly industrialized regions of the world, where the atmospheric sulfur dioxide concentration has been relatively high: sulfurous smog and acid rain. *Sulfurous smog* is the haze that develops in the atmosphere when molecules of sulfuric acid accumulate, growing in size as droplets until they become sufficiently large to serve as light scatterers. The second problem, *acid rain*, is precipitation contaminated with dissolved acids such as sulfuric acid. Acid rain has posed a threat to the environment by causing certain lakes to become devoid of aquatic life.

✓ **Key Point:** Sulfur dioxide primarily affects the respiratory tract, producing increased mucous secretion, irritation, and increased air resistance. It is also harmful to plants, causing leaf necrosis and/or chlorosis (yellowing) of the green portions of the plant.

Nitrogen Oxides   Nitrogen oxides (NO_x) comprise a group of seven oxides of nitrogen—NO, NO_2, NO_3, N_2O, N_2O_3, N_2O_4, and N_2O_5—but only two are important in the study of air pollution: nitric oxide (NO) and nitrogen dioxide (NO_2).

✓ **Key Point: Nitrous oxide** (N_2O) is generated by microbes and is relatively unreactive, although it could contribute to ozone depletion. Colorless, odorless nitric oxide (NO) and pungent red-brown nitrogen dioxide (NO_2) are collectively known as NO_x and are very significant in polluted air.

Nitric oxide is a colorless, slightly sweet, relatively nontoxic gas, which is produced by both natural and human actions. Soil bacteria are responsible for the production of most of the nitric oxide produced naturally and released into the atmosphere. Within the atmosphere, nitric oxide readily combines with oxygen to form nitrogen dioxide; together, these two oxides of nitrogen are usually referred to as NO_x (nitrogen oxides). NO_x is formed naturally by lightning and by decomposing organic matter. Approximately 50% of anthropogenic NO_x is emitted by motor vehicles and about 30% comes from power plants, with the other 20% produced by industrial processes.

Scientists distinguish between two types of NO_x—thermal and fuel—depending on the mode of formation. Thermal NO_x is created when nitrogen and oxygen in the combustion of air (such as those within internal combustion engines) are heated to a high enough temperature (above 1,000 K) to cause nitrogen (N_2) and oxygen (O_2) in the air to combine. Fuel NO_x results from the oxidation (combining with oxygen in the air) of nitrogen contained within a fuel such as coal. Both types of NO_x generate nitric oxide first, and then when vented and cooled, a portion of nitric oxide is converted to nitrogen dioxide. Although both thermal and fuel NO_x can be significant contributors to the total NO_x emissions, fuel NO_x is usually the dominant source, with approximately 50% coming from power plants (stationary sources) and the other half released by automobiles (mobile sources).

Nitrogen dioxide is about four times more toxic than nitric oxide and is a much more serious air pollutant. Nitrogen dioxide, at high concentrations, is believed to contribute to heart, lung, liver, and kidney damage. In addition, because nitrogen dioxide occurs as a brownish haze (giving smog its reddish-brown color), it reduces visibility. When nitrogen dioxide combines with water vapor in the atmosphere, it forms nitric acid (HNO_3), a corrosive substance that when precipitated out as acid rain, causes damage to plants and corrosion of metal surfaces.

NO_x levels rose in several countries during the first half of the 20th century and then leveled off or declined during the 1970s. During this same time frame, levels of nitrogen oxide did not drop as dramatically as those of sulfur dioxide, primarily because a large part of total NO_x emissions comes from millions of motor vehicles, while most sulfur dioxide is released by a relatively small number of emission-controlled, coal-burning power plants.

Acid Rain   Most rainfall is slightly acidic because of decomposing organic matter, the movement of the sea, and volcanic eruptions, but the principal factor is atmospheric carbon dioxide, which causes carbonic acid to form. *Acid rain* (pH< 5.6) is a broad term used to describe several ways that acids fall out of the atmosphere. A more precise term is *acid deposition*, which has two parts: wet (acid precipitation) and dry (dry deposition, dry gases). Acid rain is produced by the conversion of the primary pollutants sulfur dioxide and nitrogen oxides into sulfuric acid and nitric acid, respectively. These processes are complex and are dependent on the physical dispersion processes and the rates of the chemical conversions.

✓ **Key Point:** Acid rain is a serious environmental problem that affects large parts of the United States and Canada.

Contrary to popular belief, acid rain is not a new phenomenon, nor does it result solely from industrial pollution. Natural processes—volcanic eruptions and forest fires, for example—produce and release acid particles into the air. The burning of forest areas to clear land in Brazil, Africa, and other countries also contributes to acid rain. However, the rise in manufacturing that began with the Industrial Revolution dwarfs all other contributions to the problem.

The main culprits are emissions of sulfur dioxide from the burning of fossil fuels such as oil and coal and nitrogen oxide, formed mostly from internal combustion engine emissions, which is readily transformed into nitrogen dioxide. These mix in the atmosphere to form sulfuric acid and nitric acid.

$$SO_2 + 1/2O_2 + H_2O \quad several\,steps \Rightarrow 2H^+ + SO_4^{-2}\,(aq)$$

$$2NO_2 + 1/2O_2 + 2H_2O \quad several\,steps \Rightarrow 2\{H^+ + NO_3^-\,(aq)$$

The Earth's ecosystems are not completely unable to abate the effects of atmospheric acid deposition; they *can* deal with a certain amount of acid through natural alkaline substances in soil or rocks that buffer and neutralize acid. The American Midwest and southern England are areas with alkaline soil (limestone and sandstone), which provides some natural neutralization. Areas without this soil and those on granite bedrock, however, have little ability to neutralize acid rain.

Despite intensive research into most aspects of acid rain, scientists still have many areas of uncertainty and disagreement. That is why the progressive, forward-thinking countries emphasize the importance of further research into acid rain. And that is why the U.S. Clean Air Act of 1990 was strengthened to initiate a permanent reduction in SO_2 levels.

✓ **Key Point:** Inorganic air pollutants contribute to many environmental problems, including poor visibility, acid rain, increased respiratory problems, and the greenhouse effect.

Chlorofluorocarbons (CFCs)   CFCs are a class of human-made chemicals known by such trade names as "Freon," "Generton," and "Isotron." They are highly volatile compounds, contributing to air pollution. CFCs are unusual because they do not break down when vaporized into the atmosphere. Instead, they rise slowly through the atmosphere, taking six to eight years to reach the stratosphere. Here CFCs can reside for more than 100 years.

These chemicals are implicated in two major threats to the global environment: the greenhouse effect and the reduction of the ozone layer. CFCs contribute to the greenhouse effect, warming the atmosphere by trapping heat, which is then radiated back into the atmosphere. They are more than 10,000 times as effective at trapping this radiated heat as carbon dioxide.

CFCs have also been shown to contribute to the depletion of the protective ozone layer in the atmosphere. This permits greater amounts of ultraviolet radiation to reach the Earth. The increase in ultraviolet radiation affects human health by increasing the likelihood of developing skin cancer and cataracts and may depress the human immune system. Increased ultraviolet radiation reduces crop yields, depletes marine fisheries, damages construction materials, and increases smog.

Organic Air Pollutants

Organic air pollutants fall into two categories:

* Direct pollutants, which cause cancer, etc.
* Secondary pollutants, which contribute to photochemical smog.

Photochemical Smog   By far the most damaging photochemical air pollutant is ozone. Other photochemical oxidants (peroxyacetyl nitrate (PAN), hydrogen peroxide [H_2O_2], aldehydes, acrolein, peroxybenzoyl nitrate [PBzN], and formaldehyde) play minor roles. All of these are secondary pollutants because they are not emitted, but are formed in the atmosphere by photochemical reactions involving sunlight and emitted gases, especially NO_x and hydrocarbons.

✓ **Key Point:** The conditions necessary for the formation of smog are present in modern cities. They include sunlight, hydrocarbons, nitrogen oxides, and particulates that act as catalysts.

On rare occasions, it is possible for upper stratospheric ozone (good ozone) to enter the lower atmosphere (troposphere). Generally, this phenomenon only occurs during an event of great turbulence in the upper atmosphere. In these rare incursions, atmospheric ozone is formed and consumed by endogenous photochemical reactions, which are the result of the interaction of hydrocarbons, oxides of nitrogen, and sunlight, which produces a yellowish-brown haze commonly called *smog* (Los Angeles–type smog).

In its very simplest terms, we can express the formation of photochemical smog as follows:

$$\text{Hydrocarbons } NO_x + \text{Sunlight} \Rightarrow \text{Photochemical smog}$$

✓ **Interesting Point:** On December 9, 1952, foggy conditions developed over London. Because temperatures were very cold, most houses kept fires burning, with coal as the major fuel. The smoke from these fires mixed with the fog and was unable to disperse, resulting in smog that persisted for four days. The pH of air during the Great London Smog was as low as 1.6. During this period, some 4,000 more people died than would be expected at this time of the year. Most of these additional deaths were due to respiratory disorders.

Although the incursion of stratospheric ozone into the troposphere can cause smog formation, the actual formation of Los Angeles–type smog involves a complex group of photochemical interactions. These interactions are between anthropogenically emitted pollutants (NO and hydrocarbons) and secondarily produced chemicals (PAN, aldehydes, NO_2, and ozone). Note that the concentrations of these chemicals exhibit a pronounced diurnal pattern, depending on their rate of emission, the intensity of solar radiation, and atmospheric stability at different times of the day.

✓ **Key Point:** Los Angeles–type smog has a long history, dating back at least to the 1860s in Los Angeles. Its characteristics are low visibility, eye irritation, and deterioration of materials. By definition, smog is identified by visibility below three miles and moderate to severe eye irritation when the relative humidity is below 60%. Photochemical smog requires UV light, hydrocarbons, and NO_x.

The considerable range of the estimates for the Northern Hemisphere reflects uncertainty in the calculation of the ozone fluxes. On average, stratospheric incursions account for about 18% of the total ozone influx to the troposphere, while endogenous photochemical production accounts for the remaining 82%. About 31% of the tropospheric ozone is consumed by oxidative reactions in vegetative and inorganic suffocates at ground level, while the other 69% is consumed by photochemical reactions in the atmosphere (Freedman, 1989).

Most organic pollutants in the atmosphere come from natural sources. For example, 85.7% of methane is naturally generated via anaerobic bacteria and domestic animals. The other 14.3% is the result of human activity.

Methane is a major source of O^3 and CO in the troposphere and water vapor in the stratosphere.

$$CH_4 + HO^* \Rightarrow H_3C^* + H_2O$$

Other natural sources of atmospheric hydrocarbons are plants, which release ethylene and a variety of terpenes and esters.

Human-made hydrocarbon sources, because of the burning of fossil fuels, are the number one class of organic air pollutants. These common hydrocarbon air pollutants are produced in quantities exceeding 1,00,000,000 kg/yr. Aromatic hydrocarbons are widely used in industry and are key components of unleaded gasoline.

Hydrocarbons are typically oxidized (by $h\nu$) to **aldehydes** and **ketones.** Billions of kilograms of other important *carbonyl* compounds are produced annually. Aldehydes are second only to NO_2 as a source of photochemically produced free radicals.

Many **alcohols** also rank among the top 50 manufactured chemicals, the most volatile of which have been identified as atmospheric pollutants (methanol and ethanol).

✓ **Key Point:** Alcohols with high water solubility and/or low volatility are quickly "scavenged" from the atmosphere.

Phenol (an aromatic alcohol) is also in the "top 50" as well as being produced as a by-product of burning coal and making coke. Other common aromatic alcohols have also been identified as atmospheric pollutants.

The three most common **organic halide pollutants** of the atmosphere are methyl chloride, methyl chloroform, and carbon tetrachloride. The destruction of the ozone by CFCs and halides has already been discussed.

Significant **organonitrogen pollutants** include amines (odor!), dimethylformamide, and acrylonitrile.

Cigarette smoke, burning vegetation, and coke ovens release heterocyclic nitrogen compounds.

Peroxyacetylnitrate (PAN) and **peroxybenzoylnitrate** (PBN) are serious organic pollutants produced by the photochemical oxidation of hydrocarbons.

Polyaromatic hydrocarbons (PAHs) are the most notorious organic particulates in our atmosphere (up to ~20 μg/m³). They are produced by the incomplete combustion of fossil fuels and cigarettes (-100 μg/m³). These compounds are typically found sorbed to soot.

Other minor but often troublesome organic pollutants are

- ethers (fossil fuels, THF),
- oxides (ethylene and propylene oxide),
- carboxylic acids (photochemical oxidation), and
- organosulfur compounds (odor!)

Samples of smog have been shown to contain PAN, aldehydes, ketones, alkyl nitrates, and alkyl nitrites, primarily from the photoxidation of hydrocarbons. These air samples also contained inorganic pollutants such as ozone and nitric acid.

✓ **Key Point:** SMOG = Hydrocarbons + hv + NO_x

The bottom line on organic air pollutants is that they contribute to many health and environmental problems, including smog, respiratory difficulties, poor visibility, damage to materials, toxicity to plants, and increased cancer risks.

Summary of Chemical Properties of Air

- Normal air consists of nitrogen (79%), oxygen (20%), dust (solid), water (solid, liquid, and gas), carbon dioxide, and trace elements (1%).
- The lowest layer of the atmosphere is the troposphere.
- Acid rain is normal, but human pollution has increased the acid concentration of rain to more than 10 times that of natural rain.
- Carbon dioxide seems to be a harmless pollutant in our air.
- Carbon monoxide is a human-made pollutant from automobiles. It is a poisonous gas that can cause death.
- The automobile is a major air polluter. It releases carbon monoxide, oxides of nitrogen, lead, and cancer-causing chemicals.
- The major categories of atmospheric chemical species are inorganic oxides, oxidants, reductants, organics, photochemically active species, acids, bases, salts, and unstable reactive species.

- Gaseous pollutants that enter the atmosphere in the greatest quantities are CO, SO_2, NO, and NO_2.
- Three relatively reactive and unstable species that are encountered in the atmosphere that are strongly involved with atmospheric chemical processes are electronically excited molecules, free radicals, and ions.
- The photochemical dissociation of nitrogen dioxide, NO_2, can produce reactive O atoms that can react with oxidizable molecules.
- A photochemical atmosphere polluted by nitrogen oxides and hydrocarbons generates strong oxidant molecules.
- The most prominent inorganic oxidant in the atmosphere is ozone.
- The two reactions by which stratospheric ozone is produced are

$$O_2 + h\nu \Rightarrow O + O \text{ and } O + O_2\, M \Rightarrow O_3 + M$$

- The effects of pollutants in the atmosphere may be divided between direct effects and the formation of secondary pollutants, such as photochemical smog.
- The fact that most organics (hydrocarbons) in the atmosphere come from natural sources is primarily the result of the release of huge quantities of methane.
- The fluorine-containing air pollutants with the greatest potential for damage to the atmosphere are the CFCs.

SOIL CHEMISTRY

The Soil Problem

Soil contamination is a major environmental concern not only throughout the United States, but worldwide. The impact on soil of industrial and agricultural practices, management of Superfund sites, exploration and production, and mining and nuclear industrial practices, among other factors, remains difficult to assess. Certainly petroleum-contaminated soil affects the largest number of sites and is the largest total volume of impacted material. The overall amount of contaminated soil generated can be staggering. For example, in some states such as Oklahoma, contaminated soil accounts for about 98% of the waste generated as a one-time occurrence (Testa, 1997).

As our concern for the environment increases, it is comforting to know that soil, when properly used, can offer an unlimited potential for disposal and recycling of waste materials.

Regardless of their origin, most soils consist of four basic components: mineral matter, water, air, and organic matter. Simply, soils are the bridge between mineral matter and life.

To gain understanding of the "soil problem" currently confronting us, we briefly describe a few environmental problem areas that contribute to the soil problem. These problem areas are monoculture, underground storage tanks (USTs), chemical sites, oil field sites, geothermal sites, manufactured gas plants, mining sites, and environmental terrorism.

Monoculture

In agriculture, the practice of monoculture, or the planting of just one crop type in a large area, can lead to breakdown of soil aggregates by leaching the soil of important nutrients that plants need to grow.

Underground Storage Tanks (USTs)

Petroleum contamination is commonly associated with USTs. Recent estimates have ranged from five to six million, but no one is quite sure just how many USTs containing petroleum products or hazardous materials are in use in the United States. Compounding the issue, no one can guess how many USTs are no longer being used (abandoned USTs). These abandoned tanks often still hold (or held) some portions of their contents, which may have been oozing out, fouling water, land, and air. Another problem is that older USTs that are not leaking today will probably leak eventually. One thing is certain, however: Environmental contamination from leaking USTs poses a significant threat to human health and the environment.

Besides the obvious problem of fouling the environment, many of these leaking USTs also pose serious fire and explosion hazards. The irony is that USTs came into common use primarily as a fire and explosion prevention measure (presumably, the hazard was buried under the ground—out of sight, out of mind, out of harm's way). Today, however, the hazards we "buried" to protect ourselves from are finding ways to cause danger in a different manner.

The problem with leaking USTs goes beyond fouling the environment (especially groundwater, which 51% of the U.S. population relies on for drinking water) and presenting fire and explosion hazards. Products released from these leaking tanks can damage sewer lines and buried cables and poison our crops.

Chemical Sites

A 1979 survey (referred to as the Eckhardt Survey) of 53 of the largest chemical manufacturing companies in the United States, conducted for the period 1950 to 1979, reported almost 17 million tons of organic generated wastes disposed. Of this total, a little over 10 million tons were untreated (in ponds, landfills, lagoons, and injection wells). A little less than 0.5 million tons were incinerated, and a little over 0.5 were either recycled or reused. Not addressed is the volume of contaminated soil generated as a one-time occurrence, as is typical of any remediation activity (Testa, 1997).

Oil Field Sites

Another source of rather large volumes of hydrocarbon-contaminated soil is production in past and existing oil fields. Experience has shown that describing the fate of petroleum in soils in merely qualitative terms is relatively easy. For example, clearly volatile petroleum products such as gasoline experience considerable loss by evaporation; normal alkanes are subject to fairly rapid biodegradation; and aromatic hydrocarbons, particularly those of lower molecular weight, are very susceptible to dissolution in water and may thus cause contamination of water supplies in the locality. However, making rigorous, scientifically justifiable statements in which these processes are described in quantitative terms is much more difficult. In very few cases has it been possible to state, for example, that in a period of one year a certain percentage of a particular mass of oil spill was lost by evaporation, a certain percentage by dissolution, and another percentage by biodegradation, and the rest was altered by photolysis. One thing is certain, however: Oil field sites, both historically and in the present, contribute to the overall volume of contaminated soil generated (Eastcott, Shir & Mackay, 1989).

Geothermal Sites

The U.S. Department of Energy defines **geothermal energy** as "when the heat contained within the Earth is recovered and put to useful work." Geothermal energy is a very efficient resource for heating and cooling buildings, drying agricultural products, and processing heating for industry (Reed, 2002). High temperature (above 150°C) geothermal resources are used in electric power generation. However, according to the *Encyclopaedia Britannica*, one of the biggest problems in using geothermal energy is extracting it. To obtain geothermal power efficiently, heat energy must be concentrated in a small area. This may be done by underground reservoirs of hot water or steam that can be funneled into a drill hole.

Geothermal energy is used best in the generation of electricity. In geothermal power plants, hot water is turned into steam, which is then used to power a turbine. The mechanical energy from the turbine is then converted to electricity by a generator. Another source of geothermal energy is hot and dry subsurface rocks (Geothermal Energy, 2002).

✓ **Key Point:** The U.S. Department of Energy has a Geothermal Energy Technical Site that provides great detail about the growth of the geothermal industry: http://www.eren.doe.gov/geothermal/.

Proponents of geothermal use point out that geothermal energy is clean and is easy on the land. Simply, it is a very beneficial energy with a strong future ahead of it. The energy is clean, reliable, and readily available.

The use of geothermal energy is a double-edged sword, however. Although geothermal sources eliminate the air pollution associated with combustive electrical generation, they are not without problems. Gases in the steam and dissolved minerals in the hot water cause equipment to erode rapidly. The cooling and disposal of the salty (briny), mineral-rich water from the spring may also present a problem. Moreover, evidence suggests that the groundwater in areas where geothermal energy is used must be replaced to prevent subsidence.

✓ **Key Point:** Geothermal-generated brine is a mineralized fluid composed of warm to hot saline waters containing calcium, sodium, potassium, chloride, and minor amounts of other elements.

Manufactured Gas Plants (MGPs)

Manufactured gas plants (MGPs) have operated since the late 1890s, with many industrial sites having undergone redevelopment.

✓ **Key Point:** Recent surveys estimate that here are about 3,000 MGP sites in the United States.

Manufactured gas plants produce a variety of largely hazardous waste products, almost all of which are found in what is referred to today as coal tar (and associated waste products). Among the toxic substances found in coal tar are the following:

- **Aromatic hydrocarbons**—comprised mainly of phenols and cresols.
- **Monocyclical aromatic hydrocarbons (MAHs)**—the so-called BTEX series: **b**enzene, **t**oluene, **e**thylbenzene, and **x**ylene.
- **Duocyclical aromatic hydrocarbons (DAHs)**—comprised mainly of naphthalene and the light oils.
- **Polycyclical aromatic hydrocarbons (PAHs)**—the coal tars and medium and heavy oils.
- **Others**—the concentrated forms of trace minerals found in the coal, including cyanides, sulfur, and some heavy metals (arsenic, chromium, lead, etc.).

Mining Sites

Mining operations often create land and water pollution problems. Erosion-causing sediment pollution is surface mining's most obvious and most thoroughly documented problem.

The effect that mining sediments and mining wastes (from mining, milling, smelting, and leftovers) have had and are having on soil is less known, because no serious study of the problem has been done. Typical mining wastes include acid produced by oxidation of naturally occurring sulfides, asbestos produced in asbestos mining and milling operations, cyanide produced in precious metal heap-leaching operations, leach liquors produced during copper-dump leaching operations, metals from mining and milling operations, and radionuclides (radium) from uranium and phosphate mining operations.

Acid mine drainage as a soil contaminant source is well known and documented. When oxygen and water react with sulfur-bearing minerals to form sulfuric acid and iron compounds, acid formations occur. These compounds may directly affect plant life that absorbs them. Acid mine drainage can also indirectly affect the flora of a region by changing the nature of the soil minerals and microorganisms in the area.

The solid waste by-products of mining cause other problems. Metals are always mixed with other materials in mining. These materials usually have little commercial value, and disposal becomes problematic. The unsightly piles of rock and rubble are prone to erosion. Leaching releases waste materials that allow environmental poisons entry into the soil, eventually affecting both surface and groundwater sources.

Environmental Terrorism

Prior to 1991 (the First Gulf War) and 9/11/2001, there was very little concern among the general public about the potential for environmental terrorism on a regional scale. Certainly the First Gulf War and 9/11 proved otherwise. The damage caused by the deliberate destruction of municipal infrastructure, oil wells and refineries, and chemical sites can result in soil pollution on a catastrophic scale, and of course, also affect air and water.

Physical and Chemical Properties of Soil

From the environmental science point of view (regarding land conservation and methodologies for contaminated soil remediation through reuse and recycling), 10 major chemical/physical properties of soil are of interest.

Cation Exchange Capacity (CEC)

Cation exchange capacity (CEC) is the soil's capacity to hold cations. More specifically, CEC is defined as the sum of positive (+) charges of the adsorbed cations that a soil can adsorb at a specific pH. Soil particles are composed of silicate and aluminosilicate clay. These particles are negatively charged colloids. Cations are bound ionically to the surface of these colloid particles. A cation is a positively charged ion; for example, H^+, Ca^{++}, Mg^{++}, K^+, NH_4^+, Na^+ are all cations.

✓ **Key Point:** CEC is expressed as meq/100 g of soil.

Typical CEC values by soil type are listed in Table 3.15.

Table 3.15. CEC Values by Soil Type

Soil Type	meq/100g soil
Sand	2–4
Loam	7–16
Clay	4–60
Organic	50–300

✓ **Key Point:** CEC increases as the clay content and the organic matter increase in a soil.

Cations with higher charge densities (smaller cations) will replace larger cations. For example, H^+ will displace Ca^{++}; Ca^{++} will displace Mg^{++}.

When an ion in the water phase is attracted to a soil surface, it must displace another (already present) cation. For example:

$$(Soil)Mg + Cu^{2+} \Rightarrow (Soil)Cu + Mg^{2+}$$

As organic matter decomposes in a soil, the chemical reactions produce protons. The bacteria in the soil causing the decomposition also respire protons (H^+). As the proton content goes up, the protons displace the other bound ions on the surface of the soil particles, and these cations become available for absorption by the plant roots.

✓ **Key Point:** All cations are not created equal!

pH

Recall that pH is the negative logarithm of the hydrogen ion activity. The pH of soil is one of the most important properties involved in plant growth.

All living organisms are sensitive to pH. Plant roots will not function optimally in soils outside a specific pH range unique to that organism. If the pH of the soil is extreme (either alkaline or acid), the plant will die. Soil microorganisms, insects, and other animals present in the rhizosphere (i.e., the zone immediately adjacent to plant roots in which the kinds, numbers, or activities of microorganisms differ from that of the bulk soil) are equally sensitive to pH.

✓ **Key Point:** Alkaline soils have pH 7.5–8.5. Acidic soils have pH 4–6.5. Soils with pH values outside these ranges are usually toxic to most plants. Alkaline components are more readily leached from soils.

Soil pH can be adjusted by amendments. Increasing organic matter will decrease pH (increase acidity). Lime can be added to increase pH (increase alkalinity). Certain fertilizers are delivered as acidic or basic solutions and will also alter soil pH. However, soils have buffering capacity—within their normal range of pH values, they can absorb lots of protons or lots of hydroxyl ions before the pH of the soil water changes. But once the buffering capacity of the soil is reached, then the pH of the soil water will change rapidly to toxic extremes. It will also take a lot of new buffering activity to repair the soil to its original pH.

Salinity

Saline soils contain lots of soluble salts. Sodic soils are nonsaline soils containing sufficient exchangeable sodium to adversely affect crop production and soil structure under most conditions of soil and plant type. Salts accumulate naturally in some surface soils of arid and semiarid regions, because not enough rainfall occurs to flush them from the upper soil layers. The salts are primarily chlorides and sulfates of calcium magnesium, sodium, and potassium. They may be formed during the weathering of rocks and minerals or brought to the soils through rainfall and irrigation. The total salt concentration of soil (or salinity) is expressed in terms of the electrical conductivity of the water and is easily and precisely determined.

Color

Just about anyone who has looked at soil has probably noticed that *soil color* is often different from one location to another. Soil colors range form very bright to dull greasy to a wide range of reds, browns, blacks, whites, yellows, and even greens. Soil color is dependent primarily on the quantity of humus and the chemical form of iron oxides present.

Soils scientists use a set of standardized color charts (the *Munsell Color Book)* to describe soil colors. The charts consider three properties of color—hue, value, and chrome—in combination to come up with a large number of color chips to which soil scientists can compare the color of the soil being investigated.

The color of a soil can give clues to its health, origin, and long-term changes. It can also indicate the color of the **parent material**. Subsoil color can be a valuable indicator of how well the soil drains, which can be influenced by the topography.

Dark colors in the topsoil usually indicate that the soil has a high organic matter content. We often see this in prairie grassland soils of the Great Plains in the United States. Generally, the more humus, the blacker the soil. It could mean that the parent material from which soil developed was also black.

✓ **Key Point:** Distinct red and yellow colors usually indicate older, more weathered soils.

Texture

Soil texture, the relative proportions of the various soil separates in a soil, is given and cannot be easily or practically changed significantly. It is determined by the size of the rock particles (sand, silt, and clay particles) or the soil separates (the size groups of mineral particles less than 2 mm in diameter or the size groups that are smaller than gravel) within the soil. The largest soil particles are gravel, which consist of fragments larger than 2.0 mm in diameter.

Particles between 0.05 and 2.0 mm are classified as sand. Silt particles range from 0.002 to 0.05 mm in diameter, and the smallest particles (clay particles) are less than 0.002 mm in diameter. Though clays are composed of the smallest particles, those particles have stronger bonds than silt or sand, and once broken apart, they erode more readily. Particle size has a direct impact on erodibility. Rarely does a soil consist of only one single size particle—most are a mixture of various sizes.

As mentioned, soil texture refers to the relative proportions of sand, silt, and clay in a soil. Soils get their textural names (12 in all) and some specific physical properties from the proportions of these three particle sizes. Note that humus content technically has nothing to do with texture.

- Loamy sand—85% sand, 10% silt, and 5% clay
- Sandy loam—72% sand, 15% silt, and 13% clay
- Loam—46% sand, 36% silt, and 18% clay
- Silt loam—25% sand, 60% silt, and 15% clay
- Sandy clay loam—65% sand, 9% silt, and 26% clay
- Clay loam—36% sand, 32% silt, and 32% clay
- Sandy clay—55% sand, 5% silt, and 40% clay
- Clay—17% sand, 17%, and 66% clay

✓ **Key Point:** Other soil types include sand, silt, silty clay loam, and silty clay. A soil's texture has a big influence on its productivity and management needs, because it affects tilth (structure), water-holding capacity, drainage, erosion potential, and soil fertility. Texture usually varies with depth, and the subsoil is usually more clayey than the topsoil.

Tilth (Structure)

Soil tilth should not be confused with soil texture—they are different. In fact, in the field, the properties determined by soil texture may be considerably modified by soil tilth. Soil tilth refers to the combination or arrangement of primary soil particles into secondary particles (units or peds)—the way various soil particles clump together. The size, shape, and arrangement of clusters of soil particles called **aggregates** determine the formation of larger clumps called **peds**. Sand particles do not clump because sandy soils lack structure. Clay soils tend to stick together in large clumps. Good soil develops small, friable (easily crumbled) clumps. Soil develops a unique, fairly stable structure in undisturbed landscapes, but agricultural practices break down the aggregates and peds, lessening erosion resistance.

✓ **Key Point:** A soil in good tilth is easily worked, is crumbly, and readily takes in water when dry.

The presence of decomposed or decomposing remains of plants and animals (organic matter) in soil helps not only fertility but also soil structure—especially the soil's ability to store water. Live organisms such as protozoa, nematodes, Earthworms, insects, fungi, and bacteria are typical inhabitants of soil. These organisms work to either control the population of organisms in the soil or aid in the recycling of dead organic matter. All soil organisms, in one way or another, work to release nutrients from the organic matter, changing complex organic materials into products that can be used by plants.

✓ **Key Point:** Factors that influence a soil's tilth include texture, organic matter, and moisture content. Therefore, tilth can vary markedly with changes in moisture content, the amount of humus present, and compaction, especially if it is clayey. Tilth can be improved, which is why farmers plow their fields to break up the clods and add manure to their fields when they can.

Water-holding Capacity

About half of soil's volume is pore space occupied by varying amounts of air and water, depending on how wet the soil is. Water is held in the pore spaces in the form of films adhering to the soil particles. Small pores are called **micropores**; large pores are called **macropores**.

Macropores do not hold water well because the water films become too thick to adhere well to the surrounding soil particles. This water is lost downward as it drains below the root zone by gravity. So macropores allow a soil to retain enough air for root growth, as long as drainage is not impeded.

The films of micropore water, however, resist being drained away by gravity and are responsible for the water-holding capacity of soils. This water is what the roots can tap into and extract for plant use.

✓ **Key Point:** As you might guess, sands have a lot of macropores due to their large grain size, but few micropores. Thus, their water-holding capacity is low, although their drainage is good. Heavy clay soils that have a lot of micropores may have a higher water-holding capacity, but because they have fewer macropores, their drainage is poor. Plants really like a soil that lies in between these two extremes, so that their roots have both the air and water that they need.

Drainage

Drainage refers to a soil's ability to get rid of excess water, or water in the macropores, through downward movement by gravity. Topography, texture, tilth, depth, and the presence of compacted layers in the subsoil affect drainage. With few exceptions (one is rice), most plants need fairly good drainage. Without good drainage, plant roots lack oxygen, nitrogen is lost, and certain elements like iron and manganese may become soluble enough to injure plant roots. Although clayey soils are more likely to have drainage problems, drainage problems also occur in sandy soils where the water table is close to the surface. The water table is the upper surface of the groundwater, below which the soil is completely saturated with water.

✓ **Key Point:** Soil color can be affected by drainage. It can be a tool to check whether a particular soil has drainage problems. For example, red, reddish-brown, or yellow subsoil colors generally indicate good drainage. The presence of sufficient air allows the soil's iron and manganese to oxidize or "rust" and gives the soil brighter color. On the other hand, dull grays and blues indicate a reduced state, with little oxygen, which means poor drainage.

Depth

Soil *depth* refers to how deep, top to bottom, the topsoil plus the subsoil is. Depth can be easily determined by digging a hole. Soils are classified as deep or shallow (see Table 3.16).

Table 3.16. Soil Depth Classification

Depth (topsoil + subsoil)	
Deep	3 inches
Moderately deep	20 inches to 3 feet
Shallow	10 inches to 20 inches
Very shallow	<10 inches

✓ **Key Point:** Soil depth is important for plants, because deeper rooting means more soil to explore for nutrients and water. Greater soil depth can also mean better drainage, as long as no restrictive layers occur in the subsoil.

Slope

The *slope* (or steepness of the soil layer) has a marked influence on the amount of water runoff and soil erosion caused by flowing water. Slope is usually measured in terms of percentages. A 10% slope has 10 feet of vertical drop per 100 feet horizontal distance. Soil conservation measures become necessary on land with a slope as little as 1–2% to avoid erosion problems.

Subsurface Fate and Transport

Understanding soil's transport mechanisms and how they affect flow regime of contaminants or pollutants is important. When a chemical spill or leak occurs, or when pollutants are intentionally discharged or accidentally released in soil, we need to ask what happens to the pollutants. The answer is rather complex and is based on the interactions among and between the chemicals, rock, soil water, and soil (Spellman, 1999).

The following list identifies and explains the properties of the pollutants that are important to the migration, retardation, transformation, and ultimate disposition or fate of pollutants in soil:

1. **Vapor pressure or volatility:** Vapor pressure is the property that determines how easily a pollutant evaporates: the lower the vapor pressure, the more easily a pollutant evaporates. Volatility is the tendency of a solid or liquid pollutant to pass into the vapor state, how quickly and easily a liquid or solid pollutant evaporates at ordinary temperatures when exposed to the air.
2. **Miscibility with soil water and groundwater:** Miscibility is how well a liquid pollutant can be mixed with and will remain mixed with the water present under normal circumstances.
3. **Solubility in soil water and groundwater:** Solubility is the ability of a pollutant to mix with water present under normal circumstances.
4. **Density or specific gravity:** Density is the ratio of the weight of a mass to the unit of volume. Specific gravity is the ratio of the weight of the volume of liquid or solid pollutant to the weight of an equal volume of water. Specific gravity of water is 1.0: pollutants with a specific gravity below 1.0 will float on water: those with a specific gravity over 1.0 will sink in water.
5. **Dynamic viscosity:** Dynamic viscosity is the internal resistance of a liquid or gaseous pollutant while moving.
6. **Reactivity:** Reactivity is the degree of ability of a pollutant to undergo a chemical combination with another substance.
7. **Susceptibility to biodegradation:** Susceptibility is the ease with which a pollutant breaks down into basic elements.

Along with the various properties that affect the fate of pollutants when they somehow enter soil, properties of the soil environment into which a pollutant is discharged are also important and must be determined, especially for remediation activities. These important properties with respect to the fate of pollutants in soil include the soil's

- infiltration capacity,
- natural organic content,
- saturated and unsaturated hydraulic conductivities,
- effective permeabilities for immiscible pollutants and soil water,
- mineralogy,
- oxygen content, and
- bacterial community.

Several processes control the rate and extent of migration of pollution in soils. These natural processes trap the pollutant, delay the pollutant from spreading, or cause the pollutant to degrade or change in chemistry to a less hazardous state. The processes that retard pollutant movement in soils include adsorption, ion exchange, chemical precipitation, and biodegradation:

- **Adsorption** is the process by which one substance is attracted to and adheres to the surface of another substance without actually penetrating its internal structure. In soil, adsorption bonds (holds) a pollutant to the surface of a soil particle or mineral in such a way that the substance is only available or disperses slowly. Clay and highly organic materials, for example, tend to adsorb pesticides rather than absorb them. Pollutant adsorption takes place on mineral surfaces where defects in crystalline structure result in imbalances of electrical charges on the mineral surface. Dissolved pollutant molecules and ions with charge imbalances are attracted to mineral surfaces with an opposite charge imbalance.
- **Ion balance** is actually another step in the adsorption process, whereby a dissolved pollutant substitutes itself for another chemical already adsorbed on the mineral surface.
- In **pollutant precipitation**, dissolved pollutants are removed (transported) from soil water and groundwater by various precipitation reactions. Chemical precipitation is also used as a pollution remediation technique, whereby the pollutant is precipitated out of the contaminated stream.
- **Biodegradation** is the breakdown of organic and pollutant compounds through microbial activity; it affects the distribution, movement (transport), and concentration of pollutants in soil.

The fate of certain pollutants applied to the soil surface or introduced into the soil profile depends on an extremely complex combination of interactive processes. The effectiveness of these interactive processes depends on several variable conditions: the nature of the pollutant, the manner of its application, the fundamental nature of the soil, and its transient state at the time and place of interest.

In addition to the various properties of pollutants and the soil environment that affect pollutant migration, retardation, and transformation of mobile pollutants in soil, certain properties and/or conditions of the soil also affect the flow regime. These properties and conditions include the following (Kostecki & Calabrese, 1989):

1. **Soil texture:** Migration of pollutants in coarse (sandy and gravelly) soil is generally faster than in fine (clay or silty) soils, which are more likely to retain pollutants and prevent their migration.
2. **Layered soils (with vertical nonuniformity):** Layered soils are more likely to retard migration in the soil profile than are soils with uniform profiles.
3. **Configuration of the soil layers:** Whether soil layers are horizontal, slanted, or sloped has an effect on pollutant flow regime. For example, if horizontal layers with concave troughs are present, pollutant flow is more likely to be retarded. In slanted or sloped layers, the pollutant's flow regime may not only be easier, but may also be directed (for instance) toward a well or groundwater.
4. **Depth of the water table:** Obviously, if the depth to the water table is extreme, the ability of a pollutant to travel the entire distance through the soil to the water table is affected, depending on the retardivity of the soil.
5. **Structure of the soil:** Natural fissures, cracks, or channels in the soil are important considerations in identifying soil pathways that enable rapid migration of pollutants.
6. **Unstable flow:** Pollutant flow not only migrates quickly through cracks and fissures but also has the tendency to concentrate in tongue-like streams (fingers), which generally begin at the transition from fine-textured to coarse-textured layers, bypassing or short-circuiting the greater volume of soil material and allowing direct transmission of pollutants to the water table.
7. **Soil moisture:** Moisture has an obvious effect on the pattern and migration of organic pollutants in the soil.

Origins of Soil Pollutants

All human societies pollute both soil and groundwater to some extent. Throughout human history, people have had to develop ways of recognizing surface-water contamination or face disease and death from contaminated water. Those pollutants were often readily apparent and caused immediate, significant problems. However, contamination of the soil and the underground environment remained virtually unnoticed until the last few decades. The history of industrialization and the wide range of hazardous materials and other chemicals that have been introduced into the environment in developed countries, either by design or accident, have resulted in industrialized nations being most seriously affected by persistent soil pollutants.

✓ **Key Point:** Contamination of the soil and underground environment remained virtually unnoticed until the last few decades because of its unseen locations and seemingly minimal impact.

We quite simply did not comprehend how effectively the mechanisms that carry contaminants through the soil could work, or the damage pollutants could do to the soil medium and the groundwater under soil's "protective" surface.

The number of human activities that cause underground contamination is much larger than most environmental scientists would have guessed even a few years ago. Soil quality problems originating on the surface include natural atmospheric deposition of gaseous and airborne particulate pollutants; infiltration of contaminated surface water; land disposal of solid and liquid waste materials; stockpiles, tailings, and spoil; dumps; salt spreading on roads; animal feedlots; fertilizers and pesticides; accidental spills; and composting of leaves and other yard wastes.

Other sources of soil contamination are related to petroleum products, including direct disposal of used oils on the ground by individuals or industries; seepage from landfills, illegal dumps, unlined pits, ponds, and lagoons; and spills from transport accidents or even auto accidents (Tucker, 1989).

Gaseous and Airborne Particulate Pollutants

Note: The following discussion focuses on contamination originating on the land surface. However, note that soil and subsurface contamination may also originate below ground (but above the water table) from septic tanks, landfills, sumps and dry wells, graveyards, USTs, underground pipeline leakages, and other sources. In addition, the soil, subsurface, and groundwater contamination may also originate below the water table from mines, test holes, agricultural drainage wells and canals, and others.

Soil figures prominently in the function of the carbon, nitrogen, and sulfur cycles—the biogeochemical cycles. Though prominent in the normal operation of these cycles, soil interfaces in powerful and essential ways with the atmosphere. Consider the nitrogen cycle, in which nitrates and ammonium ions in rain water are absorbed by plant roots and soil microorganisms and converted to amino acids or gaseous N_2 and N_2O, which diffuse back into the atmosphere. The N_2 uptake and conversion to amino acids (nitrogen fixation) by symbiotic and free-living soil microorganisms balances this loss of gaseous nitrogen. NO, NO_2, and NH_3 (other nitrogen gases) are also emitted and absorbed by soils. Soil reactions are major determinants of trace gas concentrations in the atmosphere.

Air pollutants—sulfur dioxide, hydrogen sulfide, hydrocarbons, carbon monoxide, ozone, and atmospheric nitrogen gases—are absorbed by soil. Because soil reactions are subtle, they are often ignored in tracing the effects of air pollution. However, two classic examples of airborne particulate soil contaminants can be seen in the accumulation of heavy metals around smelters and in soils in urban areas contaminated by auto exhaust emissions. While these two soil polluters can be serious in localized areas, long-range effects of such contamination are considered minor.

Infiltration of Contaminated Surface Water

When wells are installed near streams and rivers, the well's presence induces recharge from the water body, providing high yield with low drawdown. However, if the water body the well draws from is polluted, the soil water in the well field can become contaminated. This most commonly occurs in a shallow well drawing water from the alluvial aquifer adjacent to the stream. The cone of depression imposed by pumping the well or well field creates a gradient on the water table directed toward the well. This pulls the polluted water through the soil and contaminates both well field and well.

Land Disposal of Solid and Liquid Waste Materials

Common practices for dealing with certain recyclable wastes (liquid and sludge [bio-solids], wastes from sewage treatment plants, food processing companies, and other sources) include land disposal, stockpiling, or land-applying wastes or materials. These practices serve as both a means of disposal and a beneficial use/reuse of such materials. These waste products often work successfully to fertilize agricultural lands, golf courses, city parks, and other areas, but the land selected for use must be carefully chosen and tested. Contamination problems arise if water-soluble, mobile wastes are carried deep into the subsurface. If water tables are near the surface, groundwater contamination problems can occur.

Stockpiles, Tailings, and Spoils

The practice of stockpiling chemical products (if not properly managed and contained) contributes to soil and subsurface pollution. Road salt stockpiles can leach into the soil. Tailings produced in mining activities commonly contain materials (asbestos, arsenic, lead, and radioactive substances) that present a health threat to humans and other organisms. Tailings may also contain contaminants such as sulfide, which forms sulfuric acid upon contact with precipitation. The precipitation runs off or is leached from tailing piles, infiltrating the surface layer and contaminating soil. It may ultimately reach groundwater. Spoil (a common result of excavations where huge amounts of surface cover are removed, piled, and then moved somewhere else) causes problems similar to tailing problems—precipitation removes materials in solutions by percolating waters (leaching). Pollutants migrate from the spoil, finding their way into the soil and thus into shallow aquifers.

Dumps

Illegal dumping is less common today than in the past, fortunately. In fact, uncontrolled dumping is now prohibited in most industrialized countries. The persistent remains of dumping are still with us, however. Dumping sites can contain just about anything. Such sites present localized threats of subsurface contamination.

Salt Spreading on Roads

The practice of spreading deicing salts on highways is widespread, especially in urban areas in the north. Not only does this practice contribute to the deterioration of automobiles, bridges, and the roadway itself, it adversely affects plants growing alongside a treated highway or sidewalk. More seriously, salt contamination quickly leaches below the land surface. The productivity of the land decreases because most plants cannot grow in salty soils. Contamination of wells used for drinking water can occur in areas with long-term use.

Animal Feedlots

Some of the largest contributors to nonpoint source water pollution are animal feed-lots. Animal waste in feedlots literally piles up. These stationary heaps, sometimes left for extended periods, create problems with runoff containing contaminants. These contaminants may not only enter the nearest surface water body, but may contaminate soil by waste seepage.

Fertilizers and Pesticides

The mainstays of high-yield agriculture are fertilizers and pesticides. The impact of these two products on the environment has been significant, with each yielding different types of contaminants.

We think of the application of fertilizers and pesticides to our soil as treating the soil. But are we treating it—or poisoning it? We are still trying to definitively answer this question. We do know that for fertilizer and pesticide application and its long-term effects, we do not know what we do not know—we don't have any proof of the long-term effects. The impact of using these chemicals is only now becoming clear, and we still have a lot to learn.

Accidental Spills

Disturbingly common, accidental spills of chemical products can be extremely damaging to any of the three environmental media: air, water, and soil. When chemical spills in the soil are not discovered right away, the contaminant may migrate through the soil (contaminating it) to the water table. As a general rule of thumb, we may assume that the impact of a chemical spill is directly related to the concentration at the point and time of release, the extent to which the concentration increases or decreases during exposure, and the time over which the exposure continues.

Composting of Leaves and Other Wastes

Composting is a common practice for many homeowners, who use the contained and controlled decay of yard and vegetable wastes as an environmentally friendly way to dispose of or beneficially reuse them. When the leaves, twigs, and other organic materials have been treated with chemical pesticides and some fertilizers, however, composting may be harmful to the soil.

Soil Pollution Remediation

The rapid expansion and increasing sophistication of the chemical industries in the past century and particularly over the last 30 years has meant that there has been an increasing amount and complexity of toxic waste effluents. At the same time, fortunately, regulatory authorities have been paying more attention to problems of contamination of the environment.

The occurrence of major incidents (including the *Exxon Valdez* oil spill, the Union-Carbide [Dow] Bhopal disaster, large-scale contamination of the Rhine River, the progressive deterioration of the aquatic habitats and conifer forests in the northeastern United States, Canada, and parts of Europe; and the release of radioactive material in the Chernobyl accident, etc.) and the subsequent massive publicity due to the resulting environmental problems has highlighted the potential for imminent and long-term disasters in the public's conscience.

Although "remediation" is the latest buzzword we hear in regard to mitigating soil contamination, pollution, or chemical spills, problems are associated with soil or subsurface remediation—soil remediation technologies are not the perfect solution to the problem. Available soil remediation technologies, though often very effective, are not necessarily complete answers to the problems caused by soil pollution.

The first problem is that soil pollution remediation practices are a still-developing branch of environmental science and engineering—lessons are still being learned. Another more obvious problem is timing and expediency. Soil pollution remediation is the very last procedure in the sequence of combating soil pollution, because action is taken only when we realize the problem exists—after the spill or release of pollutants into the soil. In water and air pollution, we can often limit or prevent pollution damage from occurring at all by collecting the pollutant at the source before it enters the media. In soil pollution, often the damage is not only done, it's years old and presents even more challenges to our ability to remediate the contamination.

The available technologies for remediating petroleum-product contaminated soil and groundwater are divided into two categories: *in situ* treatment and non-*in situ* treatment—the treatment of soil in place and treatment of soil removed from the site.

Table 3.17 presents a compilation of various soil remediation technologies.

Although the goals of regulatory agencies monitoring environmental cleanup efforts generally include removing every trace of contamination and restoring the landscape to its natural condition, achieving that end result is highly unlikely.

Summary of Chemical Properties of Soil

Important chemical properties of soil include the following:

- Soil contamination is a major environmental concern, not only throughout the United States, but worldwide.
- Regardless of the origin, most soils consist of four basic components: mineral matter, water, air, and organic matter.
- Petroleum contamination is commonly associated with USTs.
- Besides the obvious problem of fouling the environment, many of these leaking USTs also pose serious fire and explosion hazards.
- Experience has shown that it is relatively easy to describe the fate of petroleum in soils in merely qualitative terms.
- Geothermal energy is used best in the generation of electricity.
- Manufactured gas plants produce a variety of largely hazardous waste products.
- Mining operations often create land and water pollution problems.
- Cation exchange capacity is the soil's capacity to hold cations.
- The pH of soil is one of the most important properties involved in plant growth.
- Saline soils have lots of soluble salts.
- Soil color is dependent primarily on the quantity of humus and the chemical form of iron oxides present.

Table 3.17. Soil Remediation Technologies

Technology	Applicable Contaminants
	In situ
Natural attenuation	Petroleum hydrocarbons
	Chlorinated solvents
Passive	Petroleum hydrocarbons
	Chlorinated solvents
	Coal-tar residues
Leaching/chemical reaction	Petroleum hydrocarbons
	Chlorinated solvents
Isolation/containment	Petroleum hydrocarbons
	Chlorinated solvents
	Coal-tar residues
Stabilization	Petroleum hydrocarbons
	Chlorinated solvents
	Metals
	Coal-tar residue
Vitrification	Petroleum hydrocarbons
	Chlorinated solvents
	Coal-tar residue
Volatilization (vapor extraction)	Volatile organic compounds
Bioremediation[a]	Petroleum hydrocarbons[b]
	Not in situ
Land treatment	Petroleum hydrocarbons[c]
	Coal-tar residues
Thermal treatment	Petroleum hydrocarbons
	Chlorinated solvents
	Coal-tar residues
Solidification/stabilization	Petroleum hydrocarbons
	Chlorinated solvents
	Coal-tar residues
	Metals
Chemical extraction	Petroleum hydrocarbons
	Chlorinated solvents
	Coal-tar residues
	Metals
Excavation/disposal	Petroleum hydrocarbons
	Coal-tar residues
	Metals

[a]Bioremediation refers to biotechnology whereby bacteria are altered to produce certain enzymes that metabolize industrial waste components that are toxic to other life; new pathways are also designed for the biodegradation of various wastes.
[b]Excludes VOCs.
[c]Petroleum hydrocarbons include gasoline and fuel oils such as diesel and kerosene.

Source: Adapted from Testa, 1997, 18.

- Soil texture refers to the relative proportions of sand, silt, and clay in soil.
- Soil tilth refers to the combination or arrangement of primary soil particles into secondary particles.
- About half of soil's volume is pore space occupied by varying amounts of air and water, depending on how wet the soil is.
- Drainage refers to a soil's ability to get rid of excess water.

- Soil depth refers to how deep, top to bottom, the topsoil plus the subsoil is.
- The slope has a marked influence on the amount of water runoff and soil erosion caused by flowing water.
- It is important to understand soil's transport mechanisms affecting flow regime of contaminants or pollutants.
- Pollutant retardants include adsorption, ion balance, pollutant precipitation, and biodegradation.
- All human societies pollute both soil and groundwater to some extent.
- When chemical spills or accidents occur and soil is contaminated, "remediation" is the most common buzzword regarding the mitigation of the contamination problem.
- Although the goals of regulatory agencies monitoring environmental cleanup efforts are generally going to include removing every trace of contamination and restoring the landscape to its natural condition, achieving that end result is highly unlikely.

Effects of Whole-Tree Harvests on Forest Soil Productivity

Have you ever wondered what happens to forest soil fertility and productivity when the entire forest is harvested—every tree cut down? Several studies have been done wherein the nutrients of aboveground biomass were determined empirically and the expected impact of intensive harvesting (i.e., nutrient drained) on the ecosystem has been calculated or predicted as changes in soil nutrient availability and productivity over time. These analyses typically used nutrient budgets and/or simulation models to forecast changes in nutrient pool sizes (i.e., plant and soil pools) and transfer rates between the pools. These typically assume that the nutrient pool sizes and transfer rates between nutrient pools are the prime regulator of nutrient availability and forest productivity. Forest harvesting (i.e., nutrient removal) is then used to predict future nutrient availability and soil productivity within the ecosystem.

The major shortcomings of these forecasts and simulations are that (1) few forest ecosystems have been studied in sufficient detail to accurately predict nutrient transfers between pools; and (2) the rates of key ecosystem processes involved in nutrient cycling (e.g., decomposition, weathering, and nutrient mobilization/immobilization) are poorly understood. As a result the predictions of the consequences of various harvesting regimes may be grossly over- or understated. Nevertheless, until long-term studies began in the 1990s, these forecasts were the best available information that resource specialists had to assess soil productivity impacts from intensive harvesting.

Nutrient Capital and Nutrient Mining: These terms are used extensively in the discussion of the effects of whole-tree harvesting. As mentioned, *nutrient capital* refers to the nutrients in the ecosystem that are available to plants depending on the internal dynamics of the ecosystem. A site's initial nutrient capital is considered the amount of nutrient stored in the soil prior to a disturbance to the ecosystem. *Nutrient mining* describes the rate of removal of nutrients that exceeds the rate of replenishments into the forest ecosystem (Grigal & Bates, 1992). There has been concern that whole-tree harvesting results in significant nutrient mining of the nutrient capital of the forest ecosystem. Research is ongoing related to this area of concern.

Chapter Summary

Chemical actions and reactions accompany everything we do, every day. For environmental scientists to perform their work properly, they must know about more than the chemical basis of how humans alter and affect their environment. But chemistry is part of the material at the foundation of environmental science—without understanding and mastery of the science of chemistry, you will not master the science of our environment.

Discussion Questions and Problems

1. What is the molarity of 12 g of salt (NaCl) dissolved in 1 L of water?
2. Identify each of the following as a physical or chemical change:
   a. Breaking a drinking glass.
   b. The freezing of water into ice cubes.
   c. Tearing of paper.
   d. Dissolving instant tea in water.
3. What is the difference between an atom and a molecule?
4. Why is air *not* considered an element?
5. How could two atoms of the same element have different atomic weights?
6. Find the formula weight for NaCl.
7. Find the formula weight for aluminum sulfate $[Al_2(SO_4)]$.
8. Find the molarity of a solution that contains 25 g of grain alcohol C_2H_5OH in 1,000 mL of solution (1,000 mL = 1 liter).
9. Draw structural formulas for the following organic compounds:
   a. benzene
   b. propane
   c. propene
10. What is a chemical bond?
11. Explain the concept of density and tell how it is different from mass.
12. Why would you write Avogadro's number (6.02×10^{23}) in powers of 10 notation?
13. Soil can act as a "degrader" or "immobilizer" of agricultural chemicals, wastes, or other potential pollutions. Explain.
14. Poorly managed agricultural fields can lead to physical degradation, chemical degradation, and/or biological degradation. Give an example of each and explain.

Suggested Research Topics and Projects

- The history of chemical nomenclature and the periodic table.
- Extended definition: chemical change/reaction, chemical bonds.
- Chemical and sediment runoff from agricultural fields into local streams.
- The Warm Fire, Arizona, June 2006.

Note

1. From F. R. Spellman & N. Whiting, 2006, *Environmental Science and Technology: Concepts and Applications*, 2nd ed. Lanham, MD: Government Institutes Press.

References and Recommended Reading

A Concise Dictionary of Chemistry (1990). Oxford, England: Oxford University Press.

"Air Pollutants." (2002). http://www.doc.mmu.ac.uk/aric/ease/airquality/older/Air_Pollutants .html.

Andrews, J. E. (1996). *Environmental Chemistry*. Cambridge, MA: Blackwell Science Publications.

Associated Press. (1998, September 6). "Town Evacuated after Acid Spill." *Lancaster (PA) New Era*.

Bohn, H. L., McNeal, B. L., & O'Connor, G. A. (1985). *Soil Chemistry*. 2nd ed. New York: John Wiley & Sons.

Bohn, H. L. L., et al. (2001). *Soil Chemistry*. New York: John Wiley & Sons, Inc.

Eastcott, L., Shir, W. Y., & Mackay, D. (1989). "Modeling Petroleum Products in Soil." In Kostecki, Paul T., & Calabrese, Edward J., eds., *Petroleum Contaminated Soils, Volume I*. Chelsea, MI: Lewis Publishers, Inc.

Evangelou, V. P. (1998). *Environmental Soil and Water Chemistry: Principles and Applications*. New York: John Wiley & Sons, Inc.

Freedman, B. (1989). *Environmental Ecology*. New York: Academic Press.

Frei, R. W. W., et al. (1983). *Analysis and Chemistry of Water Polluted, Volume 6*. New York: Gordon and Breach.

Graedel, T. E., & Crutzen, P. J. (1995). *Atmosphere, Climate, and Change*. New York: Scientific American.

Grigal, D. F. (2004). "An Update of Forest Soils." A technical paper for a generic environmental impact statement on timber harvesting and forest management in Minnesota. Virginia, MN: Laurentian Energy Agency.

Grigal, D. F., & Bates, P. C. (1992). "Forest Soils." A technical paper for a generic Environmental Impact Statement on timber harvesting and forest management in Minnesota. Prepared for Minnesota Environmental Quality Board. Tarrytown, NY: Jaako Poyry Consulting, Inc.

Hansen, J. E., et al. (1986). "Climate Sensitivity to Increasing Greenhouse Gases." In Barth, M. C., & Titus, J. G., eds., *Greenhouse Effect and Sea Level Rise: A Challenge for This Generation*. New York: Van Nostrand Reinhold.

Hastie, D. R. (2002). "Atmospheric Particulate Matter." http://www.cac.yoku.ca/people/ hastie/.

Henry, J. G., & Heinke, G. W. (1989). *Environmental Science and Engineering*. Englewood Cliffs, NJ: Prentice-Hall, Inc.

Hobbs, P. V. (1993). *Introduction to Atmospheric Chemistry*. Cambridge University Press.

Kostecki, P. T., & Calabrese, E. J. (1989). *Petroleum Contaminated Soils: Volume 1 Remediation Techniques, Environmental Fate, and Risk Assessment*. Chelsea, MI: Lewis Publishers.

Manahan, S. E. (1997). *Environmental Science and Technology*. Boca Raton, FL.

MacKenzie, J. J., & El-Ashry, T. (1988). *Ill Winds: Airborne Pollutant's Toll on Trees and Crops*. Washington, DC: World Resource Institute.

Masters, G. M. (1991). *Introduction to Environmental Engineering and Science*. Englewood Cliffs, NJ: Prentice-Hall.

Meyer, E. (1989). *Chemistry of Hazardous Materials*. 2nd ed. Englewood Cliffs, NJ: Prentice-Hall.

Orlov, D. S., *Soil Chemistry*. Russia: Balkem, A. A., 1992.Manahan, S. E., *Fundamentals of Environmental Chemistry*, Boca Raton, FL: CRC Press/Lewis Publishers.

Peavy, H. S., Rowe, D. R., & Tchobanoglous, G. (1985). *Environmental Engineering*. New York: McGraw-Hill.

Reed, M. J. (2002). "Environmental Compatibility of Geothermal Energy." U.S. Department of Energy Technical Site. http://geotherm.inel.gov/geothermal/articles:read/index.html.

Schaefer, V. J., & Day, J. A. (1981). *Atmosphere: Clouds, Rain, Snow, Storms*. Boston: Houghton Mifflin.

Seinfeld, J. H., & Pandis, S. N. (1997). *Atmospheric Chemistry and Physics: From Air Pollution & Climate Change*. New York: Wiley-Interscience.

Shipman, J. T., Adams, J. L., & Wilson, J. D. (1987). *An Introduction to Physical Science*. 5th ed. Lexington, MA: D.C. Heath & Company.

Snoeyink, V. L., & Jenkins, D. (1980). *Water Chemistry*. New York: Wiley.

Sparks, D. L. (1998). *Soil Physical Chemistry*. 2nd ed. Boca Raton, FL: CRC Press.

Spellman, F. R. (1999). *The Science of Environmental Pollution*. Lancaster, PA: Technomic Publishing Company.

Spellman, F. R. (2003). *The Science of Water*. Boca Raton, FL: CRC Press.

Spellman, F. R., & Drinan, J. E. (2001). *Stream Ecology & Self-Purification: An Introduction*. 2nd ed. Lancaster, PA: Technomic Publishing Company.

Spiro, T. G., & Stigliani, W. M. (1996). *Chemistry of the Environment*. Upper Saddle River, NJ: Prentice-Hall.

Stumm, W., & Morgan, J. J. (1996). *Aquatic Chemistry: Chemical Equilibria and Rates in Natural Waters*. New York: Wiley.

Testa, S. M. (1997). *The Reuse and Recycling of Contaminated Soil*. Boca Raton: CRC/Lewis Publishers.

Tucker, R. K. (1989). "Problems Dealing with Petroleum Contaminated Soils: A New Jersey Perspective." In Kostecki, P.T., & Calabrese, E. J., eds., *Petroleum Contaminated Soils, Volume I*. Boca Raton: Fl: CRC/Lewis Publishers.

U.S. Environmental Protection Agency (EPA) (1988). *National Air Pollutant Emission Estimates 1940–1986*, Washington, DC: Environmental Protection Agency

Wallace, J. M., & Hobbs, P. V. (1997). *Atmospheric Science: An Introductory Survey*. Academic Press.

Hrubec, Juri, ed. (1995). *Water Pollution: Drinking Water and Drinking Water Treatment*. New York: Springer-Verlag.

"What Is Geothermal Energy" (2002). *Geothermal Technologies*. http://www.eren.doe.goc/geothermal/about.html.

WRI & IIED. (1988). *World Resources 1988–1989*. New York: Basic Books.

CHAPTER 4

Environmental Biology

A bumper sticker in Germany said long ago: We are treating this
planet as if we had another one in the trunk compartment.

Chapter Objectives

After studying this chapter, you should be able to:

- Discuss the interface between environmental science and microbiology.
- Define, describe, and demonstrate microbiology concepts as they apply to environmental science, including enzyme and metabolic processes.
- Define and use Linnaeus's binomial classification as it relates to microbiology and environmental science.
- Define, discuss, and draw the parts of a cell.
- Define and discuss cell function and structures.
- Define, discuss, draw, and apply the information presented on bacteria, viruses, bacteriophages, fungi, algae, and protozoa and their classification, identification, forms, structure, characteristics, reproduction, nutrition, metabolism, and cultivation as used in environmental science.
- Discuss the considerations connected with airborne particulate matter.
- Define and discuss how enzymes function to break down organics.
- Define and apply the concepts associated with the activated biosolids process.
- Discuss how enzymes are classified and what effect temperature has on enzymatic action.
- Define, discuss, and apply the concepts of metabolic transformation, including respiration, Krebs cycle, ETS, auto and heterotrophic metabolism, nutrition, growth, temperature, pH, water availability, and oxygen.
- Define, discuss, and apply the concepts, factors, and associated problems of pathogenicity and the emergence of infectious diseases for environmental science.

Chapter Outline

- Response Scenario 4.1: *pfiesteria,* environmental science, and microbiology
- Definition and discussion: microbiology
- Definition and discussion: classification
- Definition and discussion: the cell and cell structure
- Definition, discussion and examples: bacteria—bacterial forms, cell surface structures and inclusions, flagella, cell walls, plasma membrane, cytoplasm, mesosome, nuclear body or region, ribosomes, storage granules, chemical composition, metabolism, chemosynthesis, autotrophic bacteria, heterotrophic bacteria, and classification of bacteria
- Definition, discussion, and examples: viruses—bacteriophage
- Definition, discussion, and examples: fungi—classification, identification, key vocabulary for fungi, cultivation, reproduction, nutrition, and metabolism
- Definition, discussion, and examples: algae—key vocabulary for algae, description, classification characteristics, cell wall structures, chlorophyll, motility, nutrition, reproduction, and division characteristics
- Example and discussion: airborne particulate matter and *Legionella pneumophila*
- Definition, discussion, and examples: protozoa and other microorganisms—classification
- Example and discussion: the activated biosolids process and stream purification
- Definition, discussion, and examples: rotifers
- Definition, discussion, and examples: crustaceans
- Definition, discussion, and examples: enzymes—nature, action, efficiency, specificity, classification, and environmental effects on activity
- Definition, discussion, and examples: metabolic transformations—general metabolism, glycolysis, respiration, Krebs cycle, electron transport system (ETS), autotrophic and heterotrophic metabolism, microbial nutrition, bacterial growth, temperature, pH, water availability, and oxygen
- Definition, discussion, and examples: pathogenicity—transmission factors of disease, parasites, and pathogens
- Definition, discussion, and examples: emergence of infectious diseases

Key Terms

aerobic	bacteria
algae	bacteriophage
amoebae	benthic
anabolism	binomial system of nomenclature
anaerobic	biology
apoenzyme	blastospore
autotrophic	budding
bacilli	capsule

catabolism
catalysis
catalyst
cell
cell membrane
cell nucleus
cell wall
chemosynthesis
chlorophyll
chloroplasts
cilia
cocci
cofactor
conidia mycelium
crustacean
cytochrome
cytoplasm
diatom
dinoflagellates
electron transport system
endergonic
endoplasmic reticulum
enzymes
eukaryotic
eutrophication
exergonic
facultative
flagella
frustule
fungi
genome
genus
glycolysis
growth
growth curve
heterotrophic
holoenzyme

hypha
inclusion
Krebs cycle
mesosome
metabolic transformation
metabolism
microbiology
mitochondria
motility
mycology
nucleoid
nutrition
organelle
oxidation
parasite
pathogen
pellicle
plankton
planktonic
plasma membrane
prokaryotic
protozoa
reduction
ribosomes
rotifer
saprophyte
species
spirilla
sporangiospore
spore
substrate
vacuole
vectors
virulence
virus
xenobiotics

Response Scenario 4.1.
Scientific Method: *Pfiesteria* and Fish Health

Note: The following is adapted from a Sea Grant Maryland (SGM) (funding provided by the National Oceanic and Atmospheric Administration) publication, *The Scientific Method, Fish Health and Pfiesteria* (related to fish health in the Chesapeake Bay), containing the writings of William T. Keeton (1996) and a presentation by David Goshorn, PhD (2006).

Goshorn (2006) points out that "*Pfiesteria* is a very small, single-celled organism without flagella. Its got an extremely complex life cycle. Most of the time populations are benign, feeding on algae and bacteria, but some populations, not all, are capable of producing a toxin which can cause fish health problems and, apparently, human health problems. In 1997, Maryland experienced four separate toxic outbreaks on three different Eastern Shore rivers. North Carolina has had its problems for quite some time."

In regard to fish health in the Chesapeake Bay, Sea Grant Maryland (SGM, 2006) reported in *Fish Disease Information: The Scientific Method, Fish Health and Pfiesteria* that its "understanding of the situation is that fish have had lesions and that fish have died. *Pfiesteria piscicida* and pfiesteria-like organisms have been cultured from water samples taken in the vicinity where fish with lesions have been observed or where fish kills have occurred. It was reported that pfiesteria-like organisms have caused lesions and mortalities in laboratory exposures."

Well, it sounds like the jury is in; this is a simple matter of cause and effect. *Pfiesteria* were present, fish had lesions, and fish died. Moreover, *Pfiesteria*-like organisms have caused lesions and mortalities in lab exposures. That seals the deal; a slam-dunk verdict, right? Not so fast, my environmental practitioner friends. We know better (hopefully) than to jump the gun, don't we?

As SGM points out, "as good scientists know, it's not that easy."

Notwithstanding that many of us are scientists or want-to-be scientists or just want to know more about science, there are some who might ask: "Why, in this case, is it not easy to conclude that fish lesions are caused by *Pfiesteria* or *Pfiesteria*-like organisms?" SGM points out that the "very same water which was cultured for *Pfiesteria* could have also grown bacteria." Therefore, to properly study the cause of the fish lesions and the possibility that *Pfiesteria* are the culprits, we need to follow Koch's postulates.

In the course of his studies of anthrax and tuberculosis, Robert Koch (1882, 1884, 1893), a German physician and bacteriologist, formulated four postulates (i.e., four criteria for judging whether a given bacterium is the cause of a given disease) in 1884 and refined and published them in 1890. To say that Koch's criteria brought some much-needed scientific clarity to what was then a very confused field is an understatement. Still used today, Koch's postulates are as follows:

1. The organism must be found in all animals suffering from the disease, but not in healthy animals.
2. The organism must be isolated from a diseased animal and grown in pure culture.
3. The cultured organism should cause disease when introduced into a healthy animal.
4. The organism must be reisolated from the experimentally infected animal.

It should now be clear why it is difficult to establish a cause-and-effect relationship between fish lesions and *Pfiesteria*. SGM (2006) points out that "*Pfiesteria* (or its toxin) has not yet been isolated from fish or fish lesions." The record shows that fish with lesions have been taken from waters where *Pfiesteria*-like organisms have not been identified (of course that does not mean that they were not present). Moreover, in tests it has been shown that lesions on fish from lab exposures are not identical to those seen in some specimens collected from their natural habitat. This fact, and especially the nonspecificity of the lesions, means that the lesions could have been caused by a number of different agents (e.g., bacteria, **virus**, etc.). SGM reports that it was unable to isolate the infectious organism from the host, culture it, and reinfect another host to observe whether the same lesions would occur.

RESPONSE

(i) Using Koch's postulates, does this account prove or disprove the association of *Pfiesteria* and fish lesions?

Introduction

Response Scenario 4.1 illustrates an environmental problem caused by an infestation of the microbe *Pfiesteria*, which has killed a billion fish in the coastal waterways of North Carolina and has been discovered in waterways as far north as Virginia and Maryland. On the surface, *Pfiesteria*—which is a common organism, but can take on a toxic form under certain environmental conditions—is the problem. But there is more to this problem. *Pfiesteria* seem to thrive where manure washes into waterways. Scientists believe that pollution triggers the toxic transformation. What we are left with is a compound environmental problem, a chain of events leading to a chain of conditions—manure-rich waters, which provide a habitat for the fish-killing microbe *Pfiesteria*.

Just as chemistry is essential to environmental science, so is **biology**. This text assumes that readers have both a fundamental knowledge of chemistry and a rudimentary knowledge of biological sciences, in particular **microbiology**. We emphasize microbiology because of the positive and negative influences tiny microbes have on our environment. We also include in this chapter some of the basic tenets of biochemistry dealing with **enzymes** and metabolic processes. These complement our discussion of environmental microbiology.

Biology is the science of life. Strictly speaking, it includes all the life sciences: anatomy and physiology, cytology, zoology, botany, ecology, genetics, biochemistry and biophysics, animal behavior, embryology, and microbiology. In this text, we are concerned with the micro-life—the study of microbiology.

Microbiology is the focus because we are concerned with those "things" (the micro-life) that impact our environment—our air, our water, our soil—our lives. One important reason for this focus involves new research topics that have emerged, and the emphasis increasingly being placed on the biological treatment of hazardous wastes and the detection and control of new **pathogens**. For example, the field of water/wastewater microbiology has blossomed during the Past two decades as new tools have been developed to study the role of microorganisms in the treatment of water and wastewater.

Another important reason for emphasizing microbiology is that we have witnessed dramatic advances in the methodology for detection of pathogenic microorganisms and **parasite**s in various environmental samples. Environmental practitioners and microbiologists are increasingly interested in toxicity (discussed in the next chapter) and the biodegradation of **xenobiotics** (any chemical present in a natural environment, but which does not normally occur in nature—e.g., pesticides and/or industrial pollutants) by **aerobic** and **anaerobic** biological processes in wastewater treatment plants.

Beyond the obvious benefits achieved in biological treatment of wastewater, you may be familiar with other microbial treatment methods that are beneficial to the environment. Consider, for example, the Deepwater Horizon oil spill (aka the BP oil disaster, or the Macondo blowout) in the Gulf of Mexico. This horrendous spill off the Mississippi River delta on April 20, 2010, caused by a wellhead blowout, left 11 dead and poured out up to 4,900,000 barrels (206,000,000 US gallons; 779,000 cubic meters) of crude oil.

The spill caused untold damage to marine and wildlife habitats as well as the Gulf's fishing and tourism industries. And when shrimpers started to pull up tar balls in their nets more than 4,100 square miles off the gulf, the waters were closed to shrimping. In all, some 320 miles of Louisiana shoreline were impacted by oil by late November 2010.

Just about every means imaginable was employed by the oil company, the U.S. Coast Guard, and various contractors to stem the flow from the seabed, including using underwater vehicles to close the blowout preventer valves. Nothing seemed to work, not even top kill methods of sealing the spill hole with cement. All the oil spill stoppage techniques failed. Eventually a more successful process was used, whereby a riser insert was positioned in the wide burst pipe, acting as a stopper. Eventually a containment cap was successfully installed to stop the leak.

It is interesting to note that as a last resort, that is, as a last defense and an actual ongoing process against the spill, billions of hydrocarbon-chewing microbes, such as *Alcanivorax borkumensis*, were used. Biello (2010) points out that one of the main benefits of using microbes to gobble up the small oil particles is that they do this faster than any other technique for removing both the oil and dispersants at the same time. A disadvantage to using microbe-chewers of hydrocarbons is that they ingest only the smallest particles. They also do not ingest the tar or asphalt ingredients. However, this is a good thing, because if they did attack tar and asphalt, we would not be able to construct our roads using these materials; the bacteria would eat them, too.

The practical use of beneficial microbes, and a discussion of those that are not beneficial and can be detrimental to the environment (e.g., contaminants of drinking water and food), are what this chapter is all about; that is, it is an exploration of the interface between environmental studies and microbiology, which will hopefully lead to fruitful interactions between microbiologists and environmental practitioners.

Microbiology

Microbiology is the study of organisms of microscopic (cannot be seen without the aid of a microscope) dimensions. Microbiologists are scientists concerned with studying the form, structure, reproduction, physiology, **metabolism**, and identification of microorganisms. The microorganisms they study generally include bacteria, **fungi**, **protozoa**, algae, and viruses. These tiny organisms make up a large and diverse group of free-living forms that exist as single **cells**, cell bunches, or clusters.

Microscopic organisms can be found in abundance almost anywhere on Earth. The vast majority are not harmful. Many microorganisms, or microbes, occur as single cells (unicellular); others are multicellular; and still others (viruses) do not have a true cellular appearance.

Because microorganisms exist as single cells or cell bunches, they are unique and distinct from the cells of animals and plants, which are not able to live alone in nature but can exist only as part of multicellular organisms. A single microbial cell, for the most part, exhibits the characteristic features common to other biological systems, such as metabolism, reproduction, and **growth**.

CLASSIFICATION

For centuries, scientists classified the forms of life visible to the naked eye as either animal or plant. The Swedish naturalist Caroulus Linnaeus organized much of the current knowledge about living things in 1735.

The importance of classifying organisms cannot be overstated. Without a classification scheme, how could we establish criteria for identifying organisms and arranging similar organisms into groups? The most important reason for classification is that a standardized system allows us to handle information efficiently—it makes the vastly diverse and abundant natural world less confusing.

Linnaeus's classification system was extraordinarily innovative. His **binomial system of nomenclature** is still in use today. Under the binomial system, all organisms are generally described by a two-word scientific name, the **genus** and **species**. Genus and species are groups that are part of a hierarchy of groups of increasing size, based on their nomenclature (taxonomy). This hierarchy is as follows:

Kingdom
    Phylum
        Class
            Order
                Family
                    Genus
                        Species

Using this hierarchy and Linnaeus's binomial system of nomenclature, the scientific name of any organism includes both the genus and the species name. The genus name is always capitalized, whereas the species name begins with a lowercase letter. On occasion, when there is little chance for confusion, the genus name is abbreviated to a single capital letter. The names are always in Latin, so they are usually printed in italics or underlined. Some organisms also have English common names. Following are some microbe names of interest:

- *Salmonella typhi*—the typhoid bacillus
- *Escherichia coli*—a coliform bacteria
- *Giardia lamblia*—a protozoan

Escherichia coli is commonly known as *E. coli*, and *Giardia lamblia* is usually referred to by only its genus name, *Giardia*.

Let's take a look at a simplified system of microorganism classification used in water and wastewater treatment. Classification is broken down into the kingdoms of animal, plant, and protista. As a general rule, the animal and plant kingdoms contain all the multicelled organisms, and the protista contain all single-celled organisms. Microorganisms can be further classified as being **eukaryotic** or **prokaryotic** (see Table 4.1). An eukaryotic organism is characterized by a cellular organization that includes a well-defined nuclear membrane. A prokaryotic organism is characterized by having a nucleus that lacks a limiting membrane.

Table 4.1.   Simplified Classification of Microorganisms

Kingdom	Members	Cell Classification
Animal	Rotifers	
	Crustaceans	
	Worms and larvae	Eukaryotic
Plant	Ferns	
	Mosses	
Protista	Protozoa	
	Algae	
	Fungi	
	Bacteria	Prokaryotic
	Lower algae forms	

The Cell

Since the 19th century, we have known that all living things, whether animal or plant, are made up of cells. The fundamental unit of all living things, no matter how complex, is the cell. A typical cell is an entity isolated from other cells by a membrane or cell wall. The **cell membrane** contains protoplasm (the living material found within a cell) and the nucleus.

In a typical mature plant cell, the cell wall is rigid and is composed of nonliving material, whereas in the typical animal cell, the wall is an elastic living membrane. Cells have a very great variety of sizes and shapes, as well as functions. Size ranges from bacteria too small to be seen with the light microscope to the largest single cell known, the ostrich egg. Microbial cells also have an extensive size range, some being larger than human cells.

CELL STRUCTURE

The cell is the fundamental unit of life. Cells consist of a small body on the order of micrometers in size. Just as microorganisms are designated prokaryotic and eukaryotic, two kinds of cells are also classified as prokaryotic (described later in the chapter) and eukaryotic (described immediately below). Single-cell bacteria are composed of prokaryotic cells, primitive and relatively simpler than the eukaryotic cells, which comprise all organisms other than bacteria. Figure 4.1 is a simplified representation of a cell.

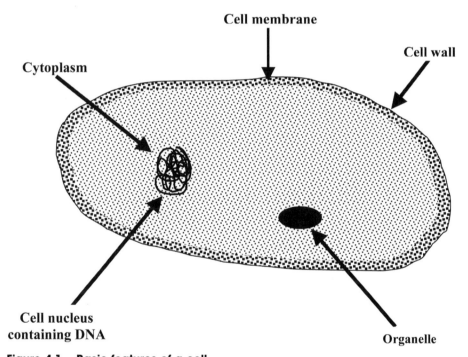

Figure 4.1. Basic features of a cell.

Eukaryotic cells can contain a cell membrane, **cell nucleus, cytoplasm, mitochondria, ribosomes, endoplasmic reticulum**, cell walls, **vacuoles**, and **chloroplast**s:

- The **cell membrane** (cytoplasmic membrane) is the lipid- and protein-containing, selectively permeable membrane that surrounds the cytoplasm in prokaryotic and eukaryotic cells. In most types of microbial cells, the cell membrane is bordered externally by the cell wall. In microbial cells, the precise composition of the cell membrane depends on the species, growth conditions, and age of the cell.

- The **cell nucleus** is a distinct region not delimited by a membrane, in which at least some species of RNA are synthesized and assembled into ribonucleoprotein subunits of ribosomes.
- **Cytoplasm** is a cellular substance located between the nucleus and the cell membrane.
- **Mitochondria** (commonly called the "powerhouse" of a cell) are **organelles** (specialized structures within cells) in which aerobic respiration produces the energy molecule ATP.
- **Ribosomes** are minute particles found attached to the endoplasmic reticulum or loose in the cytoplasm that are the site of protein synthesis.
- **Endoplasmic reticulum (ER)** is a complex system of tubules, vesicles, and sacs in cells, sometimes having attached ribosomes. When no ribosomes are attached, the ER is called the *smooth ER.*
- **Cell walls** (in plants) are strong structures composed mostly of cellulose that provide stiffness and strength.
- **Vacuoles** are various membrane-delimited compartments within a cell.
- **Chloroplasts** (in plants) are the sites for photosynthesis.

Bacteria

Of all microorganisms, bacteria are the most widely distributed, the smallest in size, the simplest in morphology (structure), the most difficult to classify, and the hardest to identify. Because of their considerable diversity, even providing a descriptive definition of what a bacterial organism is can be difficult. About the only generalizations that can be made for the entire group is that they are single-celled plants, are prokaryotic, are seldom photosynthetic, and reproduce by binary fission.

Did You Know?

There are more bacterial cells in the body than human cells. Scientists have estimated that about 95% of all the cells in the body are bacterial. The vast majority of these microbes can be found in the digestive tract.

Bacteria are found everywhere in our environment. They are present in soil, water, and the air. Bacteria are also present in and on the bodies of all living creatures—including people. Most bacteria do not cause disease. They are not pathogenic. Many bacteria carry on useful and necessary functions related to the life of larger organisms.

However, when we think about bacteria in general terms, we usually think of the damage they cause. In water, for example, the form of water pollution that poses the most direct menace to human health is **bacteriological contamination**, part of the reason that bacteria are of great significance to water and wastewater specialists. For water treatment personnel tasked with providing the public with safe, potable water, disease-causing bacteria pose a constant challenge (see Table 4.2).

Table 4.2.   Disease-Causing Bacterial Organisms Found in Polluted Water

Microorganism	Disease
Salmonella typhi	Typhoid fever
Salmonella sp.	Salmonellosis
Shigella sp.	Shigellosis
Campylobacter jejuni	Campylobacter enteritis
Yersinia entercolitice	Yersiniosis
Escherichia coli	

As far as controlling pathogenic bacteria, wastewater specialists face the same challenge that water treatment specialists do. Domestic wastewater normally contains huge quantities of microorganisms, including bacteria, viruses, protozoa, and worms.

Even though wastewater can contain bacteria counts in the millions per mL, in wastewater treatment, under controlled conditions, bacteria can help to destroy pollutants. In such a process, bacteria function to stabilize organic matter (activated biosolids [sludge] processes) and thereby assist the treatment process in producing effluent that does not impose an excessive oxygen demand on the receiving body.

Cholera Fact Sheet[1]

You may have noticed that one of the most important, certainly one of the better known, bacteria was left off the list of waterborne-borne bacteria in Table 4.2: cholera. This is an intentional oversight, so that we may place particular emphasis on this infamous killer bacterium.

Cholera is an infection of the small intestine that causes a large amount of watery diarrhea. It is caused by the bacterium *Vibrio cholerae*. The bacterium releases a toxin that causes increased release of water in the intestines, which as mentioned, produces severe diarrhea. Cholera occurs in places with poor sanitation, crowding, war, and famine. Common locations where cholera occurs are Africa, Asia, India, Mexico, and South and Central America.

People get the infection by eating or drinking contaminated food or water. A type of *Vibrio* bacteria also has been associated with shellfish, especially oysters. Risk factors include exposure to contaminated or untreated drinking water and living in or traveling to areas where there is cholera. Symptoms of cholera include the following:

- Abdominal cramps
- Dry mucus membranes or mouth
- Dry skin
- Excessive thirst
- Glassy or sunken eyes
- Lack of tears
- Lethargy
- Low urine output
- Nausea

(continued)

Cholera Fact Sheet (*continued*)

- Rapid dehydration
- Rapid pulse (heart rate)
- Sunken "soft spots" (fontanelles) in infants
- Unusual sleepiness or tiredness
- Vomiting
- Watery diarrhea that starts suddenly and has a "fish" odor

Note: Symptoms can vary from mild to severe.

Examinations and tests for detecting cholera include blood cultures and stool cultures.

The objective of treatment is to replace fluid and electrolytes lost through diarrhea. Depending on one's condition, fluids may be given by mouth or through a vein (intravenously). Antibiotics may shorten the length of time that the patients feel ill.

The outlook/prognosis is generally good. Severe dehydration can cause death, but given adequate fluids, most people will make a full recovery.

After reviewing the information from the NIH's Cholera Fact Sheet, you might think that identifying cholera and determining its origin and treatment are rather straightforward, maybe requiring nothing more than applying common sense. But until the early 1900s, this was not the case; before then common sense was not so common, and the germ theory of disease was unknown. When people became ill from drinking contaminated water or from exposure to some other disease, it was thought that they must have done something wrong; that is, they had sinned, they were evil, and they were diseased because of the wrath of their God. When the residents of an entire village fell ill, the disease was blamed on vapors or foul odors from sewage. Others assumed that epidemics were caused by *miasmas*, poisonous vapors created by planetary movements affecting the Earth or by disturbances within the Earth itself.

It was not until the invention of the microscope by Robert Hooke and Anton Van Leeuwenhoek that scientists could observe microorganisms. During this period a debate raged among biologists regarding the concept of *spontaneous generation*. For centuries, people based their beliefs on their interpretations of what they saw going on in the world around them without testing their ideas to determine the validity of their theories—in short, they didn't use the tools in the scientist's toolbox, the scientific method, to find correct answers to their questions. Rather, their conclusions were based on unverified and untested observations.

Among these observations, for centuries, since at least the time of Aristotle (4th century BC), people (including many scientists) believed that simple living organisms could come into being spontaneously. In *History of Animals*, Aristotle stated in no uncertain terms:

> Now there is one property that animals are found to have in common with plants. For some plants are generated from the seed of plants, whilst other plants are self-generated through the formation of some elemental principle similar to a seed; and of these latter plants some derive their nutriment from the ground, whilst others grown inside other plants, as is mentioned, by

the way, in my treatise on Botany. So with animals, some spring from parent animals according to their kind, whilst others grow spontaneously and not from kindred stock; and of these instances of spontaneous generation some come from putrefying Earth or vegetable matter, as is the case with a number of insects, while others are spontaneously generated in the inside of animals out of the secretions of their several organs. (Aristotle 343 BCE)

According to this theory, nonliving objects can give rise to living organisms. It was common belief that simple organisms like worms, frogs, beetles, and salamanders could come from dust, mud, etc., and that food left out quickly swarmed with life. For example, when meat spoiled and rotted, it would soon be covered with maggots that turned to flies; people thought that these maggots and flies were generated from the meat, spontaneously. Actually, while Aristotle recognized that many living things emerged from putrefying matter, he pointed out that the putrefaction was not the source of life, but the by-product of the action of the "sweet" element of water.

Animals and plants come into being in Earth and in liquid because there is water in Earth, and air in water, and in all air is vital heat so that in a sense all things are full of soul. Therefore living things form quickly whenever this air and vital heat are enclosed in anything. When they are so enclosed, the corporeal liquids being heated, there arises as it were a frothy bubble. (Aristotle 350 BCE)

With the passage of time, experimentation began to transform science, increase knowledge, and disprove ancient beliefs such as spontaneous generation. For example, in 1668, Francesco Redi challenged the idea that maggots arose spontaneously from rotting meat. He placed meat in a variety of sealed, open, and partially covered containers (Levine and Evers 1999). Realizing that the sealed containers were deprived of air, he covered the meat with "fine Naples veil," observing that no maggots appeared on the meat, but they did appear on the cloth (Redi, 1669).

Let's fast-forward to the mid-1850s, when germ theory was still about 40 years in the future, and people were still dying from cholera. For example, consider London in 1854, where cholera outbreaks were killing off people in droves. The news was not all bad, however. An uncommon doctor with lots of common sense and a detective-like intellect appeared on the scene to solve London's cholera problem. This brilliant doctor's work is described in Sidebar 4.1.

Sidebar 4.1. A Sherlock Holmes Type at the Pump[2]

He wandered the foggy, filthy, garbage-strewn, corpse-ridden streets of 1854 London, searching, making notes, always looking . . . seeking a murdering villain (no, not the Ripper, but a killer just as insidious and unfeeling)—and he did find the miscreant. He took action, removing the handle from a water pump. Fortunately for untold thousands of people, this was the correct action—the lifesaving action.

(continued)

Sidebar 4.1 (*continued*)

He was a detective—of sorts. No, not the real Sherlock Holmes, but just as clever, skillful, knowledgeable, and intuitive—and definitely as driven. His real name was Dr. John Snow. His middle name? Common Sense. Snow's master criminal, his target, was a mindless, conscienceless, brutal killer: cholera.

Let's take a closer look at this medical super sleuth and his quarry, the deadly cholera—and at Doctor Snow's actions to contain the spread of cholera. More to the point, let's look at Dr. Snow's subsequent impact on water treatment (disinfection) of raw water used for potable and other purposes.

An unassuming and creative London obstetrician, Dr. John Snow (1813–1858) achieved prominence in the mid-19th century for proving his theory (in *On the Mode of Communication of Cholera*) that cholera is a contagious disease caused by a "poison" that reproduces in the human body and is found in the vomitus and stools of cholera patients. He theorized that the main (though not the only) means of transmission was water contaminated with this poison. His theory was not held in high regard at first, because a commonly held and popular counter-theory stated that diseases are transmitted by inhalation of vapors. Many theories about cholera's cause were expounded. In the beginning, Snow's argument did not cause a great stir; it was only one of many hopeful theories proposed during a time when cholera was causing great distress. Eventually, Snow was able to prove his theory. We describe how Snow accomplished this later, but for now, let's take a look again at Snow's target: cholera.

CHOLERA

According to the U.S. Centers for Disease Control (CDC) and as mentioned, cholera is an acute diarrheal illness caused by infection of the intestine with the bacterium *Vibrio cholera*. The infection is often mild or without symptoms, but sometimes can be quite severe. Approximately 1 in 20 infected persons has severe disease symptoms such as profuse watery diarrhea, vomiting, and leg cramps. In these persons, rapid loss of body fluids leads to dehydration and shock. Without treatment, death can occur within hours.

How does a person contract cholera? This is a good question. Again, we refer to the CDC for our answer. A person may contract cholera (even today) by drinking water or eating food contaminated with the cholera bacterium. In an epidemic, the source of the contamination is usually feces of an infected person. The disease can spread rapidly in areas with inadequate treatment of sewage and drinking water. Disaster areas often pose special risks. For example, the aftermath of Hurricane Katrina in New Orleans raised concerns about a potential cholera outbreak.

Cholera bacteria also live in brackish river and coastal waters. Raw shellfish have been a source of cholera, with a few people in the United States having contracted it from eating shellfish from the Gulf of Mexico. The disease is not likely to spread directly from one person to another; therefore, casual contact with an infected person is not a risk for transmission of the disease.

This information was updated and provided by the CDC in 1996. Basically, for our purposes, the CDC confirms the fact that cholera is a waterborne disease.

FLASHBACK TO 1854 LONDON

Today, we know quite a lot about cholera and its transmission, as well as how to prevent infection and how to treat it. But what did they know about cholera in the 1850s? Not much. However, one thing is certain: They knew cholera was a deadly killer. And that was just about all they knew—until Dr. Snow proved his theory. He believed that cholera is a contagious disease caused by a poison that reproduces in the human body and is found in the vomitus and stools of cholera victims. He also believed that the main means of transmission was contaminated water.

Dr. Snow's theory was correct, of course. The question is, how did he prove his theory 20 years before the development of the germ theory? The answer involves an account of one of the all-time legendary quests for answers in epidemiological research—and an interesting story.

Dr. Snow proved his theory in 1854, during yet another severe cholera epidemic in London. Though ignorant of the concept of bacteria carried in water (germ theory), Snow traced an outbreak of cholera to a water pump located at the intersection of Cambridge and Broad Streets (London). How did he isolate the source to this particular pump? He began his investigation by determining in which area in London persons with cholera lived and worked. He then used this information to map the distribution of cases on what epidemiologists call a "spot map." His map indicated that the majority of the deaths occurred within 250 yards of that communal water pump. The water pump was used regularly by most of the area residents. Those who did not use the pump remained healthy. Suspecting the Broad Street pump as the plague's source, Snow had the water pump handle removed and thus ended the cholera epidemic.

Did You Know?

You don't need to be a rocket scientist to figure out just how deadly cholera was during the London cholera outbreak of 1854. Comparing the state of "medicine" at that time to ours is like comparing the speed of a horse and buggy to a state-of-the-art NASCAR race car today. Simply stated, cholera was the classic epidemic disease of the 19th century, as the plague had been in the 14th. Its defeat was a reflection of both common sense and progress in medical knowledge—and of enduring changes in European and American social thought.

Sounds like a rather simple solution, doesn't it? For us, it is simple, but remember that in that era, aspirin had not even been formulated yet, to say nothing of other medical miracles we now take for granted, such as antibiotics. Dr. Snow, by the methodical process of elimination and linkage (Sherlock Holmes would have been impressed), proved his point and his theory. Specifically, he painstakingly documented the cholera cases and correlated the comparative incidence of cholera among subscribers to the city's two water companies. He learned that one company drew water from the lower Thames River, whereas the other company obtained water from the upper Thames.

(continued)

Sherlock Holmes (*continued*)

Snow discovered that cholera was much more prevalent in customers of the water company that drew its water from the lower Thames, where the river had become contaminated with London sewage. Snow tracked and pinpointed the Broad Street pump's water source. You guessed it: the contaminated lower Thames, of course.

Dr. Snow the obstetrician became the first effective practitioner of scientific epidemiology. His creative use of logic, common sense (removing the handle from the pump), and scientific information enabled him to solve a major medical mystery—to discern the means by which cholera was transmitted—and earned him the title "the father of field epidemiology." Today he is known as the father of modern epidemiology.

Pump Handle Removal—To Water Treatment (Disinfection). Dr. Snow's major contribution to the medical profession, society, and humanity in general can be summarized rather succinctly: He determined and proved that the deadly disease cholera is a waterborne disease. (His second medical accomplishment was being the first person to administer anesthesia during childbirth.)

What does all of this have to do with water treatment (disinfection)? Actually, Dr. Snow's discovery—his stripping of a mystery to its barest bones—has quite a lot to do with water treatment. Combating any disease is rather difficult without a determination of how the disease is transmitted—how it travels from vector or carrier to receiver. Dr. Snow established this connection, and from his work and the work of others, progress was made in understanding and combating many waterborne diseases.

Today, sanitation problems in developed countries (those with the luxury of adequate financial and technical resources) deal more with the consequences that arise from inadequate commercial food preparation and the results of bacteria becoming resistant to disinfection techniques and antibiotics. We simply flush our toilets to rid ourselves of unwanted wastes and turn on our taps to get high-quality drinking water, from which we have all but eliminated cholera and epidemic diarrheal diseases. This is generally the case in most developed countries today—but it certainly wasn't true in Dr. Snow's time.

The progress in water treatment from that notable day in 1854, when Snow made the "connection" (actually the "disconnection" of handle from pump) between deadly cholera and its means of transmission, its "communication," to the present is a chronology of discovery leading to our modern water treatment practices. With the passage of time, pivotal events and discoveries occurred that have had a profound effect on how we live today. Let's take a look at a few elements of that progression.

After Snow's discovery that cholera is a waterborne disease emanating primarily from human waste, a number of events began to drive the water/wastewater treatment process. In 1859, five years after Snow's discovery, the British Parliament was suspended during the summer because the stench coming from the Thames was unbearable. According to one account, the river began to "seethe and ferment under a burning sun." As was the case in many cities at that time, storm sewers carried a combination of storm water, sewage, street debris, and other wastes to the nearest body of water. In the 1890s, Hamburg, Germany, suffered a cholera epidemic. Detailed studies by Koch tied the outbreak to the contaminated water supply. In response to the epidemic, Hamburg was among the first cities to use chlorine as part of a wastewater treatment regimen. About the same time, the town of Brewster, New York, became the first U.S. city to disinfect its treated wastewater. Chlorination of drinking water was done on a temporary basis in 1896, and its first known continuous use in water supply disinfection occurred in Lincoln, England, and Chicago in 1905. In 1908, Jersey City, New Jersey, became one of the first routine users of chlorine.

With the passage of time came an increased realization of the need to treat and disinfect both water supplies and wastewater. Between 1910 and 1915, technological improvements in gaseous and then solution feed of elemental chlorine (Cl_2) made the process more practical and efficient. Disinfection of water supplies and chlorination of treated wastewater for odor control increased over the next several decades. In the United States, disinfection in one form or another is now being used by more than 15,000 of approximately 16,000 publicly owned treatment works (POTWs). The significance of this number becomes apparent when we consider that fewer than 25 of the more than 600 POTWs in the United States in 1910 were using disinfectants.

Pump Handle Removal: Lessons Learned. There are a number of lessons to be learned from Dr. John Snow's removing the handle from the pump in London and effectively stopping the cholera outbreak. For our purposes, there are four important ones.

In the first place, Dr. Snow's experiments with finding the culprit that caused the 1854 cholera outbreak in London demonstrate the most important reason why we need science and why it is important: Science saves lives. If there is anything more important than this, we can't find it.

Second, we simply can't go through life ignorant of our surroundings and the laws that literally make the world go round. We all face pressing problems such as the swine flu (H1N1 virus); the prospects of global climate change and global warming or global freezing and pending sea-level rise; worldwide economic problems, which many people feel are going to require science and innovation to resolve; growing concerns about environmental pollution problems affecting all four environmental media (air, water, soil, and biota); and the pending energy crisis and the urgent need to jumpstart science and technology to bring renewable energy sources on line. All of these issues are important, and they certainly point to a need for science.

In light of all of this, we can't point out strongly enough the importance of an understanding of science for members of a democratic society. We simply cannot be ignorant of science and the facts. How are we to participate in a democracy if we don't understand basic science concepts? When the naysayer warns us about the need for this or that because if we take no action doomsday is surely near, and when so-called experts justify their expertise based on their positions of authority or power, we need to be able to filter the information to determine the truth. Science is the filter—the ultimate micro-filter.

Third, from the account of Dr. Snow's activities in attempting to find the cause of the 1854 cholera epidemic in London, it should be apparent that he followed a step-by-step procedure in finding the culprit. We can say he used his toolbox (the scientific method) to track down the dreadful killer. In this particular case, Dr. Snow used the six major tools in the scientist's toolbox:

- He *observed* that several residents of London were becoming ill and many had succumbed to some unknown agent.

(continued)

Sherlock Holmes (*continued*)

- He *questioned* why some Londoners were becoming ill and dying.
- He formed a *hypothesis*: Dr. Snow believed that sewage dumped into the river or cesspools near town could contaminate the water supply, leading to a rapid spread of disease. In 1883, a German physician, Robert Koch, took the search for the cause of cholera a step further when he isolated the bacterium *Vibrio cholerae*, the "poison" Snow had contended caused cholera. Dr. Koch determined that cholera is not contagious in person-to-person contact, but is spread only through unsanitary food or water supplies.
- He *experimented*: Dr. Snow made a spot map of the downtown London area. The spots indicated locations where people contracted and died of cholera. His spot map indicated that most of the fatalities occurred in proximity to the Broad Street pump. Therefore, he had the handle to the Broad Street pump removed.
- He *collected and recorded data*: Dr. Snow's data collected after removing the pump handle from the Broad Street pump indicated immediate results, in that no further occurrences of cholera occurred in the Broad Street area.
- He *concluded* that London's 1854 cholera epidemic was caused by sewage in the water pumped by the Broad Street pump.

The fourth lesson from Dr. Snow's cholera experiment is that science is flexible, never bends the truth, and has many branches, from acoustics, the branch of science related to the study of transmission of sound waves, to zoology, a branch of biology that is related to the study of the animal kingdom, including evolution, classification, distribution, structure, habits, and embryology of animals.

Finally, although Dr. Snow's experiments were more in line with epidemiology and the protocols and procedures followed therein, the important lesson to be learned by the environmental scientist from his research and investigations is that in science it is wise to be a generalist. The study of causes and distribution of diseases in human populations is a narrow field of expertise that could easily be enhanced by a repertoire of wide-ranging knowledge. Complex problems face us all in finding out how to prevent deadly exposure to toxins, prevent environmental damage, and live the "good life" without the huge costs incurred when we ignore and abuse our surroundings. In short, we advocate the importance of a generalist view of the environment and all the sciences involved.

Did You Know?

Cholera entered both South America (for the first time this century) and Africa in the 1980s. Molecular typing shows that the South American isolates were of the current pandemic strain, supporting the suggestion that the organism was introduced in contaminated bilge water from an Asian freighter. Other evidence indicates that cholera was only one of many organisms to travel in ballast water; perhaps hundreds, of species have been exchanged between distant places through this means of transport alone (Wachsmuth et al., 1993; Anderson, 1991).

HOW WELL DO WE KNOW BACTERIA?

Although Dr. John Snow did not discover and develop the germ theory of disease, he certainly laid the groundwork for the work of Louis Pasteur and Robert Koch, who made the determination that many diseases are caused by microorganisms. The conquest of disease has placed bacteria high on the list of microorganisms of great interest to the scientific community. There is more to this interest and accompanying large research efforts than just an incessant search for understanding and the eventual conquest of disease-causing bacteria. Not all bacteria are harmful to people. Some, for example, produce substances (antibiotics) that help in the fight against disease. Others are used to control insects that attack crops. Bacteria also have an impact on the natural cycle of matter. They increase soil fertility, which increases the potential for more food production. With the burgeoning world population, increasing future food productivity is no small matter.

We still have a lot to learn about bacteria, because we are still principally engaged in making observations and collecting facts, trying wherever possible to relate one set of facts to another and still lacking much of a basis for grand unifying theories. Like most learning processes, gaining knowledge about bacteria is slow and deliberate. With more knowledge about bacteria, we can minimize their harmful potential and exploit their useful activities.

SHAPES, FORMS, SIZES, AND ARRANGEMENTS OF BACTERIAL CELLS

Bacteria come in three shapes: elongated rods called **bacilli**, rounded or spherical cells called **cocci**, and spirals (helical and curved) called **spirilla** (the less rigid form) and **spirochaete** (those that are flexible). Elongated, rod-shaped bacteria may vary considerably in length; have square, round, or pointed ends; and be motile (possess the ability to move) or nonmotile. The spherical-shaped bacteria may occur singly, in pairs, in tetrads, in chains, and in irregular masses. The helical and curved spiral-shaped bacteria exist as slender spriochaetes, spirillum, and bent rods (see Figure 4.2).

Bacterial cells are usually measured in microns (m) or micrometers (mm); 1 mm = 0.001 or 1/1,000 of a millimeter (mm). A typical coliform bacterial cell that is rod-shaped is about 2 μm long and about 0.7 μm wide. The size of each cell changes during growth and death.

Bacterial cells, viewed under the microscope, may be seen as separate (individual) or in groupings. Within their species, cells may appear in pairs (diplo), chains, groups of four (tetrads), cubes (Sarcinae), and clumps. Long chains of cocci result when cells adhere after repeated divisions in one plane; this pattern is seen in the genera *Enterococcus* and *Lactococcus*. In the genus *Sarcina*, cocci divide in three planes, producing cubical packets of eight cells (tetrads). The shape of rod-shaped cells varies, especially the rod's end, which may be flat, cigar-shaped, rounded, or bifurcated. Although many rods do occur singly, they may remain together after division to form pairs or chains (see Figure 4.2). These characteristic arrangements are frequently useful in bacterial identification.

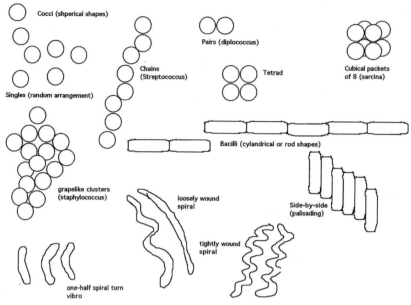

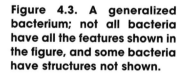

Figure 4.2. Bacterial shapes and arrangements.

BACTERIAL CELL SURFACE STRUCTURES AND CELL INCLUSIONS

Cell structure can best be studied in the rod form (see Figure 4.3). Keep in mind that cells may differ greatly both in their structure and chemical composition; for this reason there is no "typical" bacterium.

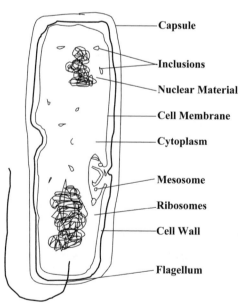

Figure 4.3. A generalized bacterium; not all bacteria have all the features shown in the figure, and some bacteria have structures not shown.

Capsule

Bacterial **capsules** (see Figure 4.3) are organized accumulations of gelatinous material on cell walls, in contrast to **slime layers** (water secretion that adheres loosely to the cell wall and commonly diffuses into the cell), which are unorganized accumulations of similar material. The capsule is usually thick enough to be seen under ordinary light microscope (**macrocapsule**), whereas thinner capsules (**microcapsules**) can only be detected by electron microscopy.

The production of capsules is determined largely by genetics, as well as environmental conditions, and depends on the presence or absence of capsule-degrading enzymes and other growth factors. The capsules vary in composition and mainly comprise water; the organic contents are made of complex polysaccharides, nitrogen-containing substances, and polypeptides.

Capsules confer several advantages on bacteria growing in their normal habitat. For example, they help (1) prevent desiccation; (2) bacteria resist phagocytosis by host phagocytic cells; (3) prevent infection by **bacteriophage**s; and (4) bacterial attachment to tissue surfaces in plant and animal hosts or to surfaces of solid objects in aquatic environments. Capsule formation often correlates with pathogenicity. On the positive side, capsule-secreted polysaccharides have been used for industrial purposes. In the food industry, for example, the polysaccharides have been used as gelling agents.

Flagella

Many bacteria are motile, and this ability to move independently is usually due to a special structure, the flagella (singular: flagellum). Depending on species, a cell may have a single flagellum (**monotrichous** bacteria; *trichous* means hair), one flagellum at each end (**amphitrichous** bacteria; *amphi* means on both sides), a tuft of flagella at one or both ends (**lophotrichous** bacteria; *lopho* means tuft), or flagella that arise all over the cell surface (**peritrichous,** bacteria; *peri* means around).

The flagellum is a threadlike appendage extending outward from the **plasma membrane** and cell wall. Flagella are slender, rigid locomotor structures, about 20 nm across and up to 15 or 20 μm long.

Bacterial cells benefit from flagella in several ways. They can increase the concentration of nutrients or decrease the concentration of toxic materials near the bacterial surfaces by causing a change in the flow rate of fluids. They can also disperse flagellated organisms to areas where colony formation can take place. The main benefit of flagellated organisms is their ability to flee areas that might be harmful.

Cell Wall

The rigid cell wall is the main structural component of most procaryotes. Some of the functions of the cell wall are to (1) provide protection for the delicate protoplast from osmotic lysis, (2) determine a cell's shape, (3) act as a permeability layer that excludes large molecules and various antibiotics and play an active role in regulating the cell's intake of ions, and (4) provide a solid support for flagella.

The cell walls of different species may differ greatly in structure, thickness, and composition. The cell wall accounts for about 20% to 40% of a bacterium's dry weight.

Plasma Membrane (Cytoplasmic Membrane)

Bordered externally by the cell wall and composed of a lipoprotein complex, the plasma membrane is the critical barrier separating the inside from outside of the cell. About 7–8 nm thick and comprising 10% to 20% of a bacterium's dry weight, the plasma membrane controls the passage of all material into and out of the cell. The inner and outer faces are embedded with water-loving (hydrophilic) lipids, while the interior is hydrophobic. Control of material into the cell is accomplished by screening, as well as by electric charge. The plasma membrane is the site of the surface charge of the bacteria.

In addition to serving as an osmotic barrier that passively regulates the passage of material into and out of the cell, the plasma membrane participates in the active transport of various substances into the bacterial cell. Inside the membrane, many highly reactive chemical groups guide the incoming material to the proper points for further reaction. This active transport system provides bacteria with certain advantages, including the ability to maintain a fairly constant intercellular ionic state in the presence of varying external ionic concentrations. The cell membrane transport system also participates in waste excretion and protein secretions.

Cytoplasm

Within a cell and bounded by the cell membrane is a complicated mixture of substances and structures called the cytoplasm. The cytoplasm is a water-based fluid containing ribosomes, ions, enzymes, nutrients, storage granules (under certain circumstances), waste products, and various molecules involved in synthesis, energy metabolism, and cell maintenance.

Mesosome

A common intracellular structure found in the bacterial cytoplasm is the **mesosome**. Mesosomes are invaginations of the plasma membrane in the shape of tubules, vesicles, or lamellae. They are seen in both Gram-positive and Gram-negative bacteria, although they are generally more prominent in the former.

The exact function of mesosomes is still unknown. Many bacteriologists believe they are artifacts generated during the chemical fixation of bacteria for electron microscopy.

Nucleoid (Nuclear Body or Region)

The nuclear region of the prokaryotic cell is primitive and in striking contrast to that of the eukaryotic cell. Prokaryotic cells lack a distinct nucleus, the function of the nucleus being carried out by a single, long, double strand of deoxyribonucleic acid (DNA) that is efficiently packaged to fit within the **nucleoid**. The nucleoid is attached to the plasma membrane. A cell can have more than one nucleoid when cell division occurs after the genetic material has been duplicated.

Ribosomes

The bacterial cytoplasm is often packed with ribosomes. They are minute, rounded bodies, made of RNA (ribonucleic acid), and are loosely attached to the plasma membrane. Ribosomes are estimated to account for about 40% of a bacterium's dry weight; a single cell may have as many as 10,000 ribosomes. Ribosomes are the site of protein synthesis and are part of the translation apparatus.

Inclusions (Storage Granules)

Storage granules or other **inclusions** are often seen within bacterial cells. Some inclusion bodies are not bound by a membrane and lie free in the cytoplasm. A single-layered membrane about 2.0 to 4.0 nm thick encloses other inclusion bodies. Many bacteria produce polymers that are stored as granules in the cytoplasm.

Volutin or **polyphosphate** granules are inorganic inclusion bodies often seen in bacterial systems. Believed to act as reservoirs of phosphate (an important component of nucleic acids), they appear to be involved with energy metabolism. These granules show the metachromatic effect; that is, they appear a different shade of color than the color they were stained with.

A variety of sulfur-metabolizing procaryotes are capable of oxidizing and accumulating free **elemental sulfur** within the cell. The elemental sulfur granules remain only under conditions when excess energy nutrients are present. As the sulfur is oxidized to sulfate, the granules slowly disappear.

CHEMICAL COMPOSITION

The normal growth of a bacterial cell in excess nutrients results in a cell of definite chemical composition. This growth, however, involves a coordinated increase in the mass of its constituent parts and not solely an increase in total mass.

Bacteria, in general, are composed primarily of water (about 80%) and dry matter (about 20%). The dry matter consists of both organic (90%) and inorganic (10%) components. All basic elements for protoplasm must be derived from the liquid environment, and if the environment is deficient in vital elements, the cell will show a characteristic lack of development.

Did You Know?

Bacteria are literally found everywhere. For example, chemolithotrophic bacteria are found in basalt deposits 4,700 ft (1,500 m) underground in solid rock. This bacterium was discovered during drilling for oil.

METABOLISM

Metabolism is bacteria's ability to grow in any environment. The metabolic process refers to the chemical reactions that occur in living cells. In this process, **anabolism** works to build up cell components, then **catabolism** breaks down or changes the cell components from one form to another.

Metabolic reactions require energy. So does locomotion and the uptake of nutrients. Many bacteria obtain their energy by processing chemicals from the environment through **chemosynthesis**. Other bacteria obtain their energy from sunlight through **photosynthesis**.

Chemosynthesis

The synthesis of organic substances such as food nutrients, using the energy of chemical reactions, is called chemosynthesis. A bacterium that obtains its carbon from carbon dioxide is called **autotrophic**. Bacteria that obtain carbon through organic compounds are called **heterotrophic** (see Figure 4.4).

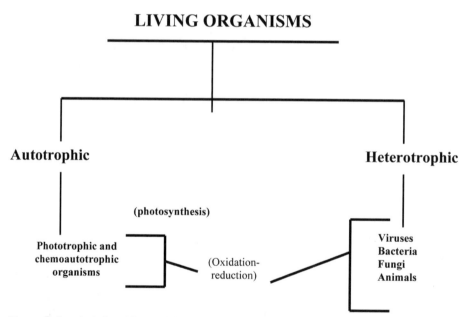

Figure 4.4.   Autotrophic and heterotrophic organism in relation to their means of obtaining energy.

Autotrophic Bacteria

Organisms that can synthesize organic molecules needed for growth from inorganic compounds using light or another source of energy are called **autotrophs**. For their carbon requirements, autotrophs are able to use ("fix") carbon dioxide to form complex organic compounds.

Heterotrophic Bacteria

Most bacteria are not autotrophic: they cannot use carbon dioxide as a major source of carbon, but must rely upon the presence of more reduced, complex molecules (mostly derived from other organisms). Bacteria that need complex carbon compounds are called **heterotrophs**. The heterotrophs use a vast range of carbon sources—including fatty acids, alcohols, sugars, and other organic substances. Heterotrophic bacteria are widespread in nature, including all those species that cause disease in humans, other animals, and plants.

CLASSIFICATION

Classifying microbes, including bacteria, is not always an easy undertaking. The classification process is complicated by the enormous variety of microorganisms, which differ widely in metabolic and structural properties. Some microorganisms are plant-like, others are animal-like, and still others are totally different from all other forms of life.

As an example of the classification process, consider bacteria in terms of activities: Bacteria can be classified as aerobic, anaerobic, or **facultative**. An aerobe must have oxygen to live. On the other extreme, the same oxygen would be toxic to an anaerobe (lives without oxygen). Facultative bacteria are capable of growth under aerobic or anaerobic conditions.

Like other microorganisms, so many different forms of bacteria exist that proper classification or identification through a systematic application of procedures that are designed to grow, isolate, and identify the individual bacteria is required. These procedures are highly specialized and technical. Ultimately, bacteria are characterized based on observation and experience. Fortunately, certain classification criteria have been established, based on observation and experience, to help in the sorting out process:

Shape
Size and structure
Chemical activities
Types of nutrients they need
Form of energy they use
Physical conditions under which they can grow
Their ability to cause disease (pathogenic or nonpathogenic)
Their staining behavior

Using these criteria, and based on observation and experience, bacteria can be identified from descriptions published in *Bergey's Manual of Determinative Bacteriology*.

Viruses

Viruses are parasitic particles that are the smallest living infectious agents known. They are not cellular—they have no nucleus, cell membrane, or cell wall. They multiply only within living cells (hosts) and are totally inert outside of living cells, but can survive in the environment. Just a single virus cell can infect a host. As far as measurable size goes, viruses range from 20 to 200 millimicrons in diameter, about 1–2 magnitude smaller than bacteria. More than 100 virus types excreted from humans through the enteric tract could find their way into sources of drinking water. In sewage, these average 100–500 enteric infectious units/100 mL. If the viruses are not killed in various treatment processes and become diluted by a receiving stream, for example to 0.1–1 viral infectious units/100 mL, the low concentrations make it very difficult to determine virus levels in water supplies. Because tests are usually run on samples of less than 1 mL, at least 1,000 samples would have to be analyzed to detect a single virus unit in a liter of water. For this reason, filtration or centrifugation prior to analysis usually concentrates viruses.

Viruses are mainly classified by phenotypic characteristics, such as morphology, host organism, mode of replication, nucleic acid type, and the type of disease they cause. Currently there are two main schemes for the classification of viruses: the Baltimore system, which places viruses into one of several groups depending on a combination of their DNA or RNA (nucleic acid), and the ICTV classification system, which shares many features (e.g., taxon structure) with the classification system of cellular organisms.

Viruses differ from living cells in at least three ways: (1) they are unable to reproduce independently of cells and carry out cell division; (2) they possess only one type of nucleic acid, either DNA or RNA; and (3) they have a simple cellular organization. They can be controlled by chlorination, but at much higher levels than those necessary to kill bacteria. Some viruses that may be transmitted by water are hepatitis A, adeno virus, polio, coxsackie, echo, and Norwalk agent. A virus that infects a bacterium is called a **bacteriophage**.

Bacteriophage

In *The Lives of a Cell*, Lewis Thomas points out that when humans "catch diphtheria it is a virus infection, *but not of us*." That is, when humans are infected by the virus causing diphtheria, it is the bacterium that is really infected—humans simply "blundered into someone else's accident" (1974, 76). The toxin of diphtheria bacilli is produced when the organism has been infected by a bacteriophage.

A bacteriophage (phage) is any viral organism whose host is a bacterium. Most of the bacteriophage research that has been carried out has been on the bacterium *Escherichia coli*, one of the Gram-negative bacteria that environmental specialists such as water and wastewater operators are concerned about because it is a dangerous typical coliform.

A virus does not have a cell-type structure from which it is able to metabolize or reproduce. However, when the **genome** (a complete haploid set of chromosomes) of a virus is able to enter into a viable living cell (a bacterium), it may "take charge" and direct the operation of the cell's internal processes. When this occurs, the genome, through the host's synthesizing process, is able to reproduce copies of itself, move on, and then infect other hosts. Hosts of a phage may involve a single bacterial species or several bacteria genera.

The most important properties used in classifying bacteriophages are nucleic acid properties and phage morphology. Bacterial viruses may contain either DNA or RNA; most phages have double-stranded DNA.

Many different basic structures have been recognized among phages. Phages appear to show greater variation in form than any other viral group. (Basic morphological structures of various viruses are shown in Figure 4.5.) The T-2 phage virus has two prominent structural characteristics: the head (a polyhedral capsid) and the tail.

The effect of phage infection depends on the phage and host, and to a lesser extent on conditions. Some phages multiply within and **lyse** (destroy) their hosts. When the host lyses (dies and breaks open), phage progeny are released.

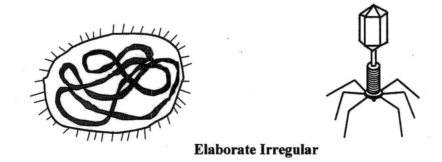

Elaborate Irregular

Long Slender Rod

Geometric Polyhedral

Figure 4.5.   Virus shapes

Fungi

The fungi (singular **fungus**) constitute an extremely important and interesting group of eukaryotic, aerobic microbes, ranging from the unicellular yeasts to the extensively mycelial molds. Not considered plants, they are a distinctive life form of great practical and ecological importance. Fungi are important because, like bacteria, they metabolize dissolved organic matter; they are the principal organisms responsible for the decomposition of carbon in the biosphere. Fungi, unlike bacteria, can grow in low moisture areas and in low pH solutions, which aids them in the breakdown of organic matter.

Fungi comprise a large group of organisms that include such diverse forms as the water molds, slime molds, other molds, mushrooms, puffballs, and yeasts. Because they lack **chlorophyll** (and thus are not considered plants), they must get **nutrition** from organic substances. They are either parasites, existing in or on animals or plants, or more commonly **saporytes**, obtaining their food from dead organic matter. The fungi belong to the kingdom **Myceteae**. The study of fungi is called **mycology**.

McKinney (1962), in *Microbiology for Sanitary Engineers*, complains that the study of mycology has been directed solely toward classification of fungi and not toward the actual biochemistry involved. He points out that for those involved in the sanitary field it is important to recognize the "sanitary importance of fungi . . . and other steps will follow" (p. 40). For students of environmental science, understanding the role of fungi in the water purification process is important. Environmental specialists need knowledge and understanding of the organism's ability to function and exist under extreme conditions, which make them important elements in biological waste stream treatment processes and in the degradation that takes place during waste-composting processes.

Fungi may be unicellular or filamentous. They are large, 5–10 m wide, and can be identified by a microscope. The distinguishing characteristics of the group, as a whole, are that they (1) are nonphotosynthetic, (2) lack tissue differentiation, (3) have cell walls of polysaccharides (chitin), and (4) propagate by **spores** (sexual or asexual).

CLASSIFICATION

Fungi are divided into five classes:

- Myxomycetes, or slime fungi
- Phycomycetes, or aquatic fungi (**algae**)
- Ascomycetes, or sac fungi
- Basidiomycetes, or rusts, smuts, and mushrooms
- Fungi imperfecti, or miscellaneous fungi

Although fungi are limited to only five classes, more than 80,000 known species exist.

IDENTIFICATION

Fungi differ from bacteria in several ways, including size, structural development, methods of reproduction, and cellular organization. They differ from bacteria in another significant way as well: Their biochemical reactions (unlike bacteria) are not important for classification; instead, their structure is used to identify them. Fungi can be examined directly or suspended in liquid, stained, dried, and examined under the microscope, where they can be identified by the appearance (color, texture, and diffusion of pigment) of their mycelia.

One of the tools available to environmental science students and specialists for the fungal identification process is the distinctive terminology used in mycology. Fungi

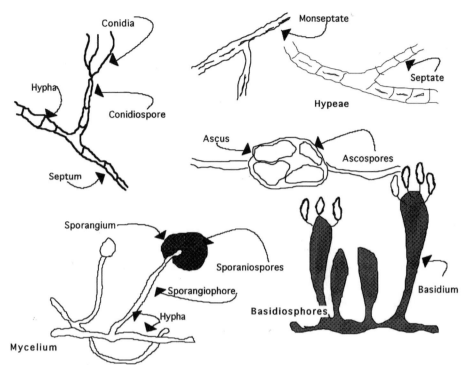

Figure 4.6.   Nomenclature of fungi. Adapted from McKinney, R. E. *Microbiology for Sanitary Engineers*, 1962, p. 36.

go through several phases in their life cycle; their structural characteristics change with each new phase. It is important to become familiar with the key terms defined below. As a further aid in learning how to identify fungi, relate the defined terms to their diagrammatic representations in Figure 4.6.

Definition of Key Terms

1. **Hypha** (pl. **hyphae**)—a tubular cell that grows from the tip and may form many branches. Probably the best-known example of how extensive fungal hyphae can become is an individual honey fungus, *Armalloria ostoyae*, which was discovered in 1992 in Washington State. This particular fungus has been identified as the world's largest living thing; it covers almost 1,500 acres. Estimations have also been made about its individual network of hyphae: it is estimated to be 500 to 1,000 years old.
2. **Mycelium**—branched hyphae, which can become large enough to be seen with the naked eye.
3. **Spore**—reproductive stage of the fungi.
4. **Septate hyphae**—when a filament has crosswalls.
5. **Nonseptate** or **aseptate**—when crosswalls are not present.
6. **Sporangiospores**—spores that form within a sac called a **sporangium**. The sporangia are attached to stalks called **sporangiophores**.

7. **Conidia**—asexual spores that form on specialized hyphae called **conidiophores**. Large **conidia** are called **macroconidia**; small conidia are called **microconidia**.

8. **Sexual spores**—In the fungi division Amastigomycota, four subdivisions are separated on the basis of type of sexual reproductive spores present. (1) Subdivision **Zygomycotina**—consists of nonseptate hyphae and **zygospores**. Zygospores are formed by the union of nuclear material from the hyphae of two different **strains.** (2) Subdivision **Ascomycotina**—fungi in this group are commonly referred to as the **ascomycetes**. They are also called **sac fungi**. They all have septate hyphae. **Ascospores** are the characteristic sexual reproductive spores and are produced in sacs called **asci** (singular, ascus). The mildews and *Penicillium* with asci in long fruiting bodies belong to this group. (3) Subdivision **Basidiomycotina**—consists of mushrooms, puffballs, smuts, rust, and shelf fungi (found on dead trees). The sexual spores of this class are known as **basidiospores**, which are produced on the club-shaped basidia.(4) Subdivision **Deutermycotina**—consists of only one group, the **deuteromycetes**. Members of this class are referred to as the **fungi imperfecti** and include all the fungi that lack sexual means of reproduction.

9. **Budding**—process by which yeasts reproduce.

10. **Blastospores** or buds—spores formed by budding.

CULTIVATION OF FUNGI

Fungi can be grown and studied by cultural methods. However, when culturing fungi, culture media that limit the growth of other microbial types are used; controlling bacterial growth is of particular importance. This can be accomplished by using special agar (culture media) that depresses the pH of the culture medium (usually Sabouraud glucose or maltose agar) to prevent the growth of bacteria. Antibiotics to prevent bacterial growth can also be added to the agar.

REPRODUCTION

As part of their reproductive cycle, fungi produce very small spores that are easily suspended in air and widely dispersed by the wind. Insects and other animals also spread fungal spores. The color, shape, and size of spores are useful in the identification of fungal species.

Reproduction in fungi can be either sexual or asexual. The union of compatible nuclei accomplishes sexual reproduction. Most fungi form specialized asexual and/or sexual spore-bearing structures (fruiting bodies). Some fungal species are self-fertilizing; other species require outcrossing between different but compatible vegetative thalluses (mycelia).

Most fungi are asexual. Asexual spores are often brightly pigmented and give their colony a characteristic color (green, red, brown, black, blue—the blue spores of *Penicillium roquefort* are found in blue or Roquefort cheese).

Asexual reproduction is accomplished in several ways:

1. Vegetative cells may **bud** to produce new organisms. This is very common in the yeasts.
2. A parent cell can divide into two daughter cells.
3. The most common method of asexual reproduction is the production of spores (see Figure 4.7). Several types of asexual spores are common:
    a. A hypha may separate to form cells (**arthrospores**) that behave as spores.
    b. If a thick wall encloses the cells before separation, they are called **chlamydo-spores.**
    c. If budding produces the spores, they are called **blastospores**.
    d. If the spores develop within sporangia (sac), they are called sporangiospores.
    e. If the spores are produced at the sides or tips of the hypha, they are called co-nidiospores.

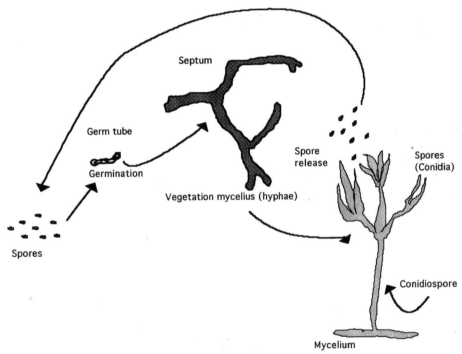

Figure 4.7. Asexual life of penicillum sp. Adapted from Wistreich, G. A., and M. D. Lechtman. Microbiology, 1980, p. 163

NUTRITION AND METABOLISM

Fungi are found wherever organic material is available. They prefer moist habitats and grow best in the dark. Most fungi are **saprophytes**, acquiring their nutrients from dead organic matter, gained when the fungi secrete hydrolytic enzymes, which digest external **substrates**. They are able to use dead organic matter as a source of carbon and energy. Most fungi use glucose and maltose (carbohydrates) and nitrogenous compounds to synthesize their own proteins and other needed materials. Knowing from what materials fungi synthesize their own nutrients in comparison to what bacteria are able to synthesize is important to those who work in the environmental disciplines for understanding the growth requirements of various microorganisms.

Algae

You don't have to be an environmental specialist to understand that algae can be a nuisance. Many ponds, lakes, rivers, and streams in the United States (and elsewhere) are currently undergoing **eutrophication**, the enrichment of an environment with inorganic substances (phosphorus and nitrogen). When eutrophication occurs, when filamentous algae like **Caldophora** break loose in a pond, lake, stream, or river and wash ashore, algae make their stinking, noxious presence known.

For environmental specialists, algae are both a nuisance and a valuable ally. In water treatment, for example, although they are not pathogenic, algae are a nuisance. They grow easily on the walls of troughs and basins, and heavy growth can cause plugging of intakes and screens. Algae release chemicals that often give off undesirable tastes and odors. In wastewater treatment, on the other hand, controlled algae growth can be valuable in long-term **oxidation** ponds, where they aid in the purification process by producing oxygen.

Before beginning a detailed discussion of algae, we define key terms:

DEFINITION OF KEY TERMS

1. **Algae (singular alga, Latin for seaweed)**—a large and diverse assemblage of eukaryotic organisms that lack roots, stems, and leaves but have chlorophyll and other pigments for carrying out oxygen-producing photosynthesis.
2. **Algology** or **phycology**—the study of algae.
3. **Antheridium**—special male reproductive structures where sperm are produced.
4. **Aplanospore**—nonmotile spores produced by sporangia.
5. **Benthic**—algae attached and living on the bottom of a water body.
6. **Binary fission**—nuclear division followed by division of the cytoplasm.
7. **Chloroplasts**—packets that contain **chlorophyll a** and other pigments.
8. **Chrysolaminarin**—the carbohydrate reserve in organisms of division **Chrysophyta**.
9. **Diatoms**—photosynthetic, circular, or oblong chrysophyte cells.
10. **Dinoflagellates**—unicellular, photosynthetic protistan algae.
11. **Epitheca**—the larger part of the **frustule** (**diatoms**).
12. **Euglenoids**—contain **chlorophylls a** and **b** in their chloroplasts; representative genus is *Euglena*.
13. **Fragmentation**—asexual algal reproduction in which the thallus breaks up and each fragmented part grows to form a new thallus.
14. **Frustule**—the distinctive two-piece wall of silica in diatoms.

15. **Hypotheca**—the small part of the frustule (diatoms).
16. **Neustonic**—algae that live at the water–atmosphere interface.
17. **Oogonia**—vegetative cells that function as female sexual structures in algal reproductive system.
18. **Pellicle**—a Euglena structure that allows for turning and flexing of the cell.
19. **Phytoplankton**—made up of algae and small plants.
20. **Plankton**—free-floating, mostly microscopic aquatic organisms.
21. **Planktonic**—algae suspended in water as opposed to attached to and living on the bottom (benthic).
22. **Prototheccosis**—a disease in humans and animals caused by the green algae *Prototheca moriformis*.
23. **Thallus**—the vegetative body of algae.

DESCRIPTION OF ALGAE

Algae are autotrophic, contain the green pigment chlorophyll, and are a form of aquatic plants. They differ from bacteria and fungi in their ability to carry out photosynthesis, the biochemical process that requires sunlight, carbon dioxide, and raw mineral nutrients. Photosynthesis takes place in the chloroplasts, which are usually distinct and visible. They vary in size, shape, distribution, and numbers. In some algal types, the chloroplast may occupy most of the cell space. They usually grow near the surface of water, because light cannot penetrate very far through water. Although in mass (multicellular forms like marine kelp) the unaided eye easily sees them, many are microscopic. Algal cells may be nonmotile, be motile by one or more flagella, or exhibit gliding **motility**, such as diatoms. They occur most commonly in water (fresh and polluted water, as well as saltwater), in which they may be suspended (**planktonic**) phytoplanktons or attached and living on the bottom (benthic). A few algae live at the water–atmosphere interface and are termed **neustonic**. Within the fresh and saltwater environments, they are important primary producers (the start of the food chain for other organisms). During their growth phase, they are important oxygen-generating organisms and constitute a significant portion of the plankton in water.

CHARACTERISTICS USED IN CLASSIFYING ALGAE

According to the five-kingdom system of Whittaker, the algae belong to seven divisions distributed between two kingdoms. Although seven divisions of algae occur, only five divisions are discussed in this text:

Chlorophyta—Green algae
Euglenophyta—Euglenids
Chrysophyta—Golden-brown algae, diatoms
Phaeophyta—Brown algae
Pyrrophyta—Dinoflagellates

The primary classification of algae is based on cellular properties. Several characteristics are used to classify algae, including (1) cellular organization and cell wall structure; (2) the nature of chlorophyll(s) present; (3) the type of motility, if any; (4) the carbon polymers that are produced and stored; and (5) the reproductive structures and methods.

Algal Cell Wall

Algae show considerable diversity in the chemistry and structure of their cell walls. Some algal cell walls are thin, rigid structures usually composed of cellulose modified by the addition of other polysaccharides. In other algae, the cell wall is strengthened by the deposition of calcium carbonate. Other forms have chitin present in the cell wall. Complicating the classification of algal organisms are the Euglenids, which lack cell walls. In **diatoms** the cell wall is composed of silica. The **frustules** (shells) of diatoms have extreme resistance to decay and remain intact for long periods of time, as the fossil records indicate.

Chlorophyll

The principal feature used to distinguish algae from other microorganisms (for example, fungi) is the presence of chlorophyll and other photosynthetic pigments. All algae contain **chlorophyll a**. Some, however, contain other types of chlorophylls. The presence of these additional chlorophylls is characteristic of a particular algal group. Other pigments encountered in algae include fucoxanthin (brown), xanthophylls (yellow), carotenes (orange), phycocyanin (blue), and phycoerythrin (red).

Motility

Many algae have flagella (threadlike appendages). The flagella are locomotor organelles that may be single polar or multiple polar. The *Euglena* is a simple flagellate form with a single polar flagellum. **Chlorophyta** have either two or four polar flagella. **Dinoflagellates** have two flagella of different lengths. In some cases, algae are nonmotile until they form motile gametes (a haploid cell or nucleus) during sexual reproduction. Diatoms do not have flagella, but have gliding motility.

Algal Nutrition/Carbon Polymers Stored

Algae can be either autotrophic or heterotrophic. Most are photoautotrophic; they require only carbon dioxide and light as their principal source of energy and carbon. In the presence of light, algae carry out oxygen-evolving photosynthesis; in the absence of light, algae use oxygen. Chlorophyll and other pigments are used to absorb light energy for photosynthetic cell maintenance and reproduction. One of the key characteristics used in the classification of algal groups is the nature of the **reserve polymer** synthesized as a result of utilizing carbon dioxide present in water.

Algal Reproduction

Algae may reproduce either asexually or sexually. Three types of asexual reproduction occur: binary fission, spores, and fragmentation. In some unicellular algae, **binary fission** occurs where the division of the cytoplasm forms new individuals like the parent cell, following nuclear division. Some algae reproduce through **spores**. These spores are unicellular and germinate without fusing with other cells. In **fragmentation**, the thallus breaks up, and each fragment grows to form a new thallus.

Sexual reproduction can involve union of cells, where eggs are formed within vegetative cells called **oogonia** (which function as female structures), and sperm are produced in a male reproductive organ called **antheridia**. Algal reproduction can also occur through a reduction of chromosome number and/or the union of nuclei.

CHARACTERISTICS OF ALGAL DIVISIONS

Chlorophyta (Green Algae)

The majority of algae found in ponds belong to this group; they also can be found in saltwater and the soil. Several thousand species of green algae are known today. Many are unicellular; others are multicellular filaments or aggregated colonies. The green algae have **chlorophylls a** and **b,** along with specific carotenoids, and they store carbohydrates as starch. Few green algae are found at depths greater than 7–10 meters, largely because sunlight does not penetrate to that depth. Some species have a holdfast structure that anchors them to the bottom of the pond and to other submerged inanimate objects. Green algae reproduce by both sexual and asexual means.

Euglenophyta (Euglenoids)

Euglenoids are a small group of unicellular microorganisms that have a combination of animal and plant properties. They lack a cell wall, possess a gullet, have the ability to ingest food, have the ability to assimilate organic substances, and in some species have no chloroplasts. They occur in fresh, brackish, and saltwaters, and on moist soils. A typical *Euglena* cell is elongated and bounded by a plasma membrane; the absence of a cell wall makes it very flexible in movement. Inside the plasma membrane is a structure called the **pellicle**, which gives the organism a definite form and allows the cell to turn and flex. Euglenoids that are photosynthetic contain **chlorophylls a** and **b**, and they always have a red eyespot (**stigma**) that is sensitive to light. Some euglenoids move about by means of flagella; others move about by means of contracting and expanding motions. The characteristic food supply for euglenoids is a lipopolysaccharide. Reproduction in euglenoids is by simple cell division.

Chrysophyta (Golden-Brown Algae)

The Chrysophyta group is quite large—several thousand diversified members. They differ from green algae and euglenoids in that (1) **chlorophylls a** and **c** are present; (2)

fucoxanthin, a brownish pigment, is present; and (3) they store food in the form of oils and leucosin, a polysaccharide. The combination of yellow pigments, fucoxanthin, and chlorophylls causes most of these algae to appear golden brown. They are also diversified in cell wall chemistry and flagellation. The division is divided into three major classes: golden-brown algae, yellow-brown algae, and diatoms.

Some Chrysophyta lack cell walls; others have intricately patterned coverings external to the plasma membrane, such as walls, plates and scales. The diatoms are the only group that have hard cell walls of pectin, cellulose, or silicon, constructed in two halves (the **epitheca** and the **hypotheca**) called a frustule. Two anteriorly attached flagella are common among Chrysophyta; some have no flagella.

Most Chrysophyta are unicellular or colonial. Asexual cell division is the usual method of reproduction in diatoms; some forms of Chrysophyta can reproduce sexually.

Diatoms have direct significance for humans. Because they make up most of the phytoplankton of the cooler ocean parts, they are the ultimate source of food for fish. Water and wastewater operators understand the importance of their ability to function as indicators of industrial water pollution. As water quality indicators, their specific tolerances to environmental parameters such as pH, nutrients, nitrogen, concentration of salts, and temperature have been compiled.

Phaeophyta (Brown Algae)

With the exception of a few freshwater species, all algal species of this division exist in marine environments as seaweed. They are a highly specialized group, consisting of multicellular organisms that are sessile (attached and not free-moving). These algae contain essentially the same pigments seen in the golden-brown algae, but they appear brown because of the predominance of and the masking effect of a greater amount of fucoxanthin. Brown algal cells store food as the carbohydrate laminarin and some lipids. Brown algaes reproduce asexually.

Rhodophyta (Dinoflagellates)

The principal members of this division are the dinoflagellates, which include a diverse group of biflagellated and nonflagellated unicellular, eukaryotic organisms. The dinoflagellates occupy a variety of aquatic environments, with the majority living in marine habitats. Most of these organisms have a heavy cell wall composed of cellulose-containing plates. They store food as starches, fats, and oils. These algae have **chlorophylls a** and **c** and several xanthophylls. The most common form of reproduction in dinoflagellates is cell division, but sexual reproduction has also been observed.

To this point, the chemical and microbial environmental contaminants we have discussed are the waterborne types most commonly found in and affecting water and wastewater treatment operations. However, while chemical contaminants are limited, microbes are not; they are ubiquitous—everywhere. The environmental science practitioner needs a well-rounded knowledge of not only microbial contaminants that are common to water bodies, water treatment systems, and water waste streams, but also those that inhabit our air and soil. Case Study 4.1 contains information on a few of the microbes common in our air (some of which also have a significant interface with our water and soil), especially indoor air; it discusses some of the environmental health problems they present.

Case Study 4.1. Airborne Particulate Matter

Bacteria, pollen, fungal and plant spores, and viruses are all airborne particles. Air conditioners and humidifiers have been identified as devices where pathogenic organisms may concentrate and later be released as concentrated viable aerosols. A variety of biological contaminants can cause significant illness and health risks. These include infections from airborne exposures to viruses that cause colds and influenza and from bacteria that cause tuberculosis (TB) and Legionnaires' disease. They also include respiratory ailments such as asthma, humidifier fever, hypersensitivity pneumonitis, and chronic allergic rhinitis. Such ailments may be caused by exposures to mold (fungi), fungal glucans (glucose residues), mycotoxins, bacterial endotoxins, microbial volatiles, or organic dust.

One of the classic and well-known cases of biological contamination of indoor air was the outbreak of Legionnaires' disease among some of those who attended the Pennsylvania American Legion convention in Philadelphia in 1976. The Centers for Disease Control (CDC) conducted an extensive investigation of this incident and isolated the causal organism, the bacterium *Legionella pneumophila*. The CDC also identified the most probable mode of transmission: contaminated air entrained in one of the air handling systems that served the hotel lobby. Legionnaires' disease causes pneumonia-like symptoms. Though it has a low attack rate (about 5%), mortality among those affected is high (15% to 20%).

Legionella pneumophila is widely present in the environment and commonly isolated from surface waters and soil. Relatively resistant to chlorine, it passes through most water treatment systems. Its optimum growth temperature is 33°C and above. As a result, significant growth can occur in cooling tower systems, evaporative condensers, domestic and institutional water heaters, spas, and hot tubs. It becomes entrained in a building's air supply via drift from cooling towers and evaporative condensers. When bacteria levels are high and *L. pneumophila* is aerosolized, disease can attack a susceptible population. The various risk factors identified for Legionnaire's disease include middle age, smoking, alcohol consumption, and travel.

Protozoa and Other Microorganisms

PROTOZOA

The protozoa ("first animals") are a large group of **eukaryotic** organisms (more than 50,000 known species that have adapted a form or cell to serve as the entire body). All protozoans are single-celled organisms. Typically, they lack cell walls, but have a plasma membrane that is used to take in food and discharge waste. They can exist as solitary or independent organisms (the stalked ciliates such as *Vorticella* sp., for example) or can colonize, like the sedentary *Carchesium* sp. Protozoa are microscopic and get their name because they employ the same type of feeding strategy as animals. Most are harmless, but some are parasitic. Some forms have two life stages: active **trophozoites** (capable of feeding) and dormant **cysts**.

As unicellular eukaryotes, protozoa cannot be easily defined, because they are diverse and, in most cases, only distantly related to each other. As stated previously, protozoa are distinguished from bacteria by their eukaryotic nature and their usually larger size. Unlike algae, protozoa obtain energy and nutrients by taking in organic molecules, detritus, or other protists rather than from photosynthesis. Each protozoan is a complete organism and contains the facilities for performing all the body functions for which vertebrates have many organ systems.

Like bacteria, protozoa depend on environmental conditions (the protozoan community quickly responds to changing physical and chemical characteristics of the environment), reproduction, and availability of food for their existence. Relatively large microorganisms, protozoans range in size from 4 m to about 500 m. They can both consume bacteria (limit growth) and feed on organic matter (degrade waste).

Interest in protozoa is high among water treatment specialists, because certain types can cause disease. In the United States, the most important of the pathogenic parasitic protozoans is *Giardia lamblia*, which causes a disease known as **giardiasis** (discussed in detail later). Two other parasitic protozoans that carry waterborne disease are *Entamoeba histolytica* (amoebic dysentery) and *Cryptosporida* (Cryptosporidosis).

To address the increasing problem of waterborne diseases, the U.S. Environmental Protection Agency (EPA) implemented its Surface Water Treatment Rule on June 29, 1989, in part because of the occurrence of *Giardia* and *Cryptosporidium* spp. in surface water supplies. The rule requires both filtration and disinfection of all surface water supplies as a means of primarily controlling *Giardia* spp. and enteric viruses. Since implementation of this rule, the EPA has also recognized that *Cryptosporidium* spp. is an agent of waterborne disease.

Classification

Protozoa are divided into four groups based on their method of motility. The **Mastigophora** are motile by means of one or more flagella, the **Ciliophora** by means of shortened modified flagella called **cilia**, and the **Sarcodina** by means of amoeboid movement; the nonmotile Sporozoa are the last group. All four groups are listed in Table 4.3, but for the purposes of this text, only the first three are discussed in detail.

Table 4.3.   Classification of Protozoans

Group	Common Name	Movement	Reproduction
Mastigophora	Flagellates	Flagella	Asexual
Ciliophora	Ciliates	Cili	Asexual by transverse fission Sexual by conjugation
Sarcodina	Amoebas	Pseudopodia	Asexual and sexual
Sporozoa	Sporozoans	Nonmotile	Asexual and sexual

Mastigophora (Flagellates)

These protozoans are mostly unicellular, lack specific shape (have an extremely flexible plasma membrane that allows for the flowing movement of cytoplasm), and possess flagella. The flagella, which can move in whiplike motion, are used for locomotion, as sense receptors, and to attract food.

These organisms are common in both fresh and marine waters. The group is subdivided into the **Phytomastigopherea**, most of which contain chlorophyll and are thus plant-like. A characteristic species of Phytomastigopherea is the *Euglena* sp., often associated with high or increasing levels of nitrogen and phosphate in the treatment process. A second subdivision of Mastigophora is the **Zoomastigopherea,** which are animal-like and nonpigmented.

Ciliophora (Ciliates)

The ciliates are the most advanced and structurally complex of all protozoans. Movement and food-getting are accomplished with short, hairlike structures called cilia that are present in at least one stage of the organism's life cycle. There are three groups of ciliates (1) free-swimmers, (2) crawlers, and (3) stalked. The majority are free-living. They are usually solitary, but some are colonial and others are sessile. They are unique among protozoa in having two kinds of nuclei: a micronucleus and a macronucleus. The micronucleus is concerned with sexual reproduction. The macronucleus is involved with metabolism and the production of RNA for cell growth and function.

Ciliates are covered by a pellicle, which may act as a thick armor. In some species, the pellicle may be very thin. The cilia are short and usually arranged in rows. Their structure is comparable to flagella, except that cilia are shorter. Cilia may cover the surface of the animal or may be restricted to banded regions.

Sarcodina

Members of this group have fewer organelles and are simpler in structure than the ciliates and flagellates. Sarcodina move about by the formation of flowing protoplasmic projections called **pseudopodia.** The formation of pseudopodia is commonly referred to as **amoeboid movement**. The **amoebae** are well known for this mode of action (see Figure 4.8). The pseudopodia not only provide a means of locomotion, but also serve as a means of feeding; this is accomplished when the organism puts out the pseudopodium to enclose the food. Most amoebas feed on algae, bacteria, protozoa, and **rotifers**.

To help you understand a specific biological process and its importance in actual use, Case Study 4.2 provides a description of the wastewater-activated biosolids process.

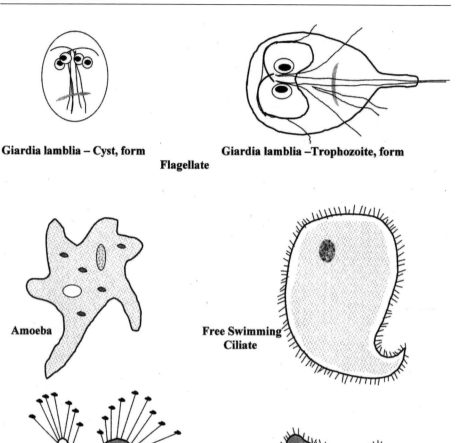

Giardia lamblia – Cyst, form

Giardia lamblia –Trophozoite, form

Flagellate

Amoeba

**Free Swimming
Ciliate**

Suctoria

Stalked - Ciliate

Figure 4.8.   Amoebae and other protozoa.

Case Study 4.2 Activated Biosolids Process (Wastewater Treatment)

The activated biosolids (sludge) process originated in England. The name comes from the production of an activated mass of microorganisms capable of aerobically stabilizing the organic content of the waste. In this process, contact with bacteria, protozoa, fungi, and other small organisms such as rotifiers and nematodes occurs. The bacteria are the most important group of microorganisms; they are responsible for the structural and functional activity of the activated biosolids "floc." The bacteria and other organisms must be brought into contact with the organic matter in the wastewater. This is usually accomplished through rapid mixing provided by large mixers, a process augmented by aeration. Agitation and aeration work hand in hand to mix the returned biosolids with effluent from primary treatment, keep the activated biosolids in suspension, and supply oxygen for the biochemical reactions necessary for wastewater stabilization.

The activated biosolids process is typified by the successive development of protozoa and mature floc particles. This succession is indicated by the type of dominant protozoa present. At the start of the activated biosolids process (or upon recovery from an upset condition), the amoebae dominate. As the process continues (uninterrupted or without upset), small populations of bacteria begin to grow in logarithmic fashion, which, as the population increases, develop into "mixed liquor." When this occurs, the **flagellates** dominate. When the biosolids attain an age of about three days, lightly dispersed floc particles begin to form, and bacteria increase. At this point, the **free-swimming ciliates** dominate. The process goes on. Floc particles begin to stabilize, taking on irregular shapes, and start to show filamentous growth. Then the crawling ciliates dominate. Eventually, mature floc particles develop and increase in size, and large numbers of **crawling** and **stalked ciliates** are present. When this occurs, the succession process has reached its terminal point.

The succession of protozoan and mature floc particle development details the occurrence of phases of development in a step-by-step progression. This is also the case when protozoan succession is based on other factors, such as dissolved oxygen and food availability.

Probably the best way to understand protozoan succession based on dissolved oxygen and food availability is to view the wastewater treatment plant's aeration basin as a "stream within a container." Using the **saprobity system** to classify the various phases of the activated sludge process in relation to the self-purification process that takes place in a stream, we can see a clear relationship between the two processes based on available dissolved oxygen and food supply. The following explanation should be useful.

The stream self-purifies and stabilizes over distance. That is, as the polluted (low dissolved oxygen and food supply) stream flows from the point of pollution, it stabilizes. In the aeration basin, waste stabilization is based on time (biosolids age), not distance. Each condition described in the saprobity system is experienced in the aeration basin, with the exception of the last phase.

In the stream, a number of distinct zones of pollution can be identified according to their degree of pollution and content of dissolved oxygen, as well

(continued)

Case Study 4.2 (*continued*)

as the types of biotic indicators present. The zones used to describe the extent of these conditions include the following:

1. *Polysaprobic Zone*—point in the stream where pollution occurs and dissolved oxygen declines.
2. *Alpha Mesoprobic Zone*—point in the stream where pollution is heavy and dissolved oxygen is low.
3. *Beta Mesoprobic Zone*—point in the stream where pollution is moderate and dissolved oxygen is increasing.
4. *Oligosaprobic Zone*—point where pollution is low and dissolved oxygen levels are almost normal.
5. *Xenosaprobic Zone*—point in the stream where pollution is nonexistent and dissolved oxygen is normal.

Except for the last zone, the zones and their associated conditions of pollution and dissolved oxygen contents are similar to the environment within the activated biosolids aeration basins.

Any change in the relative numbers of bacteria in the activated biosolids process has a corresponding change in microorganism population. Decreases in bacteria increase competition between protozoa and result in succession of dominant groups of protozoans.

The degree of success or failure of protozoa to capture bacteria depends on several factors. For example, those with more advanced locomotion capability are able to capture more bacteria. Individual protozoan feeding mechanisms are also important in the competition for bacteria. At the beginning of the activated sludge process, amoebae and flagellates are the first protozoan groups to appear in large numbers. They are aided in surviving on lower quantities of bacteria because their energy requirements are lower than other protozoan types. Since few bacteria are present, competition for dissolved substrates is low. However, as the bacteria population increases, these protozoans are not able to compete for available food. This is when the next group of protozoans enters the scene: the **free-swimming** protozoans.

The free-swimming protozoans take advantage of the large populations of bacteria because they are better equipped with food-gathering mechanisms than the amoebae and flagellates. The free-swimmers are important not only because of their insatiable appetites for bacteria, but also in floc formation. By secreting polysaccharides and mucoproteins that are absorbed by bacteria, which make the bacteria "sticky" through biological agglutination (biological gluing together), they stick together, and more important, stick to floc. Large quantities of floc are prepared for removal from secondary effluent and are either returned to aeration basins or wasted.

The crawlers and stalked ciliates succeed the free-swimmers. The free-swimmers are replaced in part because of the increasing level of mature floc that retards their movement. The environment provided by the presence of mature floc is more suited to the needs of the crawlers and stalked ciliates. The crawlers and stalked ciliates also aid in floc formation by adding weight to floc particles, thus enabling removals.

Protozoa are important members of the microorganism population of the activated sludge process in wastewater treatment. Not only do they consume and thus remove bacteria from the activated sludge and secondary effluent, they also help with nitrification. In addition, the protozoans act as parameters of sludge health and effluent quality. By simple examination and identification of the protozoan population in activated biosolids, determining whether or not loading (i.e., a quantity of material added to the process at one time) is at acceptable or unacceptable levels is possible. The presence of a particular species of protozoa can also indicate whether or not the process is operating correctly. The protozoan varieties indicate changes taking place in the strength and composition of the wastewater.

The importance of using protozoans as parameters to indicate biosolids health and effluent quality cannot be overemphasized. The following parameters demonstrate how protozoan indicators are used to determine process operation quality:

- Healthy biosolids is indicated when large varieties of crawlers and stalked ciliates are observed. This condition can indicate to the wastewater specialist that the process is producing a high-quality effluent with BOD ranging from 1 to 10 mg/L.
- Intermediate biosolids is indicated by a preponderance of all three ciliated groups. When this occurs, the indication is that the effluent is of satisfactory quality, with a BOD ranging from 11 to 30 mg/L.
- Poor biosolids is indicated when the population is dominated by free-swimmers and flagellates. The effluent is generally turbid and of low quality, with BOD at levels greater than 30 mg/L.

The indicators of effluent quality can be used in other ways. A significant shift from the patterns described may indicate that the sludge age is significantly high and/or the presence of excessive nutrient levels (nitrogen or phosphate). The absence of (or too few) protozoans in activated sludge processes can also be indicative of process problems. For example, when the protozoan population is too low or absent, the F/M ratio may be too high (an overloaded condition).

FACTORS AFFECTING PROTOZOAN POPULATION

The population, activity, and diversity of the protozoa in activated biosolids and other treatment processes are affected by environmental factors. The availability of nontoxic bacteria is important. The dissolved oxygen levels are important even though the protozoans are generally aerobic. (Dissolved oxygen content is indicative of degree of pollution in the system.) Toxicants like chemical surfactants affect the plasma membrane and enzyme systems of protozoans; using surfactants could also lead to the development of bacteria that are harmful to protozoa. pH level is also important. Most protozoans have an optimum upper and lower pH range. Shifting pH may favor one variety of protozoa over the other. Significant amounts of rainfall can affect the protozoa; significant decreases in overall population can occur through hydraulic washout.

ROTIFERS

Rotifers make up a well-defined group of the smallest, simplest multicellular microorganisms and are found in nearly all aquatic habitats. They are strict aerobes that range in size from about 0.1 to 0.8 nm. Often associated with aerobic biological processes in wastewater treatment plants, they are seen either grazing on bacteria or attached to debris by their forked tail or toe (see Figure 4.9). Rotifers promote microfloral activity and decomposition, enhance oxygen penetration in activated sludge and trickling filters, and recycle minerals in each. Most descriptions apply to the female, because the male is much smaller and structurally simpler. Rotifers form into various shapes—spherical, sac-shaped, and/or worm-shaped. Their forms are composed of three zones. At their anterior end, they possess actively moving cilia that frequently beat in a circular motion for motility and food gathering. The main body, below the head, possesses a thick cuticle that terminates at the foot end. The foot possesses adhesive (cement) glands and toes for attachment to substratum. Rotifers are unique in that they can chew their food by using a modified muscular pharynx called a **mastax**. Rotifers require high levels of dissolved oxygen; thus their presence indicates water with a high level of biological purity.

Figure 4.9. *Philodina*, a common rotifer.

Rotifers possess reproductive organs in the form of gonads. They are separated into two orders according to the number of gonads they possess. For example, in the order **Monogononta**, the rotifers possess one gonad; in the order **Digononta**, they possess two gonads.

Movement by rotifers is accomplished by either the free-swimming or crawling mode. Free-swimmers move by the beating action of rings of cilia on the epidermal area of the head. When each ring of cilia beats, it gives the impression of a wheel with spokes. The frequency of this beating motion is quite high. Rotifers of this type move in a forward direction at a slow pace.

Rotifers that move using a crawling motion employ an interesting technique. While attached by adhesive glands and toes to an old substratum, the rotifer extends its body. While extending, the rotifer's head uses its adhesive glands to attach to a new substratum, then the toes release from the old substratum. The body contracts so that the foot reaches around and attaches to the substratum close to the head. The head then releases and the body extends to its normal posture.

Rotifers feed on algae, bacteria, protozoa, and dead organisms.

CRUSTACEANS

Because they are important members of freshwater zooplankton, microscopic **crustaceans** are of interest to water and wastewater specialists. These microscopic organisms are characterized by a rigid shell structure. They are multicellular animals that are strict aerobes, and as primary producers, they feed on bacteria and algae. They are important as a source of food for fish. In addition, microscopic crustaceans have been used to clarify algae-laden effluents from oxidation ponds.

WORMS

Along with inhabiting organic muds, **worms** (**nematodes** and **flatworms**) also inhabit biological slimes. Microscopic in size, they range in length from 0.5 to 3 mm and in diameter from 0.01 to 0.05 mm. Most species are similar in appearance. They have bodies covered by cuticle, are cylindrical and nonsegmented, and taper at both ends.

Aquatic flatworms (improperly named because they are not all flat) feed primarily on algae, and because of their aversion to light, they are found in the lower depths of pools. Surface waters that are grossly polluted with organic matter (especially domestic sewage) have fauna capable of thriving in very low concentrations of oxygen. A few species of tubificid worms dominate this environment. The bottoms of severely polluted streams can be literally covered with a writhing mass of these tubificids.

One variety, the *Tubifix* (commonly known as sludge worms), are small, slender, reddish worms that normally range in length from 25 to about 50 mm. They are burrowers; their posterior end protrudes to obtain nutrients. When found in streams, *Tubifix* are indicators of pollution.

Enzymes

In many environmental treatment processes, biological activities are used to degrade organic matter. To do this, the environments in these processes must accommodate the appropriate types of microorganisms capable of performing the organic degradation function.

Enzymes present in the microorganisms and the surrounding environmental media (water, air, and soil) are the essential biological **catalyst**s that enable microorganisms to break down organics. A catalyst is defined as a substance that modifies and increases the rate of chemical reaction without being consumed in the process.

Microorganisms must first acclimate to their environments before they can produce the enzymes they need to break down organics. Specific enzymes break down different organics. In this breaking down process, the enzyme works to speed up the rate of hydrolysis of complex organic compounds and the rate of oxidation of simple compounds by decreasing the activation energy required.

The living cell is the site of tremendous biochemical activity called *metabolism* (discussed in detail later), which is the process of chemical and physical change that goes on continually in living organisms. Conversion of food to usable energy, buildup of new tissue, replacement of old tissue, disposal of waste products, and reproduction are all activities characteristic of life.

For illustrative purposes, consider the activities that characterize life as being similar to the activities that take place on the assembly line in a factory. Breslow (1990) described this correlation when he called enzymes the "machines of life." Breslow's metaphor of the machine-like enzyme is fitting when we take into account how an enzyme can repeat a particular process several times a second, or even faster (like a machine), with similar results. Taking this concept a step further for the purpose of clarity, consider the enzyme as a small machine: raw material goes in, and finished product comes out. Just like a machine, an enzyme is specialized. Finally, when one considers a living cell as a small factory containing thousands of different types of specialized machines (enzymes), enzyme function becomes clear.

The phenomenon of **catalysis** makes possible biochemical reactions necessary for all life processes. Catalysis is defined as the modification of the rate of a chemical reaction by a catalyst. The catalysts of biochemical reactions are enzymes; they are responsible for bringing about all of the chemical reactions in living organisms. Without enzymes, these reactions take place at a rate far too slow to keep pace with metabolism.

THE NATURE OF ENZYMES

Enzymes are essentially proteins formed by the polymerization of some or all of the amino acids; 20 amino acids are found in proteins. They are high molecular weight compounds (ranging from 10,000 to 2,000,000) made up of chains of amino acids linked together by peptide bonds. In the overall linking process, a water molecule is removed between the carboxyl group of one amino acid and the amino group of the next one. Several steps are involved in the actual sequence used for synthesis of proteins, including enzymes, so that chemical energy can be supplied from other molecules.

Most enzymes are pure proteins. However, some require the participation of small nonprotein groups, which may be organic or inorganic, before their catalytic activity can be exerted. These nonprotein groups are called **cofactors** (the activator). In some cases, these cofactors are nonprotein metallic ion activators (ions of iron) that form a functional part of the enzyme. When the cofactor and the protein part (the **apoenzyme**) of the enzyme are present, the entire active complex is called the **holoenzyme:**

$$\text{Apoenzyme} + \text{Cofactor} = \text{Holoenzyme} \qquad (4.1)$$

The structural nomenclature of enzymes is affected by the way in which the cofactor is attached to the apoenzyme (see Figure 4.10). For example, if the cofactor is firmly attached to the apoenzyme, it is called a **prosthetic group**. When the cofactor is loosely attached to the cofactor, it is called a coenzyme.

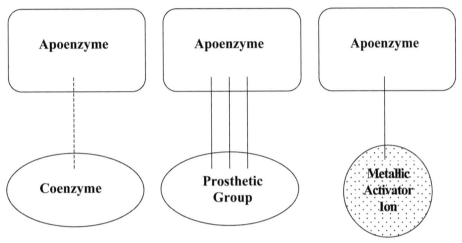

Figure 4.10. Holoenzymes showing apoenzymes and various types of cofactor. Adapted from Witkowski and Power, 1975, p. 7

ACTION OF ENZYMES

Keep in mind that enzymes increase the speed of reactions, without themselves undergoing any permanent chemical change (they do not alter their equilibrium constants). They are neither used up in the reaction, nor do they appear as products of the reaction. This basic enzymatic reaction process is:

$$\text{Substrate + Enzyme (catalyzes reaction) Product + Enzyme} \qquad (4.2)$$

In the enzymatic reaction process, note that the end product includes the enzyme, which was not altered or destroyed. The enzyme functions by combining in a highly specific way with its **substrate**, changing the substrate, without being changed itself.

Much research has been devoted to trying to determine how enzymes lower the activation energy of reactions. What is clear is that enzymes bring substrates together at the enzyme's **active site** to form an **enzyme-substrate complex** (see Figure 4.11).

In the enzyme-substrate complex, weak bonds attach the substrate to several points in the active site of the enzyme. This bringing together of enzyme and substrate allows for their concentration, which lowers the activation energy required to complete the reaction. Note that most of these reactions take place at relatively low temperatures ranging from 0° to 36°C.

Enzyme

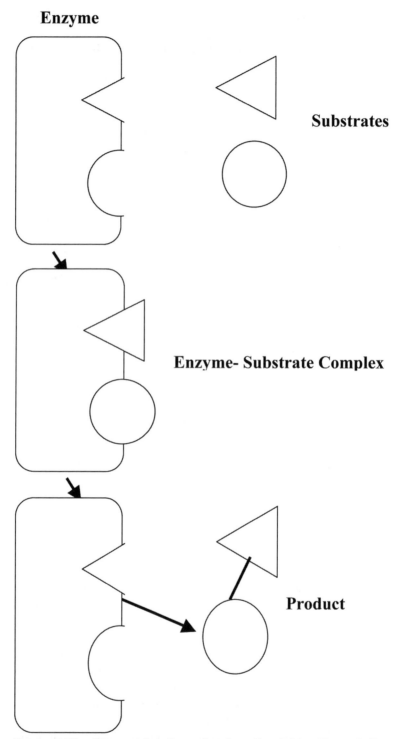

Substrates

Enzyme- Substrate Complex

Product

Figure 4.11. Enzyme function showing the interaction of the substrate and enzyme with the resulting product. Adapted from Prescott et al., 1993, p. 141

EFFICIENCY, SPECIFICITY, AND CLASSIFICATION OF ENZYMES

Enzymes are extremely efficient. Only minute quantities of an enzyme are required to accomplish at low temperatures what normally would require, by ordinary chemical means, high temperatures and powerful reagents. For example, one ounce of pepsin can digest almost two tons of egg whites in a few hours, whereas without the enzyme, digestion would take about 15 tons of strong acid 36 hours at high temperature.

Along with being efficient and extremely reactive, enzymes are characterized by a high degree of **specificity**. That is, just as a key will not fit or unlock each and every lock, enzymes require an exact molecular fit between the enzyme and the substrate.

By 1956, the number of known enzymes was rapidly increasing. In 1961, the International Union of Biochemistry published an enzyme classification scheme that is universally used today. With the exception of the originally studied enzymes (rennin, pepsin, and trypsin), most enzyme names end in *ase*. Standards of enzyme nomenclature, initiated by the International Union of Biochemistry, recommend that enzymes be named for both the substrate acted upon and the type of reaction catalyzed.

EFFECTS OF ENVIRONMENT ON ENZYME ACTIVITY

Several factors affect the rate at which enzymatic reactions proceed. They include substrate concentration, enzyme concentration, pH, temperature, and the presence of activators or inhibitors.

Substrate Concentration

At low substrate concentrations, an enzyme makes product slowly. However, if the amount of enzyme is kept constant and the substrate concentration is gradually increased, the reaction velocity increases until it reaches a maximum (usually expressed in terms of the rate of product formation). After this point, increases in substrate concentration will not increase the velocity, because the available enzyme molecules are binding substrate and converting it into product as rapidly as possible—the enzyme has reached the saturation point and is operating at maximal velocity. To gain an in-depth understanding of this enzyme saturation process, you must study in detail saturation kinetics (Michaelis-Menten kinetics), a study beyond the scope of this text. However, a fundamental appreciation of what is occurring during the enzyme-saturated-with-substrate phenomenon can be obtained by studying the graphical representation in Figure 4.12.

In Figure 4.12, you can see that the maximum velocity (V max) is the rate of product formation when the enzyme is saturated with substrate and making product as fast as possible. The **Michaelis constant (Km)** is the substrate concentration required for the enzyme to operate at half its maximal velocity. Theoretically, when the maximum velocity has been reached, all the available enzyme has been converted to enzyme-substrate complex. This point on the graph is designated **Vmax**. By using this maximum velocity and an equation, Michaelis developed from measurable data a set of mathematical expressions to calculate enzyme activity in terms of reaction speed.

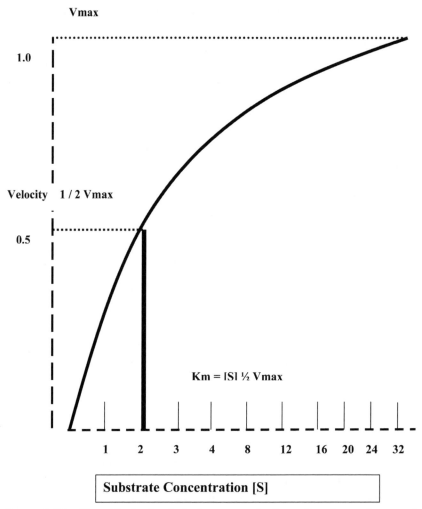

Figure 4.12.   The effect of substrate concentration—the dependence of Velocity on Substrate Concentration for a simple One-Substrate Enzyme-catalyzed Reaction. This substrate curve fits the Michaelis equation, which relates reaction velocity (v) to the substrate concentration (S).

Enzyme Concentration

To study the effect of increasing the enzyme concentration on the reaction rate, the reaction must be independent of the substrate concentration. Any change in the amount of product formed over a specific timeframe depends on the level of enzyme present.

pH

Enzymes also change activity with alterations in pH. The most favorable pH value (the point where the enzyme is most active) is known as the *optimum pH*. When the pH is much higher or lower than the enzyme's optimum value, activity slows, and the enzyme is damaged.

Temperature

Enzymes also have temperature optima for maximum activity. Like most chemical reactions, the rate of an enzyme-catalyzed reaction increases with temperature. However, if the temperature rises too much above the optimum, an enzyme's structure becomes denatured (disrupted), and its activity is lost. The temperature optima of a microorganism's enzymes often reflect the temperature of its habitat. Bacteria that grow best at high temperatures demonstrate this; they often have enzymes with high temperature optima.

Inhibitors

Enzyme inhibitors are substances that slow down (or in some cases stop) catalysis. An inhibitor competes with the substrate at an enzyme's catalytic site and prevents the enzyme from forming product.

Metabolic Transformations

Between initial absorption and final excretion, many substances are chemically converted by the organism. The assembly-line activity that occurs in microorganisms during the processing of raw materials into finished products is called **metabolic transformation**. Enzymes mediate metabolic transformations. Environmental science students and practitioners must have an understanding of these metabolic transformations.

GENERAL METABOLISM

Metabolism is derived from the Greek word *metabole*, which means "to change." Change is what metabolism is all about. In attempting to further characterize a living organism's metabolic process(es) (its metabolism), several descriptions are available. For instance, in an organizational sense, an organism's metabolism (with its associated processes) is its capability to self-organize. Metabolism can also be defined as the total chemical and physical processes by which the functional and nutritional activities of an organism are maintained. In scientific terms, metabolism is generally referred to as the entire set of chemical reactions by which a cell produces and forms the various molecules it needs to maintain itself. In simple terms, metabolism can be characterized as the flow of energy through the organism.

Any definition or explanation of an organism's metabolism must include an explanation of the metabolic processes involved. These processes are well known and documented. For instance, the two general categories of metabolism are catabolism and anabolism. In **catabolic** reactions, complex compounds are broken down, with a release of energy. These reactions are linked to **anabolic** reactions, which result in the formation of important molecules. As a result of chemicals and associated reactions, biological cells are dynamic structures that are continually undergoing change.

During metabolism, the cell takes in nutrients (discussed later), converts them into cell components, and excretes waste into the external environment (see Figure 4.13). Microbial cells are made up of chemical substances, and when the cell grows, these chemical constituents increase in amount. The chemical substances cells need come from the environment; that is, from outside the cell. Once inside the cell, the basic constituents of which the cell is composed transform these substances.

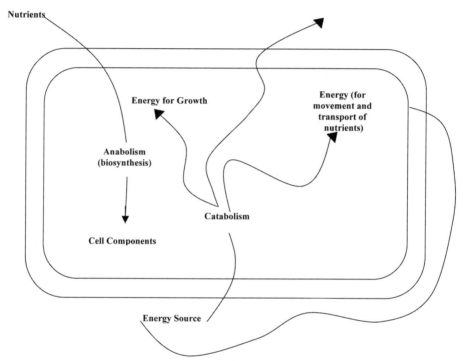

Figure 4.13. A simplified view of cell metabolism. Adapted from Brock, T. D., and M. T. Madigan. *Biology of Microorganisms*, 1991

Metabolic reactions require energy for the uptake of various nutrients and for locomotion in motile species. Microorganisms are placed in metabolic classes based on the source of energy they use. In describing these classes, the term **troph** is used (from the Greek meaning "to feed"). Thus, microorganisms that use inorganic materials as energy sources are called **lithotrophs** (*litho* is from the Greek for rock). Microorganisms that use organic chemicals as energy sources are called **heterotrophs** (feeding from sources other than oneself). Microorganisms that use light as an energy source are called **phototrophs** (*photo* is from the Greek for light). Most bacteria obtain energy from chemicals taken from the environment and are called **chemotrophs**.

Although an in-depth discussion of the metabolic processes of all microorganisms is beyond the scope of this text, environmental science practitioners should be well-grounded in the fundamental concepts that we cover briefly in the following discussion. In particular, we provide information to enhance familiarity with cell metabolism and the basics of biochemistry of microbial growth.

The chemical reactions occurring in cells are accompanied by changes in energy. A chemical reaction can occur with the release of free energy (called **exergonic**) or with the consumption of free energy (called **endergonic**). The free energy of these reactions can be expressed quantitatively.

Before a chemical reaction can take place, the reactants in a chemical reaction must first be activated. This requires energy. The amount of activation energy required can be decreased by the use of a catalyst, and the catalysts of living cells are enzymes. As stated in the preceding section, enzymes are proteins that are highly specific in the reactions that they catalyze.

The utilization of chemical energy in living organisms involves oxidation-**reduction** reactions, which includes the transfer of electrons from one reactant to another. Oxidation is defined as the removal of an electron or electrons from a substance. A reduction is defined as the addition of an electron (or electrons) to a substance. In the oxidation-reduction reaction, a transfer of electrons from one reactant to another takes place. The energy source, which is the **electron donor**, moves up one or more electrons, which are transferred to an **electron acceptor**. In this process, the electron donor is oxidized and the electron acceptor is reduced. One of the most common electron acceptors of living organisms is molecular **oxygen**. The ability of a compound to accept or release electrons is expressed quantitatively by its **reduction potential**.

The transfer of electrons from donor to acceptor in a cell involves one or more intermediates, referred to as **electron carriers**. Some electron carriers are freely diffusible, transferring electrons from one place to another in the cell; others are firmly attached to enzymes in the cell membrane.

Two of the most common electron carriers are the coenzymes **NAD** and **NADP**. NAD^+ (mincotinamide-adenine dinucleotide) and $NADP^+$ (NAD-phosphate) are freely diffusible carriers of hydrogen atoms and always transfer two hydrogen atoms to the next carrier in the chain.

In most cases, biological reactions are catalyzed by specific enzymes, which can react only with a limited range of substrates. Oxidation-reduction reactions generally proceed in three stages: (1) removal of electrons from the primary donor, (2) transfer of electrons through a series of electron carriers, and (3) addition of electrons to the terminal acceptor. Each step in the reaction is catalyzed by a different enzyme, each of which binds to its substrate and its specific coenzyme. After a coenzyme has performed its chemical functions in one reaction, it can diffuse through the cytoplasm until it attaches to another enzyme that requires the coenzyme to return to its original form—then the process can be repeated again.

Neither chemicals from the environment nor sunlight can be used directly to fuel a cell's energy-requiring processes. Therefore, the cell must have ways of converting sources of energy into a usable form. In the presence of sunlight and certain chemicals, cells can make specific high-energy compounds with which they can satisfy their energy demands; one of these important compounds is **adenosine triphosphate (ATP)**.

The process of making ATP involves combining adenosine diphosphate (ADP) and inorganic phosphate (**Pi**):

$$ADP + Pi + ENERGY \Rightarrow ATP \tag{4.3}$$

The energy required for this reaction can be obtained in one of three ways—**photosynthetic phosphorylation** (the changing of an organic substance into an organic phosphate), **substrate phosphorylation**, or **oxidative phosphorylation** (occurs on the membranes of mesosomes and related structures of procaryotes)—depending on the source of energy.

In photosynthetic phosphorylation, the required amount of energy is absorbed by chlorophyll as light. For example, photosynthesis supplies the blue-green bacteria, algae, and plants with the ATP needed for synthesis (the formation of a compound from its constituents) of all materials.

The catabolic reactions by which organic compounds are converted into other organic compounds are called substrate reactions. As stated previously, a substrate is the substance acted upon by the enzyme. During some substrate reactions, energy-rich bonds are formed, and the energy can be used to combine ADP and inorganic phosphates into ATP. These molecules of ATP are formed by **substrate phosphorylation**, which occurs in the cytoplasm of cells. During this process, ATP is synthesized during specific enzymatic steps in the catabolism of the organic compound. A process called fermentation (discussed in the following section) produces this ATP.

GLYCOLYSIS

Glycolysis is one of three phases in the catabolism of glucose to carbon and water. (The other two phases, the **Krebs cycle** and the **electron transport system**, are discussed later.) Glycolysis can occur under both aerobic and anaerobic conditions. Some of the anaerobic processes are called **fermentation**. Fermentation is a process whereby the anaerobic decomposition of organic compounds takes place. These compounds serve both ultimate electron donors and acceptors. Thus, fermentable substances often yield both oxidizable and reducible metabolites (organic compounds produced by metabolism).

The energy-converting metabolism (fermentation) in which the substrate is metabolized without the involvement of an external oxidizing agent is more easily understood by looking at a **metabolic pathway**. For example, in some bacteria, the fermentation of glucose begins with a pathway called **glycolysis**.

Glycolysis (sometimes referred to as the **Embden-Meyerhof-Parnas pathway**—EMP pathway) involves the breakdown or splitting of glucose (sugar) in a catabolic reaction that converts one molecule of glucose into two molecules of the end product, **pyruvic acid**. In this pathway, energy from energy-yielding (exergonic) reactions is used to phosphorylate ADT—that is, ATP is synthesized from ADP, an example of substrate phosphorylation, where energy from a chemical reaction is used directly for the synthesis of ATP from ADP.

The end product in the energy-yielding glycolysis process is the release of a small amount of energy used for various cell functions and the loss of larger amounts of energy in the form of fermentation products. Common fermentation products of glycolysis include ethanol, lactic acid, alcohols, and gaseous substances that are produced, for example, by certain bacteria.

Respiration

The process by which a compound is oxidized using oxygen as an **external** electron acceptor is called **respiration**. Using an external electron acceptor is important, because in the fermentation process, little energy is yielded, mainly because only a partial oxidation of the starting compounds occurs in this process. However, if some external terminal acceptor (oxygen, for example) is present, all substrate molecules can be oxidized completely to a by-product (carbon dioxide). When this occurs, a far higher yield of ATP is possible.

Because an external oxidizing substance is used, the substrate undergoes a **net** oxidation (see Figure 4.14). The oxidation of a substrate provides more energy than is obtainable from the same substrate as fermentation.

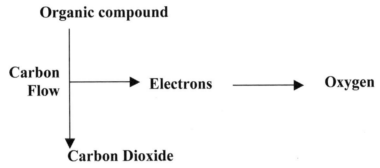

Figure 4.14.   Aerobic respiration—the process by which a compound is oxidized using oxygen as external electron acceptor.

KREBS CYCLE

The Krebs cycle is sometimes called the **citric acid cycle** or tricarboxylic acid cycle (TCA) and commonly called the "energy wheel" of cellular metabolism (see Figure 4.15), because it is a cyclical sequence of reactions crucial to supplying the energy needs of cells.

When oxygen is available to the cell, the energy in pyruvic acid is released through aerobic respiration. In the TCA cycle, pyruvate is first decarboxylated (the removal of a carboxyl group from a chemical compound), leading to the production of one molecule of NADH and an acetyl coupled to coenzyme A (acetyl-CoA). The addition of the activated 2-carbon derivative acetyl CoA to the 4-carbon compound oxaloacetic acid forms citric acid, a six-carbon organic acid. The energy of the high-energy acetyl-CoA bond is used to drive the synthesis. After undergoing dehydration,

KREBS CYCLE

Overall Reaction: **Pyruvate + 4NAD + FADE →3CO2 + 4NADH + FADH**

       GDP + Pi   →   **GTP**

       GTP + ADP   →   **GDP + ATP**

                         15 ATP

Electron-transport **4 NADH**   =   **12 ATP**

phosphorylation **FADH**   =   **2 ATP**

Figure 4.15.   Summary of the overall reaction of Krebs cycle.

decarboxylation, and oxidation, two additional carbon dioxide molecules are released. Eventually, oxalacetate is regenerated and serves again as an acetyl acceptor, thus completing the cycle. In the course of the cycle, three NADHs, one FADH, and one ATP are produced by substrate phosphorylation. The presence of an electron acceptor in respiration allows for the complete oxidation of glucose to carbon dioxide, with a greater yield of energy.

ELECTRON TRANSPORT SYSTEM (ETS)

The **electron transport system** (ETS) is a common pathway for the use of electrons formed during a variety of metabolic reactions. Most molecules are prevented from going into and out of an organism's cells by the cytoplasmic membrane, the control device of the cellular internal environment. During metabolism, however, the cell must be able to take in various substrates and get rid of waste; this is accomplished by transport systems. In some organisms—Gram-negative bacteria, for example— the transport system is located in membranes other than the cytoplasmic membrane (see Figure 4.16).

 A typical ETS is composed of electron carriers. In a bacterium, the ETS involved with respiration occurs in the cytoplasmic membrane. The ETS has two functions: (1) to accept electrons from electron donors and transfer them to electron acceptors, and (2) to save energy during electron transfer by synthesis of ATP.

 The two protein components that form the ETS are the **flavoproteins** and **cy-tochromes**. Flavoproteins are proteins (enzymes) containing riboflavin, which act as dehydrogenation catalysts or hydrogen-carriers in a number of biological reactions. The flavin portion, which is bound to a protein, is alternately reduced as it accepts hydrogen atoms and oxidized when electrons are passed on. Riboflavin (also called vitamin B-2) is a required organic growth factor for some organisms.

 Cytochromes are iron-containing proteins that receive and transfer electrons by the alternate reduction and oxidation of iron atoms and are important in cell metabo-lism. Cytochromes in the ETS are known for (among other things) their reduction

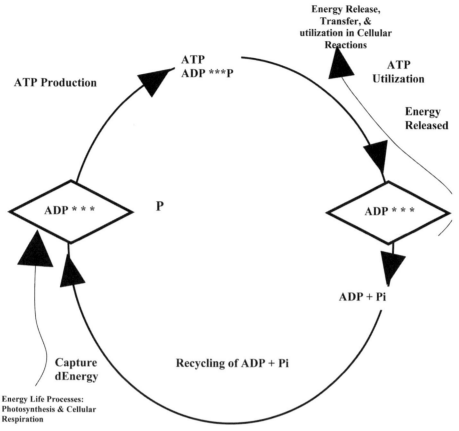

Figure 4.16. The formation of ATP, a substance that fuels all living organisms. By means of phosphorylation, energy-rich bonds (* * *) are formed, and used to combine ADP and Pi into ATP—which is used to fuel the life processes. Then Pi and ADP are used again in a continuous cycle. Adapted from Wistreich and Lechtman (1980), p. 273.

potentials. One cytochrome can transfer electrons to another with a more positive reduction potential and can itself accept electrons from cytochromes with a less positive reduction potential.

AUTOTROPHIC AND HETEROTROPHIC METABOLISM

Autotrophs can use carbon dioxide as their major carbon source for the formation of essential biochemical compounds. Photosynthetic autotrophic bacteria combine carbon dioxide with ribulose diphosphate to form other macromolecules, which can be used for energy. The nonsynthetic chemosynthetic autotrophs rely on oxidation of inorganic compounds, including hydrogen, for the energy to fix carbon dioxide.

In heterotrophic metabolism, carbon dioxide cannot be used as a major carbon source. Chemosynthetic heterotrophs perform metabolic reactions involving proteins, lipids, and carbohydrates, similar to those performed by other organisms. Heterotrophic organisms that are phototrophic can adjust to varying amounts of oxygen.

MICROBIAL NUTRITION

In previous sections, we presented various aspects of the chemical makeup of cell constituents. It may be useful at this point to review a summary of data about the chemical composition of a bacterial cell (see Table 4.4).

Table 4.4. Chemical Composition of a Bacterial Cell

Molecule	Percent Wet Weight	Percent Dry Weight
Water	70	—
Total Macromolecules	**26**	**92**
Proteins	15	55
Polysaccharide	3	5
Lipid	2	9
DNA	1	3
RNA	5	20
Total Monomers	**4**	**4**
Amino acids	0.5	0.5
Sugar	2	2
Nucleotides	0.5	0.5
Inorganic ions	1	1
Totals	**100**	**100**

Source: Data taken from Neidhart, 1987.

In Table 4.4, we see that cells contain large numbers of water, inorganic, and organic molecules, but consist primarily of macromolecules such as proteins and nucleic acids. The cell is capable of obtaining most of the water (small molecules) it needs from the environment in usable form, whereas macromolecules are synthesized inside the cell.

The mass of the cell primarily consists of four types of atoms: carbon, oxygen, nitrogen, and hydrogen. A number of other atoms are functionally important to the cell, but are less apparent. These include calcium, magnesium, iron, zinc, and phosphorus, all present in microbial cells, but in lesser amounts than carbon, hydrogen, oxygen, and nitrogen.

NUTRITION

Nutrients used by organisms and obtained from the environment can be divided into two classes: **macronutrients**, which are required in large quantities, and **micronutrients**, which are required in lesser quantities.

Macronutrients

Most procaryotes require an organic compound as their source of carbon. Bacteria have demonstrated that they can assimilate a wide variety of organic carbon compounds to make new cell material. Major macronutrients such as amino acids, fatty acids, organic acids, sugars, and others are known to be used by a variety of bacteria. The major macronutrients in the cell, after carbon, are nitrogen, sulfur, phosphorus, potassium, magnesium, calcium, sodium, and iron. Table 4.5 shows some of the common forms of these major elements needed for biosynthesis of cell components.

Table 4.5. Macronutrients

Elemental Forms Found in Environment	Element
Carbon dioxide	Carbon
Organic compounds	
Water	Hydrogen
Organic compounds	
Water	Oxygen
Oxygen gas	
Ammonia	Nitrogen
Nitrate	
Amino acids	
Phosphate	Phosphate
Hydrogen sulfide	Sulfur
Sulfate	
Organic compounds	

Micronutrients

Micronutrients (trace elements) are also required and are just as critical to the overall nutrition of a microorganism as macronutrients. For example, **cobalt** is needed for the formation of vitamin B-2, **zinc** plays a role in the structure of many enzymes, **molybdenum** is important for nitrate reduction, and **copper** is important in enzymes involved in respiration.

Bacterial Growth

In microbiology, growth may be defined as an increase in the number of cells or cellular constituents. If the microorganism is a multinucleate (**coenocytic**) organism, in which nuclear division is not accompanied by actual cell division (as with bacteria), growth results only in an increase in cell size, not cell number. In bacteria, as a general rule, growth leads to a rise in cell number, because reproduction is by **binary fission**, wherein two cells enlarge and divide into two progeny of about equal size. Other bacterial species increase their cell numbers asexually by budding, as does mycoplasma.

POPULATION GROWTH

For environmental scientists, investigating the growth of individual microorganisms is not usually convenient or practical, because of their small size. They normally follow changes in the total **population number** when studying growth.

Growth (defined previously as an increase in the number of microbial cells in a population) is measured as an increase in microbial **mass**. The change in cell number or mass per unit time is the **growth rate**.

When bacterial cells are introduced into a suitable medium and held at the optimal growth temperature, and at set intervals a small volume of medium is withdrawn and cultured (bacteria growing in or on a medium), a count can be made of the cells it contains (counting methods are discussed later). In this way, the development of a population (the increase in cell numbers with time) can be observed and followed. By plotting the number of cells against time, a **growth curve** can be obtained. The actual shape of each portion of the curve and the actual numbers of organisms obtained vary between species and types of media used.

BACTERIAL GROWTH CURVE

The growth of bacteria can be plotted as the logarithm of cell number versus the incubation time. The resulting curve has four distinct phases. Note that these phases are reflections of the events in a population of bacteria or other microorganisms, not of individual cells. The terms **lag**, **log**, **stationary**, and **death** phase do not apply to individual cells, only to populations of cells (see Figure 4.17).

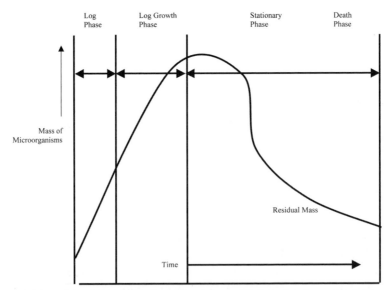

Figure 4.17. Bacterial Growth Curve. The four phases of the growth curve are identified on the curve and discussed in the text. Adapted from McKinney, R. E. *Microbiology for Sanitary Engineers*, 1962, p. 118

The Lag Phase of Growth

When bacteria are inoculated into a culture medium, growth usually does not begin immediately. Apparently this lag in growth, which may be brief or extended, represents a transition period on the part of bacteria transferred to new conditions. During this transition period, time is required for acclimation and for performing various functions, such as synthesis of new enzymes. When conditions are suitable, binary fission begins, and, after an acceleration in the rate of growth, the cells enter the logarithmic (log) phase.

The Logarithmic Phase

During the log phase, the number of bacteria is growing at the maximum rate possible. The bacteria increase in a geometric progression—one splits to make two, two splits to make four, four to eight, and so on. Because each individual divides at a slightly different moment, the growth curve rises smoothly (in a straight line), rather than in discrete jumps. From this logarithmic increase in cell number, the average time for a cell to divide, the **generation time**, can be calculated.

The Stationary Growth Phase

Eventually population growth ceases, and the growth curve becomes horizontal (Figure 4.17). When this occurs, the growth and death rates are more nearly identical, and a fairly constant population of bacteria is achieved. This uniformity in population number is reached primarily because either an essential nutrient of the culture medium is used up, or (for aerobic organisms) oxygen is limited to an inhibitory level and logarithmic growth ceases. The stationary phase leads eventually to the death phase, in which the number of living cells in the population decreases.

The Death Phase

In the limited environment of the batch culture, conditions develop that accelerate the rate of death. When this occurs, the population is said to be in the death phase. This phase is brought about by environmental changes such as nutrient deprivation and the buildup of toxic wastes. For a while, the cells will persist. Some will tolerate the ever-increasing accumulation of wastes and will survive on the lysed cellular contents of the dead cells. At some point, however, further degradation of conditions causes even the hardiest organism to die.

THE EFFECT OF ENVIRONMENTAL FACTORS ON GROWTH

The growth of microorganisms is greatly affected by the chemical and physical conditions of their environments. An understanding of environmental influences helps in the control of microbial growth and in understanding the ecological distribution of microorganisms.

Temperature

Temperature is one of the most important environmental factors affecting the growth and survival of microorganisms. In turn, one of the most important factors influencing the **effect** of temperature upon growth is **temperature sensitivity** of enzyme-catalyst reactions. As temperature rises, enzyme reactions in the cell proceed at more rapid rates (along with increased metabolic activity), and the microorganism grows faster. However, above a certain temperature, growth slows. Eventually, as the temperature continues to increase, enzymes and other proteins are denatured, and the microbial membrane is disrupted. The microorganism is damaged or killed off. Usually, as the temperature is increased, functional enzymes operate more rapidly, up to a point where the microorganism may be damaged and inactivation reactions set in.

Because of these opposing temperature influences, every organism has a **minimum temperature**, below which growth no longer occurs; an **optimum temperature**, at which growth is most rapid; and a **maximum growth temperature**, above which growth is not possible (see Figure 4.18). The temperature optimum is always nearer the **maximum** than the minimum. Although these three temperatures, called the **cardinal temperatures**, are generally characteristic for each type of organism, they are not rigidly fixed, but often depend to some extent on other environmental factors such as available nutrients and pH.

The cardinal temperatures of different microorganisms differ widely (see Table 4.6). Some microbes have temperature optimums ranging from 0°C to as high as

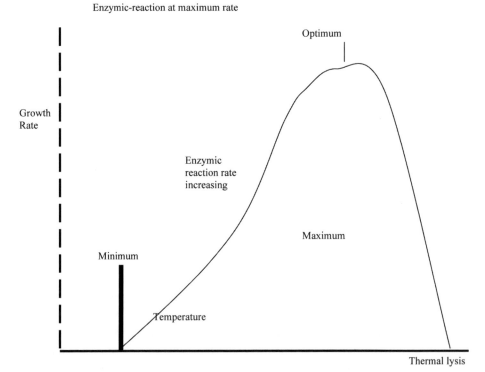

Figure 4.18. Effect of temperature on growth rate and the enzymic-reaction activity that occurs as the temperature increases.

Table 4.6. Approximate Temperature Ranges for Microbial Growth

Microorganism	Temperature Ranges (°C)		
	Minimum	Optimum	Maximum
Bacteria (nonphotosynthetic)	–10 to 85	10 to 105	25 to 110
Bacteria (photosynthetic)	70	30 to 80	45 to 85
Eucaryotic algae	–40 to 35	0 to 50	5 to 57
Fungi	0 to 25	5 to 50	15 to 60
Protozoa	2 to 29	20 to 45	31 to 49

Source: Adapted from Prescott et al., 1993, 126.

75°C. The temperature range through which growth occurs is even wider, from below freezing to greater than boiling. Generally, the growth temperature range for a particular microbe is about 30° to 40°.

Microorganisms occupying those groups listed in Table 4.7 can be placed in one of four other groups based on their temperature ranges for growth:

1. *Psychrophiles*—(low-temperature optima) grow optimally at or below 15°C, do not grow above 20°C, and have a lower limit for growth of 0°C or below. These microorganisms are readily isolated from polar seas. Psychrophilic microorganisms have adapted to their cold environments in several ways. For example, their transport systems, protein synesthetic mechanisms, and enzymes function at low temperature. Because psychrophiles are found in environments that are constantly cold, and warming to room temperature rapidly kills them, studying them in a laboratory is difficult. Psychrophilic microorganisms include a number of Gram-negative bacteria, certain fungi and algae, and a few Gram-positive bacteria.

2. *Psychotrophic*—bacteria (low enzyme and low temperature optima) can grow at low temperatures ranging from 0° to 5°C, but they grow optimally above 15°C, with an upper limit for growth ranging between 25° and 30°C, and a maximum of about 35°C. Psychrotrophic fungi and bacteria are major contributors to spoilage of refrigerated food such as meat, milk, vegetables, and fruits; only when these foods are frozen is microbial activity (growth) not possible.

3. *Mesophilic*—bacteria (mid-range-temperature optima) grow optimally at temperatures between 20° and 45°C. Most microorganisms probably fall within this category, and they include those bacteria pathogenic to man and other animals.

4. *Thermophilic*—bacteria (high-temperature optima) can grow at temperatures of 55°C or higher. Their growth minimum is around 45°C, and they often have optima between 55° and 65°C. A few thermophiles have maxima above 100°C. These thermophiles occur in composts, hydrothermal vents on the ocean floor, and hot springs.

Table 4.7. Approximate Effect of pH on Microbial Growth

Microorganism Type	Lower Limit Range	Upper Limit Range
Bacteria	0.5	9.5
Algae	0.0	9.9
Fungi	0.0	7.0
Protozoa	3.2	9.0

Source: Adapted from Prescott et al., 1993, 125.

pH

When attempting to control microbial growth, controlling pH is one of the best methods. Most bacteria grow best at or near neutral pH 7, and the majority cannot grow under either acidic or alkaline conditions. Acidity or alkalinity of a solution is expressed by its **pH value**, defined as the measure of the hydrogen ion activity of a solution. pH can be defined as the negative logarithm of the hydrogen ion concentration. This hydrogen concentration is important, because it affects the equilibrium relationship of many biological systems that function only in a very narrow pH range.

As previously stated, pH dramatically affects microbial growth. Each species has a definite pH growth range and pH growth optimum, listed in Table 4.7.

When culturing microorganisms, pH adjustment of the culture medium is a common practice. For example, if the pH is too acidic, an alkaline substance such as sodium hydroxide (caustic solution) can be added. If the culture medium pH is too alkaline, an acidic substance may be added. In general, different groups of microorganisms have different pH preferences. Most bacteria and protozoa, for example, prefer a pH between 5.0 and 8.0. Most fungi and some algae prefer slightly more acidic surroundings, ranging from a pH of about 3 to 6.

Sometimes adding a pH **buffer** to the culture medium to compensate for changes (to keep the pH relatively constant) in pH fluctuations caused by microorganisms as they grow is desirable. Often indicator dyes are added to culture media and can provide a dual visual indication of the initial pH and changes (in the color of the dye) in pH resulting from growth activity of microbes.

Each species has a definite pH growth range and optimum. This important characteristic allows the water and wastewater specialist to have significant control of various microbial populations. Most natural environments have pH values between 5 and 9; organisms in this optima range are most common. Microorganisms that live at low pH are called **acidophiles**. Those microorganisms with high optima (ranging from 8.5 to 11.5) are called **alkalophiles**. Note that acidophiles and alkalophiles may not grow at all or only very slowly at pH 7 (neutral pH).

Water Availability

The availability of water is another environmental factor that can affect the growth of microbes. For some microbes (bacteria), approximately 80% or more of their mass is water. In the growth phase, nutrients and water products enter and leave the cell, respectively, in solution. For these microbes to grow, they must be in or on an environment with adequate available water or ions in solution.

All microorganisms (like all other organisms) need water for life. Indeed, availability of water is critical. Water availability does not depend only on water content of the environment, but also on the substances present; that is, some substances can absorb water and do not readily give it up.

Water availability is generally expressed in physical terms as **water activity** (**a**w), the amount of free or available water in a given substance. The water activity of a solution is 1/100 the relative humidity of the solution when expressed as a percent. Water availability is expressed as a ratio of the vapor pressure of the air over the solution, divided by the vapor pressure at the same temperature of pure water:

$$a_w = \frac{P\,Solution}{P\,Water} \qquad (4.4)$$

Values of water activity vary between 0 and 1. Some representative values are given in Table 4.8.

Table 4.8. Water Activity of Various Materials

Material	Water Activity Value
Pure water	1.000
Human blood	0.995
Bread	0.950
Ham	0.900
Jams	0.800
Candy	0.700

Source: Adapted from Brock & Madigan, 1991, 329.

Water diffuses from a region of high water–low solute concentration to a region of lower water–higher solute concentration. If pure water and a salt solution are separated by a semipermeable membrane, water will diffuse *from* the pure water *into* the salt solution by **osmosis**. The cytoplasm of most cells has a higher solute concentration than the environment; thus water diffuses into the cell. If the cell is in an environment of low water activity, water will flow out of the cell. An environment such as salt or sugar in solution has low water activity and causes the cell to give up water. When this occurs, the plasma membrane shrinks away from the wall (plasmolysis) and the cell dehydrates, damaging the membrane, and the cell ceases to grow.

Oxygen

Microorganisms vary in their need for, or tolerance of, oxygen. Some bacteria, for example, need oxygen for growth. Others need the *absence* of oxygen for growth. Still others can grow regardless of the presence or absence of oxygen. Microorganisms can be grouped depending on the effect of oxygen. A microorganism that is able to grow in the presence of atmospheric oxygen is an **aerobe**, whereas one that can grow in its absence is an **anaerobe**. Organisms that are dependent upon atmospheric oxygen for growth are called **obligate aerobes**. Microorganisms that do not require oxygen for growth, but grow better in its presence, are called **facultative anaerobes**. The **strict** or **obligate anaerobes** do not tolerate oxygen at all and will die in its presence.

Some aerobes must be aerated to grow, because oxygen is poorly soluble in water. The oxygen used up by microorganisms during growth is diffused from air too slowly. To compensate for this shortage of oxygen in cultured aerobes, forced aeration is desirable. This can be accomplished by forcing sterilized air into the medium or by simply shaking the tube or flask vigorously.

The anaerobic culture requires the **exclusion** of oxygen, a difficult task; oxygen, obviously, is readily available in the air. To vacate air from the culture medium in which anaerobes are to be grown, completely filling the tubes to the top with culture medium and sealing with tight-fitting stoppers is necessary. This procedure is useful for providing anaerobic conditions for organisms not too sensitive to small amounts of oxygen. Adding a **reducing agent** to the medium that reacts with oxygen and excludes it from the culture medium is also possible. A common reducing agent used in this procedure is **thioglycollate**. The nature of bacterial oxygen responses can be readily determined by growing bacteria in culture tubes filled with a solid culture medium or media treated with a reducing agent. To easily detect the presence of oxygen in the medium, an indicator dye is usually added; the dye changes color and indicates the penetration level of oxygen in the medium.

Pathogenicity

> I can think of a few microorganisms, possibly the tubercle bacillus, the syphilis spirochete, and malarial parasite, and a few others, that have a selective advantage in their ability to infect human beings, but there is nothing to be gained, in an evolutionary sense, by the capacity to cause illness or death. Pathogenicity may be something of a disadvantage for most microbes, carrying lethal risks more frightening to them than to us. The man who catches a meningococcus is in considerably less danger for his life, even without chemotherapy, than meningococci with the bad luck to catch a man. Most meningococci have the sense to stay out on the surface, in the rhinopharynx. During epidemics this is where they are to be found in the majority of the host population, and it generally goes well. It is only in the unaccountable minority, the "cases," that the line is crossed, and then there is the devil to pay on both sides, but most of all for the meningococci. (Thomas, 1974, 76–77)

Thomas's account of the dilemma meningococci face upon entering the body notwithstanding, the prevention of an invasion by water-, air-, or soil-borne pathogens into human beings and other forms of life is what environmental scientists are most concerned with. For example, the most frequent cause of waterborne disease in public water supplies in the United States is inadequate water treatment, whether treatment is nonexistent or is ineffective because of treatment process breakdown, especially in disinfection. When inadequate water treatment or treatment system breakdown occurs, most diseases transmitted via the untreated water are caused by contaminated fecal material. Table 4.9 shows the public water system breakdowns in the United States reported by the Centers for Disease Control (CDC) during the 1986–1988 time frame.

Even before Mary Mallon (a.k.a. Typhoid Mary, an American cook in the late 1800s and early 1900s) was "cooking up" her daily food preparations and passing on typhoid to her unsuspecting victims, people had suspected a relationship between microorganisms and disease. As a matter of historical record, even before the discovery of waterborne, disease-causing microorganisms, people suspected a relationship between

Table 4.9. Water System Breakdowns Leading to Waterborne Disease Outbreaks 1986–1988

Type of Breakdown or Deficiency	Community Water Systems	Noncommunity Water Systems	Total
Untreated surface water	1	1	2
Untreated ground water	3	9	12
Treatment	11	12	23
Distribution system	6	0	6
Miscellaneous	1	2	3
Total	22	24	46

Source: Centers for Disease Control, Atlanta

water and the spread of disease. People's quest for the truth about disease and disease-causing microorganisms began almost 2,600 years ago, when Hippocrates, the father of medicine, suspected that "different" waters caused several different diseases. Proof took many more centuries, until Leeuwenhoek invented the microscope in 1675. Leeuwenhoek's microscope, with several later refinements, opened up the microscopic world. *Giardia lamblia* was the first microorganism studied and described by Leeuwenhoek. Eventually, in the 19th century, other great men of science such as Koch and Pasteur, disproved the ancient theory of poisonous vapors arising from decaying filth as the cause of disease; they developed the germ theory.

In the quote at the beginning of this section, Lewis Thomas discussed the plight of the meningococci that might have the misfortune of entering a human body. After having read Thomas's discussion, you may have developed the misperception that pathogenic microorganisms are defenseless and not at home within human bodies. This is not the case. Microorganisms can adapt. As a case in point, consider the following descriptive account of the adaptive challenges faced by waterborne pathogenic bacteria some unfortunate person ingests:

> In water, this bacterium was experiencing an environment where the temperature was well below 37 degrees C, nutrient concentrations and osmotic strength were low, and pH was near neutral. At least some oxygen was available. When the bacterium is ingested, it suddenly encounters a higher temperature, higher osmotic strength, a transient exposure to low pH in the stomach, followed by a rise in pH in the intestine and high concentrations of membrane-disrupting bile salts. Also, the environment of the small intestine, and to a greater extent the colon, is anaerobic.
>
> The bacterium will find abundant sources of carbon and energy in the intestine, but the forms of these compounds will be different from those it may have been using in water. Keep in mind that the incoming bacterium does not have much time to adapt to its new environment because it takes only a few hours to transit the small intestine and reach the colon, where it also will encounter stiff competition from the resident microflora. (Salyers & Whitt, 1994, 64–65)

Given the adaptive challenges faced by the waterborne bacteria and their ability to make these adaptations, it is not surprising that pathogenic bacteria have evolved defense mechanisms that make their destruction increasingly difficult. Combating these mechanisms is the ultimate challenge confronting water and wastewater treatment specialists of the future. Given the fact that pathogenic microorganisms have the remarkable ability to adapt and survive, advanced biological treatment methodologies must evolve and **adapt** as well.

CAUSAL FACTORS FOR TRANSMISSION OF DISEASE

Certain factors must exist for the transmission of disease. These factors are related to the diseased individual (the **host**), the microorganism (the **agent**), and the environment. Among the many diseases of microbial origin, some are caused by viruses, some by fungi, some by bacteria, and others by protozoa. Note that disease does not necessarily follow exposure to a given pathogen. For disease to develop, several factors must *all* be present, including the following:

1. *Pathogen* (causative agent). Any microorganism that can cause disease is called a pathogen. Normally this **pathogen** is parasitic and lives on or in another organism. In some diseases, the link between pathogen and disease is very specific; that is, the pathogen may only infect certain species. Along with being selectively specific, for a pathogen to cause the occurrence of disease is dependent on various factors. These factors include the extent or degree of resistance of the host and the capacity to produce disease (the **virulence**) of the pathogen.
2. *Pathogen's reservoir.* The pathogen lives and reproduces (multiplies) in a reservoir and is unable to reproduce or grow outside it. Humans, animals, plants, organic matter, and soils can serve as the pathogen's reservoir. Human bodies are a significant reservoir of microbial pathogens; these organisms are a normal part of human microflora and usually do not behave as pathogens unless disturbed by surgery or injury. When this occurs, our specific or nonspecific defenses are impaired; the type of pathogenic contamination that takes place is known as **opportunistic**.
3. *Movement of pathogens from reservoir.* Movement of pathogens in human physical systems may be from body openings in the respiratory, urinary, and intestinal systems; from open infections; and by mechanical means delivered by disruptions or damage caused by injuries.
4. *Transmission of disease to another host.* Transmission can be accomplished directly or indirectly. In direct transmission, disease passes (e.g., via an animal bite) immediately to a new host. Indirect transmission is accomplished through **vectors** or vehicles. These vectors can be mosquitoes, ticks, fleas, or other invertebrates. The vehicles are substances, such as milk, food, air, and other nonliving substances.
5. *Virulence of the pathogen.* The occurrence of disease depends on the pathogen's virulence (its capacity to cause disease).
6. *Degree of resistance to transmission.* Humans possess mechanisms of defense against disease. For example, human skin provides the primary defense against infectious disease. For most diseases to pass or be transmitted through the skin's resistance barrier, wounding or insect bites (as explained in point 4) must break the skin.

For disease to spread, some vehicle, medium, or opportunity for spread must exist. This is where water and wastewater treatment specialists play such a vital role. If an individual ingests untreated water, that individual may become a carrier of waterborne disease. Typhoid Mary infected several people with typhoid fever, but she never demonstrated obvious symptoms of this deadly disease; thus, she was a carrier.

Pathogenic organisms found in water and wastewater may be from carriers of disease. The principal categories of pathogenic organisms found in water and wastewater are bacteria, viruses, protozoa, and helminths. Such highly infectious organisms have been responsible for countless deaths and continue to cause the deaths of large numbers of people and animals in underdeveloped parts of the world.

Problems with waterborne diseases in underdeveloped parts of the world are well documented. In one instance, a report filed by Ries and others (1992) recorded that in 1991 in Piura, Peru, a city of more than 350,000, within a two-month period there were more than 7,922 cases and 17 deaths attributed to cholera—an epidemic. During the investigation, a hospital-based culture survey showed that approximately 80% of diarrhea cases were cholera. A study of 50 case-patients and 100 matched controls demonstrated that cholera was associated with drinking unboiled water, drinking beverages from street vendors, and eating food from vendors. Note that in a second study, patients were more likely than controls to consume beverages with ice. Ice was produced from municipal water. Testing of municipal water supplies revealed no, or insufficient, chlorination, and *fecal coliform* bacteria were detected in most samples tested. With epidemic cholera spreading throughout Latin America, these findings emphasize the importance of safe municipal drinking water. More specifically, the results of this study indicate that even though we have come a long way in the fight against waterborne disease and are successful in most instances, parts of the world still struggle with this life-threatening problem. Natural disasters and wars, in particular, can disrupt both water and wastewater treatment, providing opportunities for diseases to flourish.

EMERGENCE OF INFECTIOUS DISEASES[3]

Throughout history, emerging infectious diseases have included some of the most feared plagues. New infections continue to emerge, while many of the old plagues are still with us. These are global problems. As demonstrated in influenza epidemics, under suitable circumstances, a new infection first appearing anywhere in the world could traverse entire continents within days or weeks.

We define as "emerging" infections those that have newly appeared in the population or have existed but are rapidly increasing in incidence or geographic range (Morse & Schluederberg, 1990; Morse 1993). Recent examples of emerging diseases in various parts of the world are HIV/AIDS; classic cholera in South America and Africa; cholera due to *Vibrio cholera* 0139; Rift Valley fever; hantavirus pulmonary syndrome; Lyme disease; and hemolytic uremic syndrome, a foodborne infection caused by certain strains of *Escherichia coli* (in the United States, serotype 0157:H7).

Numerous examples of infections originating as zoonoses (Fiennes, 1978; McNeill, 1976) suggest that the "zoonotic pool"—introduction of infections from other species—is an important and potentially rich source of emerging diseases; periodic discoveries of "new" zoonoses suggest that the zoonotic pool appears by no means exhausted. Once introduced, an infection might then be disseminated through other factors, although rapid course and high mortality combined with low transmissibility are often limiting. However, even if a zoonotic agent is not able to spread readily from person to person and establish itself, other factors (e.g., nosocomial infection) might transmit the infection. In addition, if the reservoir host or vector becomes more widely disseminated, the microbe can appear in new places. Bubonic plague transmitted by rodent fleas and ratborne hantavirus infections are examples.

Most emerging infections appear to be caused by pathogens already present in the environment, brought out of obscurity or given a selective advantage by changing conditions and afforded an opportunity to infect new host populations (on rare occasions, a new variant may also evolve and cause a new disease) (Morse 1993, 1990, 1991). The process by which infectious agents may transfer from animals to humans or disseminate from isolated groups into new populations can be called "microbial traffic" (Morse 1990a, 1991). A number of activities increase microbial traffic and as a result promote emergence and epidemics in some cases, including many of the most novel infections. The agents are zoonotic, crossing from their natural hosts into the human population because of the many similarities. In other cases, pathogens already present in geographically isolated populations are given an opportunity to disseminate further. Surprisingly often, disease emergence is caused by human actions, however inadvertent; natural causes, such as changes in climate, can also at times be responsible (Rogers & Packer 1993). Although this discussion is confined largely to human disease, similar considerations apply to emerging pathogens in other species.

Table 4.10 summarizes the underlying factors responsible for emergence. Any categorization of the factors is, of course, somewhat arbitrary, but should be representative of the underlying processes that cause emergence. Responsible factors include ecological changes, such as those due to agricultural or economic development or other anomalies in climate; human demographic changes and behavior; travel and commerce; technology and industry; microbial adaption and change; and breakdown of public health measures. Each of these is described in turn.

Ecological interactions can be complex, with several factors often working together or in sequence. For example, population movement from rural areas to cities can spread a once-localized infection. The strain on infrastructure in the overcrowded and rapidly growing cities may disrupt or slow public health measures, perhaps allowing establishment of the newly introduced infection. Finally, the city may also provide a gateway for further dissemination of the infection. Most successful emerging infections, including HIV, cholera, and dengue, have followed this route.

Consider HIV as an example. Although the precise ancestry of HIV-1 is still uncertain, it appears to have had a zoonotic origin (Myers, MacInnes & Korber 1992; Allan, Short & Taylor, 1991). Ecological factors that would have allowed human exposure to a natural host carrying the virus that was the precursor to HIV-1 were therefore instrumental in the introduction of the virus into humans. This probably occurred in a rural area. A plausible scenario is suggested by the identification of an HIV-2-infected man in a rural area of Liberia whose virus strain resembled viruses isolated

Table 4.10.   Factors in Infectious Disease Emergence

Factor	Examples of Specific Factors	Examples of Diseases
Ecological changes	Agriculture, dams, changes in water ecosystems; deforestation/reforestation; flood/drought; famine; climate changes	Schistosomiasis (dams); Rift Valley fever (dam, irrigation); Argentine hemorrhagic fever (agriculture); Hantann (Korean hemorrhagic fever) (agriculture)
Human demographics, behavior	Societal events: Population growth and migration (movement from rural areas to cities); war or civil conflict; urban decay; sexual behavior; intravenous drug use; use of high-density facilities.	Introduction of HIV; spread of dengue; spread of HIV and other sexually transmitted diseases.
International travel and commerce	Worldwide movement of goods and people; air travel	"Airport" malaria; dissemination of mosquito vectors; ratborne hantaviruses; introduction of cholera into South America; dissemination of 0139 *V. cholerae*
Technology and industry	Globalization of food supplies; changes in food processing and packaging; organ or tissue transplantation; drugs causing immunosuppression; widespread use of antibiotics	Hemolytic uremic syndrome (*E. coli* contamination of hamburger meat); bovine spongiform encephalopathy; transfusion-associated hepatitis
Microbial adaptation and change	Microbial evolution, response to selection in environment	Antibiotic-resistant bacteria; "antigenic drift" in influenza virus
Breakdown in public health measures	Curtailment or reduction in prevention programs; inadequate sanitation and vector control measures	Resurgence of tuberculosis in the U.S.; cholera in refugee camps in Africa; resurgence of diphtheria in the former Soviet Union

Sources: Institute of Medicine, 1992; CDC, 1994a.

Did You Know?

Airport malaria is defined as malaria acquired through the bite of an infected tropical anopheline mosquito by persons whose geographic history excludes exposure to this vector in its natural habitat (Isaacson, 1989). The vector is usually introduced into a nonendemic-disease country on an international flight. For example, random searches of airplanes at Gatwick Airport (London) found that 12 of 67 airplanes from tropical countries contained mosquitoes (Curtis & White 1984). After a mosquito leaves the aircraft, it may survive long enough to take a blood meal and transmit the disease, usually in the vicinity of an airport. In temperate climates, temperature and humidity can be favorable in the summer for the mosquito not only to survive but also to move around and perhaps lay eggs. With the enormous and continuing increase in air traffic, cases of airport malaria may increase.

---

from the sooty mangabey monkey (an animal widely hunted for food in rural areas and the putative source of HIV-2) more closely than it did strains circulating in the city (Gao et al., 1992). Such findings suggest that zoonotic introductions of this sort may occur on occasion in isolated populations, but may well go unnoticed as long as the recipients remain isolated. But with increasing movement from rural areas to cities, such isolation is increasingly rare. After its likely first move from a rural area into a city, HIVC-1 spread regionally along highways, then by long distance routes, including air travel, to more distant places. This last step was critical for HIV and facilitated today's global pandemic. Social changes that allowed the virus to reach a larger population and to be transmitted despite its relatively low natural transmissibility were instrumental in the success of the virus in its newfound human host. For HIV, the long duration of infectivity allowed this normally poorly transmissible virus many opportunities to be transmitted and to take advantage of such factors as human behavior (sexual transmission, intravenous drug use) and changing technology (early spread through blood transfusions and blood products).

Ecological Changes and Agricultural Development

Ecological changes, including those due to agricultural or economic development, are among the most frequently identified factors in emergence. They are especially frequent as factors in outbreaks of previously unrecognized disease with high case-fatality rates, which often turn out to be zoonotic introductions. Ecological factors usually precipitate emergence by placing people in contact with a natural reservoir or host for an infection hitherto unfamiliar but usually already present (often a zoonotic or arthropod-borne infection), either by increasing proximity or, often, also by changing conditions so as to favor an increased population of the microbe or its natural host (Morse 1993, 1991). The emergence of Lyme disease in the United States and Europe was probably due largely to reforestation (Barbour & Fish, 1993), which increased the population of deer and the deer tick, the vector of Lyme disease. The movement of people into these areas placed a larger population in close proximity to the vector.

Agricultural development, one of the most common ways in which people alter and interpose themselves into the environment, is often a factor. Hantaan virus, the cause of Korean hemorrhagic fever, causes over 100,000 cases a year in China and has been known in Asia for centuries. The virus is a natural infection of the field mouse *Apodemus agrarius*. The rodent flourishes in rice fields; people usually contract the disease during the rice harvest from contact with infected rodents. Junin virus, the cause of Argentine hemorrhagic fever, is an unrelated virus with a history remarkably similar to that of Hantaan virus. Conversion of grassland to maize cultivation favored a rodent that was the natural host for this virus, and human cases increased in proportion with the expansion of maize agriculture (Johnson, 1993). Other diseases, in addition to those already known (Morse, 1993; Johnson, 1993), are likely to appear as new areas are placed under cultivation.

Perhaps most surprisingly, pandemic influenza appears to have an agricultural origin, integrated pig-duck farming in China. Strains causing the frequent annual or biennial epidemics generally result from mutation ("antigenic drift"), but pandemic influenza viruses do not generally arise by this process. Instead, gene segments from two influenza strains reassert to produce a new virus that can infect humans (Webster et al., 1992). Evidence amassed by Webster, Scholtissek, and others indicates that water fowl, such as ducks, are major reservoirs of influenza and that pigs can serve as "mixing vessels" for new mammalian influenza strains (Webster et al., 1992). Pandemic influenza viruses have generally come from China. Scholtissek and Naylor suggested that integrated pig-duck agriculture, an extremely efficient food production system traditionally practiced in certain parts of China for several centuries, puts these two species in contact and provides a natural laboratory for making new influenza recombinants (Scholtissek & Naylor, 1988). Webster has suggested that, with high-intensity agriculture and movement of livestock across borders, suitable conditions may now also be found in Europe (Webster et al., 1992).

Water is also frequently associated with disease emergence. Infections transmitted by mosquitoes or other arthropods, which include some of the most serious and widespread diseases (WHO 1989; Monath 1993), are often stimulated by expansion of standing water, simply because many of the mosquito vectors breed in water. There are many cases of diseases transmitted by water-breeding vectors, most involving dams, water for irrigation, or stored drinking water in cities. The incidence of Japanese encephalitis, another mosquito-borne disease that accounts for almost 30,000 human cases and approximately 7,000 deaths annually in Asia, is closely associated with flooding of fields for rice growing. Outbreaks of Rift Valley fever in some parts of Africa have been associated with dam building as well as with periods of heavy rainfall (Monath 1993). In the outbreaks of Rift Valley fever in Mauritania in 1987, the human cases occurred in villages near dams on the Senegal River. The same effect has been documented with other infections that have aquatic hosts, such as schistosomiasis.

Because humans are important agents of ecological and environmental change, many of these factors are anthropogenic. Of course, this is not always the case, and natural environmental changes, such as climate or weather anomalies, can have the same effect. The outbreak of hantavirus pulmonary syndrome in the southwestern United States in 1993 is an example. It is likely that the virus has long been present in mouse populations, but an unusually mild and wet winter and spring in that area led to an increased rodent population in the spring and summer and thus to greater opportunities for people to come in contact with infected rodents (and hence with the virus); it has been suggested that the weather anomaly was due to large-scale climatic effects (Levins et al., 1993). The same causes may have been responsible for outbreaks of hanta viral disease in Europe at approximately the same time (Le Guenno et al., 1993; Rollin, Coudrier, & Sureau, 1993). With cholera, it has been suggested that certain organisms in marine environments are natural reservoirs for *Vibrio cholerae*, and that large-scale effects on ocean currents may cause local increases in the reservoir organism, with consequent flare-ups of cholera (Epstein, Ford & Colwell, 1993).

Changes in Human Demographics and Behavior

Human population movements or upheavals, caused by migration or war, are often important factors in disease emergence. In many parts of the world, economic conditions are encouraging the mass movement of workers from rural areas to cities. The United Nations has estimated that, largely as a result of continuing migration, by the year 2025, 65% of the world's population (also expected to be larger in absolute numbers), including 61% of the population in developing regions, will live in cities (UN, 1991). As discussed above in reference to HIV, rural urbanization allows infections arising in isolated rural areas, which may once have remained obscure and localized, to reach larger populations. Once in a city, the newly introduced infection would have the opportunity to spread locally among the population and could also spread further along highways and interurban transport routes and by airplane. HIV has been, and in Asia is becoming, the best-known beneficiary of this dynamic, but many other diseases, such as dengue, stand to benefit. The frequency of the most severe form, dengue hemorrhagic fever, which is thought to occur when a person is sequentially infected by two types of dengue virus, is increasing as different dengue viruses have extended their range and now overlap (Gubler & Trent, 1993). Dengue hemorrhagic fever is now common in some cities in Asia, where the high prevalence of infection is attributed to the proliferation of open containers needed for water storage (which also provide breeding grounds for the mosquito vector) as the population size exceeds the infrastructure (see Figure 4.19; Monath, 1993). In urban environments, rained-filled tires and plastic bottles are often breeding grounds of choice for mosquito vectors. The resulting mosquito population boom is complemented by the high human population density in such situations, increasing the chances of stable transmission cycles between infected and susceptible persons. Even in industrialized countries, infections such as tuberculosis can spread through high-population-density settings (e.g., day-care centers or prisons) (Institute of Medicine, 1992; Krause, 1992; Bloom & Murray, 1992; Hoge et al., 1994).

Human behavior can have important effects on disease dissemination. The best-known examples are sexually transmitted disease, and the ways in which such human behavior as sex or intravenous drug use has contributed to the emergence of HIV are now well known. Other factors responsible for disease emergence are influenced by a variety of human actions, so human behavior in the broader sense is also very important. Motivating appropriate individual behavior and constructive action, both locally

Figure 4.19.   Potable water collector in Amazonia, Ecuadorian Jungle. Photo by Frank R. Spellman

and on a larger scale, will be essential for controlling emerging infections. Ironically, as AIDS prevention efforts have demonstrated, human behavior remains one of the weakest links in our scientific knowledge.

International Travel and Commerce

The dissemination of HIV through travel has already been mentioned. In the past, an infection introduced into people in a geographically isolated area might, on occasion, be brought to a new place through travel, commerce, or war (McNeill, 1976). Trade

Did You Know?

Dengue (pronounced den' gee) is a disease caused by any one of four closely related dengue viruses (DENV1, DENV2, DENV3, or DENV4). The viruses are transmitted to humans by the bite of an infected mosquito. In the Western Hemisphere, the *Aedes aeqypti* mosquito is the most important transmitter or vector of dengue viruses, although a 2001 outbreak in Hawaii was transmitted by *Aedes albopictus*. It is estimated that there are over 100 million cases of dengue worldwide each year. Dengue hemorrhagic fever (DHF) is a more severe form of dengue infection. It can be fatal if unrecognized and not properly treated in a timely manner. DHF is caused by infection with the same viruses that cause dengue fever. With good medical management, mortality due to DHF can be less than 1% (CDC, 2009).

between Asia and Europe, perhaps beginning with the Silk Route and continuing with the Crusades, brought the rat and one of its infections, the bubonic plague, to Europe. Beginning in the 16th and 17th centuries, ships bringing slaves from West Africa to the New World also brought yellow fever and its mosquito vector, *Aedes aegypti*, to the new territories. Similarly, smallpox went on from Old World origins to wreak havoc in the New World. In the 19th century, cholera had similar opportunities to spread from its probable origin in the Ganges plain to the Middle East, and from there, to Europe and much of the remaining world. Each of these infections had once been localized and took advantage of opportunities to be carried to previously unfamiliar parts of the world.

Similar stories are being repeated today, but opportunities in recent years have become far richer and more numerous, reflecting the increasing volume, scope, and speed of traffic in an increasingly mobile world. Rats have carried hantaviruses virtually worldwide (LaDuc, Childs & Glass, 1992). *Aedes albopictus* (the Asian tiger mosquito) was introduced into the United States, Brazil, and parts of Africa in shipments of used tires from Asia (CDC, 1991a). Since its introduction in 1982, this mosquito has established itself in at least 18 states of the United States and has acquired local viruses, including Eastern equine encephalomyelitis (CDC, 1991b), a cause of serious disease. Another mosquito-borne disease, malaria, is one of the most frequently imported diseases in non-endemic-disease areas, and cases of "airport malaria" are occasionally identified.

Technology and Industry

High-volume rapid movement characterizes not only travel, but also other industries in modern society. In operations, including food production, that process or use products of biological origin, modern production methods yield increased efficiency and reduced costs, but can increase the changes of accidental contamination and amplify the effects of such contamination. The problem is further compounded by globalization, allowing the opportunity to introduce agents from far way. A pathogen present in some of the raw material may find its way into a large batch of final product, as happened with the contamination of hamburger meat by *E. coli* strains causing hemolytic uremic syndrome (CDC, 1993). In the United States, the implicated *E. coli* strains are serotype 0157:H7; additional serotypes have been identified in other countries. Bovine spongiform encephalopathy (BSE), which emerged in Britain within recent years, was likely an interspecies transfer of scrapie from sheep to cattle (Morse, 1990b) that occurred when changes in rendering processes led to incomplete inactivation of scrapie agent in sheep by-products fed to cattle (Wilesmith, Ryan & Atkinson, 1991).

The concentrating effects that occur with blood and tissue products have inadvertently disseminated infections unrecognized at the time, such as HIV and hepatitis B and C. Medical settings are also on the front line of exposure to new diseases, and a number of infections, including many emerging ones, have spread nosocomially in health-care settings (see Table 4.11). Among the numerous examples, in the outbreaks of Ebola fever in Africa, many of the secondary cases were hospital acquired, most transmitted to other patients through contaminated hypodermic apparatus and some to the health-care staff by contact. Transmission of Lassa fever to health-care workers has also been documented.

On the positive side, advances in diagnostic technology can also lead to new recognition of agents that are already widespread. When such agents are newly recognized, they may at first be labeled, in some cases incorrectly, as emerging infections. Human herpes virus 6 (HHV-6) was identified only a few years ago, but the virus appears to be extremely widespread (Inoue, Dambaugh & Pellett, 1993) and has recently been implicated as the cause of roseola (exanthema subitum), a very common childhood disease (Yamanishi et al., 1988). Because roseola has been known since at least 1910, HHV-6 is likely to have been common for decades and probably much longer. Another recent example is the bacterium *Helicobacter pylori*, a probable cause of gastric ulcers (Peterson, 1991) and some cancers (Nomura et al., 1991; Parsonnet, 1991). We have lived with these diseases for a long time without knowing their cause. Recognition of the agent is often advantageous, offering new promise of controlling a previously intractable disease, such as treating gastric ulcers with specific antimicrobial therapy.

Microbial Adaptation and Change

Microbes, like all other living things, are constantly evolving. The emergence of antibiotic-resistant bacteria as a result of the ubiquity of antimicrobials in the environment is an evolutionary lesson on microbial adaption, as well as a demonstration of the power of natural section. Selection for antibiotic-resistant bacteria (Soares et al., 1993; Davies, 1994) and drug-resistant parasites has frequently been driven by the wide and sometimes inappropriate use of antimicrobial drugs in a variety of applications (Bloom & Murray, 1992; Cohen, 1992; Neu, 1992). Pathogens can also acquire new genes for antibiotic resistance from other, often nonpathogenic, species in the environment (Davies, 1994), selected or perhaps even driven by the selection pressure of antibiotics.

Many viruses show a high mutation rate and can rapidly evolve to yield new variants (Domingo & Holland, 1994). A classic example is influenza (Kilbourne, 1976). Regular annual epidemics are caused by "antigenic drift" in a previously circulating influenza strain. A change in an antigenic site of a surface protein, usually the hemagglutinin (H) protein, allows the new variant to reinfect previously infected persons, because the altered antigen is not immediately recognized by the immune system.

On rare occasions, perhaps more often with nonviral pathogens than with viruses (Morse, 1994), the evolution of a new variant may result in a new expression of disease. The epidemic of Brazilian purpuric fever in 1990, associated with a newly emerged clonal variant of *Haemophilus influenzae*, biogroup *aegyptius*, may fall into this category. It is possible, but not yet clear, that some recently described manifestations of disease by group A *Streptococcus*, such as rapidly invasive infection or necrotizing fasciitis, may also fall into this category.

Breakdown of Public Health Measures and Deficiencies in Public Health Infrastructure

Classical public health and sanitation measures have long served to minimize dissemination and human exposure to many pathogens spread by traditional routes such as water or preventable by immunization or vector control. The pathogens themselves often still remain, albeit in reduced numbers, in reservoir hosts or in the environment or in small pockets of infection and therefore are often able to take advantage of the opportunity to reemerge if there are breakdowns in preventive measures.

Reemerging diseases are those, like cholera, that were once decreasing but are now rapidly increasing again. These are often conventionally understood and well-recognized public health threats for which (in most cases) previously active public health measures had been allowed to lapse, a situation that unfortunately now applies all too often in both developing countries and the inner cities of the industrialized world. The appearance of reemerging disease may therefore often be a sign of the breakdown of public health measures and should be a warning against complacency in the war against infectious diseases.

Cholera, for example, has recently been raging in South America (Glass, Libel & Branding-Bennett, 1992) and Africa. The rapid spread of cholera in South America may have been abetted by recent reductions in chlorine levels used to treat water supplies (Moore, 1992). The success of cholera and other enteric diseases is often due to the lack of a reliable water supply. These problems are more severe in developing countries, but are not confined to these areas. The U.S. outbreak of waterborne *Cryptosporidium* infection in Milwaukee, Wisconsin, in the spring of 1993, with over 400,000 estimated cases, was in part due to a nonfunctioning water filtration plant (McKenzie et al., 1994); similar deficiencies in water purification have been found in other cities in the United States (CDC, 1994b).

PARASITES AND PATHOGENS

One form of pathogenicity is demonstrated when **parasitic** microorganisms derive their nutrients for growth and reproduction from living on or in a viable host. Another form of pathogenicity occurs when toxic substances are produced by pathogens.

Microbial parasites include viruses, protozoans, and helminths; bacteria, fungi, and actinomycetes are pathogens. *All* viruses are parasitic. Protozoans are parasites that commonly enter and live in the gastrointestinal system of humans and animals. The helminths (worms) have two parasitic forms: roundworms and flatworms (tapeworms).

Parasites and pathogens are not defenseless against our efforts to destroy or remove them. This ability of pathogenic microorganisms to adjust or adapt should come as no surprise, because humans, through evolution, have also been able to develop ways to protect themselves (build up resistance) from parasites and bacteria.

Remember that during the human evolutionary process, and even with our ability to fight off disease, pathogenic microorganisms have not remained static. Pathogenic microorganisms have also evolved. Consider the effect that certain antibiotics have today on the pathogens they were successfully used against only a few years ago. Today, these antibiotics may not be as effective because pathogens have evolved ways to circumvent their effects, to the point that they may no longer provide a defense against disease. Salyers and Whitt (1994) point out that it is almost striking the way in which pathogenic bacteria have been able to develop strategies that enable them to survive against the various defensive actions we implement. For example, bacteria cellular structures such as capsule formation, thickened cell walls, and spore formation are defensive mechanisms bacteria have developed with time and constant exposure to various antibiotics. "Bacteria are clearly Machiavellian" (1994, 2).

Bacteria are not alone in their resistance to their own destruction. Take for example the viruses; they are protected from most chemical treatment processes because of the very nature of their own chemical composition. Protozoans are another example of adaptation and adjustment. For instance, they have developed a specialized hyaline wall structure that protects their cyst forms. The helminths are often able to resist destruction because of the tough shell that surrounds their eggs.

Parasitic protozoans can survive outside the intestinal tract in feces as a **cyst** with a thick hyaline wall that provides resistance to treatment.

The highest prevalence of giardiasis in the United States is in communities using surface water supplies, where potable water treatment consists primarily of disinfection. Giardiasis can also be contracted from contaminated food, mountain streams, and wastewater contaminated with infected feces. The best control that can be used to protect against protozoan waterborne infection is to use proper sanitation procedures (i.e., boil water and wash hands with soap and water).

CONTROL OF DISEASE

Ewald (1996) reports that disease control could be made more manageable if focusing attention on the pathogens most likely to become dangerous was possible—even though disagreement exists about the ability to predict and prevent the occurrence of these new pathogens. However, Ewald (1996) emphasizes that the identification of these pathogens rests on two major characteristics, the ability to spread easily from human to human through vectors and transmission features that select for high levels of virulence.

✓ **Interesting Point:** Examples of vectors are viruses, bacteria, rodents, and insects.

The transmission features that promote virulence include

- being vector-borne with humans as part of the life cycle,
- durability in the external environment if directly transmitted,
- being needle-borne or borne by attendants in medical care, and
- being sexually transmitted and mutation-prone with an attraction to critical cell types (WHO, 1995).

There is a long-term threat of emerging disease organisms, and the resources needed to keep pace with that threat are bolstered by the knowledge of these evolutionary characteristics.

Sidebar 4.2. West Nile Virus

Diseases transmitted by mosquito bites are becoming a more and more critical safety issue for anyone who spends time outside. Not only are mosquito bites itchy and annoying, the rapid spread of the West Nile virus means that avoiding mosquito bites altogether is becoming more and more important, especially for at-risk populations. West Nile was first reported in the United States in 1999, in four East Coast states. By 2000, the virus was in 12 states in the Northeast and mid-Atlantic regions. Reports for the summer of 2001 of the West Nile virus in both people and horses suggested an expanding zone of transmission for the 2002 mosquito season, one that was borne out in actuality—27 states, including some in the Midwest. In 2002, West Nile was in 44 states and had reached the West Coast. According to the CDC figures for 2003 (reported in April 2004), the West Nile virus is now in all but 4 states (Washington, Oregon, Alaska, Hawaii) and is responsible for 2,863 known cases of neuroinvasive disease, 6,829 cases of fever—a total of 9,858 total human cases reported to the CDC—and 262 deaths in 2003 alone (Penn State).

Activity spread from the initial zone, centered around the New York City area, with more and more cases of infection reported in several northeastern and mid-Atlantic states, spreading rapidly south and west.

Big cities, especially those that have international ports for travel and commerce, are frequently the starting point for the introduction of exotic diseases—something linked to, but not necessarily associated with, the spread of invasive species. As our world becomes more and more mobile, infectious diseases associated with one part of the world can migrate with startling speed. If the pathogens or their vectors find amenable conditions, they can thrive, just as exotic plants or animals can establish a foothold and thrive because their natural enemies don't exist. We don't have a societal immunity built up against exotic diseases.

Mosquitoes and infected birds spread West Nile virus to humans and other mammals. Migrating birds may spread the virus to other regions, where local mosquitoes pick up infected blood and transmit the infection further. Halting a disease spread by migrating birds is not possible, though cold winter weather could freeze out pockets of the disease-bearing mosquitoes.

For information you need on West Nile encephalitis, visit these Web pages:

Penn State College of Agricultural Sciences/AgriculturalResearchandCooperativeExtension, http://pubs.cas.psu.edu/freepubs/pdfs/uo207.pdf
2003 West Nile Virus Activity in the United States (reported as of April 14, 2004), http://www.cdc.gov/ncidod/dvbid/westnile/surv&control.htm

The bottom line on disease control: Moore (2002) points out that we cannot predict where, when, or how the next disease will emerge or reemerge, or the impact it will have on individuals, society, each nation, or the world. What's the answer? Increased vigilance and the application of more resources is the ultimate answer.

Chapter Summary

Microbiology is basic to the groundwork of environmental science and to the day-to-day functioning of tools working environmental scientists use every day. This technical information and the hands-on skills of identification and classification, testing, enumeration, and assessment tie in directly with organic chemistry and with the toxicology concepts presented in the next chapter.

Discussion Questions and Problems

1. Distinguish among aerobic, anaerobic, and facultative organisms.
2. How are fungi able to ingest food?
3. Distinguish between eukaryotic cells and prokaryotic cells.
4. What is an enzyme? What do they do?
5. What is a catalyst? What does it do?
6. What is the purpose of metabolism?
7. Explain the Krebs cycle.
8. Why is the study of microorganisms important to environmental scientists?
9. Are all microbes harmful? Explain your answer.
10. Explain the self-purification process in streams.

Suggested Research Topics and Projects

- Examine microbial epidemics, such as "Red Tide" or "*Pfiesteria*: Biography of Linnaeus."
- Examine the history and development of the binomial system of nomenclature.
- Research disease-causing bacteria life cycles.
- Research what is at the cutting edge of bacterial research.
- Research the world's largest living organism.
- Research the fungal identification process.
- Research Legionnaires' disease: history, causes, and effects.
- Research pathogenic parasitic protozoa linked to disease or human health issues.
- Examine the bacterial life cycles and changes in the activated sludge process.
- Examine the International Union of Biochemistry's enzyme classification system.
- Research metabolic transformation more thoroughly.
- Explore osmosis and water activity for microorganisms.
- Research water service breakdowns or failures in your area.

- Explore the history or write a biography of Typhoid Mary.
- Explore the history or write a biography of Leeuwenhoek.
- Examine microbial adaptation and survival and associated human health issues (e.g., antibiotic-resistant TB).
- Examine how pathogens invade the human body.
- Examine how pathogens develop drug resistance.
- Examine the treatments and precautions that can be taken to reduce the risk of contracting and spreading disease.

Notes

1. Information in this section is from *Cholera*, accessed April 24, 2011, www.NIH.gov/medlineplus/ency/article/000303.htm; F. Seas & E. Gotuzzo, 2009, "Vibrio Cholera," in G. L. Mandell, J. E. Bennett, and R. Dolin, eds., *Principles and Practice of Infectious Diseases*, 7th ed. Philadelphia, PA: Elsevier Churchill Livingstone, chapter 214.

2. This section is adapted from F. R. Spellman, 2006, *Environmental Science and Technology*, 2nd ed. Rockville, MD: Government Institutes Press.

3. Material in this section is from S. S. Morse, "Factors in the Emergence of Infectious Disease," January–March 1995, *Emerging Infectious Diseases* 1, no. 1: 7–11.

References and Recommended Reading

Allan, J. S, Short, M., Taylor M. E., et al. (1991). "Species-specific Diversity among Simian Immunodeficiency Viruses from African Green Monkeys." *Journal of Virology* 65: 2816–28.
American Heritage Dictionary of the English Language. 4th ed. (2000). Boston: Houghton Mifflin.
Anderson, C. (1991). "Cholera Epidemic Traced to Risk Miscalculation." *Nature* 354: 255.
Aristotle, 343 BCE. *The History of Animals.* Translated by D'Arcy Wentworth Thompson. Oxford: Clarendon Press.
Aristotle, 350 BCE. *On the Generation of Animals.* Translated by Arthur Platt. Oxford: Clarendon Press.
Barbour, A. F., & Fish, D. (1993). "The Biological and Social Phenomenon of Lyme Disease." *Science* 260: 1610–16.
Bergey's Manual of Systematic Bacteriology. 8th ed. (1974). Edited by Buchanan, R. E., & Gibbons, N. E. Williams & Wilkins.
Biello, D. (2010). "Slick Solution: How Microbes Will Clean up the Deepwater Horizon Oil Spill." *Scientific American.*
Bloom, B. R., & Murray, C. J. L. (1992). "Tuberculosis: Commentary on a Reemergent Killer." *Science* 257: 1055–64.
Breslow, R. *Enzymes: The Machines of Life.* (1990). Burlington, NC: Carolina Biological Supply Co.
Brock, T. D., & Madigan, M. T. (1991). *Biology of Microorganisms.* Englewood Cliffs, NJ: Prentice-Hall.
Campbell, N. A. (2004). *Biology: Concepts & Connections.* 4th CD-ROM ed. Benjamin-Cummings.
CDC (1991a). "*Aedes albopictus* Introduction into Continental Africa." *MMWR* 40: 836–38.

CDC (1991b). "Eastern Encephalitis Virus Associated with *Aedes albopictus*—Florida." *MMWR* 41: 115, 121.

CDC (1993). "Update: Multistate Outbreak of *Escherichia coli* 0157:H7 Infections from Hamburgers—Western United States, 1992–1993." *MMWR* 42: 258–63.

CDC (1994a). *Addressing Emerging Infectious Disease Threats: A Prevention Strategy for the United States.* Atlanta, GA: U.S. Department of Health and Human Services, Public Health Service.

CDC (1994b). "Assessment of Inadequately Filtered Public Drinking Water—Washington, D.C." *MMWR* 43: 661–63.

CDC (2009). "Dengue: Frequently Asked Questions." Accessed April 28, 2011, http://www .cod.gov/dengue/fAQFacts/index.html.

Cohen, M. L. (19920. "Epidemiology of Drug Resistance: Implications for a Post-antimicrobial Ear." *Science* 257: 1050–55.

Curtis, F. F., & White, G. B. (1984). "*Plasmodium falciparum* Mission to England: Entomological and Epidemiological Data Relative to Cases in 1983." *Journal of Tropical Medicine and Hygiene* 87: 101–14.

Davies, J. (1994). "Inactivation of Antibiotics and the Dissemination of Resistance Genes." *Science* 264: 375–82.

Domingo E., & Holland, J. J. (1994). "Mutation Rates and Rapid Evolution of RNA Viruses." In Mores, S. S., ed., *The Evolutionary Biology of Viruses*, 161–84. New York: Raven Press.

Epstein, P. R., Ford, T. E., & Colwell, R. R. (1993). "Marine Ecosystems." *Lancet* 342: 1216–19.

Ewald, P. W. (1996, October–December). "Guarding against the Most Dangerous Emerging Pathogens: Insights from Evolutionary Biology." *EID* 2, no. 4.

Fiennes, R.W. (1978). *Zoonoses and the Origins and Ecology of Human Disease*. London: Academic Press.

Gao, F., Yue, L., White, A. T., et al. (1992). "Human Infection by Genetically Diverse SIVSM Related HIV-2 in West Africa." *Nature* 358: 495–99.

Glass, R. I., Libel, M., & Branding-Bennett, A. D. (1992). "Epidemic Cholera in the Americas." *Science* 265: 1524–25.

Goshorn, D. (2006). *Proceedings of the DELMARVA Coastal Bays Conference III: Tri-State Approaches to Preserving Aquatic Resources.* Washington, DC: USEPA.

Gubler, D. J., & Trent, D. W. (1993). "Emergence of Epidemic Dengue/Dengue Hemorrhagic Fever as a Public Health Problem in the Americas." *Infectious Agent and Disease* 26: 383–93.

Hoge, C. W., Reichler, M. R., Dominguez, E. A., et al. (1994). "An Epidemic of Pneumococcal Disease in an Overcrowded, Inadequately Ventilated Jail." *New England Journal of Medicine* 331: 643–48.

Huxley, T. H. (1876). *Science & Education, Volume III: Collected Essays*. New York: D. Appleton & Company.

Inoue, N., Dambaugh, T. R., & Pellett, P. E. (1993). "Molecular Biology of Human Herpes Viruses 6A and 6B." *Infectious Agents and Disease* 26: 343–60.

Institute of Medicine. 1992. *Emerging Infections: Microbial Threats to Health in the United States.* Edited by Lederberg, J., Shope, R. E., & Oaks, S. C., Jr. Washington, DC: National Academy Press.

Isaacson, M. (1989). "Airport Malaria: A Review." *Bulletin of the World Health Organization* 67: 737–43.

Johnson, K. M. (1993). "Emerging Viruses in Contest: An Overview of Viral Hemorrhagic Fevers." In Mores, S. S., ed., *Emerging Viruses*, 46–47. New York: Oxford University Press.

Jones, A. M. (1997). *Environmental Biology*. New York: Routledge.

Keeton, W. T. (1996). *Biological Science*. R.S. Means Company.

Kilbourne, E. D. (1978). "The Molecular Epidemiology of Influenza." *Journal of Infectious Diseases* 172: 478–87.

King, R. M. (2003). *Biology Made Simple*. New York: Broadway Books.

Koch, R. (1882). "Uber die Atiologie der Tuberkulose." In *Verhandlungen des Knogresses fur Innere Medizin*. Wiesbaden: Erster Kongress.

Koch, R. (1884). *Mitt Kaiser Gesundh* 2: 1–88.

Koch R. (1893). *Journal of Hyg. Inf.* 14: 319–33.

Krause, R. M. (1992). "The Origin of Plagues: Old and New." *Science* 257: 1073–78.

Larsson, K. A. (1993). "Prediction of the Pollen Season with a Cumulated Activity Method." *Grana* 32:111–14.

LaDuc, J. W., Childs, J. E., & Glass, G. E. (1992). "The Hantaviruses, Etiologic Agents of Hemorrhagic Fever with Renal Syndrome: A Possible Cause of Hypertension and Chronic Renal Disease in the United States." *Annual Review of Public Health* 13: 79–98.

Le Guenno, B., Camprasse, M. A., Guilbaut, J. C., Lanoux, P., & Hoen, B. (1993). "Hantavirus Epidemic in Europe." *Lancet* 343: 114–15.

Levine, R., & Evers, C. (1999). *The Slow Death of Spontaneous Generation (1668–1859)*. Washington, DC: National Health Museum.

Levins, R., Epstein, P. R., Wilson, M. E., Morse, S. S., Slooff, R., & Eckardt, I. (1993). "Hantavirus Disease Emerging." *Lancet* 342: 1292.

Lynn, L. (1995). *Environmental Biology*. Northport, NY: Kendall-Hunt.

McKenzie, W. R., Hoxie, N. J., Proctor, M. E., et al. (1994). "A Massive Outbreak in Milwaukee of Cryptosporidium Infection Transmitted Through the Water Supply." *New England Journal of Medicine* 331: 161–67.

McKinney, R. E. (1962). *Microbiology for Sanitary Engineers*. New York: McGraw-Hill.

McNeill, W. H. (1976). *Plagues and Peoples*. New York: Anchor Press/Doubleday.

Med Net (2006). "Definition of Koch's Postulates." Medicine Net.com.

Metcalf & Eddy (1991). *Wastewater Engineering, Treatment, Disposal, and Reuse*. 3rd ed. Revised by Tchobanoglous, G., & Burton F. L. New York: McGraw-Hill.

Monath, T. P. (1993). "Arthropod-borne Viruses." In Morse, S. S., ed., *Emerging Viruses*. New York: Oxford University Press.

Moore, G. S. (2002). *Living with the Earth*. 2nd ed. Boca Raton, FL: Lewis Publishers.

Moore, P. S. (1992). "Meningococcal Meningitis in sub-Saharan Africa: A Model for the Epidemic Process." *Clinical Infectious Diseases* 14: 515–25.

Moore, P. S., & Broome, C. V. (1994). "Cerebrospinal Meningitis Epidemics." *Scientific American* 271, no. 5: 38–45.

Morse, S. S. (1990a). "Regulating Viral Traffic." *Issues in Science and Technology* 7: 81–84.

Morse, S. S. (1990b). "Looking for a Link." *Nature* 344: 297.

Morse, S. S. (1991). "Emerging Viruses: Defining the Rules for Viral Traffic." *Perspect Bil Med*, 34: 387–409.

Morse, S. S. (1993). "Examining the Origin of Emerging Viruses." In Morse, S. S., ed., *Emerging Viruses*, 10–28. New York: Oxford University Press.

Morse, S. S. (1994). "Toward an Evolutionary Biology of Viruses." In Morse, S. S., ed., *The Evolutionary Biology of Viruses*, 1–28. New York: Raven Press.

Morse, S. S., & Schluederberg, A. (1990a). "Emerging Viruses: The Evolution of Viruses and Viral Diseases." *Journal of Infectious Diseases* 162: 1–7.

Myers, G., MacInnes, K., & Korber, B. (1992). "The Emergency of Simian/Human Immunodeficiency Viruses." *AIDS Research and Human Retroviruses* 8: 373–86.

Neidhart, F. C., ed. (1987). *Escherichia coli and Salmonella typhimurium—Cellular and Molecular Biology.* Washington, DC: American Society of Microbiology.

Neu, J. C. (1992). "The Crisis in Antibiotic Resistance." *Science* 257: 1064–72.

Nomura, A., Stemmermann, G. N., Chyou, P. H., Kato, I., Perez-Perest, G. I., and Blaser, M. J. (1991). "*Helicobacter pylori* Infection and Gastric Carcinoma among Japanese Americans in Hawaii." *New England Journal of Medicine* 325: 1132–36.

Parsonnet, J., Friedman, G. D., Vandersteen, D. P., et al. (1991). "*Helicobacter pylori* Infection and the Risk of Gastric Carcinoma." *New England Journal of Medicine* 335: 12127–131.

Peterson, W. L. (1991). "*Helicobacter pylori* and Peptic Ulcer Disease." *New England Journal of Medicine* 324: 1043–48.

Prescott, et al. (1993). *Microbiology.*

Redi, F. (1669). *Experiments on the Generation of Insects.* Translated by Mab Bigelow. Accessed April 24, 2011, http://books.google.com/.

Riddihough, G. (1993). "Picture of an Enzyme at Work." *Nature* 362: 793.

Ries, A. A., Vugia, D. J., Beingolea, L., Palacios, A. M., Vasquez, E., Wells, J. G., Garcia, N., Swerdlow, D. L., Pollack, M., & Bean, N. H. (1992). "Cholera in Piura, Peru: A Modern Urban Epidemic." *Journal of Infectious Disease* 166, no. 6: 1429–33.

Rogers, D. F., & Packer, M. J. (1993). "Vector-borne Disease, Models, and Global Change." *Lancet* 342: 1282–84.

Rollin, P. E., Coudrier, D., & Sureau, P. (1994). "Hantavrus Epidemic in Europe, 1993." *Lancet* 343: 115–16.

Salyers, A. A., & Whitt, D. D. (1994). *Bacterial Pathogenesis: A Molecular Approach.* Washington, DC: American Society for Microbiology.

Scholtissek, C., & Naylor, E. (1988). "Fish Farming and Influenza Pandemics." *Nature* 331: 215.

SGM. (2006). *The Scientific Method, Fish Health and Pfiesteria.* University of Maryland; NOAA.

Singleton, P. (1992). *Introduction to Bacteria.* 2nd ed. New York: John Wiley & Sons.

Singleton, P., & Sainsbury, D. (1994). *Dictionary of Microbiology and Molecular Biology.* 2nd ed. New York: John Wiley & Sons.

Soares, S., Kristinsson, K. G, Musser, J. M., & Tomasz, A. (1993). "Evidence for the Introduction of a Multiresistant Clone of Serotype 6B Streptococcus Pneumonia from Spain to Iceland in the Later 1980s." *Journal of Infectious Diseases* 168: 158–63.

Spellman, F. R. (1997). *Microbiology for Water/Wastewater Operators.* Lancaster, PA: Technomic.

Spellman, F. R., & Whiting, N. E. (2006). *Environmental Science and Technology.* 2nd ed. Rockville, MD: Government Institutes.

Spieksma, F. T. (1991). "Aerobiology in the Nineties: Aerobiology and Pollinosis." *International Aerobiology Newsletter* 34: 1–5.

Thomas, L. (1974). *The Lives of a Cell.* New York: Viking Press.

United Nations (UN). (1991). *World Urbanization Prospects, 1990.* New York: United Nations.

U.S. Environmental Protection Agency (EPA) (2006). *What Is the Scientific Method?* http://www.epa.gov/maia/html/scientific.html.

Wachsmuth, I. K, Evins, G. M., Fields, P. I., et al. (1993). "The Molecular Epidemiology of Cholera in Latin America." *Journal of Infectious Disease* 167: 621–26.

Webster, R. G., Bean, W. J., Gorman, O. T., Chambers, T. M., & Kawaoka, Y. (1992). "Evolution and Ecology of Influenza A Viruses." *Microbiology Review* 56: 152–79.

World Health Organization (WHO). (1989). *Geographical Distribution of Arthropod-borne Disease and Other Principal Vectors*. Geneva: World Health Organization.

World Health Organization (WHO) (1995, November). "WHO Reports on New, Re-emerging Disease Threatening World Health." *The Nation's Health* 24.

Wilesmith, J. W., Ryan, J. B. M., & Atkinson, M. J. (1991). "Bovine Spongiform Encephalopathy: Epidemiological Studies on the Origin." *Veterinary Record* 128: 199–203.

Wistreich, G. A., & Lechtman, M.D. (1980). *Microbiology*. 3rd ed. New York: Macmillan.

Yamanishi, K., Okuno, T., Shiraki. L., et al. (1988). "Identification of Human Herpesvirus-6 as a Causal Agent for Exanthem Subitum." *Lancet* 1: 1065–67.

CHAPTER 5

Environmental Toxicology

> Most human decisions are made with incomplete knowledge. In daily life, a physician may diagnose disease from a single drop of blood or a microscopic section of tissue; a housewife judges a watermelon by its "plug" or by the sound it emits when thumped; and amid a bewildering array of choices and claims we select toothpaste, insurance, vacation spots, mates, and careers with but a fragment of the total information necessary or desirable for complete understanding. All of these we do with the ardent hope that the drop of blood, the melon plug, and the advertising claim give a reliable picture of the population they represent.
>
> —Frank Freese, 1976

"Don't Eat the Lettuce!"[1]

In a June 1994 outbreak of *Shigella sonnei* food poisoning in several countries in northwestern Europe, the vehicle of infection appeared to be iceberg lettuce. Several small outbreaks and clusters were reported during June. Various official reporting agencies and national and private laboratories were alerted, and studies were started to determine the causal factors involved with the food poisoning events.

The international researchers investigated sporadic cases associated with consumption of lettuce from particular restaurants or public houses; they were able to compare the date of onset with the date of delivery of iceberg lettuce by the wholesalers. The distribution chain was traced back through importers supplying wholesale markets in England. These wholesalers were supplied by packers in Spain. This was consistent with the findings of the investigators in the Norwegian outbreak. Iceberg lettuce investigated by the Public Health Laboratory service during the second week of June 1994 did not grow *SS. sonnei*. However, the iceberg lettuce season in Spain, which began in October, ended early in June, and the source of lettuce available for testing could not be traced.

The work performed in many international laboratories by epidemiologists (remember Dr. Snow?), toxicologists, and other scientists, together with reports from other European countries, including Scotland, Sweden, and Norway, determined through strong statistical evidence that consumption of iceberg lettuce was associated with the risk of becoming ill, and the temporal association of the outbreak with iceberg lettuce season in Spain implicated that lettuce as the vehicle of infection. This was corroborated by laboratory studies, which showed a change in predominant phage type during the period of the outbreak. The predominance of the same phage types in lettuce-associated *SS. sonnei* infections in a number of countries added further weight to the conclusion.

Because of coordinated laboratory results, epidemiological and toxicological investigation, and rapid communications and common typing techniques in various European countries, the causal factors of the contamination of iceberg lettuce and its resolution were determined and preventative measures put in place.

So, what was the plausible explanation for the contaminated iceberg lettuce? A plausible explanation is that fecally contaminated water was used to irrigate the lettuce or to cool it after packing. If iceberg lettuce, like many other leafy vegetables, is not washed thoroughly before consumption, contamination could be retained in the leaves.

Chapter Objectives

After studying this chapter, you should be able to:

- Describe and discuss the importance of dose/response.
- Describe how the biotic index works, and how it indicates pollution levels.
- Define and discuss the principles behind the biotic index and determine other potential uses for it.

Chapter Outline

- Introduction: Definition and discussion—toxicology
- Definition and discussion—dose–response relationship, curve, and threshold of effect
- Discussion: practical applications of environmental toxicology, laboratory work, and fieldwork
- Example: biotic index—definition, discussion, and application
- Discussion: biotic index concepts applied to other areas in environmental science

Key Terms

biotic index
dose–response curve
dose–response relationship
ecological toxicology
ecotoxicology

environmental toxicology
oxygen sag curve
threshold of effect
toxicity
toxin

Introduction

Toxicology is the study of the adverse effects of chemicals on living organisms. Often, toxicology is more simply defined as the science that deals with the nature and effects of poisons, or (even simpler) as the science of poisons. The development of toxicology as an independent science closely follows and parallels the growth pattern of the chemical industry and its production of non-natural toxicants. **Environmental toxicology** (which blends the principles and practices of environmental science with those of toxicology)—sometimes referred to as **ecological toxicology** or **ecotoxicology**—is the branch that addresses the effects of toxic substances, not only on the human population (population dynamics, community structure, and ecosystems), but also on the environment in general, including air, soil, surface water, and groundwater. To devise, then recommend, mitigation procedures for the effects of pollution, environmental toxicologists attempt to understand, monitor, and predict the consequences of a wide variety of toxic pollutants.

A toxicant or **toxin** is a chemical that can cause serious illness or death. **Toxicity** is a physiological property of matter that defines the capacity of a chemical to harm or injure a living organism by other than mechanical means. It entails a definite dimension—amount or quantity. The toxicity of a chemical depends on the degree of exposure.

Dose–Response

In the science of toxicology, a phrase has become well known to most students and practitioners: *It's the dose that makes the poison.* What this means, of course, is that a person can be exposed to just about any chemical and not receive or feel any ill effects—if the exposure dose is small or below the "toxic" level.

Consider arsenic. Arsenic is a poison. Anyone who has been exposed to crime shows on television or has had the opportunity to see or read Joseph Hesselring's *Arsenic and Old Lace* is familiar with the potent effects of arsenic. Arsenic trioxide has been a known poison since at least the Middle Ages.

Most people immediately correlate the word arsenic with another word: poison. Yet most people do not know that arsenic itself does not kill— the amount of arsenic (the dose) ingested kills. Arsenic, like several other heavy metals, tends to accumulate in the body. Thus, ingestion of a small dose of arsenic may seemingly exert no adverse effect. However, ingestion of multiple small doses could cause death.

Toxicologists base all toxicological considerations on the **dose–response relationship**. A dose is administered to test animals and, depending on the outcome, is increased or decreased until a range is found wherein at the upper end all animals die and at the lower end all animals survive. The data collected are used to prepare a **dose–response curve** relating percent mortality to dose administered.

To understand the dose–response relationship and its importance to environmental scientists and others, let's take a closer look at the dose–response curve and how it is used.

To determine what dose of a particular chemical causes which kinds of toxic effects, scientists generally administer a wide variety of doses to experimental animals.

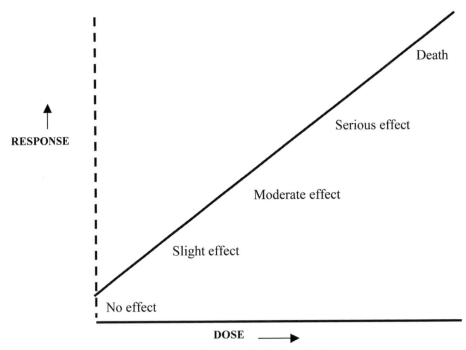

Figure 5.1.   Dose-response curve for a typical chemical.

During this process, the usual response pattern is that a very small dose causes no observable effects, at a higher dose some toxicity is observed, at still a higher dose there is greater toxicity, and at a high enough dose the animal dies. This gradual increase in toxic effects is known as dose–response and is often presented graphically (see Figure 5.1).

If we assume that the dose–response curve shown in Figure 5.1 represents what happens when chemical T is given to a mouse, the next question is: What happens if chemical T is given to a rat? Will the dose–response curve look the same? If not, how will it differ? The answer is that the dose–response curve will probably have a similar shape, but it will start rising at either a lower or higher dose than in the mouse. An entire group of curves describing what happens when chemical T is given to a number of different animals has been determined (see Figure 5.2), demonstrating that some animals are more sensitive to chemical T than others. This is important because what it is really showing is that a smaller dose is needed to produce the same toxic affect—the "toxic dose" varies from one kind of animal to another. The dose is species-specific.

Remember that a sufficiently small amount of most chemicals is not harmful. These chemicals possess a **threshold of effect**—a "no effect" level. The most toxic chemical known, if present in small enough amounts, will have no measurable effect. It might damage a few cells, but it will produce no measurable effect (e.g., liver damage). As the dose increases, a point when the first measurable effect is noted occurs. The toxic potency of a chemical is defined by the relationship between the dose of the chemical and the response it produces in a biological system. A high concentration of

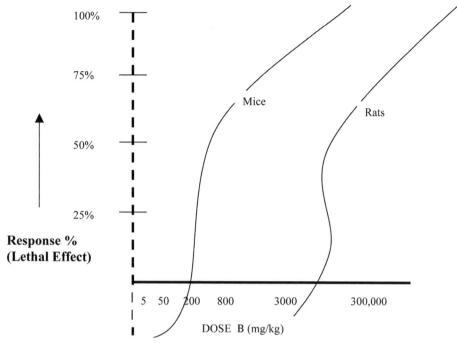

Figure 5.2. Variation of dose-response for the same chemical in two different species.

a toxic substance in a target organ (e.g., the liver) will cause a severe reaction, and a low concentration, a less severe reaction.

The "qualitative" information provided above is a rough estimate of the relative toxicity of various chemicals. In science, however, we are interested in making reproducible "quantitative" determinations of toxicity. To do this we use and follow specific experimental protocols.

The toxicologist, who is interested in determining whether or not a specific substance is harmful to organisms, understands that this determination depends on the properties of the chemical, the dose, the route by which the substance enters the body (the four routes of entry are inhalation, ingestion, injection, and contact with or absorption through the skin), and the susceptibility or resistance of the exposed individual.

Environmental Toxicology: Practical Applications

The environmental toxicologist is concerned with determining the concentration of toxic contaminants and how they affect all living organisms that inhabit our environment. Taking the lead in making these determinations is the US Environmental Protection Agency. The EPA is required to characterize and evaluate known hazardous waste sites where toxic releases to the environment have been observed. Under congressional mandate, the EPA must provide a means of responding to such toxic substance releases.

What role do environmental scientists and/or toxicologists play in the EPA's national monitoring and cleanup efforts for toxic waste sites and chemical spills and releases? Most of the personnel performing these tasks for the EPA are environmental scientists and toxicologists.

On a local level (in the everyday work world), environmental toxicologists do most of their experimentation, studies, and analysis in the laboratory. However, they also do a fair amount of work in the field, even though most toxicological analysis requires extensive work in a fully equipped laboratory. Let's take a look at an example of field level work the environmental scientist/toxicologist might be involved with, determining water quality without the aid of a laboratory.

Case Study 5.1. Biotic Index

Environmental scientists find of interest and often use four different indicators of water quality: coliform bacteria count, concentration of dissolved oxygen (DO), biochemical oxygen demand (BOD), and the **biotic index**. The biota that exist at or near a stream, for example, are direct indicators (a biotic index) of the condition of the water. This biotic index is often more reliable than many of the laboratory chemical tests that environmental scientist/toxicologists use in attempting to determine the pollutant level in a stream. Indicator species help determine when pollutant levels are unsafe.

How does the biotic index work? How does it indicate pollution?

Certain common aquatic organisms, by signifying the extent of oxygenation of a stream, may be regarded as indicators of the intensity of pollution from organic waste. The responses of aquatic organisms in streams to large quantities of organic wastes are well documented; they occur in a predictable, cyclical manner. For example, upstream from an industrial waste discharge point, a stream can support a wide variety of algae, fish, and other organisms, but in the section of the stream where oxygen levels are low (below 5 ppm), only a few types of worms survive. As stream flow courses downstream, oxygen levels recover, and those species that can tolerate low rates of oxygen (such as gar, catfish, and carp) begin to appear. Eventually, at some further point downstream, a clean water zone reestablishes itself, and a more diverse and desirable community of organisms returns.

During this characteristic pattern of alternating levels of dissolved oxygen (in response to the dumping of large amounts of biodegradable organic material), a stream goes through a cycle called an **oxygen sag curve**. Its state can be determined using the biotic index as an indicator of oxygen content.

The biotic index is a systematic survey of invertebrate organisms. Since the diversity of species in a stream is often a good indicator of the presence of pollution, the biotic index can be used to correlate with water quality. A knowledgeable person (such as an environmental scientist or toxicologist) can easily determine the water quality of any stream simply through observation of types of species present or missing, used as an indicator of stream pollution. The biotic index, used in the determination of the types, species, and numbers of biological organisms present in a stream, is commonly used as an auxiliary to BOD determination in gauging stream pollution.

The biotic index is based on two principles:

1. A large dumping of organic waste into a stream restricts the variety of organisms at a certain point in the stream.

2. As the degree of pollution in a stream increases, key organisms disappear in a predictable order.

The disappearance of particular organisms indicates the water quality of the stream.

Several forms of the biotic index are commonly used. In Great Britain, for example, the Trent Biotic Index (TBI), the Chandler score, the Biological Monitoring Working Party (BMWP) score, and the Lincoln Quality Index (LQI) are widely used. Most forms use a biotic index that ranges from 0 to 10. The most polluted stream, which contains the smallest variety of organisms, is at the lowest end of the scale (0); the clean streams are at the highest end (10). A stream with a biotic index of greater than 5 will support game fish; a stream with a biotic index of less than 4 will not support game fish.

Because they are easy to sample, macroinvertebrates have predominated in biological monitoring. In addition, comparison with identification keys, which are portable and conveniently used in field settings, can easily identify invertebrates. Present knowledge of invertebrate tolerances and responses to stream pollution is well documented. In the United States, for example, the EPA has required states to incorporate narrative biological criteria into their water quality standards since 1993.

Macroinvertebrates are a diverse group. They demonstrate tolerances that vary between species. Discrete differences tend to show up and often contain both tolerant and sensitive indicators.

The biotic index provides a valuable measure of pollution, especially for species that are very sensitive to lack of oxygen. Consider the stone fly. Stone fly larvae live underwater and survive best in well-aerated, unpolluted waters with clean gravel bottoms. When the stream deteriorates from organic pollution, stone fly larvae cannot survive. The degradation of stone fly larvae has an exponential effect on other insects and fish that feed off them; when the stone fly larvae disappear, so in turn do many insects and fish.

Table 5.1 shows a modified version of the BMWP biotic index. Because the BMWP biotic index indicates ideal stream conditions, it takes into account the sensitivities of various macroinvertebrate species to stream contamination. Aquatic macroinvertebrate species are represented by diverse populations and are excellent indicators of pollution. These organisms are large enough to be seen by the unaided eye. Most aquatic macroinvertebrates live for at least a year. They are sensitive to stream water quality, on both a short-term and long-term basis. Mayflies, stone flies, and caddis flies are aquatic macroinvertebrates considered clean-water organisms; they are generally the first to disappear from a stream if water quality declines and are therefore given a high score. Tubicid worms (tolerant to pollution) are given a low score.

In Table 5.1, a score from 1 to 10 is given for each family present. A site score is calculated by adding the individual family scores. The site score (total score) is then divided by the number of families recorded to derive the Average Score Per Taxon (ASPT). High ASPT scores result from such taxa as stone flies, mayflies, and caddis flies present in the stream. A low ASPT score is obtained from heavily polluted streams dominated by tubicid worms and other pollution-tolerant organisms.

(continued)

Case Study 5.1. (*continued*)

Table 5.1.   The BMWP Score System (Modified for Illustrative Purposes)

Families	Common-Name Examples	Score
Hepatagenidae	Mayflies	10
Leuctridae	Stone flies	10
Aeshnidae	Dragonflies	8
Polycentropidae	Caddis flies	7
Hydrometridae	Water striders	
Gyrinidae	Whirligig beetles	5
Chironomidae	Mosquitoes	2
Oligochaera	Worms	1

*Organisms with high scores, especially mayflies and stone flies (the most sensitive), and others (dragonflies and caddis flies) are very sensitive to any pollution (deoxygenation) of their aquatic environment.

Case study 5.1 shows that environmental scientists/toxicologists make use of the fact that unpolluted streams normally support a wide variety of macroinvertebrates and other aquatic organisms with relatively few of one kind in making determinations about water quality in the field. While some aquatic species, such as mayflies and stone flies, are more sensitive than others to certain pollutants and succumb more readily to the effects of pollution, other species, such as mussels and clams, accumulate toxic materials in their tissues at sublethal levels. These species can be monitored (*must be* monitored to protect public health) to track pollution movement and buildup in aquatic systems.

Using a biotic index to determine the level of pollution in a body of water demonstrates only one application. B. M. Levine, et al. (1989) point out that similar determinations regarding soil quality can be made by observing and analyzing organisms (such as earthworms) in the soil. Studies conducted to assess the impact of sewage biosolids (sludge) treatments on old-field communities revealed that earthworms concentrate cadmium, copper, and zinc in their tissues at levels that exceed those found in the soil. Cadmium levels even exceed the concentrations found in the biosolids. Thus, earthworms may provide an "index" for monitoring the effects of biosolids disposal on terrestrial communities.

In addition to determining the level of pollution in water and soil, environmental scientists/toxicologists also monitor the air we breathe. A few horrendous incidents involving acute exposure to dangerous airborne chemicals have been well documented. The sudden accidental release of methylisocyanate (MIC) at Bhopal, India, is one infamous example. Such acute exposures make headlines in the press, but chronic (long-term) exposures to sublethal quantities of toxic materials present a much greater hazard to public health and are of major concern to environmental toxicologists. Millions of urban residents are continually exposed to low levels of a wide variety of pollutants. Many deaths attributed to heart failure or diseases like emphysema may actually be brought on by long-term exposure to sublethal amounts of pollutants in the air.

Response Scenario 5.1.
Migrant Farmworker Poisoned

Note: The following is a fictional account of an incident—not unlike similar incidents that actually occur in growing numbers in agricultural settings throughout the world—involving pesticide misuse. These common incidents demonstrate only one way the misapplication of toxic chemicals can impact people exposed to them. As someone studying environmental science, however, you should view this incident beyond its immediate effects. Think about its possible significance in the "bigger picture": environmental damage.

A 41-year-old migrant farm worker was brought to Rachel's Creek Hospital emergency department by his coworkers. All spoke only Portuguese; no interpreter was available. However, the coworkers indicated that the patient had suffered from severe abdominal pain, nausea, vomiting, weakness, diarrhea, and increased salivation for several hours.

The patient was a well-developed, well-nourished Portuguese woman who seemed anxious and restless. Her speech slurred, and despite profuse sweating she appeared somewhat dehydrated. Her blood pressure was 165/110, pulse 94, and respiration 25 and labored. Physical findings included a watery nasal discharge, bilateral pinpoint pupils, profuse salivation, and marked respiratory wheezing. Occasional, diffusely distributed, uncoordinated, uncontrolled twitching of muscles (fasciculation) were noted. The patient was oriented to day and place, but mental status could not be evaluated further due to the language barrier.

Arterial blood gases showed mild respiratory acidosis, serum electrolytes were normal, and glucose was 195 mg per deciliter. An appropriate drug was administered, without improvement.

During the hour following her arrival, the patient became progressional and dyspneic and finally required intubation. When an interpreter arrived, he learned from the patient's coworkers that she had been accidentally sprayed by a pesticide applicator a few hours earlier at the cabbage field where they all worked. She had sustained a concentrated exposure, both respiratory and percutaneous, to the pesticide. Her coworkers were unable to identify the pesticide.

Within an hour of the exposure, the patient had begun to complain of chest tightness, nausea, and difficulty swallowing (dysphagia). She vomited several times, passed three loose stools, and developed generalized muscular weakness over several hours. It was then that she had been brought to the hospital.

(i) From the information provided, what do you think is the possible contaminant?

(ii) In a case such as this, to whom (which regulatory agency) would this incident be reported?

Note: Many pesticides are used throughout the world. Those at risk of occupational poisoning include individuals involved in its production or application, and field workers. Incidents of pesticides carried home on clothing (and affecting the health of young children in particular) are increasing also. Greater use of pesticides at home has also been associated with a growing number of childhood poisonings, and pesticides are frequently implicated in suicidal ingestions.

(continued)

Response Scenario 5.1. (*continued*)

RESPONSE—EXPLANATION

The patient described in this example was acutely exposed to parathion (an organophosphate). After receiving proper medical treatment, she went on to complete recovery. Her poisoning was reported to the departments of public health and environmental quality as required by state law. A follow-up study of the farm hands at the cabbage field revealed that most had suffered from nausea, vomiting, diarrhea, and increased secretions during work. Under intense regulatory and legal pressure, the grower soon introduced a series of procedural safeguards for pesticide application.

Response Scenario 5.2. Poisoned Picnic

The picnic started at 6:00 p.m., Tuesday evening, at Grand City Park. The park is located by the Grand River and contains several gazebos and picnic areas. The administration and faculty of Grand City Middle School organized the picnic as a relaxing event to be held before the faculty meeting. Many faculty and staff brought members of their families.

Mrs. Smith and Ms. Johnston arrived at 5:30 to set up. Mr. Albert arrived next to set up the grill. He brought his grill from home and had to take a few minutes to clean it off because it had not been used since the previous summer. Mr. Drake arrived next, after having bought the hamburgers at the supermarket. After the charcoal was lit and aluminum foil was placed over the grill, Mr. Albert began to cook.

At 5:55, Mrs. Smith realized that there was only one serving spoon. At that point, she left to get some more spoons. The other teachers waited for awhile, but finally decided to start eating at about 6:20.

When all of the food arrived there was a full menu that included baked beans, chicken, ham, green bean casserole, tuna casserole, cherry pie, pudding, potato salad, macaroni salad, corn, and hamburgers. Drinks included soda, water, coffee, and tea.

Mr. Drake was first through the line. He had

green bean casserole,
ham, and
a hamburger.

Ms. Cummings was next. She ate

potato salad,
ham, and
a hamburger.

The third person through the line was Mr. Carlson. He ate

green bean casserole,
potato salad, and
a hamburger.

Mrs. Albert was next in line. She sampled

potato salad,
a hamburger, and
cherry pie.

At this point, Mrs. Smith returned with more serving spoons. Mrs. Bell came at the same time. She was a little late because she had to be sure that her chicken was done.
Mrs. Wolfe went through the line next. She ate

green bean casserole,
chicken,
a hamburger, and
pudding.

Next was Mr. Lewis, who ate

baked beans,
green bean casserole,
macaroni salad, and
corn.

The line became a little unorganized at this point, and it is not clear who went through next. Mrs. Smith and Ms. Johnston were two of the last people through because they helped to serve.
Mrs. Smith ate

green bean casserole,
potato salad,
a hamburger, and
pudding

Others in attendance included Mr. Harvey, Ms. Jackson, Mr. Dooley, Mrs. Jones, and Mrs. Darwin. A lot of the guests said they could not remember exactly what they ate, but Mr. Harvey, Mr. Dooley, Mrs. Jones, and Mrs. Bell all had hamburgers, baked beans, and macaroni salad.
Ms. Jackson and Mrs. Darwin had ham, baked beans, corn, and some pudding for dessert.
Ms. Cain, Mrs. Williams, Dr. Oakton, Mrs. Corning, and Mrs. Reid have not yet been interviewed. Some other staff members arrived just in time for the faculty presentations, which started at 7:45 p.m. These included Mrs. Robinson, Mrs. Brown, and Mrs. Wright.
Some of the faculty and staff walked around while they ate, but most sat in one of the gazebos. The presentations were held in the main gazebo, which was a relief for some of the faculty because it seemed to be one of the few places free of duck droppings.
Even during the meeting, some of the kids chased ducks with their water guns. These kids never seemed to run out of water, because the guns held

(continued)

Response Scenario 5.1. (*continued*)

almost a gallon each, but even if they did run out, they quickly refilled them from the river. Just about everyone at the picnic, except for those who came only for the meeting, was soaked. Because it was a hot day, the only time anyone seemed to mind the soaking was when one of the kids missed the intended target and almost put out the grill. After this incident, which happened at about 6:10 p.m., the kids stayed away from the main gazebo, where the food was located, and turned their attention to the ducks and teachers walking around.

Grand City officials were alarmed by the illnesses and deaths that seemed to be associated with the event. They have promised a full investigation. Even the wastewater treatment plant just a few hundred yards up the river will have to submit a report on its procedures for water treatment. This is the first time anything like this has happened at the park, and officials want to be sure that it does not happen again.

Park managers said that most of the symptoms, such as dehydration, stomach cramps, nausea, and vomiting, indicate some type of food poisoning. However, at this point they cannot be certain.

You are now part of a team of epidemiologists that has been called in to get to the bottom of this mystery. You will need to identify the cause of the disease and prevent any further outbreaks. Time is of the essence. The first thing you will want to do is meet with your team members and outline the information you have been given, then decide what additional information you need. Grand City authorities have promised complete cooperation in this matter. Good luck!

DATA COLLECTION

The first order of business for the team of epidemiologists is to determine the goal of their investigation and to compile data related to the picnic. The goal is to determine the cause of the mysterious disease and how to prevent future outbreaks. Item 1, the picnic menu, and other collected items are shown below.

Item 1: Grand City Middle School Faculty Picnic Menu

Baked beans: Simply purchased two large cans of baked beans and heated on stove top to boiling.
Pudding: Mixed four packets of chocolate pudding with four cups of milk. Heated and then refrigerated.
Chicken: Baked chicken legs for one hour.
Ham: Baked ham for two hours thirty minutes, until thermometer read 150 degrees for twenty minutes.
Green bean casserole: Covered cracker crust with two cans of cream of mushroom soup and two jars of green beans. Topped with two cans of small onions. Baked for 20 to 25 minutes to warm.
Potato salad: Added one jar of salad dressing (mayonnaise) to assorted diced vegetables, 2 tablespoons sugar, ½ cup mustard, and 6 cups diced and cooked potatoes.

Macaroni salad: Cooked one box of elbow macaroni, added 3 T mustard, one jar salad dressing (mayonnaise), and various diced vegetables.
Tuna casserole: Took cracker crust, three cans tuna, one can cream of mushroom soup, one can cream of chicken soup. Mixed and topped with parmesan cheese topping.
Hamburgers: Purchased at the supermarket just before the picnic (receipt showed time was 12:25).
Corn: Heated two large cans of corn to simmering.
Cherry pie: Baked premade mountain top cherry pie, premade, baked 40 minutes.

Item 2: Poisoned Picnic Faculty Information Cards

See Table 5.2.

Pause 1: It's Got to Be the Potato Salad or Macaroni Salad!

We feel it is important to pause for a moment. We want to point out to readers that we have presented this particular case to undergraduate environmental health students in a few of our 300 level college courses for several years. We know this is the right place to pause in our presentation, because right after we introduce the above picnic menu to our students, many of their faces light up and beam that look of knowing the answers. We are used to this occurrence and always cease our presentation to allow the students the chance to comment on what they think. Invariably their statements relate the following: "Ah, they all got sick because of the potato and/or macaroni salad . . . . It was probably the mayonnaise that poisoned 'em." We allow the students to banter round and round with their statements without our interjecting anything. But as with all bubbles that eventually burst into nothingness, the time soon arrives to put the students back on the correct scientific approach to finding the picnic poison.

We explain that commercially prepared mayonnaise gets a bad rap when it comes to making picnickers sick from eating potato salad and/or macaroni salad. A commercially made jar of mayonnaise is set with a pH level point that bacteria can't survive in. The pH level makes mayonnaise safe to eat even if it is not refrigerated.

When people become sick from eating these salads, the causal factors are related to how long the salads have sat in the sun, along with the potatoes and onions. Bacteria have never found a freshly cut potato or onion that they did not immediately attack. They can't resist either one, and it is these potatoes and onions that are the culprits—not mayonnaise. However, in this case the potato and macaroni salads are not the culprits.

Item 3 consisted of specific additional information about the poisoned picnic event.

Item 3: Picnic Information Card

It was determined that there was only one burger on the grill when it was soaked. Mr. Albert decided to throw it away because he had to lift up the grill and add more charcoal. He walked away from the grill many times to talk to someone and return to some very well done burgers. No one seemed to mind; that's the way they wanted them.

(continued)

Response Scenario 5.1. (*continued*)

Table 5.2. Poisoned Picnic Faculty Information Cards

Mrs. Cain: Brought plates and cups to the picnic. Had chicken, potato salad, pudding, and green bean casserole. Became sick Tuesday evening. Symptoms included nausea, vomiting, and dizziness.

Mrs. Williams: Recovering. Became ill Tuesday night and was rushed to the hospital by her husband. Her son enjoyed his water gun, dousing teachers with river water. She loved the burgers made by Mr. Albert. She also tried some green bean casserole, chicken, and pudding. Her son did not become ill.

Dr. Oakton: Recovering. Had a great time except for when she stepped in duck droppings, which seemed to be everywhere. She didn't even mind being soaked. She tried a little bit of everything to eat.

Mrs. Corning: Arrived late, just in time to grab a burger and some green bean casserole. Most of the utensils and food were already put away. She became ill Wednesday morning and had to leave work around 8:30. She suffered from nausea and dizziness and was so disoriented that she could not drive home.

Mr. Lewis: Organized a game of volleyball set up by the gazebo. The players were a favorite target for the water guns! The only foul was when Mrs. Cain stepped on a duck going after the ball. Mr. Lewis became ill Tuesday evening. He was treated and released from the hospital Wednesday morning.

Mrs. Reid: Sampled a little bit of everything. She became ill Tuesday night and finally went to the hospital Wednesday morning. She complained of stomach cramps and nausea. Doctors quickly began an IV to help replenish lost fluids. She briefly went into a coma, then slowly recovered.

Mr. Albert: Mr. Albert took control of the grill. Mr. Drake soon showed up with the hamburger meat and started making the burgers. Mr. Albert had some potato salad, green bean casserole, a hamburger, and pudding for dessert. Mr. Albert became ill, suffering from numbness, disorientation, nausea, and vomiting. He was treated and released after several days in the hospital.

Mrs. Smith: She arrived early with her son and helped set up for the picnic. After many of the staff arrived, she realized that there was only one serving spoon, so she went home to get some more. She returned about 30 minutes later with spoons (after several faculty had gone through the line) to find her son chasing ducks with the water guns. Both Mrs. Smith and her son became ill.

Mrs. Johnston: Helped set up for the picnic. She had a hamburger, baked beans, pudding, and corn. She and several other teachers spent their time sitting in one of the gazebos talking and watching the children dash about after the ducks. Mrs. Johnston is lactose intolerant. She became ill just a couple of hours after the picnic, suffering from severe stomach pains. She went to bed and recovered overnight.

Mrs. Albert: Complained of stomach cramps early Tuesday night. Her condition continued to worsen until she finally had to be taken to the hospital. She was given massive doses of antibiotics. Her condition became worse as symptoms began to include vomiting and disorientation. She soon found that she could not remember much about the picnic. After some time, her condition improved.

It was also learned that the wastewater treatment plant performed several tests on the water coming from the plant (effluent). The effluent was virtually devoid of bacteria. The plant was doing a good job. They also did tests on the water around the park and found no notable bacterial contamination.

The epidemiological team obtained item 4, the pathology reports on victims.

Item 4: Pathology Reports

Victim: Mrs. Wolfe—Admitted to hospital suffering from abdominal pain and vomiting. Began diagnostic tests, but patient's condition deteriorated. Death due to respiratory and heart failure. Time of death: 3:30 a.m. 9/21/05.

Victim: Mr. Carlson—Paramedic response to home. Pronounced dead on arrival. Attempts to revive failed. Time of death: 11:30 p.m. 9/20/05.

Victim: Mr. Drake—Admitted to hospital suffering from abdominal pain, headache, and paralysis of extremities. Lapsed into shock. Pulmonary failure followed. Time of death: 2:30 a.m. 9/21/05.

Victim: Mrs. Cummings—Admitted to hospital suffering paralysis. Unable to communicate to hospital staff. Died of heart and respiratory failure. Time of death: 1:20 a.m. 9/21/05.

Item 5 Round Up the Usual Suspects

Because the epidemiological investigative team determined the culprit in the poisoned picnic episode was likely food poisoning, they listed specific disease-causing microbes that could be responsible. The suspect list is provided in Table 5.3.

From the toxin suspect list in Table 5.3 and the information and clues gathered from other sources, the team was able to select the correct food item and toxin responsible for the incident. The results of their findings are detailed in the incident explanation below.

Pause 2: The Culprit Identified?

Before presenting the poisoned picnic team's findings, we thought we would ask: Have you identified the food and the toxin? Let's see if your decision matches the team's findings.

(continued)

Response Scenario 5.1. (*continued*)

Table 5.3.   Poisoned Picnic: List of Suspect Disease-Causing Microbes

Microbe Name	Description
Staphylococcus aureus	*Staph* bacteria are very common on the skin of most animals, including humans. The bacteria can, in rare instances, be very dangerous when ingested. Food poisoning can result if the bacteria are allowed to multiply and produce toxins on handled food before eating. Foods commonly contaminated in the United States include turkey, ham, processed meats, chicken salad, pastries, and ice cream in which *staph* has grown. Infection is characterized by sudden nausea, vomiting, diarrhea, and often shock within a few hours of eating contaminated food. Usually other bacteria in the body help to keep *staph* at bay, but if something happens to upset this balance, such as the introduction of massive doses of antibiotics, infection can occur, with fatal results.
Bacillus cereus	*Bacillus cereus* is one of the many types of bacteria that cause food poisoning. General symptoms of stomach cramps, dizziness, and vomiting can be attributed to it, but the infection is rarely fatal. The illnesses caused by this intestinal intruder are actually caused by toxins it produces.
Escherichia coli	*E. coli* are found in the intestines of healthy animals, including humans. There are many different strains or types of this bacterium, and most are harmless to humans. However, some strains have been known to cause *E. coli* food poisoning. People can become infected by eating undercooked meat products (especially ground meat) that have been contaminated with animal feces. *E. coli* also can be contracted by ingesting other types of food, water, or anything else that has been contaminated with human or animal waste. Upon infection, the bacteria multiply and produce toxins. Victims usually suffer severe bloody diarrhea and stomach cramps. Some suffer vomiting. Infection can be fatal, especially for the elderly and the young, because their immune systems are not as strong as those in other age groups. Death can result from dehydration or damage to the red blood cells and kidneys.

Salmonella typhimurium	This bacterium causes salmonella food poisoning. It is usually caused by eating undercooked fowl (such as chicken or turkey), but can also be contracted from a contaminated water supply. Symptoms include headache, chills, and stomach pain and are usually followed by nausea, vomiting, diarrhea, and fever. Symptoms usually last three to four days. After this time, an individual may become a carrier of the disease. Rarely fatal if treated quickly.
Clostridium botulinum	This bacterium causes botulism. Botulism is actually caused by the toxins produced by the bacterium and not the presence of the bacterium itself. This organism reproduces by forming spores, which can be found in soil and therefore on vegetation. The bacteria are often found in meats and improperly canned foods. Infected individuals initially suffer from nausea, vomiting, and diarrhea. If enough toxin is ingested or produced, death can result from a general breakdown of the nervous system. Individuals may become paralyzed, and death usually occurs as result of respiratory paralysis.
Clostridium perfringens	This bacterium causes gas gangrene. The condition can lead to a buildup of gases in the muscles of the body, rendering them useless. Infection also causes stomach pain and cramping (gastroenteritis). Disease is usually caused by eating meat that has been stewed or boiled and then set aside before reheating and serving.
Streptococcus pyogenes	This bacterium is widely distributed among humans. Infected individuals may spread this pathogen through respiratory droplets. This organism can cause sharp outbreaks of sore throats and scarlet fever. High fever and skin lesions characterize infection by this pathogen. Individuals with known infection should be isolated.

POISONED PICNIC: INCIDENT EXPLANATION

In determining the food item and correct toxin that caused the poisoned picnic event, the investigation team pieced together the following clues from a variety of sources:

- The opening information states that there was only one serving spoon when the teachers began going through the line. Moreover, the first person through

(continued)

Response Scenario 5.1. (*continued*)

the line had green bean casserole. That person was one of the four fatalities. The next person through the line was also a fatality. This person did not eat green bean casserole, but the toxin was on the serving spoon after being used for the casserole and then for the potato salad. The second person through the line got it from the spoon! After this, the other serving spoons arrived, and the cross-contamination soon ended.

- Team members realized that everyone who had the green bean casserole contracted the illness. Two people became ill (one of whom died) who did not have the green bean casserole. The second person through the line contracted the disease from the serving spoon. The other person was lactose intolerant and became ill because of the pudding, which was made with milk.
- From the list of usual suspects, team members were able to link the symptoms of the disease to botulism. From this and other research, team members knew that botulism can come from improperly canned vegetables. The menu states that the green bean casserole was made using canned green beans. Botulism is easily destroyed by high heat. However, the menu also states that the casserole was only heated to warm. This would not have provided enough heat to destroy the toxin.
- In addition to identifying the cause of the disease, team members were also able to outline a strategy to prevent future outbreaks of the disease. Because this outbreak was due to food poisoning, team members realized that they needed to educate the teachers, students, and parents about proper food handling techniques. For this specific contaminant, information should include inspection of canned foods for bulges (a result of gas buildup from growth of the bacteria) and also stress the importance of using sufficient heat to destroy the toxin. Other general information should include cleanliness in food preparation areas, washing of hands, and the use of clean utensils in food preparation. This information could be presented in the form of a brochure or a school auditorium skit that would be broadcast on CCTV, local television stations, or radio stations.

Final Pause

So, did you determine that the green bean casserole was the bad food, that the spoon was the source of cross-contamination, and that the deadly toxin was *Clostridium botulinum*? If so, great! If not, no problem. The point is that the poisoned picnic event demonstrates the need for a step-by-step approach based on actual facts in determining causal factors related to an event such as this one.

For those of you who immediately jumped on the potato salad or macaroni salad (laced with copious amounts of mayonnaise, of course) as being the bad food, as mentioned, you are not alone in your assumptions. And this is the point about the need for science and the scientists' toolbox: Investigative opinions should be based on facts and good science—peer-reviewed and verified facts and the practice of good science only, please!

Chapter Summary

All organisms are exposed to toxic substances. Some of these substances (lead and mercury, for example) have always been in the environment in trace amounts. However, present-day industrial processes (technological advancements) concentrate substances like lead and mercury to dangerous levels—and then release them into the environment. Many of the toxic chemical products and by-products that enter the environment produced today were unknown a few decades ago. An increasing concern is that the environment we live in today—the air that we breathe, the water we drink, and the food we eat—endangers our health. This is where environmental scientists/toxicologists come in. Their concern is with the study, detection, and mitigation of all such toxicants and their potential impact on our environment—and on our lives and life around us.

Discussion Questions and Problems

1. Which of these factors is considered least important in evaluating exposure to toxicant materials?
   a. route of entry
   b. frequency of exposure
   c. duration of exposure
   d. weaning age of the animals
2. A city has an infestation of mosquitoes. There is a public fear of meningitis and demands that the city take some remedial action. A city worker sprays malathion mixed with kerosene. What dangers, if any, are there for the worker?
3. What are the three main routes of entry into the body for chemicals?
4. It is not the poison that kills, it is the dose. Explain.
5. What ecosystems are found in the area where you live? What environmental problems are caused by the different ways in which these ecosystems are managed or mismanaged?
6. Imagine that an accident at a chemical factory released a large quantity of a previously unknown chemical into the local source of drinking water, but that no increased illnesses in the community were noted for six years. Would you be reassured that the accident was harmless? Explain. What more, if anything, would you want to know?
7. Distinguish between acute and chronic toxicity.
8. Although much less spectacular, chronic exposure to toxic materials is a greater threat to human health than acute exposure. Explain.

Suggested Research Topics and Projects

• Research problems associated with residential use of pesticides: human health effects, environmental effects.

- Research acute environmental toxins sensitivity.
- Research products in common use that may cause toxicity problems.
- Research arsenic in literature.
- Research species-specific toxic accumulation and the food chain.
- Research how environmental toxins reach entry in humans. Example: In *A Civil Action*, the people affected were exposed in all three ways. How could that be?
- Research stream purification using biotic index analysis.

Note

1. From Centers for Disease Control, 1996, "An Outbreak of *Shigella sonnei* Infection Associated with Consumption of Iceberg Lettuce," accessed May 5, 2011, http://www.cdc.gov/ncidod/eid/vol1no1/frost.htm.

References and Recommended Reading

Centers for Disease Control (1996). "An Outbreak of *Shigella sonnei* Infection Associated with Consumption of Iceberg Lettuce." Accessed May 5, 2011, http://www.cdc.gov/ncidod/eid/vol1no1/frost.htm.

Environ (1988). *Elements of Toxicology and Chemical Risk Assessment.* Washington, DC: Environ.

Haas (1997). *A Civil Action.*

Huff, W. R. (1993). "Biological Indices Define Water Quality Standards." *Water Environment and Technology* 5: 21–22.

Jefferies, M., & Mills, D. (1990). *Freshwater Ecology: Principles and Applications.* London: Belhaven Press.

Kamrin, M. A. 1989. *Toxicology.* Chelsea, MI: Lewis Publishers.

Levine, M. B., Hall, A. T., Barret, G. W., & Taylor, D. H. (1989). "Heavy-Metal Concentration During Ten Years of Sludge Treatment to an Old-Field Community." *Journal of Environmental Quality* 18, no. 4: 411–18.

Mason, C. F. (1990). "Biological Aspects of Freshwater Pollution." In Harrision, R. M., ed., *Pollution: Causes, Effects, & Control.* Cambridge, UK: The Royal Society of Chemistry.

Meyer, E. (1989). *Chemistry of Hazardous Materials.* 2nd ed. Englewood Cliffs, NJ: Prentice-Hall.

O'Toole, C., ed. (1986). *The Encyclopedia of Insects.* New York: Facts on File.

Spellman, F. R. (1996). *Stream Ecology and Self-Purification: An Introduction for Wastewater and Water Specialists.* Lancaster, PA: Technomic.

US Environmental Protection Agency (1986). *Superfund Public Health Evaluation Manual.* Washington, DC: Office of Emergency and Remedial Response.

Wooten, A. (1984). *Insects of the World.* New York: Facts on File.

CHAPTER 6

Environmental Geology and Groundwater Hydrology

Plants absorb energy from the sun. This energy flows through a circuit called the biota, which may be represented by a pyramid consisting of layers. The bottom layer is the soil. A plant layer rests on the soil, an insect layer on the plants, and so on up through various animal groups to the apex layer, which consists of the larger carnivores.

—Aldo Leopold

The science of hydrology would be relatively simple if water were unable to penetrate below the Earth's surface.

—Harold E. Thomas

Under heaven nothing is more soft and yielding than water.
Yet for attacking the solid and strong, nothing is better;
It has no equal.

—Lao Tzu, *The Tao Te Ching*

Chapter Objectives

After studying this chapter, you should be able to:

- Describe the major components of soil and explain how it is formed.
- List the physical, chemical, and biological factors that are responsible for soil formation.
- Describe a typical soil profile.
- Differentiate between soil texture and soil structure.
- List the major uses for land and describe how various land uses affect agriculture and the environment.
- Explain the role of living things in soil formation and fertility.

Chapter Outline

- Discussion: soil and its relationship with water hydrology
- Definition: geology
- Definition and discussion: rock formation and type
- Discussion: how soil is formed; weathering, abrasion, and pioneer communities and organisms
- Definition and discussion: characteristics of soil types
- Definition and discussion: soil profile and horizons
- Discussion: soil function
- Discussion: soil as a medium for plants
- Discussion: soil in recycling
- Discussion: soil as an engineering medium
- Discussion: soil as a medium for organisms
- Discussion: soil as a purifier for water supplies
- Definition and discussion: groundwater hydrology and the water cycle

Key Terms

aquifer
atmosphere
evapotranspiration
geology
groundwater
horizon
humus
hydrologic
hydrological cycle
hydrosphere
igneous
lithosphere

loam
magma
metamorphic
oxidize
parent material
pioneer community
sedimentary
soil profile
soil texture
tilth
water table
weathering

Introduction

As with biology, chemistry, ecology, and other related sciences, a fundamental knowledge of **geology** is a prerequisite for meeting and understanding the many environmental science challenges into the 21st century. Geology is a wide field, but in this text, we focus on only one division of geological science—soil science—because of its natural interface with the other environmental media, air and water. Not only can the study of soil be fascinating and intellectually stimulating; soil is also the ideal medium in which to observe practical applications for basic principles of biology, chemistry, other related sciences, and water hydrology.

To discuss soil without discussing the natural interface that is soil plus water hydrology would be like launching a hot air balloon without the hot air needed to lift it skyward. More specifically (and correctly stated), a natural interface occurs among air, soil (minerals), living organisms, and water. This natural interface can be seen in any good-quality **loam** surface soil where these four media are mixed in complex patterns. Figure 6.1 shows the proportions of soil volume occupied by each medium.

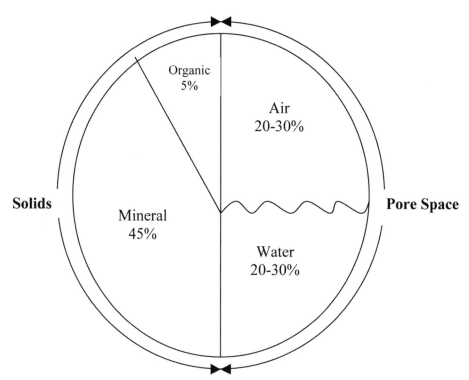

Figure 6.1. Typical volume concentration of a loam surface soil. The curved line between water and air indicates that the proportion of these two components fluctuates as soil becomes wetter or drier.

To better understand and appreciate the message presented in Figure 6.1, consider a handful of dirt, a clump you turn over and over in your hand. You ask yourself, "Is this clump of dirt solid?" It appears to be—but it is not. The clump is really a mixture of components. Only about half of the soil volume contains solid material (mineral and organic). The other half consists of pore spaces filled with air and water.

In water hydrology (especially **groundwater** hydrology), the environmental scientist must have a thorough understanding of the machinations of the **hydrological cycle**, the water–soil surface interface, and the role soils play in subsurface water supplies, because the focus of environmental legislation has been on cleaning up our waters, both on the surface and below ground. The environmental practitioner must have a fundamental understanding of geology and water hydrology to effect cleanup of the problems of pollution and make use of the technology to prevent contamination or to decontaminate subsurface problems. The following sections are intended to raise your understanding of the basic science involved and in turn will help you understand the more complex environmental issues related to soil and groundwater problems discussed in detail later in this text.

What Is Geology?

In a traditional sense, we can say that geology is the science of Earth, its origin, composition, structure, and history. On a much simpler plane, we can say that the Earth comprises three main areas, or spheres: the **lithosphere** (rock and soil), the **hydrosphere** (water), and the **atmosphere** (air). In this chapter, we are concerned with the study of geologic material (primarily rocks and soils—the lithosphere) through which groundwater moves.

Formation and Types of Rocks

Rocks are classified into three types: **igneous, sedimentary**, and **metamorphic**. The igneous (at one time in a molten or liquid state) are the many types of volcanic material that then harden into rock form. Granite, for example, is an igneous rock found in the core of many mountain areas.

Sedimentary rocks have one thing in common: They are all composed of small units, ranging in size from molecules through dust particles, to pebbles and large boulders, all brought together and deposited on the surface of the Earth's crust. All of the mineral matter comprising these rocks was once part of other rocks.

The third and final category of rocks is metamorphic. The term *metamorphic* means simply "changed in form." The name concentrates attention on the processes by which the rock evolves. All of the rocks in this class were once either igneous or sedimentary, but have been changed by pressure, heat, or chemical action of liquids or gases so that their original nature has been significantly altered. Pressure is caused by burial of rock types beneath the surface, and heat is applied as a function of either depth or proximity to molten rock from **magma** beneath the surface of igneous intrusions into the upper rock layers.

Soil is derived from **parent material** rock.

Formation of Soil

Soil is a complex mixture of minerals, organic material, billions of living organisms, air, and water, and is the thin covering over the surface of the Earth. It is a renewable resource. Soil is initially formed from rock, the parent material, through a combination of physical and biological events. Soil building begins with the physical fragmentation of ancient layers of rock or more recent geologic deposits from lava flows or glacial activity. The kind of parent material and climate determines the kind of soil formed. Physical factors that bring about the fragmentation or chemical change of the parent material are known as **weathering**. Weathering is the process whereby rocks are broken down into smaller pieces. There are two types of weathering: mechanical and chemical. *Mechanical weathering* occurs when rocks are broken into smaller pieces by physical means. Plant and animal activity, abrasion, tree-fall, and temperature change (ice wedging) are primary mechanical agents of weathering.

Plant and animal activity breaks rocks into smaller pieces in a variety of ways. Plants grow strong roots that grow into existing rock cracks. As the roots grow, they expand and add pressure to the rock, until small pieces of rock begin to flake or break away. Tree roots can also grow around rock segments, and when tree fall occurs the underlying rock is pulled up and exposed to surface conditions, where continued weathering takes place. Burrowing animals like rabbits and moles dig holes that expose new rocks to the effects of weathering. The holes allow water and other weathering agents to reach the rock layer that had been covered by the soil. With exposure and time, large rocks are made into smaller rocks.

Did You Know?

Earthworms are a major factor in the weathering of rock. They tunnel through the soil looking for food. As they tunnel, they bring rock pieces (flakes) to the surface and expose covered rock to the effects of air and water.

Because rock does not expand evenly, heat can cause a large rock to fracture. Pieces fall off, resulting in smaller chunks that are eventually reduced in size by other processes. One of these processes is the repeated freezing and thawing of water. Water finds its way into cracks and crevices, then expands as it freezes, causing the rock to be broken into smaller pieces over time. In the seasonal cycles of freeze and thaw, the cracks become progressively wider and wider, causing the rock to eventually fracture, crack, and break into smaller pieces.

Abrasion is the grinding of rocks and is also an important weathering process that eventually reduces large, solid rock masses to soil. This physical breakdown of rock is commonly caused by glacial action, wherein rock fragments grind against each other. This results in small fragments and smoother surfaces. Carried by glaciers, these fragments and particles are deposited when the ice melts. Weathering by abrasion also occurs when wind and moving water cause small particles to collide. Moving water in streams and rivers also cause rock fragments to collide and rub together, making their surfaces smooth. Similarly, wind picks up particles and causes them to collide with objects like rock formations, eventually resulting in fragmentation of both the rock formation and the wind-driven particles.

Moving water and wind cause smaller particles to be pushed along to some other location, where new surfaces are exposed to further weathering. Many of the landscapes throughout the world were created by a combination of moving water and wind that removed easily transported fragments and particles, while more resistant rock formations remained. These remaining formations are still undergoing the weathering process; someday they too will be reduced to small fragments and particles that will end up as soil.

In addition to these mechanical forces, certain chemical forces and activities also alter the size and composition of parent material and participate in the soil-making process. These chemical activities include (1) the action of atmospheric air working to chemically **oxidize** small rock fragments into different compounds; and (2) hydrolysis, through which water combines with water molecules—oxidized and hydrolyzed molecules are more readily soluble in water and may be removed by rain or moving water. Acid rain also assists in dissolving rocks.

This rock fragmentation process continues as the first organisms gain a foothold in broken down or modified parent material. Lichens often form a **pioneer community**—the first successful integration of plants (including animals and decomposers) into a bare rock community. The lichen-formed pioneer community traps small particles and chemically alters the underlying rock. When plants and animals become established, they contribute increasing amounts of organic matter, which is incorporated with small rock fragments to form soil. **Humus**, dead organic matter, becomes mixed with the top layers of rock particles, constituting a critical soil ingredient. It supplies some of the nutrients needed by plants and also increases soil acidity so that inorganic nutrients become more available to plants. These inorganic soil constituents are more soluble under acidic conditions. Some crops (corn and wheat, for example) grow best in soils with a pH between 5.0 and 7.0. When humus is added to a soil with a pH above 7.0, the soil becomes more productive, because the humus increases the soil acidity. Along with affecting the soil's nutrient availability, humus modifies **soil texture**. A soil with a loose, crumbly texture allows water to soak in and permits air to be incorporated into it. A compact soil allows water to run off and prevents adequate aeration.

Burrowing animals, fungi, soil bacteria, and the roots of plants are also important in the biological process of soil formation. The earthworm is one of the most important burrowing animals. These animals literally eat their way through soil, mixing organic and inorganic material as they go. This mixing action obviously results in an increase in the amount of nutrients available for plant use. Earthworms also increase the fertility of the soil by bringing nutrients from the deeper layers of the soil up into the area where the roots of plants are concentrated. Burrowing earthworms improve soil aeration and drainage. When earthworms collect dead organic matter from the surface and transport it into burrows, this adds organic matter to the soil.

Earthworms are not the only organisms that improve soil quality. Bacteria and fungi are decomposers. They, along with other organisms, reduce organic matter to smaller particles, improving soil quality.

Over time (from as little as a few weeks to hundreds of years, depending on climate conditions), physical, chemical, and biological processes have formed the soils we have today. Soil formation is a slow but continuous process.

Response Scenario 6.1. Doing Dirt

Natural soil evolution is both variable and long term; some soils develop quickly, others more slowly—from over 1,000 years for quick-developing soils, to over a million years for slow-developing soils. The equilibrium stage of primary succession represents the highest natural soil development possible from existing environmental factors. Ecological factors that impact soil evolution include climate and area, the original formation rock, and drainage. Soils evolve through processes related to humification and alternation.

When soil is in balance at an ecological climax stage, if left undisturbed the balance tends to remain. The existing vegetation produces the needed humification, protects the ground from erosion, and binds soil particles together. Small-scale disturbances at the climax stage cause retrogression, but if the disturbance halts, secondary succession naturally occurs rapidly. Large-scale disturbances, however, destroy the balance. Whether they are natural or introduced by humans, when soil is significantly disturbed, erosion quickly destroys the exposed soils, reverting upper soil horizons to earlier succession stages.

Although most soil degradation is the result of erosion caused by human activity, specific agricultural practices damage soil as well, causing soil to degrade and destructure. Using mineral rather than organic fertilizers gradually breaks apart soil structure, causing a decrease in soil organic matter and biological activity. The consequences of these breakdowns and decreases are terrific strains on soil systems, which will eventually cause human populations serious problems.

RESPONSE

(l) List at least four problems stemming from too much interference in natural soil cycles. Compare your answers with those provided in the chapter summary.

Soil Enhancement and Rebuilding

Although improving soil stewardship can slow soil erosion, and improved practices can enhance and rebuild soil, without wide-scale cooperation, soil degradation will continue. Improving soil structure, adding organic matter, and limiting runoff works very well for soil improvement. But human-scale technique cannot totally restore a soil (and the life associated with it) that took nature more than 1,000 years to create.

Soil Characteristics

Soil characteristics include soil texture, structure, atmosphere, moisture, biotic content, and chemical composition. *The mineral present in the soil determines soil texture (or feel).* It determines the oxygen (proportions of sand, silt, and clay) present in the soil and the oxygen- and water-holding capacity of soil. Gravel and sand, the larger particles, allow water and air to penetrate the soil because their shapes permit many tiny spaces between individual particles. Not only do water and air flow through these spaces, but water also drains very rapidly; as it drains, it carries valuable nutrients to lower soil layers, where they are normally beyond the reach of the roots of plants. Clay particles are generally packed close together to form waterproof layers, so soils with large amounts of clay content do not drain well, are poorly aerated, and retain nutrients.

Soil rarely consists of one type or size of particle. It is a mixture of various particle sizes and types, resulting in soils being classified into several different types. Those with roughly equal mixtures of clay, sand, silt, and humus are called loam. **Loam** is the ideal soil because it combines the good aeration and drainage properties of large particles with the nutrient retention ability of clay particles.

Although texture helps to determine soil structure, remember that soil structure and texture are different. **Soil texture**, or **tilth**, refers to the way various soil particles clump together, or how the soil particles are arranged. It helps determine soil *porosity*, a measure of the volume of pores or spaces per volume of soil and of the average distance between those pores.

The structure of a particular soil is strongly influenced by the amount of clay and organic matter it contains. Sand particles do not clump; therefore, sandy soils lack structure. Clay soils tend to stick together in large clumps. Clay and organic particles, because of their chemical and physical properties, are able to link with other particles, forming larger soil aggregates. Being small and numerous, clay particles create a large surface area in a given amount of soil, which provides a surface for water and nutrients to cling to. In contrast, soils lacking clay or organic matter have an unstable structure and are likely to form dust or loose sand, which can easily blow away.

A good soil, composed of small clumps, crumbles easily when squeezed by hand. This ability to crumble is known as *friability*. Sandy soils are friable; clays are not. Soil that will crumble has adequate spaces to allow air and water to mix with soil. The air in these spaces provides a source of oxygen for plant root cells. Water for the roots occupies the remaining soil space.

Soil Profile

The **soil profile** is a series of horizontal layers of different chemical composition, particle size, and different amounts of organic matter that differ greatly from region to region. Each recognizable layer is known as a **horizon**. Each soil horizon has a characteristic color, texture, structure, acidity, and composition. Road cuts and other excavations can expose soil profile. Horizons within a soil may vary in thickness and have somewhat irregular boundaries, but generally they parallel the land surface.

The uppermost layer of the soil contains more nutrients and organic matter (decomposed plant leaves and roots) than the deeper layers. This layer is known as the **A horizon** or **topsoil**. The A horizon may vary in thickness from a few centimeters to over a meter in some areas. The majority of the living organisms and nutrients are found near the top of the A horizon. The lower portion of the A horizon often contains few nutrients, because they are leached to the B horizon by flowing water.

The layer underlying the A horizon, the **B horizon** (also known as the subsoil), contains comparatively less organic matter than the horizon nearer the surface. The B horizon also contains less organic material and fewer organisms, but it accumulates nutrients leached from higher levels.

The area below the B horizon is known as the **C horizon** and consists of weathered, unconsolidated parent material. The C horizon is outside the zones of major biological activities, lies above the impenetrable layer of bedrock, and is generally little affected by the processes that formed the horizons above it.

Note that soil profiles and the factors that contribute to soil development are extremely varied.

Functions of Soils

Soil's primary function is to support the growth of plants by providing a medium for plant roots and supplying nutrient elements essential for the plant. The various properties of the soil determine the nature of the vegetation present, and to a lesser degree, the number and types of animals that the vegetation can support. A secondary function of soil is to act as a recycling system for nature (and for us). Within the soil, dead bodies of animals, plants, and people, and their waste products, are assimilated, and their basic elements (nutrients) are made available for reuse. Soil also functions as an engineering medium. It not only provides the foundation for virtually every type of construction project, but also is an important building material (Earth fill and bricks). Obviously, one of the most important functions soil provides is habitat for a host of living organisms. Finally, soil functions to control the fate of water in the **hydrologic** system. Soil affects water loss, usage, purification, and contamination.

SOIL PROVIDES A MEDIUM FOR PLANT GROWTH

That soil provides physical support for and anchors the root systems of plants so they won't fall over is obvious. Less obvious is what else soil provides to plants. We all know soil is the primary medium for plant growth, but what is involved in this process? What goes on beneath the surface?

Plant roots are the primary residents of subsurface soil. Roots depend on the process of respiration to obtain energy. Because root respiration, like our own respiration, produces carbon dioxide (CO_2) and uses oxygen (O_2), an important function of soil is "gas transfer"—allowing CO_2 to escape and fresh O_2 to enter the root zone. This gas transfer is accomplished via the network of soil pore spaces.

An equally important function of soil is to absorb rainwater and hold it where it can be used by plant roots. When exposed to sunlight, plants require a continuous stream of water to use in nutrient transport, cooling, turgor maintenance (swelling or distension from water), and photosynthesis. Whether it's raining or not, plants use water continuously. Thus, the water-holding capacity of soils is essential for plant survival. The deeper the soil, the more holding capacity it normally has for storing water to allow plants to survive long periods without rain.

The soil also moderates temperature fluctuations. The insulating properties of soil protect the deeper portion of the root system from the extremes of hot and cold that often occur at the soil surface.

As well as moderating moisture and temperature changes in the root environment, the soil supplies plants with inorganic mineral nutrients in the form of dissolved ions, including potassium, iron, copper, nitrogen, phosphorus, sulfur, and many others. The plant takes these elements out of the soil solution (the thin aqueous film surrounding soil particles) and incorporates most of them into the various organic compounds that constitute plant tissue. Soil supports plant growth by providing a continuing supply of dissolved mineral nutrients in amounts and relative proportions appropriate for plant growth. Enzymes, organic metabolites, and structural compounds making up a plant's dry matter consist mainly of carbon, oxygen, and hydrogen, which the plant obtains via photosynthesis from air and water, not from the soil.

SOIL RECYCLES RAW MATERIALS

How important is the raw-material recycling continuously performed by soil? It is so essential that without the constant reuse of nutrients that this natural recycling provides, plants and animals would have run out of nutrients eons ago, and in fact, Earth would not have been able to establish life on any large scale. Instead of layers of plants, the world would be covered with a layer of dead plants, animals, and waste. Soil also plays a key role in geochemical cycles. It assimilates large quantities of organic waste, turning it into humus; converting the nutrients to forms used by plants and animals; and returning the carbon to the atmosphere as gaseous carbon dioxide, where it will be reused again via plant photosynthesis. Large accumulations of carbon in soil organic matter can have a major impact on the *greenhouse effect* (discussed in detail later).

SOIL IS AN ENGINEERING MEDIUM

Generally, soil is a firm, solid base on which to build roads and all kinds of buildings. However, some soils are not as stable as others and are unsuitable to build on. Whether a soil is or is not suitable for a particular type of construction or excavation is a decision that can only be accurately made by professional soil engineers.

SOIL PROVIDES A MEDIUM FOR ORGANISMS

For those who consider soil nothing more than a pile of organic debris and broken rocks, consider picking up a handful of dirt. When you do, what you really have in your hand is an entire ecosystem. A handful of certain types of soil may be the home of several hundred million organisms, belonging to several thousand species. One handful of soil could contain a full range of organisms, including predators, prey, producers, consumers, decomposers, and parasites. When someone questions the validity of placing soil in the same category of importance as the other two environmental media, water and air, he or she only need study the microworld contained in one handful of soil to find the answer.

SOIL REGULATES WATER SUPPLIES

Excluding the relatively small quantity of precipitation that falls directly into bodies of fresh water, nearly every drop of water in our lakes, rivers, streams, estuaries, and **aquifers** has either traveled through the soil or flowed over its surface. Consider a steep hillside, joined by a gully housing a slow-moving stream. Some of the rain falling on the steep hillside may soak into the ground, where the water may be stored in the soil and used by the trees, bushes, flowers, and grass that cover it, while some may seep slowly down through the soil layers to the groundwater, eventually entering the stream over a period of a few months or years. As the water flows through the soil, soil processes remove many impurities and kill disease organisms.

Soil is not only a natural storehouse for water, it is also a filter—probably the best filter there is. Mother Nature has a way of perfecting processes that we attempt to imitate but never really duplicate, at least not to the same degree.

Environmental scientists are concerned with the quality and quantity of the water in our lakes, rivers, streams, and underground aquifers. A primary mission (obligation) in environmental science is to prevent, mitigate, or abate pollution that threatens the quality of our waters for fishing, drinking, and swimming. To better fulfill this obligation, environmental science practitioners must have a fundamental knowledge of soil science and groundwater hydrology.

Groundwater Hydrology

Ralph C. Heath (2005) makes a good point when he states that it is surprising, considering that groundwater is so widely used and so important to the health and economy of the country, that the occurrence of groundwater is not only poorly understood but also the subject of many widespread misconceptions. Common misconceptions include the belief that groundwater occurs in underground rivers resembling surface streams, whose presence can be detected by certain individuals. This misconception and others have hampered the development and conservation of groundwater and have adversely affected the protection of its quality.

Hydrology is the science concerned with the occurrence and circulation of water in all its phases and modes. Groundwater hydrology is the subdivision of the science of hydrology that deals with the occurrence, movement, and quality of water beneath the Earth's surface. Hydrology begins with the hydrological cycle, the means by which water is circulated in the biosphere (see Figure 6.2). **Evapotranspiration**—the combination of evaporation and transpiration of liquid water in plant tissue and the soil

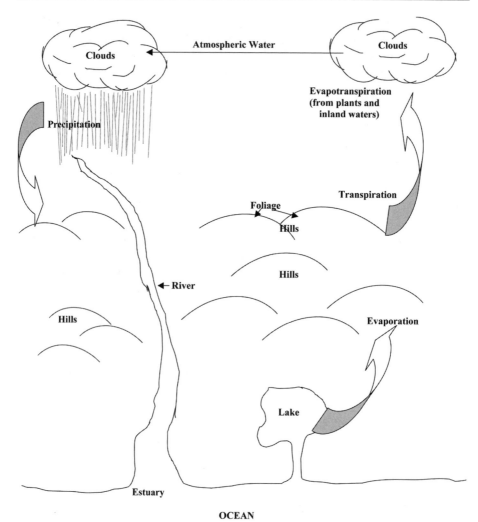

Figure 6.2.   Water cycle. Adaptation from Spellman, F. R., 1999. *The Handbook for Waterworks Operator Certification, Vol II*. Lancaster, PA: Technomic

to water vapor in the atmosphere—from the land mass, plus evaporation from the oceans, is counterbalanced by cooling in the atmosphere and precipitation over both land and oceans (see Figure 6.2). The hydrological cycle requires that on a worldwide basis, evaporation and precipitation are equal. However, oceanic evaporation is greater than oceanic precipitation; thus excess precipitation is given to the land. Eventually this land precipitation ends up in lakes, rivers, and streams and returns to the sea, completing the cycle.

Most of the Earth's water (about 97%) is salty; only a small portion (less than 3%) is fresh. Three-quarters of all fresh water is found in polar ice caps and glaciers, and nearly one-quarter, **groundwater**, is found underground in water-bearing porous rock or sand or gravel formations. Some 96% of the U.S. water supply is groundwater.

Groundwater percolates down through the soil after a rain or snow or seeps downward from surface water and is stored in an aquifer. This percolation is quite slow, typically only two feet per year and rarely more than one foot per day. An **aquifer** is a water-bearing geologic formation composed of layers of sedimentary material, including sand, gravel, and porous rock. Water fills the cracks and crevices of the rock and the pores between the particles of sand and gravel. The depth at which the aquifer begins is known as the **water table**. Before it reaches the aquifer, water passes through an unsaturated zone, where pores contain both water and air. Plants remove some of the water; the rest continues to move downward to the saturated zone. Thus groundwater is that part of underground water below the water table, and soil moisture is that part of underground water above the water table. Shallow, unconfined aquifers are recharged by water percolating downward from soils and materials directly above the aquifer. Eventually most groundwater flows into rivers, lakes, wetlands, and oceans.

Historically, groundwater has been considered to be so safe to drink that many water companies deliver it untreated to their customers. We have learned, however, that some of our groundwater is becoming—or already is—contaminated with hazardous substances from landfills, septic systems, and surface impoundments. One challenge for environmental practitioners is to prevent groundwater contamination and to restore quality and quantity when contamination has occurred. However, remember that once groundwater becomes contaminated, restoration is difficult, if not impossible. According to Sandra Postel, director of the Global Water Policy Project, "If we're to have any hope of satisfying the food and water needs of the world's people in the years ahead, we will need a fundamental shift in how we use and manage water."

Chapter Summary

For most of us, soil is easier to ignore than are water and air. Most people don't realize how directly our water supply is linked to healthy soil. The study of soil science and groundwater hydrology has never been more important to environmental scientists, practitioners, students—and to all other organisms on Earth.

Plausible Answers to Response Scenario 6.1

1. Increased damage from natural disasters.
2. Water quality degradation from turbidity, increased nitrogen and phosphorus levels, increased pollution levels caused by industrialization, urbanization, and agriculture, more rapid eutrophication.
3. Loss of biological diversity through reduction of climax vegetation and habitat loss.
4. Yield reduction because of soil quality degradation. Increased human populations increase the need for high-yield crop production; in some places, crop failure means devastation and starvation without intervention. Today's world population of over 5.5 billion people uses roughly 10% of Earth's land area for food production (both crops and livestock). Slight degradation can reduce production by 10%; moderate

degradation can cause yield decreases from 10 to 50%; severely degraded soils lose over 50% of their production potential. Soils in developing countries are most severely affected.

Discussion Questions and Problems

1. List the following soils in order of increasing porosity to water: clay, loam, and sandy loam.
2. Why should everyone, not just environmental scientists, be concerned with soil conservation?
3. Name the key properties of soil that are good for growing most crops.
4. What problems can occur from overuse of groundwater?
5. Explain why soils with very large or very small particle sizes are not optimal for the growth of plants.
6. Explain how organic matter alters both the physical and the chemical nature of soils.
7. What factors affect the formation of soil?
8. Name four major components of soil.
9. Describe the process of soil formation.
10. How does soil particle size affect texture and drainage?
11. What is erosion?
12. Why is groundwater depletion such an urgent problem?

Suggested Research Topics and Projects

- Extended definition of soil/dirt.
- Research soil pH and pH levels' effects on specific crops.
- Perform a soil analysis of a site in your area.
- Perform a soil profile for a site in your area.
- Examine a clump of soil—analyze the soil community.
- Examine soil as a water purifier/filter.
- Examine the history of soil/land/agricultural conservation.
- Research agricultural practices that preserve soil integrity.

References and Recommended Reading

Bohn, H. L., McNeal, B. L., & O'Connor, G. A. (1985). *Soil Chemistry*. 2nd ed. New York: Wiley.

Bouwman, A. F., ed. (1990). *Soils and the Greenhouse Effect*. New York: Wiley.

Brady, N. C. (1974). *The Nature and Properties of Soils*. New York: Macmillan.

Courtney, F. M., & Trudgill, S. T. (1984). *Soil: An Introduction to Soil Study*. Baltimore, MD: E. Arnold.

Ellis, B. G. & Foth, H. D. 1997. *Soil Fertility.* 2nd ed. Boca Raton, FL: CRC Press/Lewis Publishers.

Freeze, R. A. & Cherry, J. A. 1979. *Groundwater.* Englewood Cliffs, NJ: Prentice-Hall.

Gupta, R. S. 1989. *Hydrology and hydraulic Systems.* Englewood Cliffs, NJ: Prentice-Hall.

Heath, R. C. (2005). *Basic Ground-Water Hydrology.* U.S. Geological Survey Water-Supply Paper 2220. Washington, DC: U.S. Government Printing Office.

Jenny, H. (1941). *Factor of Soil Formation: A System of Quantitative Pedology.* New York: McGraw-Hill.

Linsley, R. K., Hohler, M. A., & Paulhus, J. L. (1975). *Hydrology for Engineers.* 2nd ed. New York: McGraw-Hill.

Paddock, J., Paddock, N., & Bly, C. (1986). *Soil and Survival: Land Stewardship and the Future of American Agriculture.* San Francisco: Sierra Club Books.

Petersen, G. W., Cummingham, R. L., & Matelski, R. P. (1971). "Moisture Characteristics of Pennsylvania Soils: III. Parent Material and Drainage Relationships." *Soil Science Society of America Proceedings* 35: 115–119.

Soil Survey Division Staff. (1993). *Soil Survey Manual.* Agricultural Handbook 18. Washington, DC: U.S. Gov't Printing Office.

Spellman, F. R. (1998). *The Science of Water: Concepts and Applications.* Lancaster, PA: Technomic.

Spellman, F. R. (1999). *Handbook of Waterworks Operator Certification.* Volume II. Lancaster, PA: Technomic.

U.S. Environmental Protection Agency (1986, September). "Drinking Water in America: An Overview." *EPA Journal.*

Willis, R. & Yek, W. W-G. (1987). *Groundwater System Planning & Management.* Englewood Cliffs, NJ: Prentice-Hall.

CHAPTER 7

Environmental Sampling and Analyses

An understanding of the underlying theories and principles of environmental sampling and analyses empowers environmental professionals to select and adapt the proper sample and analysis protocols for specific contaminants as well as for specific project applications.

Chapter Objectives

After studying this chapter, you should be able to:

- Define and describe representative sampling and the components important to sampling successfully.
- Define, describe, and discuss the four reasons for sampling, and why environmental planners monitor media.
- Choose sampling locations and what makes a good location.
- Define, describe, and discuss the two types of samples and their uses, strengths, and weaknesses.
- Define, describe, and discuss the two types of sample collection methods and the advantages and disadvantages of each.
- Describe and discuss the key considerations for choosing a media flow measurement site.
- Describe and discuss the keys to successful field sampling programs.
- Describe and discuss how air is contaminated by pollutants and what conditions affect air quality.
- Define, describe, and discuss the most common methods for evaluation of air quality.
- Define, describe, and discuss the mechanics of soil/groundwater pollution.
- Define, describe, and discuss the common methods used for soil and groundwater sampling.

Chapter Outline

- Discussion: contamination of air, soil, and water
- Discussion and definition: planning, representative sampling, analysis, and reporting
- Discussion: sampling program considerations
- Discussion: sampling program objectives
- Discussion: choosing sampling locations
- Discussion and definition: sampling types
- Discussion and definition: collection methods—manual and automatic
- Discussion: accurate measurements
- Discussion: field procedures
- Discussion and definition: general evaluation methods
- Discussion and definition: ambient air quality evaluation
- Discussion and definition: soil and groundwater evaluation
- Discussion and definition: soil and groundwater sampling
- Discussion: lab analysis

Key Terms

auger
automatic samplers
composite sample
depletion
dispersion
excavation
geophysical testing
grab samples

modeling
monitor wells
monitoring
representative sample
soil boring
transformation
trenching

Introduction

Through improper use, storage, and/or disposal, contaminants find their way into air, groundwater, and soil. Once a hazardous material has spilled, discharged, or leaked, its impact and movement depend on several factors. In air, quality is impacted by those things we can see with the naked eye or under the microscope (pollen, dust, etc.), and those substances we can't see (ozone, sulfur dioxide, carbon dioxide, etc.). In soil and groundwater contamination, when a contaminated material has leaked or been discharged to the surface, its movement depends on the nature of the material and the soil horizon. In this chapter, we discuss various means of sampling air, soil, and groundwater. This chapter provides the environmental practitioner with additional "tools" to perform the critical task of evaluating environmental contamination problems.

Environmental Sampling and Analysis: What's It All About?

Anyone working in any branch of science, environmental science included, must have scientifically reliable data to work with. *Reliable* means that proper procedures for sampling and analysis are followed so that the results accurately reflect the content of the sample.

Obtaining reliable environmental samples is a difficult process. Again, the key word here is "reliable." In general, for the purpose of reliability, the sampling effort should be directed toward taking and obtaining **representative samples**. According to the U.S. EPA's Office of Research and Development, a representative sample (representativeness) expresses the degree to which data accurately and precisely represent a characteristic of a population, parameter variations at a sampling point, a process condition, or an environmental condition. Taking representative samples is critical.

However, sampling is more involved than just ensuring representativeness. Sampling operations require that you start with a sampling plan, then execute it in a reliable fashion. Specific needs, of course, dictate which techniques are actually incorporated into a sampling plan and which ones are rejected. Techniques not selected should be rejected only because they don't meet sampling goals, not because they were overlooked.

In the sampling plan, the main objective is to take representative samples of a heterogeneous and dynamic (changing) piece of our environment, to analyze them for components that constitute a very small fraction of the samples (often at or below the parts-per-billion [ppb] range. Working with tiny fractions of samples is only one of many problems involved in sampling. Other complicating factors are that the matrix is usually very complex, opening the door for analytical interferences such as false positives and masking. Other interference can be introduced during sample transport and preservation. Further complicating the sampling and analytic process is the reactivity (unstableness) of some analytes.

So what does all this mean? That sampling is, without a doubt, the weakest link in the *planning-sampling-analysis-reporting process*. In short, we can say that the reliability of the overall data obtained cannot be greater than that of the reliability of the weakest part of the chain of events constituting an environmental sampling and analysis effort.

The bottom line is this: What good is any analytical report if the samples are not representative of their source?

Response Scenario 7.1.
The Environmental Practitioner's Toolbox

In a serious mechanic's, carpenter's, machinist's, or handyman's toolbox, you would expect to find a complete set of tools, including pliers, sockets, wrenches, drive tools, screwdrivers, handsaws, clamps, tap and die sets, micrometers, calipers, combination squares, tape measures, hammers, hack saw, woodworking tools, and other specialty tools. The serious mechanic, carpenter, or machinist has other tools that are not as obvious, including knowledge, experience, and skill. This makes sense: a full toolbox is useless without someone who knows how to properly use the tools.

The environmental technician, scientist, or practitioner also has a toolbox, which includes the tools of chemistry, biology, ecology, toxicology, geology, groundwater hydrology, soil science, and other related sciences. And like the mechanic, carpenter, and machinist, the environmental practitioner must know how to use these tools.

The environmental practitioner needs a well-rounded education in the basic sciences and well-rounded knowledge of the sciences related to the environment to be able to properly evaluate environmental contamination.

Remember, the mechanic, carpenter, machinist, handyman, and environmental practitioner not only must all have their sets of basic tools, they must also know how to use them.

From the environmental practitioner's standpoint, possession of scientific knowledge puts the tools in one's hand—but more is required. The environmental practitioner must take those tools and apply them. The principal way in which they are applied is through sampling and analyzing the media (air, water, or soil) with which they are concerned.

RESPONSE

(i) Besides the tools listed above, what tools would you add to the environmental practitioner's toolbox?

General Considerations for a Sampling Program

Note: Much of the general sampling information provided in the following section is based on the U.S. Department of Commerce's *Handbook for Sampling and Sample Preservation of Water and Wastewater* (1982), which has applications for all three environmental media types.

No single sampling program can apply to all types of environmental media. Nevertheless, each sampling program should consider:

- location of sampling points,
- types of samples,

- sample collection methods,
- measurements, and
- field procedures.

OBJECTIVES OF SAMPLING PROGRAMS

We use sampling and analysis programs for four major reasons: planning, research or design, process control, and regulation. These objectives in an overall environmental media quality program are interrelated and cover various stages from planning to enforcement. Based on these objectives, we compare the different sampling programs in general terms.

An environmental planner monitors to

1. establish representative baseline media quality conditions,
2. determine assimilative capacities of specific media,
3. follow effect of a particular project or activity,
4. identify pollutant source,
5. assess long-term trends,
6. allocate waste load, and
7. project future media characteristics.

SAMPLING LOCATIONS

Usually, the sampling program's objectives define the approximate locations for sampling (e.g., influent and effluent to/from a treatment plant or water supply intake). Often, however, the objectives give only a general indication (the effect of surface runoff on stream quality) when assessing the quality of drinking water supplies for a community.

Most sampling surveys and subsequent analyses are performed to meet the requirements of federal, state, or local regulations. Examples of regulatory monitoring are the National Pollutant Discharge Elimination System (NPDES), established in accordance with the Federal Water Pollution Control Act Amendments, and the EPA's 503 regulations dealing with the disposal and incineration of wastewater biosolids in accordance with the Clean Air Act (CAA). Specific objectives in collecting regulatory data vary considerably and often overlap, but generally they are designed to

1. verify self-monitoring data;
2. verify compliance with a regulatory permit;
3. support enforcement action;
4. support permit reissuance and/or revision; or
5. support other program elements, such as media quality standards requiring various data.

TYPES OF SAMPLES

The type of sample collected depends on the variability of flow, variability of media (water, air, soil) quality, the accuracy required, and the availability of funds for conducting the sampling and analytical programs. We are concerned with two types of sampling techniques: grab and composite samples.

Grab samples are individual, discrete samples collected over a period of time not exceeding 15 minutes. A grab sample can be taken manually, using a pump, scoop, vacuum, or other suitable device. Collecting a grab sample is appropriate when it is needed to

1. characterize media quality at a particular time,
2. provide information about minimum and maximum concentrations,
3. allow collection of variable sample volume,
4. collaborate composite samples, or
5. meet a requirement of a discharge permit.

Use a grab sample when (1) the medium being sampled does not flow continuously; (2) the media or waste characteristics are relatively constant; (3) the parameters to be analyzed are likely to change with storage, such as dissolved gases, residual chemical, soluble chemical, oil and grease, microbiological parameters, organisms, and pH; (4) information on maximum and minimum air variability is desired; (5) the history of media quality is to be established based on relatively short time intervals; and (6) the spatial parameter variability is to be determined (for example, the parameter variability throughout the cross-section and/or depth of a stream or large body of water).

A **composite sample** is a sample formed by mixing discrete samples taken at periodic points in time or a continuous proportion of the flow. The number of discrete samples that make up the composite depends on the variability of pollutant concentration and flow. A sequential composite is defined as a series of periodic grab samples, each of which is held in an individual container, then composited to cover a longer time period.

A composite sample is used when (1) determining average concentrations and (2) calculating mass/unit time loading.

SAMPLE COLLECTION METHODS

Samples can be collected manually or with automatic samplers. Whichever technique is employed, the success of the sampling program is directly related to the care exercised in sample collection. Optimum performance is obtained by using trained technicians.

Manual sampling involves a minimal initial cost. The human element is the key to the success or failure of manual sampling programs. Well suited to a small number of samples, it is costly and time-consuming for routine and large sampling programs. The advantages of manual sampling include low capital cost, no maintenance, and that extra samples can be collected in a short time. Disadvantages of manual sampling include the probability of increased variability from sample handling, inconsistency in collection, and high cost of labor. In addition, sampling is a repetitious and monotonous task for personnel.

Automatic samplers are cost effective, versatile, and reliable. They also increase and improve capabilities—greater sampling frequency and increased sampling needs because of regulatory requirements. They are available with widely varying levels of sophistication, performance, mechanical reliability, and cost. Additional advantages of using automatic samplers include the consistency of the samples, minimal labor requirements, and the capability of collecting multiple samples for a visual estimate of variability and analysis of individual samples. The disadvantages include that considerable maintenance is required, that size is restricted to general specifications, inflexibility, and the ever-present potential of sample contamination.

MEASUREMENTS

Inaccurate measurements for samplings such as flow measurements lead to inaccurate proportional composite samples, which in turn lead to inaccurate results. Care must be exercised in selecting a measurement site. The ideal site provides desired measurement to meet program objectives, ease of operation and accessibility, and personnel and equipment safety.

A media flow measurement system usually consists of a primary device having some type of interaction with the media and a secondary device that translates this interaction into a desired readout or recording.

Flow measurement methods, depending on the type of media to be sampled, can be broadly grouped into four categories:

1. Closed circuit flow measurement
2. Flow measurement for pipes discharging to atmosphere
3. Open channel flow measurement
4. Miscellaneous methods of measurement

FIELD PROCEDURES

In environmental sampling, field operations are critical. If proper precautions are not exercised in field procedures, the entire sampling program becomes meaningless—despite adequate planning, analytical facilities, and personnel. The key to the success of a field sampling program is good housekeeping, collection of representative samples, proper handling and preservation of samples, and appropriate chain of custody procedures. Improper procedures in any sampling task can cause inaccurate results.

Sidebar 7.1. Sydney, Australia

From the end of July to the end of September 1998, on three occasions, residents of the city of Sydney, Australia, had to take the precaution of boiling their drinking water. Testing found giardia and cryptosporidium in the public water supply. According to the Sydney authorities, at these levels, the giardia and cryptosporidium cysts posed little, if any, health threat. No incidents of illness were linked to the presence of giardia and cryptosporidium—however, businesses that relied on large quantities of pure water could not function on boil-alert quality water.

Evidence seemed to indicate that the plant itself was creating the problem, and that the results of water tests performed by the lab (Australian Water Technologies) were improperly read (or performed) and misinterpreted. The aftermath of the incidents left the Sydney Water Corporation (the privately owned organization handling the treatment systems since privatization in January 1995) in shambles. Beginning on July 29, the three boil alerts (the last ended September 19) resulted in a massive investigation into the causes and sources of the contamination and the resignation of Sydney Water's managing director and chairman (whose blossoming political career crashed and burned). Sydney Water Corporation was also stripped of responsibility and major assets, losing control of treatment plants, dams, and catchment areas to the government's new Sydney Catchment Authority. Sydney Water Corporation had to make repayments to residential water users for the expense and trouble of using bottled water, and a whopping lawsuit was filed by the businesses and industries affected by the shutdown. On the positive side, Australia put an American-style Clean Water Act into place (which if nothing else established guidelines to follow in such a case), and Sydney is working to ensure good preventive maintenance measures for watershed protection.

Of special interest are the tests, their results, and the difficulty in pinpointing the source (or sources) and cause of the contamination. American experts warned that actually finding a direct source was unlikely (causes of the 1995 outbreak in Milwaukee were similarly uncertain) and recommended either an ozonation system or microfiltration be installed to ensure completely safe drinking water. That expert advice, though, presumed that actual giardia and cryptosporidium contamination existed—which was in more than a little doubt.

During that two-month period, test results on the same water samples varied widely. Tests for the later shutdowns were less accurate than those for the initial shutdown—not surprising with panic conditions at the lab, which was under pressure to find the causes and gun-shy about risking either consumer wrath about the inconvenience or consumer illness and death from contamination. One test sample was read at 1,000 cryptosporidium oocysts initially. Sample reexamination found only two. Technicians may also have mistaken harmless algae similar in appearance to giardia and cryptosporidium for the dangerous cysts, raising false (and expensive) alarms. Even in retesting, test results were shaky. The New South Wales Health Department counted what it thought were more than 9,000 oocysts per hundred liters of treated water in one sample—higher levels than testing should find in raw sewage. An expert from the department of civil engineering at the University of New South Wales who saw lots of different algae and no cryptosporidium in his own tests on the water pointed out that the highest U.S. level ever reported was 1,000—and that those U.S. reports included Milwaukee (aka the "bug that made Milwaukee famous") in 1995, when hundreds of thousands of people fell ill. He also pointed out that other common fecal bacteria should be present in the sample as well, but were not (The Age, 1998).

The moral of the story? Know your stuff. Be sure of your technique and do everything you can to ensure the accuracy of your samples and test results. As an environmental scientist, you may have to turn in test results that open a similar can of worms at some point—or announce unsafe water supplies to the press.

Did You Know?

Standard operating procedures (SOPs) are documents that provide a step-by-step description of how a specific operation, method, or procedure is performed. Generally, SOPs are submitted in lieu of applicable portions of a sampling and analysis plan.

General Evaluation Methods for Environmental Media

AMBIENT AIR QUALITY EVALUATION

To evaluate ambient air quality, you need some fundamental knowledge of how air is contaminated by pollutants. The air contamination process begins with a source, either stationary or mobile, that releases contaminants into the atmosphere. When contaminants are released, they are subject to atmospheric **dispersion**, **transformation**, and **depletion** mechanisms.

The dispersion of contaminants (pollutants) in the atmosphere is determined by wind conditions and atmospheric turbulence. Horizontal winds play a significant role in the transport and dilution of pollutants. As the wind speed increases, the column of air moving by a source in a given period of time also increases. The concentration of pollutant is an inverse function of wind speed; that is, if the emission rate is relatively constant, a doubling of the wind speed will halve the pollutant concentration. Atmospheric turbulence is the result of two factors: (1) air does not flow smoothly near the Earth's surface because of friction created by that surface and human-made structures such as buildings; and (2) atmospheric heating also causes turbulence.

Transformation refers to the chemical changes that take place in the atmosphere (such as the conversion of an original pollutant into a secondary pollutant, e.g., ozone).

Depletion refers to the fact that pollutants emitted into the atmosphere do not remain there forever. Weather affects air pollution in several ways. Precipitation helps cleanse the air of pollutants, although those pollutants are then transferred to the other media (soil and water). Winds and storms may deplete air pollutants by dilution, making pollutants less troublesome in the area of their release. Air heated by the sun rises, carrying pollution with it. When the rising air mass is accompanied by wind, the pollution is carried aloft and diluted with clean air.

For evaluating ambient air quality, the most widely used methods are **monitoring** and **modeling**. Monitoring involves the use of measuring devices to determine the concentration of a specific contaminant, at a specific location, at a specific time. The main advantage of monitoring is that an exact level of contaminant can be determined, subject only to the accuracy and level of detection limitations of measurement method. The main disadvantages are that (1) monitoring is expensive; (2) the actual contribution of specific emission sources to the total measured concentration can be difficult to determine; and (3) the impact of proposed sources not yet in operation cannot be assessed with monitoring methods.

Modeling refers to the use of mathematical representations of contaminant dispersion and transformation to estimate ambient pollutant concentrations. The main advantage of modeling is that it can be used to estimate concentrations at several hundred locations at relatively low cost. The main disadvantage of modeling is that a mathematical model cannot exactly replicate the complexities of atmospheric dispersion and transformation. To be effective, a model must be tested with actual data over an appropriate period of time.

AIR SAMPLE COLLECTION

When collecting ambient or indoor air samples, soil vapor samples, or gas samples (e.g., landfill gas), the sampling and analysis plan should identify the types of samples to be collected, the methods and procedures for collecting the samples, the sampling locations, the constituents for which to analyze, the laboratory methods to be used, and the sampling frequency.

Typically two methods are used for collecting air, vapor, or gas samples. The most common is drawing air into an evacuated vessel (e.g., Tedlar bag, glass bulb, or stainless-steel canister). This is often referred to as a whole air sample. The second method involves pulling air through a sorbent. The contaminants are removed from the air either by absorption on the sorbent surface or by reacting with a coating on the sorbent to form a derivative of the contaminant.

To extract vapors or gas below the ground surface or below a landfill, gas monitoring wells or probes are often installed. If the wells or probes are not part of an active soil vapor extraction system, the well/probe will have to be purged prior to sample collection. A vacuum pump, lung box, or syringe is typically used to purge the air from a well. A least three well probe and tubing volumes should be purged.

Did You Know?

The methods for analyzing air samples typically require a specific sample collection method, type of vessel, etc., and should be reviewed prior to preparing a sampling plan.

SOIL AND GROUNDWATER QUALITY EVALUATION

The soil is a primary recipient (a sink or depository) of the waste products and chemicals used in modern society. Once these pollutants enter the soil, they become part of a cycle that affects all forms of life. When soils are polluted, the degradation goes well beyond the soil itself. In many cases, the damage also extends to water, air, and living organisms. In this section we are primarily concerned with evaluating the quality of soil and groundwater. To do so, we must have an understanding of the mechanics of soil/groundwater pollution.

Once contaminants such as organic chemicals (hydrocarbons or pesticides) reach the soil, they move in one or more directions (depending in part on their chemical structures). They may (1) vaporize into the atmosphere; (2) be absorbed by the soil; (3) move downward through the soil and be leached from the soil; (4) undergo chemical reactions on the surface or within the soil; (5) be broken down by soil microorganisms; (6) wash into streams, rivers, or lakes in surface runoff; and (7) be taken up by plant or soil animals and move up the food chain.

Before environmental practitioners can evaluate the horizontal or vertical extent of contaminated horizons, they must understand the general principles (the mechanics) of how contaminants are transported. The permeability of the soil and the viscosity of the contaminants influence the speed at which contaminants move through the soil. Gravity (the main cause of vertical movement of a contaminant through the soil) is dependent on the volume of contaminant, the depth of the water table and the density and viscosity of the contaminants. Not every contaminant reaches the water table. On their journey downward through soils, contaminants often are stopped naturally whenever they encounter an impermeable soil layer. Movement is also stopped whenever the surrounding soils absorb the contaminant.

If a certain contaminant is discharged directly onto soil in a large enough quantity (a large spill), chances are good that it will eventually reach the groundwater. Once a contaminant reaches the groundwater, its movement is dependent on the physical properties (specific gravity and solubility) of the contaminant. The specific gravity of the contaminant determines the extent that the contaminant will move through the water, while the solubility will help determine how fast the contaminant will be transported through the groundwater.

Contaminants less dense than water and with high solubility often are found moving horizontally in the upper sections of the aquifer. Contaminants more dense than water and with low solubility will generally be found moving vertically through the aquifer and at higher concentrations at depth.

SOIL AND GROUNDWATER SAMPLING

Several tools and methods are available for and commonly used in soil and groundwater sampling. One of the most common methods used for large spill areas is **geophysical testing**, which involves using resistivity and conductivity meters (which can evaluate site conditions up to 200 feet below land surface) to evaluate the subsurface layers, locate the water table, and map contaminant contours. These surveys can be conducted easily and quickly by traversing the suspect contaminated area to locate and evaluate the horizontal perimeter of the contaminated area.

Probably the easiest and most commonly used method to obtain accurate soil samples is **soil boring**, which normally involves the use of **augers**. A hand-operated soil auger is a pole-like device with a T handle that usually features a three-inch-diameter, high-strength barrel sample collection device on one end. The device is hand operated by rotating the T bar and turning the device vertically through the soil up to a depth of about 10 feet. General purpose augers are used in wet sands and gravels, dry or damp soils, and loams. Open-sided augers are used in clay soils. Augers are also available for use in sand and muddy soils. The key advantage in using soil augers is that they permit direct evaluation of soil samples collected from various depths. Augered soil samples can be immediately examined visually for contamination with field equipment during soil boring, or they can be preserved and evaluated in the laboratory. When samples need to be taken at a depth greater than 10 feet, usually a *split spoon* type sampler is attached to a drilling rig.

An even easier method of soil sampling can be accomplished by using a shovel, spade, or scoop. The *shovel, spade,* and *scoop* method is normally used in shallow **excavations**. The shovel breaks the soil surface (surficial soil) to the required depth. A normal lawn and garden spade is used to remove the soil. After the topsoil is removed, a steel scoop is used to remove a sample for field or laboratory analysis.

When a large amount of contaminant is spilled, trenching and excavation is used. **Trenching** and excavation normally involve the use of large Earth-moving machines to remove large layers of soil. The obvious advantage of this operation is that it allows for direct observation of site-specific conditions and field and lab analysis.

Normally, soil borings are conducted where the resulting data will provide conclusions about the potential migration of contaminants onto a particular property. In some cases, groundwater monitoring well installation may be favored over random soil borings, because the cost-effective characterization of groundwater quality is the main objective of many investigations.

Groundwater **monitor wells** are installed after the contaminated area has been identified. These wells provide access to groundwater for sampling purposes. Samples are evaluated for dissolved contaminant and free product.

Several common drilling methods are available for well construction, and usually the "one up three down" layout rule is followed in their installation. This consists of one well placed up-gradient from the spill area and three placed down-gradient. The up-gradient well provides data on groundwater that are not influenced by contamination from the spill. The down-gradient wells are strategically placed to intercept any waste migrating from the spill area.

After the monitor wells are installed, groundwater samples are collected. These samples are collected for laboratory analysis to confirm the type of contaminant and concentration of dissolved contaminants in the groundwater.

<table>
<tr><td>**Did You Know?**</td></tr>
</table>

For all sampling events, a complete record of field activities, measurements, and observations should be maintained. This information should be recorded in field notebooks and appropriate field sampling forms (e.g., log of exploration forms, sample collection forms, as-built well completion forms, well development records, etc.). Other documentation that should be maintained includes sample container labels, photographs, and sample custody forms (typically known as chain-of-custody forms).

LABORATORY ANALYSIS

To accurately evaluate the extent and concentration of contamination at a spill site, samples are taken to an environmental laboratory for analysis. All laboratory analyses must be performed at an approved analytical laboratory, using EPA-approved protocol and quality assurance/quality control (QA/QC) measures. All groundwater samples undergo analyses for temperature, pH, organic vapor concentration and conductivity. Additional parameters may also be chosen based on the results of subsequent investigations and regulatory requirements.

Chapter Summary

The basic techniques for air, soil, and water sampling are relatively simple. Learning the techniques presents little problem—but to be able to properly collect samples in the field is harder than the techniques suggest. Sampling and analysis requires practice—practical experience is using the environmental practitioner's available tools.

Discussion Questions and Problems

1. Which "tools" would you add to the practitioner's toolbox?
2. What factors affect the quality of samples taken in the field?
3. Briefly describe some of the problems associated with sampling air, water, and soil.
4. Compare and contrast manual versus automatic sampling.
5. Explain the practice of geophysical testing.

Suggested Research Topics and Projects

- Create a detailed sampling plan for a site-specific location.
- Analyze the NPDES and EPA 503 requirements for sampling. What general and specific procedures do they demand?
- Research and set up a mathematical model for air sampling.

- Evaluate the soil in a specific region using geophysical testing.
- Research other means and methods of sampling used in air, water, and soil evaluation.

References and Recommended Reading

American Conference of Governmental Industrial Hygienists. (1995). *Air Sampling for Evaluation of Atmospheric Contaminants.* 8th ed. Cincinnati, OH: ACGIH.

Black, H. H. (1952, January). "Procedure for Sampling and Measuring Industrial Wastes." *Sewage & Industrial Wastes* 24: 45–65.

Boulding, J. R. (1994). *Description and Sampling of Contaminated Soils: A Field Guide.* 2nd ed. Boca Raton, FL: Lewis Publishers.

Cahill, L., & Kane, R. (1989). *Environmental Audits.* 6th ed. Rockville, MD: Government Institutes.

Handbook for Sampling & Sample Preservation of Water and Wastewater. (1982). Springfield, VA: U.S. Department of Commerce.

Kemmer, F. N., ed. (1988). *The NALCO Water Handbook.* 2nd ed. New York: McGraw-Hill.

Metcalf & Eddy, Inc. (1991). *Wastewater Engineering: Treatment, Disposal, Reuse.* 3rd ed. New York: McGraw-Hill.

Pasquill, F., & Smith, F. B. (1990). *Atmospheric Diffusion.* New York: Ellis Horwood.

Tan, K. H. (1994). *Environmental Soil Science.* New York: Marcel Decker, Inc.

Testa, S. M. (1997). *The Reuse & Recycling of Contaminated Soil.* Boca Raton, FL: CRC/Lewis Publishers.

Testa, S. M., & Patton, D. (1993, December). "Don't Dig Clean Soils—Selective Excavation Can Cut Project Costs." *Soils,* 31–33.

Turner, D. B. (1979). "Atmospheric Dispersion Modeling: A Critical Review." *JAPCA* 29: 502–19.

U.S. Bureau of Reclamation. (1967). *Water Measurement Manual,* 16. Washington, DC: U.S. Government Printing Office.

CHAPTER 8

Technology and Environment

> Technology will bring about the end of the World . . . as we know it! Have you ever heard anyone say this before? Have you had the bejesus spooked out of you when folks talk about (whisper about) "technology eating our environment?"
>
> —a scenario known as *ecophagy*

Do you suffer from white nights when sleep is somewhere else, elusive, nonexistent, worrying yourself sick and silly about Drexler's (1986) grey goo? You know, that end-of-the-world scenario involving molecular nanotechnology in which out-of-control, self-replicating machines (robots) consume all matter on Earth while building more of themselves. Or, are you one of those who sleep well in a warm bed in a comfortably furnished home—surrounded by all the modern conveniences that have resulted from technological advances?

Would you give up any of the technologically derived modern comforts willingly?

Chapter Objectives

After studying this chapter, you should be able to:

- Identify, describe, and discuss the principal ways technology has impacted our air, water, and soil.
- Compare and contrast mobile and stationary sources of air pollution and the toxins they produce.
- Identify, define, describe, and discuss the importance of ozone in the troposphere and the problems related to ozone in the atmosphere.
- Define, describe, and discuss sulfur dioxide and its relationship to the problems, effects, and significance of acid deposition.
- Identify the sources of lead, airborne toxic chemicals, and airborne particulate matter, and discuss related problems and adverse health effects.

- Define, discuss, and describe what factors make controlling water pollution diverse and complex.
- Define, describe, and discuss BOD and oxygen-demanding waste.
- Identify sources and discuss adverse effects of and problems related to waterborne pathogens, toxic and hazardous substances, and sediments.
- Describe and discuss the problems related to oyster population, nitrogen, and sediment in the Chesapeake Bay.
- Define, describe, and discuss the factors and problems related to thermal pollution, plant nutrients in water supplies, persistent substances, and radioactive substances in our water systems.
- Identify, define, and discuss the chief soil pollutants.
- Discuss and describe the role the petroleum industry and petroleum hydrocarbon wastes play in soil pollution.

Chapter Outline

- Discussion: technology and its environmental consequences and impact
- Discussion: natural and technological contaminants that affect air quality, their sources, and the health risks associated with them
- Discussion and definition: air quality and the effects of carbon monoxide, ozone, sulfur dioxide, and lead
- Discussion and definition: air quality and the effects of toxic chemical pollutants, airborne particulate matter, and acid deposition
- Discussion: natural and technological contaminants that effect water quality, their sources, the health risks associated with them, and the complications that arise from the complex nature of our water system
- Discussion and definition: water quality and the effects associated with oxygen-demanding wastes, disease-causing wastes, toxic and hazardous substances, and sediments
- Discussion and definition: environmental problems in the Chesapeake Bay
- Discussion and definition: water quality and the effects associated with thermal pollution, plant nutrients, persistent substances, and radioactive substances
- Discussion: natural and technological contaminants that affect soil quality, their sources, and the health risks associated with them
- Discussion and definition: soil quality and the effects associated with waste disposal, hazardous wastes, petroleum hydrocarbons and the petroleum industry, coal gasification, and mining

Key Terms

acid rain
acidic deposition
airborne particulate matter

alternative energy
anthropogenic sources
biological oxygen demand

biological nutrient removal
biomass
coal gasification
decomposition
dissolved oxygen
geothermal power
groundwater
hydrogen
hydropower
leachate
mining waste
mobile sources
mobilization
ocean energy
organic wastes
persistent substance

radioactive substance
renewable energy
sediment
silage liquor
smog
solar energy
stationary sources
stratosphere
sulfurous smog
tailings
thermal pollution
toxic or hazardous substances
troposphere
waterborne pathogens
wind energy

Weathering the Storm[1]

What's going on in the United States isn't pretty. For almost 36 straight months now, the U.S. economy has been hemorrhaging jobs. Nearly 25 million Americans, about 17%, are underemployed, out of work, or have given up looking. The current recession has wiped out 15% of our manufacturing jobs, most of which will likely never come back. Economic prosperity is impossible without job growth. We must create more jobs, not the temporary, Band-aid type jobs that are resulting from TARP and so-called bailout money. Think about it: When bailout money is used to employ workers to replace or repair the country's infrastructure (e.g., roads and bridges), what happens to this small number of additional workers when these short-term projects are completed?

Moreover, a recent article in the *Virginian-Pilot* (2010) points out that localities' jobless rates remain unmoved by the spending binge on highways, undercutting the argument for a second stimulus bill. The article also points out that an analysis of stimulus spending "found that it didn't matter whether a lot of money was spent on highways, or none at all: Local unemployment rates rose and fell regardless. And the stimulus spending only barely helped the beleaguered construction industry." Reality check: Band-aid-like, pie-in-the sky temporary fixes applied in desperation to a hemorrhaging economy are not the answer. The damage to the American workforce has been deep and profound. We can't allow it to get any worse. No one knows this better than those who have lost their jobs or can't find jobs.

We have found that when we interview people about current issues or problems, for example about their being laid off from a long-term job, usually they are eager to talk. Right after a plant shutdown and the loss of several hundred or thousands of jobs, former employees will answer questions, state their opinions about the plant closure, and discuss their new status as members of the unemployed. However, these answers are usually delivered with an attitude and tone of shock, sadness, and/or extreme bitterness. This stands to reason because of the gripping aftershock associated with losing one's job. The effects can reverberate for years, decades, even lifetimes, and take an enduring toll on everything, from countless upended personal lives to government finances. For this reason, we have found it is best to wait a day or two after plant closures and mass layoffs before attempting to question former employees.

While conducting the post-layoff interviews reported in this text, we found that after several minutes of answering our questions, the tables were turned, and the respondents became the interviewers. The number one question we were asked was always simply stated: "What do you think about all this . . . this mess the United States is in?" Usually we do not answer that question or similar general questions, because we do not know the answer(s); we have no clue. We do have opinions, but they ask for answers.

However, one question has been a different matter for us; it always solicits a different kind of response. Whether we are right or wrong in our reply to this question is for others to judge. Based on our experience, however, we feel we are correct in our assessment. The question is three simple words: "What went wrong?" Usually this query is made with a string of qualifiers such as, "What went wrong? This is America; this is not supposed to happen . . . not to hard-working, God-fearing folks like us! We have a right to work for a living. Where are the jobs? Where have they gone? What happened to them? Will the jobs come back? When will the jobs come back?"

We found that this last question—When will the jobs come back?—prevails in the thoughts of almost all job losers. Many assume that when economic times get better, they will go back to work (what we describe as the "white knight riding into town to fill empty factories with new jobs" syndrome). Laid-off workers often don't quite get the long-lasting impact of current conditions. The current economic situation and the loss of jobs will bend the trajectory of their lives in unexpected ways. Some have been dealt blows from which they will never truly recover, the economic impact hardening like a footprint in wet cement. The reality is that many of these workers have lost their hold on the labor market and will see their incomes become permanently reset to a much lower level. Those who made $20+ per hour with full benefits as factory workers will be lucky to find employment that pays $8 per hour (and without benefits.) Moreover, there are ripple effects. Young people currently entering the workforce can expect to earn substantially less during their careers than those who started their careers when the economy was booming.

The question that reverberates is: "What do we do now, and how can this job problem be fixed?" In response to this question, our standard reply is: "You can go to school and learn a new skill set . . . and the job problem in the US can only be solved by innovation. The solution today can be summed up in one word: Innovation! Innovation! Innovation!" We are greeted with either quizzical looks or blank stares whenever we say this. We are used to this; we expect it. When we speak of innovation in America, what we mean is a multifaceted approach to correcting the current situation for finding permanent jobs in the United States. First, we mean that we can't survive as the globe's privileged, leading-edge country unless we end our dependence on foreign oil. We must throw off our oil hostage chains, break the links through innovation, and harvest energy by using post-oil energy technology. Simply, dependence on foreign oil is not an option for restoring our economy. We must end our dependency on foreign supplies of energy.

Energy innovation must be the first step in replacing lost American jobs.

Though it is true that unemployment wounds, it is also true that these wounds can be healed. We must start this process by converting from gasoline to natural gas. Not that natural gas conversion is the panacea for all our energy needs; however, it is a lifeline to get us off foreign oil and other energy imports and on our way to innovation via renewable energy. According to EIA (2008), the United States has natural gas reserves, both dry and liquid natural gas, that exceed 245 trillion cubic feet. Thus, we have enough natural gas supplies to get us through this century.

What we had hoped the Obama administration would do (it is never too late) with that TARP and/or stimulus money was to put it to work on energy renewal. In January 2009, the new administration should have sat down with the troubled automobile manufacturers and told them, first, that the government was going to bail them out by giving them money to stabilize, and second, that all new cars must be built to run on natural gas only. At the same time, the government would pay for gas station conversion to natural gas at the approximately 122,000 gas stations in the United States (Census, 2002).

Once innovation is under way, our next move must be research and development.

At the same time the administration was doling out TARP and other stimulus funds, its officials should have gone to an outstanding engineering and technology university like Virginia Tech in Blacksburg, Virginia, and informed the school administrators that they would be given a $250 million grant to do whatever it takes to develop some sort of super battery or fuel cell to power the cars of the future.

Accompanying specifications and directions would simply state that this battery or fuel cell has to be large capacity (large ampere-hour capacity) and able to be continuously recharged with supersensitive solar sensors. In order to charge a battery, a certain amount of current or electron flow is necessary. Solar supersensors will produce current flow. These supersensors will be wired from the battery itself to at least four positions on the roof of the automobile, where they can constantly be exposed to daylight—any level of daylight.

We know what you're thinking: it does get dark at night, so how are we going to continuously recharge the car's battery, fuel cell, or whatever we call it? Good question; it has a simple answer. Two additional wires and super-super light sensors are to be run from the battery to the car's headlamps, one to each. Thus, during nighttime driving, the light from the head lamps would be sensed by the super-super sensors and sent back to the battery.

Now, we know electrical engineers out there are scratching their heads and wondering where we got such an unworkable idea. We are not finished with our explanation . . . hold onto your brain cells. An amplification or booster device (like a transistor that amplifies a signal) can be placed in the wiring between the battery and the external and headlamp cells connections.

Is this scenario possible? Anything, absolutely anything is possible. We are Americans; we think we can do anything if we put our minds to it, and history has shown this to be true. Now is the time.

Let's say that we are able to create or devise a power plant arrangement consisting of a powerful battery or fuel cell with a built-in recharge system; what's next? Another good question. What's next is the final ingredient: education, training, and on-the-job training (OJT).

In order to come up with innovation and research and development grants, we must have personnel who are highly educated and trained. Unfortunately, in the United States at present, we are losing (or have already lost in some areas) our edge in higher education. The country will not restore itself to preeminence in science, technology, engineering, and mathematics unless we shift our focus, money, and talent to educate our youth in these critical subjects.

Response Scenario 8.1

Consider the following account and answer the response question.

By today's calendar, it is June 26, 15,543 BC. The place is a large, natural cave set deep under a solid outcropping that formed a fairly significant mountain meadow before the last glacial ice sheet gouged, gorged, ground, and pulverized it down to its present size and shape.

The colossal sheet of ice is in retreat. When it was at its full width, depth, and length, it extended several hundred miles beyond the cave site to a V-shaped valley, where glacial melt fed a youthful, raging river that ran through the valley's bottomland.

A small, steady stream of meltwater courses almost in a straight line past one side of the cave, down toward that valley, where it joins and feeds that river.

On the other side is a sloping field of young grass, brush, and flowers—flowers everywhere. Up close, we see the stark remnants of the terminal moraine that formed this abrupt slope, with its fresh cover of grass and blossoms. A closer look reveals a dark heap at the base of the slope—a heap of trash composed of skin, sinew, bone, decaying corpses, and burnt remnants of past hunts and feasts. We know only too well the refuse, filth, and discards that people leave behind as their foulest signature; somebody, maybe many bodies, live close by. Where? Of course—in the cave.

Let's take a look inside.

We wander up to the huge hole in the rock that forms the mouth of the cave. We tread carefully—we do not want to disturb (startle, frighten, anger) the occupants. Remember, we're talking about cavepeople here. We have no language in common, no culture in common. Could we have anything in common with such primitive people?

But all is quiet—and with no overt threat present, our curiosity overcomes our caution, and we walk into the opening chamber.

Something reaches out and grabs us—not a caveman, but a stench—a horrible stench—too horrible to describe. With our fingers clamped tightly to our noses, crushing to the bone, we move on, too interested, despite the reek, to retreat.

We can see fairly well in this chamber, because daylight pours in through the entrance. We take a few steps and stop to look around, religiously not breathing through our noses.

The walls of the cave are covered with black soot. A pit near the cave wall to the right, under attack by millions of flies and other insects, is the source of much of the stench—the latrine. A heap of detritus similar to the dump outside provides the rest of the reek.

That this cave is abandoned dawns on us. We have no doubt about why. The largest by-product manufactured by humans has taken over—the cave is a garbage dump.

Perhaps, back in other chambers, deeper in the cave, there are cave paintings and remnants of ceremony. But we don't have the tools to explore them with us today, and we retreat, grateful for a breath of fresh air.

Outside, a few hundred feet from the smelly cave and within sight of the garbage heap, we stop to contemplate what we've seen. Fifteen thousand years from now, archaeologists will find this cave and explore it thoroughly, learning information that will give us insights into the world of the people whose former home we have just visited. But the remains the archaeologists will find will be altered by 15,000 years of history. The picture they see will be incomplete, scattered by the natural interferences life causes, giving mystery to the short and brutal lives of our ancestors.

But here, right now, we see similarities. We foul our environment in the same ways, and in more. But the caveman had a huge advantage over modern man in that respect. When his living quarters became too foul for comfort, he could pick up whatever he considered of value that he and his tribe could carry and move on. A fresh site was always just around the next bend in the river. The pollution he created was completely (eventually) naturally biodegradable—in a few years, this cave could house humans again.

Although we have similarities with those far-off ancestors, one stark difference is plain: modern man cannot destroy and pollute his environment with impunity. We can no longer simply pick up stakes and move on. What we do to our environment has ramifications on a scale that we cannot ignore—or avoid.

RESPONSE

(i) Do you think humans are destined to reoccupy caves and live that lifestyle in order to survive?

Modern Technology

In prehistoric times, people had many of the same bad habits of environmental abuse that many of us have today. However, cave people did have a distinct advantage over modern folks: When prehistoric humans contaminated their environment (their caves), the damage was local and on a much smaller scale. Prehistoric people simply pulled up stakes and moved on to another cave. Their environmental abuse was on a much smaller impact-of-scale for two reasons: (1) Earth supported fewer human inhabitants, and (2) technology had not progressed beyond the use of fire for cooking/heating and the manual manufacturing of a few rudimentary tools for hunting and gathering.

Today's technology would drive prehistoric people to seek shelter in terror in the depths of their caves. We take for granted great advances in technology, which have given us the potential to completely destroy life on Earth as we know it. We also possess the chronic potential to destroy all life (in an insidious manner like cancer) through many of our practices that pollute the environment.

What have advances in technology allowed us to do? Many things. We can (and do) clear-cut entire forests in short order. We can (and do) blow megatons of pollutants into the atmosphere. We can (and do) pour endless streams of toxic wastes into our oceans, rivers, streams, and lakes. We can (and do) carve out huge, gaping holes in our soil and dump massive quantities of waste into them. Because of these great advances in technology, we can literally change the landscape of the Earth, the quality of the air we breathe, the quality of the water we drink, and the quality of our soil, which all life depends on. We can do all these things—and we do them.

The consequences of our technological progress have taken us from caves to "life-styles" with amenities most people in modern societies have come to expect today. But with these changes come tradeoffs. Some people question whether these technological advances are advantageous in the long run—or a bust.

Perhaps the problem is with science and technology. Several years ago, blaming environmental ills on increased knowledge of science (nature) and the ability to put that knowledge to work became common, and such statements now seem to be made almost by rote. Adherents of the "back-to-nature" movement purport to reject technology, while at the same time making considerable use of the fruits of the technology they eschew: virtually any item they purchase, the clothes they wear, the food they eat, the tools they use, the home they live in, and for that matter, the money obtained from employment.

Remember that those who blame technology for environmental problems forget that those who alerted us early to the environmental crisis, like Rachel Carson in *Silent Spring*, Aldo Leopold in *A Sand Country Almanac*, and Barry Commoner in *The Closing Circle*, were *scientists*. Their knowledge, skill, foresight, and use of scientific observation opened our eyes to environmental problems. That is, our very knowledge of technology (nature and science) is precisely what alerted us to the threats posed by environmental degradation (Pierce et al., 1998).

Not all technologies should be automatically labeled bad—few would argue that the technological advances in medicine, agriculture, weather forecasting, and many other important areas are all bad. Technology has a plus side; it can be put to work for the betterment of humankind. We can only hope that in the coming years we will use technology to our benefit—to make our lives better and to sustain and protect our environment at the same time.

One of the results of technological advance that many of us are experiencing at the present time (2011) has to do with the significant industrialization of China, India, and other emerging countries. Specifically, we are starting to feel the pinch of tighter supplies of Middle Eastern crude oil supplies, a direct result of technological advances in emerging countries that have increased appetites for crude oil and its by-products as they enter the so-called modern industrial world. Of course, all energy problems are also impacted by world futures' speculation and turmoil (war, rebellion, revolution, terrorism, etc.) within or near the oil-rich Middle Eastern suppliers. Consider for a moment that the emerging Asian countries contain most of the world's populace, and that as these populations progress technologically, their demands on energy products also increase. Their demand for automobiles and the products needed to operate them increases at a correspondingly almost exponential rate. With only so much energy available, increasing demand is having an impact not only on availability of crude oil products, but also on the price we pay at the pump for gasoline. It is our belief that in the future, energy and clean, safe potable water are going to be the limiting factors affecting continued technological growth, worldwide relationships (war or peace), and life itself. Certainly these factors will have an effect on life (or lifestyle) as we know it today.

In this chapter we briefly discuss technology and its impact on our environment—its impact on our air, water, and soil quality. We also include a discussion on renewable energy, because there is a correlation between clean, alternative/renewable energy and a clean, sustainable environment. Later, in media-specific chapters, we discuss how technology can be used to neutralize the adverse effects people have on our environment. We stress the positive—how advanced technology can be used in an Earth-friendly manner.

The Impact of Technology on Air Quality

When a volcano erupts and spews millions of tons of ash into the atmosphere; or when a large forest area is struck by lightning and a small fire turns into a rampaging, blazing swath of death and destruction, producing and pouring out millions of tons of smoke, ash, and cinders into the atmosphere; or when, at the local level, a neighborhood house catches on fire and the smoke and ash contaminate the local air, you have no difficulty recognizing what air pollution is all about. It is about having to draw air into your lungs that makes you cough, can make you sick, smells foul, tastes foul, and fills your lungs with particulate matter—that is contaminated.

These natural and accidental human-made air contaminant producers are, if not common, at least well known. However, several other events—processes, chemical reactions, and machines—also contaminate our atmosphere, the air that we all must breathe.

In terms of effects on the environment, we have made a huge leap forward from the smoke-producing fire of the prehistoric cave dweller to the plume of a 380-meter-tall "super-smokestack" venting pollutants from a modern copper smelter. This huge leap forward is the direct result of the technological advances that developed slowly from about 4000 BC to the rapid, ever-increasing, mind-boggling pace of modern times.

Air pollution presents one of the greatest risks to our health and environment. The water most of us drink comes clean and pure (because of technology) from the taps in our houses, or we choose to purchase bottled water. Most of the food we eat comes ready to cook, wrapped in plastic at a supermarket, and we can pay extra for organically grown products if we wish. But we must breathe whatever air surrounds us, constantly. The health problems caused or aggravated by air pollution are extensive and include lung diseases (cancer, chronic bronchitis, and pulmonary emphysema) and other conditions (eye irritation, bronchial asthma, and neural disorders). Environmental problems range from vegetation and crop damage to increased lake and pond acidity, which makes them uninhabitable by aquatic life.

As you know, air pollution is not limited to the actions of humans (anthropogenic causes) but is also the result of natural phenomena—vulcanism, lightning storms, earthquakes, and others. However, we focus on the **anthropogenic sources** of air contaminants. Man has no control over—and cannot accurately predict—when natural disasters will occur. But we must be concerned with the sources of air pollution related to technological advances. These sources of pollution can be classified into two categories: mobile and stationary sources.

Mobile sources of air pollution account for about 50% of the air pollution produced in the United States. They include any nonstationary source of air pollution: aircraft, boats, trucks, trains, motorcycles, and passenger cars. Exhaust vapors from such sources contains carbon monoxide, volatile organic compounds (VOCs), nitrogen oxide, lead, and particulate matter. VOCs, along with nitrogen oxides, contribute to the formation of **smog**.

Stationary sources of air pollution are those emanating from any fixed or stationary point. These range from large chemical processing plants to neighborhood gas stations and dry cleaners. Some of the common sources are power plants, printing plants, steel plants, and coke plants.

Stationary sources generate air pollutants primarily by combusting fuel for energy, and to a lesser degree, as by-products of industrial processes. Factories, utilities, commercial and residential buildings that burn oil, wood, coal, natural gas, and other fuels are principal sources of pollutants such as sulfur dioxide, nitrogen oxides, carbon monoxide, VOCs, lead, and particulate matter.

Toxic air pollutants also come from a variety of manufacturing and industrial processes. Hazardous waste disposal facilities, municipal incinerators, utilities, landfills, and fuel oil contaminated with hazardous materials are potential sources of toxic air pollution.

The major pollutants generated by mobile and stationary sources are carbon monoxide, ozone, sulfur dioxide, lead, air toxins, airborne particulates, and acid deposition. We provide a brief description of each of these major pollutants in the following sections. We also discuss the technological advances used to mitigate the effects of these pollutants in those sections dealing with each specific environmental media type—air, water, and soil.

CARBON MONOXIDE

Carbon monoxide (CO) is a colorless, odorless, and flavorless product of the incomplete combustion of fossil fuels and **biomass**. Although the dominant producers of CO are natural sources, large emissions to the atmosphere result from a number of anthropogenic sources. When inhaled, CO replaces the oxygen in the bloodstream and can impair alertness (slow reflexes), vision, and other physical and mental capacities. For those suffering with lung and heart ailments, inhalation of CO can bring about severe health effects.

If you wanted to locate the highest concentrations of CO at any given time in a particular part of a country (e.g., the United States), all you would have to do is find an area with a high concentration of people and motor vehicles. Motor vehicles are the main source of carbon monoxide, especially when their engines are burning fuel inefficiently. Industrial processes, incinerators, and wood stoves are other sources of CO.

OZONE

Ozone is a variation of oxygen that possesses a set of physical and chemical properties significantly different from the "normal" form of oxygen. Ozone has three instead of the usual two atoms of oxygen per molecule; thus O_3 represents its chemical formula. At ambient room temperature, ozone is a pale blue gas with a pungent odor. It is heavier (more dense) than oxygen (vapor density of 1.7) and considerably more soluble in water. Ozone is particularly hazardous for two reasons: (1) It is extremely reactive, and (2) it is very toxic.

Individuals are often familiar with ozone as the protective ozone layer in Earth's **stratosphere** (extending roughly 7 to 30 miles above the surface), which acts as a protective shield, preventing (by absorption) harmful amounts of ultraviolet radiation from penetrating the **troposphere** (the bottom layer of Earth's atmosphere extending about 7 miles above Earth's surface) and reaching Earth's surface.

The benefits of ozone in the upper atmosphere notwithstanding, the presence of ozone in the lower atmosphere is one of the most widespread environmental problems: it can be hazardous, poisonous to most living organisms. The presence of ozone in the lower atmosphere is what we are concerned with.

Ozone is produced naturally in the atmosphere when sunlight triggers chemical reactions between atmospheric gases and pollutants such as VOCs and nitrogen oxides. The main source of VOCs and nitrogen oxides is internal combustion engines used in automobiles, buses, trucks, etc. During heavy commuter traffic, ozone levels are usually highest, because large amounts of VOCs and nitrogen oxides are being produced.

Two problems with ozone are related to advancements in technology. First, the overproduction of ozone by anthropogenic emissions disturbs the natural equilibria among stratospheric ozone reactions, consequently decreasing ozone concentration. Because stratospheric ozone absorbs much of the incoming solar ultraviolet radiation, it serves as a UV shield, protecting organisms on the Earth's surface. Reducing the ozone concentration in the stratospheric regions strips away that protective shield.

The second problem with ozone normally occurs under two conditions. Turbulence in the upper atmosphere sometimes causes stratospheric ozone to enter the troposphere. On these rare occasions, ozone usually enters for short durations only. But on those occasions, endogenous photochemical reactions take place in the lower troposphere—a primary cause of oxidants in Los Angles–type smog.

SULFUR DIOXIDE

Sulfur dioxide (SO_2) is a colorless gas that has the sharp, pungent odor of burning rubber. The product of combustion resulting from burning of sulfur-containing materials (e.g., coal and other fossil fuels), other sources of it include refineries, pulp and paper mills, steel and chemical plants, smelters, and energy facilities related to oil and gas production. Residential neighborhoods are directly affected by SO_2 emitted from home furnaces and wood-burning stoves. Near major industrialized areas, sulfur dioxide is a common air pollutant. Excessive levels of sulfur dioxide in the ambient air are associated with significant increases in acute and respiratory diseases.

When emitted to the atmosphere, sulfur dioxide can be transported long distances, because it bonds to particles of dust or aerosols. With time, sulfur dioxide oxidizes to sulfur trioxide, which dissolves in atmospheric water vapor, forming highly corrosive sulfuric acid. In highly industrialized regions, two major environmental problems develop: **acid rain** and **sulfurous smog**.

Acid rain (as the name implies, although not quite accurately) is precipitation contaminated with dissolved acids like sulfuric acid. Acid rain is a threat to the environment because of the damage it causes to aquatic life when it falls in freshwater lakes. The second problem, sulfurous smog, is the haze that develops in the atmosphere when droplets of sulfuric acid accumulate, growing in size until they become sufficiently large to serve as light scatterers.

LEAD

Lead is a heavy metal that can cause serious physical and mental impairment. Children are particularly vulnerable to the effects of high lead levels. Stationary sources of lead were nonferrous smelters and battery manufacturers, but their levels of lead emissions have been substantially reduced via EPA regulation. Another significant former contributor of atmospheric lead contamination was the automobile, especially in densely populated areas. Up until the 1970s, tetraethyl lead was a component of gasoline. When combusted (in internal combustion engines), it was transformed into lead oxide. Tiny particles of lead oxide were emitted as components of vehicular exhaust and were subsequently inhaled or consumed, directly or indirectly.

The adverse health effects caused by overexposure to lead prompted the U.S. EPA to take action to reduce the lead content of all gasoline over time. In addition to phasing down lead in gasoline, the EPA instituted an automotive emissions control program in 1975 that required the use of unleaded gas in any car. At the present time, about 70% of the gas sold in the United States is unleaded.

TOXIC CHEMICALS

A category of toxic pollutants overlooked in the past (or not understood until recently) is toxic chemical pollution, found in all environmental media. Emission of toxic chemicals into the air by human activities has both acute and chronic effects on human health and the environment. The sources that emit toxic chemicals into the atmosphere include industrial and manufacturing processes, solvents, hazardous waste handling and disposal sites, incinerators, motor vehicles, and sewage treatment plants. Toxic heavy metals (such as cadmium, chromium, mercury, arsenic, and beryllium) are emitted by smelters, manufacturing processes, and metal refiners. Plastic and chemical manufacturing plants emit toxic organics such as benzene and vinyl chloride. In processes where plastics are burned at high temperatures in incinerators, chlorinated dioxins are emitted.

For people, the most common exposure of these contaminants is by inhalation in the industrial workplace, but most of these toxins are emitted from smokestacks and tailpipes. More problems occur when these toxins leave the air and fall to the Earth, where they are consumed or absorbed by animals, fish, or crops eaten by humans. These airborne toxins also contaminate water sources that supply drinking water to communities. When these toxins enter the body, they accumulate and can become highly concentrated in human tissues.

Response Scenario 8.2.
Xenoestrogens and Estrogen Dominance

Alligators in Florida's Lake Apopka are failing to reproduce; many males have reduced genitalia. Female-female pairs of gulls in California are building nests, and some young males in the same population show partially feminized reproductive tracts. Male rainbow trout in Great Britain living near sewer outlets are generating proteins in their tissues normally found only in females' eggs.

Meanwhile, several studies suggest that over the last 40 years, human males have suffered a steep, worldwide decline in the numbers and quality of their sperm cells. Incidences of abnormal or incomplete genital development, such as undescended testes and malformed penises, are reported to be increasing in certain Scandinavian countries. And a variety of human cancers known to be affected by sex hormones appear to be on the rise, including breast cancer, testicular cancer, and prostate cancer (Harvard Center for Risk Analysis 1996).

Some scientists are becoming increasingly concerned that these diverse and widespread reproductive system anomalies all represent manifestations of an emerging environmental problem: environmental accumulation of xenoestrogens—persistent chemicals that mimic sex hormones. Because of their reproductive system action, these chemicals are known as disruptors of endocrine function.

The estrogen mimics function by binding to estrogen receptors in the same way and in about the same amounts as does estrogen itself. This has the potential to wreak havoc on reproductive anatomy and physiology. The functions of the natural hormones (including estrogen, progesterone, and testosterone) produced by human reproductive systems include controlling the normal processes of development, growth, and control of sexual differentiation; sexual behavior; and reproductive function. Throughout the human life cycle, however, they are also tied to many other physical functions.

As an example of the pervasiveness of xenoestrogens, the American government banned DDT for use in the United States in the early 1970s. Unfortunately, it is still manufactured in the country and sold abroad. U.S. retailers purchase produce treated with DDT, which is then sold in U.S. stores. DDE, a principal metabolite derived from DDT, is a xenoestrogen that persists for decades in fat deposits in the human body. Estrogen-mimicking effects, including feminization and hermaphroditism, in males have been reported in various fish species in places such as the Great Lakes, which have high residual concentrations of DDT and PCBs (polychlorinated biphenyls). Fish now serve as barometers of xenoestrogen contamination in bodies of water.

(continued)

Response Scenario 8.2. (*continued*)

Environmental xenoestrogens have been linked to early puberty in girls. The normal, average age of onset is between 12 and 13. A recent study of 17,000 girls in the United States indicated that 7% of white and 27% of black girls exhibited physical signs of puberty by age seven. For 10-year-old girls, the percentages increased to 68 and 95, respectively. Studies from the United Kingdom, Canada, and New Zealand have shown similar changes in the age of puberty onset.

Some xenoestrogens act by binding to and filling receptor sites, which prevents the genuine hormone from binding. Others block access by genuine hormone molecules to their receptors, which may prevent the body's own hormones from acting in normal biological modulations. Still others affect the metabolism, which affects the concentrations of the body's natural hormones. Compounds with xenoestrogenic properties include certain chlorinated organic compounds (principally pesticides such as DDT, kepone, and others, but also certain polychlorinated biphenyls); some plasticizers and breakdown products of polycarbonate plastic; and some pharmaceuticals, such as diethylstilbestrol (DES).

In short, xenoestrogens (including the man-made estrogens used in pharmaceutical birth control products now linked to increased levels of cancer), by producing inappropriate hormonal stimulation, may result in the proliferation of reproductive-tissue cells (increasing cancer risk) and deviations in embryonic sexual differentiation. The sources of xenoestrogens are pervasive in modern American society, and since some environmental compounds tend to reduce the response to sex-hormonal stimuli at low doses and to increase response at high doses, properly defining and controlling the problem becomes increasingly difficult:

> Many who study the phenomenon of premature puberty attribute it to environmental estrogens in plastics and secondhand exposure through the meat and milk of animals treated with steroid hormones. An alarming increase in the numbers of girls experiencing precocious puberty occurred in the 1970s and '80s in Puerto Rico. Among other effects, breast development occurred in girls as young as one year. Premature puberty was traced to consumption of beef, pork, and dairy products containing high concentrations of estrogen. Another study from Puerto Rico revealed higher concentrations of phthalate—a xenoestrogen present in certain plastics—in girls who showed signs of early puberty, compared with controls.
>
> It may be that excess body fat and exposure to estrogenic substances operate in concert to hasten puberty. Body fat is one site of endogenous estrogen synthesis. Exposure to environmental estrogens may add just enough exogenous hormone to exert the synergistic effect necessary to bring on puberty, much like the last drop of water that causes the bucket to overflow. (Trankina 2001)

RESPONSE

The book *Risk in Perspective: Are Chemicals in the Environment Disrupting Hormonal Control of Growth and Development?* calls for answers to five questions; respond to these questions:

(i)   How good is the evidence for changes over time in human male sperm counts and the incidence of genital abnormalities? What is the basis for linking any such trends with environmental chemicals?

(ii) Should hormonally acting agents be presumed to have exposure thresholds for their toxic effects, and if so, how can such thresholds be experimentally characterized?

(iii) Are phytoestrogens at the levels typically encountered exerting significant endocrine effects? If so, do they act primarily as agonists or antagonists?

(iv) Since male organisms typically have much less natural estrogen, are they particularly sensitive to xenoestrogens in comparison to females? If so, why are they not affected by phytoestrogens?

(v)   Are there key times during development of the embryo when even small, inappropriate exposures to estrogenic stimuli can divert normal sexual development pathways or affect future fertility?

REFERENCES

Body Burden: The Pollution in People. http://www.ewg.org/reports/bodyburden/.

Harvard Center for Risk Analysis. (1996, April 1). *Risk in Perspective: Are Chemicals in the Environment Disrupting Hormonal Control of Growth and Development?* http://c3.org/chlorine_issues/health/hormgrow.html.

Trankina, Michele L. (2001). *The Hazards of Environmental Estrogens,* http://www.worldandi.com/public/2001/October/ee.html.

ADDITIONAL READING

EPA. Endocrine Disruptors Research Initiative. www.epa.gov/endocrine/gedri/.

Tulane and Xavier Universities. "Environmental Estrogens and Other Hormones." www.som.tulane.edu/ecme/eehome/.

World Wildlife Fund. "Toxic Chemicals, Endocrine Disruptors." www.worldwildlife.org/toxics/progareas/ed/index.htm.

The CDC and the Environmental Working Group (EWG) provide strong evidence that those who live in industrialized societies carry the traces of a startlingly high number of unnatural chemical compounds in their bodies (see Table 8.1). The CDC and the EWG performed two studies with related goals, but opposite purposes. While the CDC studied "individual chemicals in a multitude of people," the EWG focused on "individuals with a multitude of chemicals." The studies found 49 chemicals in common and "an average of 91 industrial compounds, pollutants, and other chemicals in the blood and urine of nine volunteers, with a total of 167 chemicals found in the group" (see the report *Body Burden: The Pollution in People,* at www.ewg.org/reports/bodyburden).

AIRBORNE PARTICULATE MATTER

Airborne particulate matter, such as dust, smoke, and aerosols, may have both long- and short-term health and environmental effects. These effects range from

Table 8.1.   Chemical Pollution in People

Health Effect or Body System Affected	Number of Chemicals Found in Nine People Tested		
	Average Number	Total	Range
Birth defects and developmental delays	55	79	37–68
Brain and nervous system	62	94	46–73
Cancer	53	76	36–65
Cardiovascular system and blood	55	82	37–68
Female reproductive system	42	61	24–56
Hearing	34	50	16–47
Hormone system	58	86	40–71
Immune system	53	77	35–65
Kidney	54	80	37–67
Liver	42	69	26–54
Lungs/breathing	55	82	38–67
Male reproductive system	47	70	28–60
Reproductive system	55	77	37–68
Skin	56	84	37–70
Stomach or intestines	59	84	41–72
Vision	5	11	4–7

*Some chemicals are associated with multiple health impacts and appear in multiple categories in this table.

Source: Environmental Working Group compilation

irritating the eyes and respiratory track, to reducing the body's resistance to infection, to causing chronic pulmonary diseases. Particulates, especially smaller particles (under 0.2 micron) that are able to reach the lower regions of the respiratory tract affect breathing, aggravate existing respiratory and cardiovascular diseases, alter the body's defense systems against foreign materials, and damage lung tissue. Particulates may also be carcinogenic (such as particulates emitted from diesel engines) and can absorb gaseous pollutants (such as sulfur dioxide) and deliver them directly to the lungs. Particulates that end up in wind-blown dusts can be toxic (such as pesticides and polychlorinated biphenyls [PCBs]).

Did You Know?

Scientific studies have linked particle pollution, especially fine particles, with a series of significant health problems, including

- increased respiratory symptoms such as irritation of the airways, coughing, and difficulty breathing;
- decreased lung function;
- aggravated asthma;
- development of chronic bronchitis;
- irregular heartbeat;
- nonfatal heart attacks; and
- premature death in people with heart or lung disease.

Major sources of particulates include diesel engines, residential wood combustion, coal-fired power plants, agricultural tilling, construction, and unpaved roads. In addition, particulates are also released into the atmosphere from steel mills, power plants, cotton gins, construction work, demolition, cement plants, smelters, and grain storage elevators.

Particulates are also responsible for soiling and corrosion of building materials, severe reduction in visibility (atmospheric haze), and damage to vegetation.

ACIDIC DEPOSITION

Acidic deposition (acid rain—an incorrect nomenclature, because snow and all other types of precipitation are also affected, causing acid fog, acid clouds, acid dew, and acid frost as well) has caused not only much confusion, but also much controversy. We have little doubt about and much scientific evidence pointing to acidic deposition as an environmental problem. Actually, acidic deposition problems have been of concern for hundreds of years—the phenomenon is not new.

Acidic deposition is the phenomenon wherein pollutants affect the chemical nature of precipitation. Precipitation is by nature somewhat acidic. Remember the pH scale? The range is 0–14; 7.0 is neutral; and the more pH drops below 7.0, the more acidity increases. Because the pH scale is logarithmic, a tenfold difference exists between one number and the next. A drop in pH from 6.0 to 5.0 represents a tenfold increase in acidity, and a drop from 6.0 to 4.0 represents a hundredfold increase. All rain is slightly acidic; however, only rain with a pH below 5.6 is considered "acid rain."

Changes in precipitation chemistry have been reported for more than 30 years. During that period, national governments in North America and Europe have come to recognize the seriousness of precipitation acidification by sulfur and nitrogen pollutants of man-made (anthropogenic) origin.

How Significant Is the "Acid Rain" Phenomenon?

In some locations, the acidity of rainfall has fallen well below 5.6. For example, in the northeastern United States, the average pH of rainfall is 4.5, and rainfalls with a pH close to 4.0 are not unusual—these levels are 1,000 times more acidic than distilled water. The increased acidity appears to be because of sulfuric (65%) and nitric acids (30%). The apparent major sources of sulfur and nitrogen oxides for these strong acids are fossil fuel–fired power plants, metal smelters, industrial boilers, and automobiles.

The middle Ohio Valley and the states immediately adjacent to it make up the major source region for sulfur and nitrogen oxides (precursors of "acid rain"). Ohio emits twice as much sulfur oxide as all the New England states combined. Significant sulfur oxide emissions also occur in Indiana, Kentucky, Illinois, West Virginia, Tennessee, Missouri, and Michigan. Data collected by various monitoring networks show that the areas of the United States receiving the most acid rainfall are downwind and northeast of those states with the highest acid precursor emissions.

Effects of Acid Deposition[2]

The effects of acid rain are normally measured in economic and environmental terms. In terms of economic costs, the effect of acid deposition is difficult to estimate, because it includes too many areas: damage to agriculture, tourism, fisheries, lakes, vegetation, and human and animal health. One fact is certain and easier to determine, however: The effects of acid deposition can be seen throughout the ecosystem. These include damage to leaf surfaces; release of harmful chemicals from soil that damage root systems; and acid-catalyzed releases of toxic metals like aluminum, which can filter into lakes and streams, threatening public water supplies and contaminating fish. Metals usually remain inert in the soil until acid rain moves through the ground (scientists call this phenomenon **mobilization**). The acidity of precipitation is capable of dissolving and *mobilizing* metals including mercury, manganese, and aluminum. Transported by the movement of this acidic water through the ecosystem, these toxic metals accumulate in lakes and streams, where they may threaten aquatic organisms. Nitrates from acid deposition in saltwater estuaries create algal blooms that cause oxygen depletion and suffocate fish and aquatic plants. In combination with ground-level ozone, acid deposition can impair plant growth and damage forests.

In regard to the effects of acid rain on forests, over the years, scientists, environmental science practitioners, foresters, and others have noted a slowed growth of some forests. Leaves and needles turn brown and fall off when they should be green and healthy. In extreme cases, individual trees or entire areas of the forest simply die off without an obvious reason.

After much analysis, environmental researchers now know that acid rain causes slower growth, injury, or death of forests. Acid rain has been implicated in forest and soil degradation in many areas of the eastern United States, particularly high-elevation forests of the Appalachian Mountains from Maine to Georgia, including areas such as the Shenandoah and Great Smoky Mountain National Parks. Of course, acid rain is not the only cause of such conditions. Other factors contribute to the overall stress on these areas, including air pollutants, insects, disease, drought, or combined effects of acid rain and these other environmental stressors. After many years of collecting information on the chemistry and biology of forests, researchers are beginning to understand how acid rain works on the forest soil, trees, and other plants.

Acid Rain on the Forest Floor

A spring shower in the forest washes leaves and falls through the trees to the forest floor below. Some trickles over the ground and runs into streams, rivers, or lakes, and some of the water soaks into the soil. That soil may neutralize some or all of the acidity of the acid rainwater. This ability is called *buffering capacity*, and without it, soils become more acidic. Differences in soil buffering capacity are an important reason why some areas that receive acid rain show a lot of damage, whereas other areas that receive about the same amount of acid rain do not appear to be harmed at all. The ability of forest soils to resist, or buffer, acidity depends on the thickness and composition of the soil, as well as the type of bedrock beneath the forest floor.

Midwestern states like Nebraska and Indiana have soils that are well buffered. Places in the mountainous northeast, like New York's Adirondack and Catskill Mountains, have thin soils with lower buffering capacity.

Did You Know?

It should be pointed out that acid rain does not kill trees directly. Instead, it is more likely to weaken trees by damaging their leaves, limiting the nutrients available to them, or exposing them to toxic substances slowly released from the soil. Quite often, injury or death of trees is a result of these effects of acid rain in combination with one or more environmental factors.

Acid rain can also damage material used in construction and sculptures. Building materials such as limestone, marble, carbonate-based paints, and galvanized steel all can be eroded and weakened by the dilute acids found in acid deposition.

Sources of Water Pollution

Protecting drinking water supplies, coastal zone waters, and surface water is complicated by the variety of sources that affect them. **Groundwater** is being contaminated by pollution from animal wastes, leaking underground storage tanks, **silage liquor**, **leachate** from landfill sites, spoil heaps, solvent discharges to sewers or land, fertilizers and pesticides, septic tanks, drainage wells, and inadequate sewage treatment plants, threatening a large percentage of the world's drinking water supplies.

Water pollution is both diverse and complex. This combination is clearly evident in the number of different pollutant categories and the way in which they overlap. These categories include oxygen-demanding wastes, disease-causing wastes, **toxic and hazardous substances**, **sediments**, **thermal pollution**, plant nutrients, **persistent substances**, and **radioactive substances**. The overlapping of these categories can be seen in improperly treated sewage waste, which may contain organic wastes, disease-causing wastes, plant nutrients, toxic substances, and persistent substances. Pollutants may also fit into more than one category; for example, PCBs are both hazardous and persistent. One type of pollutant may enter water attached to another type; for example, organic chemical pollutants often adhere to sediments. Pollutants from all categories can contaminate water systems. Various contaminants may also act *synergistically* (together) to form deadly pollutants.

OXYGEN-DEMANDING WASTES

Oxygen-demanding or **organic wastes** are small particles of once-living plant or animal matter. Usually suspended in the water column, they can also accumulate in thick layers of sediments on the bottom of lakes or rivers. Human and animal wastes and/

or plant residues make up most of the suspended matter. Other sources of oxygen-demanding wastes are natural runoff from land; industrial wastes from oil refineries, paper mills, food processing plants; and urban runoff. In a process called **decomposition**, aerobic bacteria use the organic matter as an energy source. As they decompose or consume the organic matter, the bacteria use **dissolved oxygen** (DO) from the water, to the detriment of other aquatic organisms, such as fish and shellfish. Bacteria residing in sediments (anaerobic bacteria) do not require oxygen to decompose organics; however, they may emit noxious gases such as methane and **hydrogen** sulfide as a by-product of decomposition.

Biological oxygen demand (BOD) is a measure of the amount of dissolved oxygen needed by decomposers to break down organic materials in a given volume of water. A natural water body (lake or stream) with a high BOD will have a low concentration of DO because bacteria are using up oxygen to decompose organic matter. (**Note:** BOD levels in pure water and typical fresh waters run 0 to 2–5 mg/L, respectively.) Dissolved oxygen is a major limiting factor in the aquatic habitat, so oxygen depletion is a serious factor affecting the water quality of a lake or stream.

DISEASE-CAUSING WASTES

Disease-causing wastes enter water bodies from sources of untreated human and animal wastes and increase the chance that infectious organisms—**waterborne pathogens**—that cause the outbreak of diseases (e.g., typhoid, infectious hepatitis, cholera, and dysentery) may contaminate the water source. Waterborne pathogens enter the water mainly through the feces and urine of infected people and animals. Many other diseases are also transmitted by organisms in water. For example, mosquitoes transmit the protozoan that causes malaria, and snails transmit the fluke that causes schistosomiasis. Every summer, the areas affected by West Nile virus (spread by mosquitoes and also transported by birds) become more extensive.

TOXIC AND HAZARDOUS SUBSTANCES

Toxic or hazardous substances are those materials injurious to the health of individual organisms. Sometimes fatal, they disrupt the metabolism of organisms as a result of ingestion or contact. Toxic substances include oils, gasoline, greases, solvents, cleaning agents, biocides, and synthetics. Many rivers, streams, lakes, and bays have thousands of toxic and hazardous chemicals in their sediments. The hazardous chemicals increasingly being found in dumps and landfills are one of the most serious environmental problems in many industrialized countries. As hazardous contaminants leach from dumps and landfills, they make their way into lakes, streams, rivers, and groundwater supplies, leading to contamination of drinking water supplies.

Several thousand organic chemicals enter aquatic ecosystems every day. Most are by-products of industrial processes or are present in hundreds of thousands of commonly used products. Some of them are carcinogenic (e.g., dioxin and PCBs). Inorganic substances (acids, salts, brine, and metals) also contaminate our water systems. Such processes as mining and manufacturing produce these contaminants and release acids into the environment. Salt from road salting and irrigating causes damage, oil and natural gas wells release brine, and manufacturing processes also release metals (chromium, copper, zinc, lead, and mercury, as well as others) into aquatic ecosystems.

Response Scenario 8.3.
Persistent Pesticide Exposure

Atrazine, a known endocrine disruptor, is the most heavily used agricultural pesticide in the United States. Commonly used to control broadleaf weeds and grasses, atrazine is used for weed control in applications from urban to rural to forestland. It is environmentally persistent and is the most common pesticide found to contaminate wells and city water supplies, as well as surface and groundwater. An estimated 60% of the U.S. population is unknowingly exposed to atrazine every day.

In one study, low levels of atrazine were given to pregnant rats. The resulting female offspring developed abnormal mammary glands, which increased their cancer risk under carcinogen exposure. With atrazine exposure, frogs demonstrate a much higher rate of hermaphroditism, and males show significantly lower testosterone levels. In utero exposure to atrazine in humans may produce similar risks over the long term.

Atrazine exposure has been linked to higher rates of prostate cancer in atrazine manufacturing workers in Louisiana and to leukemia in migrant farmworkers in California.

Several European countries, including France, Denmark, Germany, Norway, and Sweden, have banned atrazine because of its endocrine-disrupting properties, although the U.S. EPA has not yet listed it.

The highest levels of risk from exposure to endocrine-disruptor pollutants, including atrazine, are to the unborn. In utero, even small exposures to endocrine disrupters can affect later reproductive organ and tissue development: breasts, ovaries, uterus, and testes.

RESPONSE

(i)   Should atrazine be outlawed for use as a pesticide?
(ii) If you outlaw atrazine for use as a pesticide, what would you use instead?

REFERENCES

Birnbaum, L. S., & Fenton, S. E. (2003, April). "Cancer and Developmental Exposure to Endocrine Disruptors." *Environmental Health Perspectives* 111, no. 4: 389–94.
"Feminized Frogs: Herbicide Disrupts Sexual Groups." (2002, April 20). *Science News Online* 161, no. 16. http://www.sciencenews.org/20020420/fob1.asp.
Hessel, P. A., Kalmes, R., et al. (2004, April). "A Nested Case-control Study of Prostate Cancer and Atrazine Exposure." *Journal of Occupational and Environmental Medicine* 46, no. 4: 379–85.
U.S. Environmental Protection Agency. (2002, May 2). "Summary of Atrazine Risk Assessment." http://www.epa.gov/oppsrrd1/reregistration/atrazine/srrd_summary_may02.pdf accessed 1/22/03.

SEDIMENTS

Soil particles dislodged by raindrops travel via runoff into streams, rivers, lakes, or oceans and are deposited there as sediments. Although rivers and streams have always transported enormous quantities of sediment to the sea, their sediment loads today are greater than ever (by weight, sediments are the most abundant water pollutant). Soils stripped of vegetation by crop cultivation, timber cutting, strip mining, overgrazing, road building, and other construction activities are subject to high rates of erosion. When eroded, sediments by the millions of tons are deposited into aquatic systems, muddying streams and rivers.

The obvious result of soil erosion is the loss of valuable agricultural soils, but other problems are associated with the wearing down of soil as well. Eroded soil particles eventually fill lakes, ponds, reservoirs, harbors, navigation channels, and river channels. As a result, the accumulation of sediments greatly reduces the attractiveness of lakes and reservoirs, which causes them to lose recreational value. Sedimentation also impedes navigation, covers bottom-dwelling organisms, eliminates valuable fish-spawning areas, and reduces the light penetration necessary for photosynthesis. Another problem with erosion is that soils eroded from farmlands sweep nutrients in the form of nitrogen and phosphorus into surface waters. In small quantities, these nutrients are not a problem. However, a dramatic increase in the sediment load can cause ecological changes. In Sidebar 8.1, we describe the ecological changes that have occurred in the Chesapeake Bay, partly caused by the influx of sediments and nutrients.

Sidebar 8.1. What's Wrong with the Chesapeake Bay?

Not all that long ago (maybe less than 40 years ago), inhabitants of towns on the Eastern Shore of the Chesapeake Bay often went wading in clear, knee-deep waters to catch crabs. The crabbers made their way through the lush, waving grasses on the bay's bottom, carrying crabpot-nets attached to long poles, dragging along a container tied by a string to their waists.

The crabbers waited until the crabs scampered out of the grasses, then netted them and flipped them into their containers, never breaking stride as they continued scooping up scampering crabs. The water was so clear the crabbers could see their own feet.

Today, the clear water of the past has been replaced with brown and turbid water. The crabs have moved on to "greener" pastures and cleaner waters. The lush, thick grasses that tickled the crabbers' feet are gone—and so are the crabs.

In less than 40 years, submerged grasses have vanished from many parts of the upper and middle bay. Scientists and environmentalists believe that they are beginning to understand why. The answers lie in assaults on the Chesapeake, many by the heavy hand of humans. The ecology of the bay has changed. Some scientists, ecologists, and other environmental specialists suspect the bay is dying.

What is going on with the Chesapeake Bay?

The answer is complex. Actually, over the past 40 years, many different groups and individuals have presented many "answers." Some of these presented much speculation about what is causing the Chesapeake Bay problem. Following is an example of one of these "answers" that isn't really the answer to the Chesapeake Bay problem.

Environmental policymakers in the Commonwealth of Virginia came up with what is called the Lower James River Tributary Strategy on the subject of nitrogen from the lower James River and other tributaries as the possible culprit contaminating the Lower Chesapeake Bay Region. Nitrogen is a nutrient. In excess, nitrogen is a pollutant. Some "theorists" jumped on nitrogen as being the cause of a decrease in the oyster and other aquatic organism populations in the Lower Chesapeake Bay Region. Oysters, like crabs, are important to the lower region, for both economic and environmental reasons, and for other reasons as well. From an environmental point of view, oysters are important to the Lower Chesapeake Bay Region because in the past, their life cycle worked to maintain relatively clean bay water. Oysters are filter feeders. They suck in water and its accompanying nutrients and other substances. The oyster sorts out the ingredients in the water and uses those nutrients it needs to sustain life. Impurities (including pollutants) are aggregated and excreted by the oyster back into the James River.

In the past (maybe 55 years ago), when oysters thrived in the Lower Chesapeake Bay, they were able to take in turbid bay water and turn it almost clear in a matter of about three days.

Of course, this is not the case today. The oysters are almost all gone.

Where did they go? Who knows?

One thing we know for certain: Oysters are no longer thriving, no longer colonizing the Lower Chesapeake Bay Region in the numbers they did in the past. They are no longer providing economic stability for watermen; they are no longer cleaning the bay.

One group of "experts" jumped to a solution. They knew the answer—it had to be nutrient contamination; nitrogen is the culprit, right?

Wrong!

Most shots taken from the hip miss the target. The proponents of nutrient contamination missed their shot.

A regional sanitation authority and a local university in the Lower Chesapeake Bay region formed a study group to formally, professionally, and scientifically study this problem. Over a five-year period, using **biological nutrient removal** (BNR) techniques at a local wastewater treatment facility, they determined that the effluent leaving the treatment plant and entering the Lower James River consistently contained below 8-mg/L of nitrogen for five consecutive years.

Has the water in the Chesapeake Bay become cleaner, clearer?

Have the oysters returned?

The answer to both of these questions is no; not really.

Wait a minute—some environmentalists, regulators, and other well-meaning interlopers stated that the problem was nitrogen. If nitrogen levels have been reduced in the Lower James River, shouldn't the oysters start thriving, colonizing, and cleaning the Lower Chesapeake Bay again?

(continued)

Sidebar 8.1. (*continued*)

You might think so, but they are not. While it is true that the nitrogen level in the wastewater effluent was significantly lowered through treatment, that a major point-source contributor of nitrogen was reduced in the Lower Chesapeake Bay is also true.

If the nitrogen level has decreased, then where are the oysters?

A more important question is: What is the real problem?

The truth is that no one at this point in time can give a definitive answer to this question.

However, a number of questions need to be answered before another theory on how to clean up the Lower Chesapeake Bay is put into practice. First, is nitrogen from the Lower James River and other tributaries feeding the Chesapeake Bay having an impact on the bay (and the oysters—and maybe the crabs)? Second, is there evidence of low dissolved oxygen in the Lower James River? Third, although concentrations of nitrogen in the Lower James River exist, are there corresponding high levels of plankton (chlorophyll a)? Finally, is it true that removing nitrogen for the sake of removing nitrogen would produce no environmental benefits, be very expensive, and divert valuable resources from other significant environmental issues?

Back to the problem with the decrease in the oyster (and crab) populations in the Lower James River/Chesapeake Bay Region. Why have the oyster and crab populations decreased?

One theory states that because the tributaries feeding the Lower Chesapeake Bay (including the James River) carry megatons of sediments into it, they add to the Bay's turbidity problem. When waters are highly turbid, oysters do the best they can to filter out the sediments, but eventually decrease in numbers and fade into the abyss.

A similar fate awaits the crabs. Highly turbid waters do not allow the sunlight to penetrate the murky water. Without sunlight, the sea grasses will not flourish. Without the sea grasses, the crab population diminishes.

Is this the answer? Is the problem with the Lower Chesapeake Bay and its oyster population, and the Eastern Shore and its crab population, related to turbidity?

Only solid, legitimate, careful scientific analysis may provide the answer.

One thing is certain. Before we leap into ill-advised actions based on nothing but that they sound "scientific" and "feel" good, we need to step back and size up the situation. This sizing-up procedure can be correctly accomplished only through the use of scientific methods.

Obviously, that we need to stop the pollution of our surface water bodies is not in question. However, shouldn't we replace the timeworn and frustrating approach that "we must start somewhere" with good common sense and legitimate science?

The bottom-line: We shouldn't do anything to our environment until science supports the tampering—the investment.

As a footnote to Sidebar 8.1, we point out that recently, from 1984 through 2008, because of reductions made in nutrient and sediment deposition in the Lower Chesapeake Bay Regions, bay grasses have rebounded. Will the oyster and crab populations also rebound? Only time will tell.

THERMAL POLLUTION

Simply stated, thermal pollution occurs when industry returns heated water to its source. Large-scale generation of electricity requires enormous quantities of water for cooling, which is sometimes drawn from lakes, rivers, or streams. Power plants that burn fossil fuels or use nuclear fuel generate great amounts of waste heat, some of which is removed by circulating cool water around and through hot power-generating equipment. This transfers heat to the water, raising its temperature. When the heated water is discharged, it can have an adverse effect on aquatic ecosystems. For example, thermally polluted water can decrease solubility of oxygen in water; kill some kinds of fish; and increase the susceptibility of some aquatic organisms to parasites, disease, and chemical toxins. Thermal pollution in general tends to disrupt aquatic ecosystems and accelerate changes in their composition. Still waters—lakes and bays—are particularly vulnerable to thermal pollution.

PLANT NUTRIENTS

The amount of nitrogen and phosphorus in a water system normally limits aquatic plant and algal growth. These plant nutrients are usually found in large amounts in sewage; phosphates are found in some detergents and in agricultural and urban runoff. When present in large amounts in still water systems (lakes, bays, and ponds), these nutrients stimulate massive, rapid reproduction and growth in algal blooms. Algae impart a green color to water and form a green scum on the surface and on rocks near shore. When algae die and decompose, additional nutrients are added to the water system, increasing the BOD.

In Sidebar 8.1, we discussed part of the problem created when too much sediment-bearing nutrient contaminant (such as phosphorus or nitrate) finds its way into our water systems. Note that excessive plant nutrients in a water system not only affect the habitats of oysters and crabs, but of course impact entire aquatic systems— and public safety. Too much phosphorus in a water system is generally not a human health problem, but excess nitrogen, in the form of nitrates, is. Nitrates are found in fertilizers and organic waste from livestock feedlots. Soluble in water, nitrates do not bind to soil particles, making them highly mobile. Because of their mobility, nitrates wash into surface water and percolate into groundwater. Nitrates in drinking water pose a significant health threat to human populations; in particular, they are a serious health threat to infants. When they reach infant intestinal tracts, nitrates oxidize the hemoglobin in the blood, rendering it unable to carry oxygen. This condition, called methemoglobinemia, can result in brain damage or death.

PERSISTENT SUBSTANCES

A water pollution threat that is (or was) often ignored is persistent substance contamination. In this modern age, some materials (products of scientific and engineering wizardry) persist; they are not normally changed or degraded to harmless substances. These persistent substances include the pesticides DDT and chlordane, metals (e.g., mercury), and organic chemicals like PCBs. These substances do not break down easily and tend to magnify throughout the food chain. Consequently, organisms at higher trophic levels (e.g., peregrine falcons, bald eagles, and other raptors) suffer the most serious effects of these nonbiodegradeable, persistent substances.

In addition to the persistent chemical substances just discussed, another category of persistent substances is playing havoc with our water systems and wildlife and is quickly gaining in notoriety as a world-class environmental problem: plastics. Plastic six-pack rings, plastic bags, and monofilament line have life expectancies of hundreds of years—they literally take hundreds of years to degrade. In marine systems, where plastics are discarded in record amounts, the problem is particularly troublesome. Balloons and bags are frequently mistaken for food and are ingested by marine wildlife, becoming entwined in the stomachs and intestines and killing the animals slowly. Sea creatures become entangled in monofilament line and six-pack rings, causing loss of movement that can eventually lead to death. On a larger scale, the fishing industry follows the deadly practice of cutting free entangled drift nets, sometimes allowing hundreds of yards of fishing nets to remain in the ocean. Called *ghost nets*, these abandoned nets entrap and drown countless sea mammals and other creatures on a much larger scale.

RADIOACTIVE SUBSTANCES

Radioactive substances are another category of pollutant affecting aquatic ecosystems. Natural radioactivity occurs in the environment (rocks and soils); however, radiation pollution arises from the use of radioactive materials. Three main sources of radiation pollution are nuclear power plants, coal-fired power plants, and nuclear explosions. Radiation pollution can cause generic defects and cancer. To control radiation pollution, the use of nuclear power plants must be strictly regulated, and the processing and shipping of nuclear fuels and wastes must be strictly controlled.

Sources of Soil Pollution

Historically, in solid waste disposal, a common saying and practice was: "I don't want it anymore. Take it to the river and throw it away." No wonder our river and stream systems became polluted over the years. We can look at the historical record of the Thames River in London and the population that grew along its banks to gain understanding of the compound problem of solid waste disposal and river pollution.

Although earlier human settlements were located along river courses (for several reasons), not all camps, settlements, and communities were located near rivers or some other water system. Eventually, as populations grew and improvements were made in transportation, population centers commonly formed in areas remote from water systems. One thing did not change, however. People continued to produce waste or "throwaways." These remote areas, however, provided no convenient body of water to dump the waste in. The waste had to be dumped somewhere. That somewhere was the land.

Land became a convenient dumping ground for wastes, including those removed from air and water. Historically, and not surprisingly, activities such as improper storage and disposal of chemicals also became—and remain—a serious problem.

When land is used for dumping waste, where do the waste products actually end up? What is affected by such dumping practices?

The answers are the same, and obvious: the soil.

With almost every country in the world experiencing a continuing increase in the amount and type of materials being discarded in landfills and other disposal sites, soil is being contaminated at an ever-increasing rate. Because of the increased rate of waste disposal on land, soil itself has become a waste product to be disposed of properly. This situation is exacerbated by the limitations of the technologies currently available for the remediation of contaminated soil, an important issue developed more fully later in this text.

Note that disposal of solid waste materials is not the only causal factor related to soil contamination. Soil contamination is also the result of certain practices conducted worldwide by other agricultural and industrial entities. These include exploration and production, mining, and nuclear industrial practices. Without question, petroleum contaminants affect the largest number of sites and the largest total volume of impacted material.

Although generally small in unit size, another large-volume contaminator of soil is underground storage tanks (USTs). In fact, petroleum contamination is commonly linked to USTs. Between 1950 and 1970, several million USTs were installed. The EPA estimates that out of approximately 2.5+ million USTs throughout the United States, more than 400,000 have leaked—or are leaking—petroleum hydrocarbons. Virtually thousands of USTs remain unrecorded, and their individual impacts on soil and the subsurface remain unknown.

Along with petroleum hydrocarbons, several other chemicals are responsible for soil contamination. The 1979 Eckhardt Committee Survey of the largest chemical manufacturing companies in the United States reported more than 16 million tons of organic generated waste had been disposed of up to that point. Of this total, almost 10 million tons were untreated (in ponds, injection wells, lagoons, and landfills). Almost 0.5 million tons were incinerated; a little more than 0.5 million tons were either reused or recycled. Manufacturing accounts for the largest percentage (85%) of the hazardous waste generated.

Oil field sites account for a large volume of hydrocarbon-contaminated soil. Sources of soil contamination include oil wells, pits and dumps, sumps, leakage from

Sidebar 8.2. Pollution Rules and Military Preparedness

Seeking broader exemptions from environmental regulation, defense officials say some environmental laws harm combat readiness and impede training. They object to rules that potentially limit maneuvers in some places during mating or nesting seasons or that restrict beaches used for practice landings.

Defense officials claim to only want better balance between military training needs and environmental protection. But according to the Government Accountability Office, readiness reports do not support claims that environmental laws are hurting preparedness. Defense officials have not been able to quantify adverse impact systematically, the GAO says, and don't even have an inventory of all their training ranges.

As the investigative arm of Congress, the GAO also wants to know why issues of preparedness should permit the Pentagon to skimp on cleanup when its activities foul soil and water or damage wildlife habitat. When environmental laws already permit case-by-case exemptions in the interest of national security, broader exemptions should not be written into law until a good case has been clearly made.

REFERENCES

"Pollution Rules Don't Hurt Military Readiness." (March 27, 2003). *Charlotte Observer* editorial.

above-ground storage containers, reservoirs, pumping stations, piping ratholes, underground storage tanks, transformers, well cellars, and random leakage or spillage.

These sites aren't the only culprits, however. Several high-volume petroleum-handling facilities, including refineries, terminals, and pipeline corridors, are situated close to production fields and residential areas. All of these sites have contributed, and still do contribute, to the overall volume of contaminated soil.

Another operation in which a close relationship between site usage and the potential for adverse environmental damage exists is **geothermal power operations**. Geothermal power operations involve conducting energy (in the form of superheated steam or water) from the Earth's interior to the surface in areas where igneous rocks are in a molten or partly molten state. Typically, geothermal plants consist of a power plant, brine storage holding tanks/ponds, drill sumps, and leach fields. Brine and lead-mine scale are the two hazardous constituents associated with geothermal operations.

For several years, **coal gasification processes** have operated in several locations throughout the United States. Using various gasification processes, these industrial plants commonly produce tars containing a wide variety of organic and inorganic compounds. These tars have contributed to a large volume of contaminated soil, groundwater, and surface water.

Mining waste (wastes from mining, milling, smelting, and refining ores and minerals) is a considerable contributor to soil contamination. Environmental problems are primarily associated with disposal of mining waste: the overburden plus **tailings**

(residue of ore processing). When they are piled into heaps and left at the site, rainwater seeps through mine wastes, which are rich in heavy metals and chemicals, and harmful by-products like sulfuric acid may be produced. This acid runoff then drains into rivers, streams, soils, and groundwater.

Alternative/Renewable Energy[3]

The current status of worldwide use of fossil fuels is impacted by supply/demand issues, who the suppliers are (i.e., unfriendly suppliers), various aspects of politics related to environmental pollution, and other persistent forces, all pushing the need for substitute, alternate, clean, and renewable fuel sources. This present need is further amplified and aggravated by the current (2011) and future economic problems, manifested by $4.00+/gallon gasoline (especially in the United States), and by the perceived crisis developing with high carbon dioxide emissions (i.e., our carbon footprint), which is the major contributing factor to global climate change.

Before proceeding with a brief, introductory discussion of alternative/renewable energy sources, it is important to make a clear distinction between the two terms, *alternative* and *renewable* energy. **Alternative energy** is an umbrella term that refers to any source of usable energy intended to replace fuel sources without the undesired consequences of the replaced fuels. The use of the term "alternative" presupposes a desirable connotation (for many people "fossil fuels" has joined that endless list of four-letter words)—that is, energy that does not use up natural resources or harm the environment. Examples are petroleum as an alternative to whale oil, coal as an alternative to wood, alcohol as an alternative to fossil fuels, and coal gasification as an alternative to petroleum. These alternate fuels need not be renewable.

Renewable energy is energy generated from natural resources—such as sunlight, wind, water (hydro), ocean thermal, wave and tide action, biomass, and geothermal heat—which are naturally replenished and thus renewable. Renewable energy resources are virtually inexhaustible—they are replenished at the same rate as they are used—but limited in the amount of energy that is available per unit of time. If we have not come full circle in our cycling from renewable to nonrenewable, we are getting close. Consider, for example, that in 1850, about 90% of the energy consumed in the United States was from renewable energy resources (hydropower, wind, burning wood, etc.). Now, however, the country is heavily reliant on the nonrenewable fossil fuels: natural gas, oil, and coal. In 2009, about 7% of all energy consumed (see Table 8.2) and about 8.5% of total electricity production was from renewable energy resources.

Most of the renewable energy is used for electricity generation, heat in industrial processes, heating and cooling buildings, and transportation. Electricity producers (utilities, independent producers, and combined heat and power plants) consumed 51% of total U.S. renewable energy in 2007 for producing electricity. Most of the rest of the remaining 49% of renewable energy was biomass, consumed for industrial applications (principally paper-making) by plants producing only heat and steam. Biomass is also used for transportation fuels (ethanol) and to provide residential and commercial space heating. The largest share of the renewable-generated electricity comes

Table 8.2. U.S. Energy Consumption by Energy Source, 2007 (Quadrillion Btu)

Energy Source	2007
Total	**101.605**
Renewable	6.830
Solar/PV	0.080
Wind	0.319
Hydroelectric conventional	2.463
Biomass (biofuels, waste, wood and wood-derived)	3.615
Biofuels	1.018
Waste	0.431
Wood-derived fuels	2.165
Geothermal	0.353

Source: EIA, 2007.

from hydroelectric energy (71%), followed by biomass (16%), wind (9%), geothermal (4%), and solar (0.2%). Wind-generated electricity increased by almost 21% between 2006 and 2007, more than any other energy source. Its growth rate was followed closely by solar, which increased by over 19% between 2006 and 2007.

From Table 8.2 it is obvious that currently there are five primary forms of renewable energy: solar, wind, hydroelectric, biomass, and geothermal. Each of these holds promise and poses challenges for future development.

SOLAR ENERGY

It is fitting to begin our discussion of the various kinds of renewable energy with the sun—the star that symbolizes life, power, strength, force, clarity, and, yes, energy. The sun nourishes our planet. When we consider the sun and **solar energy** first, we quickly realize that there is nothing new about renewable energy. The sun was the first energy source; it has been around for 4.5 billion years, as long as anything else we are familiar with. On Earth, without the sun there is nothing—absolutely nothing. The sun provided light and heat to the first humans. During daylight, the people searched for food. They hunted and gathered and probably stayed together for safety. When nightfall arrived and they were in the dark, we can only imagine that they huddled together for warmth in the light of the stars and moon, waiting for the sun and its live-giving and sustaining light to return.

Solar energy (a term used interchangeably with solar power) uses the power of the sun, through various technologies, "directly" to produce energy. Solar energy is one of the best renewable energy sources available, because it is one the cleanest. Direct solar radiation absorbed in solar collectors can provide space heating and hot water. Passive solar can be used to enhance the solar energy use in buildings for space heating and lighting requirements. Solar energy can also be used to produce electricity, and this is the renewable energy area that is the focus in this section.

According to U.S. DOE (2009), the two solar electric technologies with the greatest potential are photovoltaics (PV) and concentrating solar power (CSP).

Photovoltaics (PV)

Photovoltaic (Gr. *photo*, light, and *volt*, electricity pioneer Alessandro Volta) technology makes use of the abundant energy in the sun, and it has little impact on our environment. *Photovoltaics* is the direct conversion of light into electricity at the atomic level. Some materials exhibit a property known as the *photoelectric effect* (discovered and described by Becquerel in 1839), which causes them to absorb photons of light and release electrons. When these free electrons are captured, an electric current results (i.e., electricity is the flow of free electrons) that can be used as electricity. The first photovoltaic module (billed as a solar battery) was built by Bell laboratories in 1954. In the 1960s, the space program began to make the first serious use of the technology to provide power aboard spacecraft. Space program use helped this technology make giant advancements in reliability and helped to lower costs. However, it was the oil embargo of the 1970s (the so-called energy crisis) that propelled photovoltaic technology to the forefront of recognition for use other than space applications. Photovoltaics can be used in a wide range of products, from small consumer items to large commercial solar electric systems.

A basic *photovoltaic cell* is also called a *solar cell*. Solar cells are made of silicon, and other semiconductor materials such as germanium, gallium arsenide, and silicon carbide are used in the microelectronics industry. For solar cells, a thin semiconductor wafer is specially treated to form an electric field, positive on one side and negative on the other. When light energy strikes the solar cell, electrons are jarred loose from the atoms in the semiconductor material. If electrical conductors are attached to the positive and negative sides, forming an electrical circuit, the electrons can be captured in the form of an electrical current—that is, again, electron flow is electricity. This electricity can then be used to power a load, such as a light, tool, toaster, or other electrical appliance or apparatus.

A number of solar cells electrically connected to each other and mounted in a support panel or frame are called a *photovoltaic module*. Modules are designed to supply electricity at a certain voltage, such as a common 12-volt system. The current produced is directly dependent on how much light strikes the module.

Multiple modules can be wired together to form an array. In general, the larger the area of a module or array, the more electricity will be produced. Photovoltaic modules and arrays produce direct-current (DC) electricity. They can be connected in both series and parallel electrical arrangements to produce any required voltage and current combination.

Concentrating Solar Power (CSP)

Concentrating solar power (CSP) offers a utility-scale, firm, dispatchable renewable energy option that can help meet a nation's demand for electricity. CSP plants produce power by first using mirrors to focus sunlight to heat a working fluid. Ultimately, this high-temperature fluid is used to spin a turbine or power an engine that drives a generator that produces electricity.

Concentrating solar power systems can be classified by how they collect solar energy, using linear concentrator, dish/engine, or power tower systems (NREL 2009).

- A *linear concentrator* collects the sun's energy using long, rectangular, curved (U-shaped) mirrors. The mirrors are tilted toward the sun, focusing sunlight on tubes (or receivers) that run the length of the mirrors. The reflected sunlight heats a fluid flowing through the tubes. The hot fluid is then used to boil water in a conventional steam-turbine generator to produce electricity. There are two major types of linear concentrator systems: parabolic trough systems, in which receiver tubes are positioned along the focal line of each parabolic mirror; and linear Fresnel reflector systems, in which one receiver tube is positioned above several mirrors to allow the mirrors greater mobility in tracking the sun.
- The *dish/engine system* uses a mirrored dish similar to a very large satellite dish. The dish-shaped surface directs and concentrates sunlight onto a thermal receiver, which absorbs and collects the heat and transfers it to the engine generator. The most common type of heat engine used today in dish/engine systems is the Stirling engine (conceived in 1816). This system uses the fluid heated by the receiver to move pistons and create mechanical power. The mechanical power is then used to run a generator or alternator to produce electricity.
- The *power tower system* uses a large field of flat, sun-tracking mirrors known as heliostats to focus and concentrate sunlight onto a receiver on the top of a tower. A heat-transfer fluid heated in the receiver is used to generate steam, which in turn is used in a conventional turbine generator to produce electricity. Some power towers use water/steam as the heat-transfer fluid. Other advanced designs are experimenting with molten nitrate salt, because of its superior heat-transfer and energy-storage capabilities. The energy-storage capability, or thermal storage, allows the system to continue to dispatch electricity during cloudy weather or at night.

Smaller CSP systems can be located directly where the power is needed. For example, a single dish/engine system can produce 3 to 25 kilowatts of power and is well suited for such distributed applications. Larger, utility-scale CSP applications provide hundreds of megawatts of electricity for the power grid. Both linear concentrator and power tower systems can be easily integrated with thermal storage, helping to generate electricity during cloudy periods or at night. Alternatively, these systems can be combined with natural gas, and the resulting hybrid power plants can provide high-value, dispatchable power throughout the day.

Solar energy has some obvious advantages in that the source is free; however, the initial investment in operating equipment is not. Solar energy is also environmentally friendly, requires almost no maintenance, and reduces our dependence on foreign energy supplies. Probably the greatest downside of solar energy use is that in areas without direct sunlight during certain times of the year, solar panels cannot capture enough energy to provide heat for homes or businesses. Geographically speaking, the higher latitudes do not receive as much direct sunlight as tropical areas. Because of the position of the sun in the sky, solar panels must be placed in sun-friendly locations such as the U.S. Southwest and the Sahara region of northern Africa.

WIND ENERGY[4]

Wind energy is the movement of wind to create power. Since early recorded history, people have been harnessing the energy of the wind for milling grain, pumping water, and other mechanical power applications. Wind energy propelled boats along the Nile River as early as 5000 BC. By 200 BC, simple windmills in China were pumping water, while vertical-axis windmills with woven reed sails were grinding grain in Persia and the Middle East.

The use of wind energy spread around the world, and by the 11th century, people in the Middle East were using windmills extensively for food production; returning merchants and crusaders carried this idea back to Europe. The Dutch refined the windmill and adapted it for draining lakes and marshes in the Rhine River delta. When settlers took this technology to the New World in the later 19th century, they began using windmills to pump water for farms and ranches, and later, to generate electricity for homes and industry. Today, there are several hundred thousand windmills in operation around the world, many of which are used for water pumping. But it is the use of wind energy as a pollution-free means of generating electricity on a significant scale that is attracting most current interest. With the present and pending shortage and high cost of fossil fuels to generate electricity and the green movement toward the use of cleaner fuels, wind energy is the world's fastest-growing energy source and will power industry, businesses, and homes with clean, renewable electricity for many years to come. In the United States since 1970, wind-based electricity-generating capacity has increased markedly, although at present it remains a small fraction of total electric capacity. But this trend is beginning to change with the advent of $4.00/gallon for gasoline, high heating and cooling costs, subsequent increases in the cost of electricity, and worldwide political unrest or uncertainty in oil-supplying countries. One need only travel the "wind corridors" encompassing parts of Arizona, New Mexico, Texas, Missouri, and north through the Great Plains to the Pembina Escarpment and Turtle Mountains of North Dakota to witness the seemingly exponential increase in wind energy development and wind turbine installations. These machines are being installed to produce and provide electricity to the grid.

We can classify wind energy as a form of solar energy. Winds are caused by uneven heating of the atmosphere by the sun, irregularities of the Earth's surface, and the rotation of the Earth. As a result, winds are strongly influenced and modified by local terrain, bodies of water, weather patterns, vegetative cover, and other factors. The wind flow, or motion of energy, when harvested by wind turbines can be used to generate electricity.

As for any other source of energy, nonrenewable or renewable, there are advantages and disadvantages associated with their use. On the positive side, it should be noted that wind energy is a free, renewable resource, so no matter how much is used today, there will still be the same supply in the future. Wind energy is also a source of clean, nonpolluting, electricity. One huge advantage of wind energy is that it is a domestic source of energy, produced in the country where it is installed and where wind is abundant. In the United States, the wind supply is abundant.

Figure 8.1. Wind turbine farm in corn field in Indiana. Photo by Frank R. Spellman

Wind turbines can be installed on farms or ranches, as shown in Figure 8.1, thus benefiting the economy in rural areas, where most of the best wind sites are found. Moreover, farmers and ranchers can continue to work the land, because the wind turbines use only a fraction of it.

On the other side of the coin, wind energy does have a few negatives. Wind power must compete with conventional generation sources on a cost basis. Even though the cost of wind power has decreased dramatically in the past 10 years, the technology requires a higher initial investment than fossil-fueled generators. The challenge for using wind as a source of power is that wind is intermittent and does not always blow when electricity is needed. Wind energy cannot be stored (unless batteries are being used), and not all winds can be harnessed to meet the timing of electricity demands. Another problem is that good sites are often located in remote locations, far from cities where the electricity is needed. Moreover, wind resource development may compete with other uses for the land, and those alternative uses may be more highly valued than electricity generation. Finally, although wind power plants have relatively little impact on the environment compared to conventional power plants, there is some concern over the noise produced by the rotor blades, aesthetic (visual) impacts, and birds being killed by flying into the rotors. Most of these problems have been resolved or greatly reduced through technological development or by properly siting wind plants.

In regard to wind energy and its future, one thing is certain: It continues to be one of the fastest-growing energy technologies and looks set to become a major generator of electricity throughout the world.

HYDROPOWER

When we look at rushing waterfalls and rivers, we may not immediately think of electricity. But hydroelectric (water-powered) plants are responsible for lighting many of our homes and neighborhoods. **Hydropower** is the harnessing of water to perform work. The power of falling water has been used in industry for thousands of years (see Table 8.3). The Greeks used water wheels for grinding wheat into flour more than 2,000 years ago. Besides grinding flour, the power of the water was used to saw wood and power textile mills and manufacturing plants.

Table 8.3.   History of Hydropower

Date	Hydropower Event
BC	Hydropower used by the Greeks to turn water wheels for grinding wheat into flour more than 2,000 years ago.
Mid-1770s	French hydraulic and military engineer Bernard Forest de Belidor wrote a four-volume work describing vertical- and horizontal-axis machines.
1775	U.S. Army Corps of Engineers founded, with establishment of Chief Engineer for the Continental Army.
1880	Michigan's Grand Rapids Electric Light and Power Company, generating electricity by dynamo belted to a water turbine at the Wolverine Chair Factory, lit up 16 brush-arc lamps.
1881	Niagara Falls city street lamps powered by hydropower.
1882	World's first hydroelectric power plant began operation on the Fox River in Appleton, Wisconsin.
1886	About 45 water-powered electric plants in the United States and Canada.
1887	San Bernardino, California, opens first hydroelectric plant in the West.
1889	Two hundred electric plants in the United States use water power for some or all generation.
1901	First Federal Water Power Act.
1902	Bureau of Reclamation established.
1907	Hydropower provides 15% of U.S. electrical generation.
1920	Hydropower provides 25% of U.S. electrical generation. Federal Power Act establishes Federal Power Commission to issue licenses for hydro development on public lands.
1933	Tennessee Valley Authority established.
1935	Federal Power Commission authority extended to all hydroelectric projects built by utilities engaged in interstate commerce.
1937	Bonneville Dam, first federal dam, begins operation on the Columbia River; Bonneville Power Administration established.
1940	Hydropower provides 40% of electrical generation. Conventional capacity tripled in United States since 1920.
1980	Conventional capacity nearly tripled in United States since 1900.
2003	About 10% of U.S. electricity comes from hydropower. Today, there is about 80,000MW of conventional capacity and 18,000 MW of pumped storage.

Source: EERE, History of Hydropower, Energy Efficiency & Renewable Energy. U.S. Department of Energy, Washington, DC: 2008 (http://www1.eere.energy.gov/windlandhydro_history.html).

The technology for using falling water to create hydroelectricity has existed for more than a century. The evolution of the modern hydropower turbine began in the mid-1700s when a French hydraulic and military engineer, Bernard Forest de Belidor, wrote a four-volume work describing using a vertical-axis versus a horizontal-axis machine.

Water turbine development continued during the 1700s and 1800s. In 1880, a brush arc light dynamo driven by a water turbine was used to provide theater and storefront lighting in Grand Rapids, Michigan, and in 1881, a brush dynamo connected to a turbine in a flour mill provided street lighting at Niagara Falls, New York. These two projects used direct-current (DC) technology.

Alternating current (AC) is used today. That breakthrough came when the electric generator was coupled to the turbine, which resulted in the world's and the United States' first hydroelectric plant, located on the Fox River in Appleton, Wisconsin, in 1882. The U.S. Library of Congress (2009) lists the Appleton hydroelectric power plant as one of the major accomplishments of the Gilded Age (1878–1889). Soon, people across the country were enjoying electricity in homes, schools, and offices, reading by electric lamp instead of candlelight or kerosene. Today, we take electricity for granted, not able to imagine life without it.

Ranging in size from small systems (100 kilowatts to 30 megawatts) for a home or village to large projects (capacity greater than 30 megawatts) producing electricity for utilities, hydropower plants are of three types: impoundment, diversion, and pumped storage. Some hydropower plants use dams and some do not. Many dams were built for other purposes, and hydropower was added later. In the United States, there are about 80,000 dams, of which only 2,400 produce power. The other dams are for recreation, stock/farm ponds, flood control, water supply, and irrigation. The sizes of hydropower plants are discussed below.

Impoundment

The most common type of hydroelectric power plant is an impoundment facility. Typically a large hydropower system, it uses a dam to store river water in a reservoir. Water released from the reservoir flows through a turbine, spinning it, which in turn activates a generator to produce electricity. The water may be released either to meet changing electricity needs or to maintain a constant reservoir level.

Diversion

A diversion, sometimes called run-of-river, facility channels all or a portion of the flow of a river from its natural course through a canal or penstock. It may not require the use of a dam.

Pumped Storage

When the demand for electricity is low, a pumped storage facility stores energy by pumping water from a lower reservoir to an upper reservoir. During periods of high electrical demand, the water is released back to the lower reservoir to generate electricity.

Hydropower offers advantages over the other energy sources, but faces unique environmental challenges. The advantages of using hydropower begin with the fact that it does not pollute the air like power plants that burn fossil fuels, such as coal and natural gas. Moreover, hydropower does not have to be imported into the United States like foreign oil does; it is produced in the country. Because hydropower relies on the water cycle, driven by the sun, it's a renewable resource that will be around for at least as long as humans. Hydropower is controllable; that is, engineers can control the flow of water through the turbines to produce electricity on demand. Finally, hydropower impoundment dams create huge lake areas for recreation, irrigation of farm lands, reliable supplies of potable water, and flood control.

Hydropower also has some disadvantages. For example, fish populations can be impacted if fish cannot migrate upstream past impoundment dams to spawning grounds or if they cannot migrate downstream to the ocean. Many dams have installed fish ladders or elevators to aid upstream fish passage. Downstream fish passage is aided by diverting fish from turbine intakes using screens or racks or even underwater lights and sounds, and by maintaining a minimum spill flow past the turbine. Hydropower can also impact water quality and flow. Hydropower plants can cause low dissolved oxygen (DO) levels in the water, a problem that is harmful to riparian (riverbank) habitats and is addressed using various aeration techniques, which oxygenate the water. Maintaining minimum flows of water downstream of a hydropower installation is also critical for the survival of riparian habitats. Hydropower is also susceptible to drought. When water is not available, the hydropower plants can't produce electricity. Finally, construction of new hydropower facilities impacts investors and others by competing with other uses of the land. Preserving local flora and fauna and historical or cultural sites is often more highly valued than electricity generation.

BIOMASS

Biomass (all the Earth's living matter) or *bioenergy* (the energy from plants and plant-derived materials; stored energy from the sun) has been used since people began burning wood to cook food and keep warm. Wood is still the largest biomass energy resource today, but other sources of biomass can also be used. These include food crops, grassy and woody plants, residues from agriculture or forestry, and the organic component of municipal and industrial wastes. Even the fumes from landfills (which are methane, a natural gas) can be used as a biomass energy source. Organic material that has been transformed by geological processes into substances such as coal or petroleum is not considered biomass. The biomass industry is one of the fastest-growing industries in the United States.

A variety of biomass feedstocks can be used to produce transportation fuels, biobased products, and power. Currently, a majority of the ethanol produced in the United States is made from corn or other starch-based crops. However, the current trend in research is to develop biomass fuels from non-foodstocks. For example, the focus is on the development of cellulosic feedstocks—nongrain, non-food-based feedstocks such as switchgrass, corn stover, and woody material—and on technologies to convert cellulosic material into transportation fuels and other products. Using cellulosic feedstocks can not only alleviate the potential concern of diverting food crops to produce fuel, but also has a variety of environmental benefits.

Environmental benefits include the use of biomass energy to greatly reduce greenhouse gas emissions. Burning biomass releases about the same amount of carbon dioxide as burning fossil fuels. However, fossil fuels release carbon dioxide captured by photosynthesis millions of years ago—an essentially "new" greenhouse gas. Biomass, on the other hand, releases carbon dioxide that is largely balanced by the carbon dioxide captured in its own growth (depending on how much energy was used to grow, harvest, and process the fuel).

Another benefit of biomass use for fuel is that it can reduce dependence on foreign oil, because biofuels are the only renewable liquid transportation fuels available.

Finally, biomass energy supports U.S. agricultural and forest-product industries. The main biomass feedstocks for power are paper mill residue, lumber mill scrap, and municipal waste. For biomass fuels, the feedstocks are corn (for ethanol) and soybeans (for biodiesel), both surplus crops. In the near future—and with developed technology—agricultural residues such as corn stover (the stalks, leaves, and husks of the plant) and wheat straw will also be used. Long-term plans include growing and using dedicated energy crops, such as fast-growing trees and grasses that can grow sustainably on land that will not support intensive food crops.

GEOTHERMAL ENERGY[5]

Approximately 4,000 miles below the Earth's surface is the core, where temperatures can reach 9,000° F. This heat—geothermal energy (*geo*, meaning Earth, and *thermos*, meaning heat)—flows outward from the core, heating the surrounding area, which can form underground reservoirs of hot water and steam. These reservoirs can be tapped for a variety of uses, such as to generate electricity or heat buildings.

The geothermal energy potential in the uppermost six miles of the Earth's crust amounts to 50,000 times the energy of all oil and gas resources in the world. In the United States, most geothermal reservoirs are located in the western states, Alaska, and Hawaii. However, geothermal heat pumps (GHPs), which take advantage of the shallow ground's stable temperature for heating and cooling buildings, can be used almost anywhere.

Again, it is important to point out that there is nothing new about renewable energy. From solar power to burning biomass (wood) in the cave and elsewhere, humans have taken advantage of renewable resources from time immemorial. For example, hot springs have been used for bathing since Paleolithic times or earlier (DOE 2009). The early Romans used hot springs to feed public baths and for under-floor heating. The world's oldest geothermal district heating system, in France, has been operating since the 14th century (Lund 2007). The history of geothermal energy use in the United States is interesting and lengthy. Following is a brief chronology of major geothermal events in the United States (DOE 2006).

Geothermal Timeline

8000 BC (and earlier): Paleo-Indians use hot springs for cooking, refuge, and respite. Hot springs are neutral zones where members of warring nations can bathe together in peace. Native Americans have a history with every major hot spring in the United States.

1807: As European settlers move westward across the continent, they gravitate toward these springs of warmth and vitality. In 1807, the first European to visit the Yellowstone area, John Colter (ca. 1774–ca. 1813), widely considered to be the first mountain man, probably encounters hot springs, leading to the designation "Colter's Hell." Also in 1807, settlers found the city of Hot Springs, Arkansas, where in 1830 Asa Thompson charges one dollar each for the use of three spring-fed wooden tubs, the first known commercial use of geothermal energy.

1847: William Bell Elliot, a member of John C. Fremont's survey party, stumbles upon a steaming valley just north of what is now San Francisco, California. Elliot calls the area The Geysers—a misnomer—and thinks he has found the gates of Hell.

1852: The Geysers is developed into a spa called The Geysers Resort Hotel. Guests include J. Pierpont Morgan, Ulysses S. Grant, Theodore Roosevelt, and Mark Twain.

1862: At springs located southeast of The Geysers, businessman Sam Brannan pours an estimated half million dollars into an extravagant development dubbed "Calistoga," replete with hotel, bathhouse, skating pavilion, and racetrack. Brannan's is one of many spas reminiscent of those in Europe.

1864: Homes and dwellings are built near springs millennia ago, to take advantage of the natural heat, but the construction of the Hot Lake Hotel near La Grande, Oregon, marks the first time that the energy from hot springs is used on a large scale.

1892: Boise, Idaho, provides the world's first district heating system, piping water from hot springs to town buildings. Within a few years, the system is serving 200 homes and 40 downtown businesses.

1900: Hot springs water is piped to homes in Klamath Falls, Oregon.

1921: John D. Grant drills a well at The Geysers with the intention of generating electricity. This effort is unsuccessful, but one year later Grant meets with success across the valley at another site, and the first U.S. geothermal power plant goes into operation. Grant uses steam from the first well to build a second well, and several wells later, the operation is producing 250 kilowatts, enough electricity to light the buildings and streets at the resort. The plant, however, is not competitive with other sources of power, and it soon falls into disuse.

1927: Pioneer Development Company drills the first exploratory wells at Imperial Valley, California.

1930: The first commercial greenhouse use of geothermal energy is undertaken in Boise, Idaho. The operation uses a 1,000-foot well drilled in 1926. In Klamath Falls, Charlie Lieb develops the first downhole heat exchanger (DHE) to heat his house.

1940: The first residential space heating in Nevada begins in the Moan area in Reno.

1948: Geothermal technology moves east when Carl Nielsen develops the first ground-source heat pump, for use at his residence. J. D. Krocker, an engineer in Portland, Oregon, pioneers the first commercial building use of a groundwater heat pump.

1960: The country's first large-scale geothermal electricity-generating plant begins operation. Pacific Gas and Electric operates the plant, located at The Geysers. The first turbine produces 11 megawatts (MW) of net power and operates successfully for more than 30 years.

1978: Geothermal Food Processors, Inc., opens the first geothermal food-processing (crop-drying) plant in Brady Hot Springs, Nevada. The Load Guaranty Program provides $3.5 million for the facility.

1979: The first electrical development of a water-dominated geothermal resource occurs, at the east Mesa field in the Imperial Valley in California. The plant is named for B.C. McCabe, the geothermal pioneer who, with his Magma Power Company, did field development work at several sites, including The Geysers.

1980: TAD's Enterprises of Nevada pioneers the use of geothermal energy for the cooking, distilling, and drying processes associated with alcohol fuels production. UNOCAL builds the country's first flash plant, generating 10 MW at Brawley, California.

1982: Economical electrical generation begins at California's Salton Sea geothermal field through the use of crystallizer-clarifier technology. The technology is the result of a joint government–industry effort to manage the high-salinity brines at the site.

1984: A 20 MW plant begins generating power at Utah's Roosevelt Hot Springs. Nevada's first geothermal electricity is generated with a 1.3 MW binary power plant beginning operation.

1987: Geothermal fluids are used in the first geothermal-enhanced heap leaching project for gold recovery, near Round Mountain, Nevada.

1989: The world's first hybrid (organic Rankine/gas engine) geopressure–geothermal power plant begins operation at Pleasant Bayou, Texas, using both the heat and the methane of a geopressured resource.

1992: Electrical generation begins at the 25 MW geothermal plant in the Puna field of Hawaii.

1993: A 23 MW binary power plant is completed at Steamboat Springs, Nevada.

1995: Integrated Ingredients dedicates a food-dehydration facility that processes 15 million pounds of dried onions and garlic per year at Empire, Nevada. A DOE low-temperature resource assessment of 10 western states identifies nearly 9,000 thermal wells and springs and 271 communities collocated with a geothermal resource greater than 50.

2002: Organized by GeoPowering the West, geothermal development working groups are active in five states—Nevada, Idaho, New Mexico, Oregon, and Washington. Group members represent all stakeholder organizations. The working groups identify barriers to geothermal development in their state and bring together all interested parties to arrive at mutually beneficial solutions.

2003: The Utah Geothermal Working Group is formed.

2011: There are four district heating systems in Boise, Idaho, providing heat to over 5 million square feet of residential, business, and governmental space. There are also 17 district heating systems in the United States and dozens more around the world. More than 500 DHEs are in use around the United States, and 69 large-scale geothermal generating facilities are in operation at 18 resource sites.

Geothermal energy can be and already is accessed by drilling water or steam wells, in a process similar to drilling for oil. Geothermal energy is an enormous, underused heat and power resource that is clean (emits little or no greenhouse gases), reliable (average system availability of 95%), and homegrown (making us less dependent on foreign oil).

Geothermal resources range from shallow ground to hot water and rock several miles below the Earth's surface, and even farther down to the extremely hot molten rock called magma. Mile-or-more-deep wells can be drilled into underground reservoirs to tap steam and very hot water that can be brought to the surface for use in a variety of applications.

OCEAN ENERGY

The **ocean** can produce two types of energy: *thermal energy* from the sun's heat and *mechanical energy* from the tides and waves. Open thermal energy can be used for many applications, including electricity generation. Electricity conversion systems either use the warm surface water or boil the seawater to turn a turbine, which activates a generator.

The conversion of both tidal and wave energy into electricity usually involves mechanical devices. It is important to distinguish tidal energy from hydropower. Recall that hydropower is derived from the hydrological climate cycle, powered by solar energy, which is usually harnessed via hydroelectric dams. In contrast, tidal energy is the result of the interaction of the gravitational pull of the moon and, to a lesser extent, the sun, on the seas. Processes that use tidal energy rely on the twice-daily tides and the resultant upstream flows and downstream ebbs in estuaries and the lower reaches of some rivers, as well as, in some cases, tidal movement out at sea. A dam is typically used to convert tidal energy into electricity by forcing the water through turbines, activating a generator. Meanwhile, wave energy, a very large potential resource to be tapped, uses mechanical power to directly activate a generator, to transfer into a working fluid, water, or air, which then drives a turbine/generator.

HYDROGEN[6]

Containing only one electron and one proton, hydrogen (H) is the simplest element on Earth. Hydrogen is a diatomic molecule—each molecule has two atoms of hydrogen (which is why pure hydrogen is commonly expressed as H_2). Although abundant as an element, hydrogen combines readily with other elements and is almost always found as part of another substance, such as water, hydrocarbons, or alcohols. Hydrogen is also found in biomass, which includes all plants and animals. Considerations about hydrogen energy include the following:

• Hydrogen is an energy carrier, not an energy source. It can store and deliver usable energy, but it doesn't typically exist by itself in nature; it must be produced from compounds that contain it.

- Hydrogen can be produced using diverse, domestic resources, including nuclear; natural gas and coal; and biomass and other renewables, including solar, wind, hydroelectric, or geothermal energy. This diversity of domestic energy sources makes hydrogen a promising energy carrier and important to our nation's energy security. It is expected and desirable for hydrogen to be produced using a variety of resources and process technologies (or pathways).
- The U.S. Department of Energy (DOE) focuses on hydrogen-production technologies that result in near-zero net greenhouse gas emissions and use renewable energy sources, nuclear energy, and coal (when combined with carbon sequestration). To ensure sufficient clean energy for our overall energy needs, energy efficiency is also important.
- Hydrogen can be produced via various process technologies, including thermal (natural gas reforming, renewable liquid and bio-oil processing, and biomass and coal gasification), electrolytic (water splitting using a variety of energy resources), and photolytic (splitting water using sunlight via biological and electrochemical materials).
- Hydrogen can be produced in large, central (50–300 miles from point of use); smaller, semi-central (located within 25–100 miles of use); and distributed (near or at point of use) facilities. Learn more about distributed versus centralized production.
- For hydrogen to be successful in the marketplace, it must be cost-competitive with the available alternatives. In the light-duty vehicle transportation market, this competitive requirement means that hydrogen has to be available untaxed at $2–$3/gge (gasoline gallon equivalent). This price would result in hydrogen fuel cell vehicles having the same cost to the consumer on a cost-per-mile-driven basis as a comparable conventional internal-combustion engine or hybrid vehicle.
- The DOE is engaged in research and development of a variety of hydrogen production technologies. Some are further along in development than others—some can be cost-competitive for the transition period (beginning in 2015), and others are considered long-term technologies (cost-competitive after 2030).

Infrastructure is required to move hydrogen from the location where it is produced to the dispenser at a refueling station or stationary power site. Infrastructure includes the pipelines, trucks, railcars, ships, and barges that deliver fuel, as well as the facilities and equipment needed to load and unload them.

Delivery technology for hydrogen infrastructure is currently available commercially, and several U.S. companies already deliver bulk hydrogen. Some of the infrastructure is already in place, because hydrogen has long been used in industrial applications, but it's not sufficient to support widespread consumer use of hydrogen. Because hydrogen has a relatively low volumetric energy density, its transportation, storage, and final delivery to the point of use involve a significant cost and result in some of the energy inefficiencies associated with using it as an energy carrier.

Options and trade-offs for hydrogen delivery from central, semicentral, and distributed production facilities to the point of use are complex. The choice of a hydrogen production strategy greatly affects the cost and method of delivery.

For example, larger, centralized facilities can produce hydrogen at relatively low cost due to economies of scale, but the delivery costs for centrally produced hydrogen are higher than the delivery costs for semicentral or distributed production options (because the point of use is farther away). In comparison, distributed production facilities have relatively low delivery costs, but the hydrogen production costs are likely to be higher—lower volume production means higher equipment costs on a per-unit-of-hydrogen basis.

Key challenges to hydrogen delivery include reducing delivery cost, increasing energy efficiency, maintaining hydrogen purity, and minimizing hydrogen leakage. Further research is needed to analyze the trade-offs between the hydrogen production options and the hydrogen delivery options taken together as a system. Building a national hydrogen delivery infrastructure is a big challenge. It will take time to develop and will likely include combinations of various technologies. Delivery infrastructure needs and resources will vary by region and type of market (e.g., urban, interstate, or rural). Infrastructure options will also evolve as the demand for hydrogen grows and as delivery technologies develop and improve.

Hydrogen Storage

Storing enough hydrogen aboard a vehicle to achieve a driving range of greater than 300 miles is a significant challenge. On a weight basis, hydrogen has nearly three times the energy content of gasoline (120 MJ/kg for hydrogen versus 44 MJ/kg for gasoline). However, on a volume basis, the situation is reversed (8 MJ/liter for liquid hydrogen versus 32 MJ/liter for gasoline). Onboard hydrogen storage in the range of 5–13 kg H_2 is required to encompass the full platform of light-duty vehicles.

Hydrogen can be stored in a variety of ways, but for it to be a competitive fuel for vehicles, the hydrogen vehicle must be able to travel a comparable distance to conventional hydrocarbon-fueled vehicles.

Hydrogen can be physically stored as either a gas or a liquid. Storage as a gas typically requires high-pressure tanks (5,000–10,000 psi). Storage of hydrogen as a liquid requires cryogenic temperatures, because the boiling point of hydrogen at one atmosphere pressure is –252.8ºC. It can also be stored on the surfaces of solids (by adsorption) or within solids (by absorption). In adsorption, hydrogen is attached to the surface of material either as hydrogen molecules or as hydrogen atoms. In absorption, hydrogen is dissociated into H atoms, and then the hydrogen atoms are incorporated into the solid lattice framework.

Hydrogen storage in solids may make it possible to store large quantities of hydrogen in smaller volumes at low pressures and at temperatures close to room temperature. It is also possible to achieve volumetric storage densities greater than liquid hydrogen, because the hydrogen molecule is dissociated into atomic hydrogen within the metal hydride lattice structure.

Finally, hydrogen can be stored through the reaction of hydrogen-containing materials with water (or other compounds such as alcohols). In this case, the hydrogen is effectively stored in both the material and the water. The phrase "chemical hydrogen storage" or chemical hydrides is used to describe this form of hydrogen storage. It is also possible to store hydrogen in the chemical structures of liquids and solids.

Hydrogen Fuel Cell

The fuel cell uses the chemical energy of hydrogen to cleanly and efficiently produce electricity, with water and heat as by-products. Fuel cells are unique in the variety of their potential applications; they can provide energy for systems as large as a utility power station and as small as a laptop computer.

Fuel cells have several benefits over conventional combustion-based technologies currently used in many power plants and passenger vehicles. They produce much smaller quantities of greenhouse gases and none of the air pollutants that create smog and cause health problems. If pure hydrogen is used as a fuel, fuel cells emit only heat and water as by-products.

Did You Know?

Hydrogen fuel cell vehicles (FCVs) emit approximately the same amount of water per mile as vehicles using gasoline-powered internal combustion engines (ICEs).

A *fuel cell* is a device that uses hydrogen (or hydrogen-rich fuel) and oxygen to create electricity by an electrochemical process. A single fuel cell consists of an electrolyte and two catalyst-coated electrodes (a porous anode and a cathode). Although there are different fuel cell types, all fuel cells work similarly:

- Hydrogen, or a hydrogen-rich fuel, is fed to the anode, where a catalyst separates hydrogen's negatively charged electrons from positively charged ions (protons).
- At the cathode, oxygen combines with electrons and, in some cases, with species such as protons or water, resulting in water or hydroxide ions, respectively.
- In polymer electrolyte membrane and phosphoric acid fuel cells, protons move through the electrolyte to the cathode to combine with oxygen and electrons, producing water and heat.
- In alkaline, molten carbonate, and solid oxide fuel cells, negative ions travel through the electrolyte to the anode, where they combine with hydrogen to generate water and electrons.
- The electrons from the anode cannot pass through the electrolyte to the positively charged cathode; they must travel around it via an electrical circuit to reach the other side of the cell. This movement of electrons is an electrical current.

Chapter Summary

Technological advances have allowed our modern culture to achieve incredible goals—along the way creating incredible problems we must address. But the technology that we have created also gives us ways to solve the problems we have caused. While we paint a bleak picture of the state of our environment, environmental engineers, scientists, and technologists—as well as concerned "civilian" environmentalists (and even some politicians)—recognize what needs to be done and work to improve our environmental situation.

Discussion Questions and Problems

1. If nature pollutes more than humans, why should we be concerned about anthropogenic air pollution? Water pollution? Soil pollution?
2. What is the atmospheric significance of anthropogenic CO emissions?
3. How do haze and smog differ?
4. What processes lead to the formation of sulfuric acid and other sulfate compounds in the atmosphere?
5. Describe two ways by which precipitation removal of contaminants from the atmosphere occurs. What are the two main sinks for these contaminants?
6. How do the concepts of acid rain, acid precipitation, and acidic deposition differ?
7. How does acidic deposition affect the ecology of freshwater lakes?

Suggested Research Topics and Projects

• Research the advances in technologies that have or can cause the most significant changes in our environment. This could work with modern advances, or you could examine previous advances, ones to which we are accustomed. Computers are a relatively new technology. The printing press is not, yet it has produced incredible change.
• Research health and/or environmental damage from air pollution.
• Research the history of ozone as an environmental concern.
• Examine the history of lead poisoning from air and soil.
• Examine the role of the media in the Chesapeake Bay environmental problems.
• Examine landfills and the persistent substances problem.

Notes

1. From F. R. Spellman & J. Price-Bayer, 2011, *In Defense of Science*. Lanham, MD: Government Institutes.
2. From U.S. EPA, *Acid Rain—Effects of Acid Rain—Forests*, accessed May 9, 2011, http://www.epa.gov/ acidrain/effects/forests.html.
3. Much of the information in this section is from EIA's *Renewable Energy Trends*, 2004, accessed June 12, 2009, http:www.eia.doe.gov/cneaf/solar.renewables/page/trends/rentrends04 .html; and EIA's (2007) *How Much Renewable Energy Do We Use?* accessed June 12, 2009, http://tonto.eia.doe.gov/energy_in_brief/renewable_energy.cfm.
4. Much of the information in this section is from U.S. DOE-EERE, 2005, *History of Wind Energy*, accessed June 12, 2009, http://www1/eere/emergu/gpv/womdamdjudrp/printable_ versions/wind_hisotry.htm.

5. Based on information from U.S. DOE, 2001, *Renewable Energy: An Overview*. Washington, DC: U.S. Department of Energy.

6. Information in this section is from U.S. DOE, 2008, Hydrogen, Fuel Cells & Infrastructure Technologies Program, http://www1.eere.energy.gov/hydrogenandfuelcells/production/basics.html.

References and Recommended Reading

Adams, D. D., & Page W. P., eds. (1985). *Acidic Deposition—Environmental, Economic and Policy Issues*. New York: Plenum Publishers.

Alexander, M. (1994). *Biodegradation and Bioremediation*. San Diego: Academic Press.

Arms, K. (1994). *Environmental Science*. 2nd ed. Saddle Brook, NJ: HBJ College and School Division.

Beaty, C. B. (1978). "The Causes of Glaciation." *American Science* 66: 452–59.

Blumberg, L., & Gottlieb, R. (1989). *War on Waste—Can America Win Its Battle with Garbage?* Washington, DC: Island Press, 301.

Bowne, N. E. (1984). "Atmospheric Dispersion." In Calvert, S., & Englund, H., eds., *Handbook of Air Pollution Technology*, 859–93. New York: John Wiley & Sons.

Bridgman, H. A. (1994). *Global Air Pollution*. New York: John Wiley & Sons.

Conner, H. R. (1992). *Chemical Fixation and Solidification of Hazardous Waste*. New York: Van Nostrand Reinhold, 692.

Drexler, E. (1986). *Engines of Creation: The Coming Era of Nanotechnology*. New York: Anchor.

EIA (2007). *U.S. Energy Consumption by Energy Source*. Accessed June 12, 2009. http://www.eia.doe.gov/enaf/alternate/page/renew_energy_conump/table 1.html.

Elsom, D. M. (19920. *Atmospheric Pollution—A Global Problem*. 2nd ed. Oxford: Blackwell Publishers.

Gates, D. M. (1993). *Climate Change and Its Biological Consequences*. Sunderland, MA: Sinuer Associates.

Harrison, R. M., ed. (1990). *Pollution—Causes, Effects and Control*. Cambridge, UK: Royal Society of Chemistry, Thomas Graham House.

Jackson, A. R., & Jackson, J. M. (1996). *Environmental Science: The Natural Environment and Human Impact*. New York: Longman.

Kerr, R. A. (1979). "Global Pollution: Is Arctic Haze Actually Industrial Smog?" *Science* 205: 290–93.

Lamb, B. (1984). "Gaseous Pollutant Characteristics." In Cavert, S., & Englund, H., eds., *Handbook of Air Pollution Technology*, 3rd ed., 65–96. New York: John Wiley & Sons.

Moore, J. W., & Ramamoorthy, S. (1992). *Heavy Metals in Natural Waters*. New York: Springer-Verlag.

PEDCO. (1979). *PEDCO Analysis of Eckhardt Committee Survey for Chemical Manufacturer's Association*. Washington, DC: PEDCO Environmental Inc.

Perkins, H. C. (1974). *Air Pollution*. New York: McGraw-Hill.

Pierce, J. J., et al. (1998). *Environmental Pollution and Control*. 4th ed. Boston: Butterworth-Heinemann.

Rizzo, J. A., ed. (1990). *Underground Storage Tank Management: A Practical Guide*. 4th ed. Rockville, MD: Government Institutes.

Rodriguez, J. M. (1989). "Probing Atmospheric Ozone." *Science* 261: 1128–29.

Seinfeld, J. H. (1986). *Atmospheric Chemistry and Physics of Air Pollution.* New York: Wiley-Inter-Science.

Stern, A. C., & Wohlers, H. C. (1984). *Fundamentals of Air Pollution.* New York: Academic Press.

Testa, S. M. (1994). *Geological Aspects of Hazardous Waste Management.* Boca Raton, FL: CRC/Lewis Publishers, 537.

U.S. EPA (1982). *Air Quality Criteria for Particulate Matter and Sulfur Oxides, Vol. II.* EPA/600/8-82-029a-c.

U.S. EPA (1988, August). *Environmental Progress and Challenges.*

U.S. EPA (1991, January/February). *EPA Journal* 17: 1.

U.S. EPA (1994). *National Air Pollutant Emission Trends, 1900–1993.* EPA/454/R-94-027.

U.S. EPA (1995a). *Air Quality Criteria for Particulate Matter. Vol. I,* EPA/600/AP-95/001a.

U.S. EPA (1995b). *Air Quality Criteria for Particulate Matter, Vol. III,* EPA/600/AP-95/001c.

Part II

AIR QUALITY

The quality of the air we breathe is not normally a concern unless we detect something unusual about the air (its odor, its taste, or that breathing is difficult or uncomfortable), or unless the authorities or news media have advised us that there is cause for concern. Air pollutants in the atmosphere cause great concern because of the potential adverse effects on our health. To have good air quality is a plus for any community. Good air quality attracts industry, as well as people who are looking for a healthy place to live and raise a family. Advertisements that push a locality's pollution-free "clean or fresh air" or "country air" are not uncommon.

CHAPTER 9

The Atmosphere: Basic Air Quality

Whether we characterize it as a caress, or a light touch against soft skin, as a gentle breeze, a warm wind, blustery gale, as tempest, typhoon, tornado, or hurricane, air is vital.

Air encapsulates us. It surrounds us. We take it in, as we must, with every breath, our bodies thrive on it, and we fail immediately without it. Literally awash with air, on Earth, all life we know of depends on it. It occurs naturally everywhere on Earth—the sky begins where the ground ends.

Air is scientifically unique. The combinations of common and rare gases we breathe have made life possible. Air, as with water, is the only chemical compound found naturally that affects most living organisms in a manner of ways.

We associate air with all the good on Earth. We cannot imagine life without breathing—we must constantly quench our thirst for air. Air sustains growth. It creates the subtle and blatant movements that provide us with changing weather patterns. But can we really say emphatically, definitively, that air is only good?

No. We cannot. Nothing—absolutely nothing—is safe from air.

Air is odorless, colorless, and tasteless. We rarely stop to think about it, unless it brings something to us as a reminder. But it covers Earth completely. Nothing can escape air's touch. Nothing.

Air is life—life and air are inseparable.

We sometimes call air the breath of life—a fitting name, especially when you consider that air can be the boon—or bane—of all life, capable, in time of sustaining or destroying all life as we define it.

Whether it pushes the blade of a windmill, a billowy cloud, a dust mote, a feather, whether it lifts a bird soaring on thermals, or wafts to us the sweet fragrance of gardenia, lavender, lilac, rose, or a seed to fertile ground, whether it sets water lapping against some distant shore, drives a gritty wind that sculpts mountains to sand, or hammers a horrendous fist that flattens whatever stands in its path—cities, forests, crops—and man—air is essential. Air is life. Air is vital.

Air gives us the blessing of communication. From our first cry to our dying breath, our voices travel on a current of air. Air carries sound. Can we hear a more pleasant sound than wind passing through pine? Can our spines tingle more than at the sound generated by wind against an ancient shutter?

Air carries warmth. Air carries cold.

Air is vital.

Our very existence depends on air, but we have created a paradox within our vital line to life. Why would we abuse something so vital—something we need to survive—something we cannot live without? Why do we foul the very essence of our lives? Why do we insult our environment at a faster pace than we can understand and mitigate the consequences? Why? Because air—air—air is everywhere. We've always had enough. Right?

Let us hope that we always will. Let us hope that we are not destroying the very air we breathe. Let us hope that technology will aid us in our efforts to retain the quality of the air we need to survive.

We need air as it should be: pure, wholesome, and sweet smelling, in the perfect mixture of elements we were evolved to inhale, vital to our existence.

Such pure air simply exists. Part of the greenhouse effect, part of ozone depletion, part of global warming, air can only be a passive presence in those processes and in the damage we cause—it can neither cause or prevent.

Should we?

—Frank R. Spellman

Chapter Objectives

After studying this chapter you should be able to:

- Define, describe, and discuss Earth's atmosphere's chemical composition and identify and quantify the composite gases.
- Define, describe, and discuss the atmosphere's structure and the roles that pressure, density, and temperature play.
- Define, describe, and discuss how solar and thermal radiation affects atmospheric conditions.
- Define albedo and discuss its part in Earth's radiation balance and how it influences the annual mean temperature.
- Identify and define the elements that affect Earth's heat balance and describe and discuss how the transference of energy affects weather and climatic conditions.
- Identify the causes of atmospheric motion and describe and discuss how they create air movement on small and large scales.

- Describe how local winds are affected by local geographic conditions.
- Describe how local air quality is affected by people's impact on the environment.

Chapter Outline

- Discussion: atmosphere as an ocean of air
- Discussion and definition: atmospheric chemical composition
- Discussion and definition: atmospheric density and pressure
- Discussion and definition: atmospheric divisions and temperatures
- Discussion and definition: solar and thermal radiation
- Discussion and definition: albedo and its effects on mean annual temperature
- Discussion and definition: the Earth's heat balance and how average surface temperature is maintained
- Discussion and definition: the atmosphere in constant motion
- Discussion and definition: the causes of atmospheric motion, gravity, density, pressure of force, and thermal circulation
- Discussion and definition: air movement on local and global scales
- Discussion and definition: changing basic air quality

Key Terms

advective winds
air
air current
albedo
atmosphere
carbon dioxide
climate
conduction
convection
density
gravity
greenhouse effect
heat balance
heat index
insolation
isobar

jet stream
mesosphere
oxygen
pressure
pressure gradient force
radiation
stratosphere
thermal circulation
thermal radiation
thermosphere
troposphere
water vapor
weather
wind
wind chill factor

Introduction

In the not too distant past, when coal miners worried about **air** quality in the mines, they took canaries with them—not for their companionship or song, but for the moment they stopped singing. Then they knew that it was time to abandon the mine, because the air contained deadly methane, which could ignite and explode. Today environmental scientists (and others) use electronic air monitors to monitor air quality. These monitors are reliable and accurate, and usually quite expensive.

Once again, nature provides its own form of monitoring air quality. For example, a living organism such as lichen can warn of bad air. Lichens, combinations of fungi and algae, are quietly trodden underfoot by animals and hikers. With no roots, stems, or leaves, they can grow almost anywhere, but rely on nutrients they accumulate from the air. Thus, they are uniquely sensitive to air pollution, making them valuable early warning indicators of reduced air quality. Scientists have used them as biomonitors for decades, including lichen evaluation as an effort to estimate the amount of nuclear fallout from the Chernobyl meltdown in 1986.

Because lichens are long lived, widespread, and anchored in place, they can also help track pollution to its source. Thus, they can replace electronic monitoring stations that cost several thousands of dollars. Lichens can alert us to danger. But as with all forms of pollution, the best solution is prevention (Miller, 2004).

When we undertake a comprehensive discussion of air, it begins and ends with the Earth's **atmosphere**. Earth's atmosphere is unique. It is often described as a thin veil, skin, shroud, envelope, blanket, or an invisible sea of gases that surround the planet, but "ocean of air" is probably more correct. This vast ocean is massive, restless, and far different from water and soil media. No matter how it is described, the atmosphere is shared by a huge variety of living things—it is vital to life itself. Composed of invisible gases and condensed **water vapor**, the atmosphere is maintained in place by Earth's gravitational pull.

In this chapter, we cover concepts important to gaining a basic understanding of the atmosphere, which in turn enables us to better understand our anthropogenic impact on it. We also discuss key parameters used to measure air quality, the feature that concerns us most. Could we have a concern greater than that of maintaining air quality to sustain life? A full understanding of environmental science requires knowledge of the atmosphere.

What Is Air?

What is air? Most of us would have little difficulty quickly answering that air is the **oxygen** that we breathe—the substance that we need to sustain life. Taking our definition to the next level and beyond, we might state that air surrounds us—it is virtually everywhere; it is that substance we feel against our faces and skin when the **wind** blows, that gas we use to fill our automobile tires; it is necessary for combustion to take place. Hot air lifts our balloons; air under pressure (pneumatic air) powers our tools and machines; it can be either warm or cold or just about right—air is air, what more needs to be said? (A lot more.)

What is air? Environmental scientists/practitioners would answer this question differently than most of us. They would state that air is a gas—that it is actually a combination of gases. They might also state that a gas is a state of matter distinguished from the solid and liquid states by very low **density** and viscosity, relatively great expansion and contraction with changes in **pressure** and temperature, the ability to diffuse readily, and the spontaneous tendency to become distributed throughout any container.

How about engineers? They always seem to have a definition for just about anything and everything (most of which cannot be understood by many of us—and maybe that is their intention). Engineers might refer to air as a fluid (because it is; like water, air is fluid—we can pour it). They are primarily interested in air as a fluid because they deal with fluid mechanics, the study of the behavior of fluids (including air) at rest or in motion. Fluids may be either gases or liquids. You are probably familiar with the physical difference between gases and liquids, as exhibited by air and water, but for the study of fluid mechanics (and the purposes of this text), it is convenient to classify fluids by their compressibility:

- Gases are very readily compressible (you've heard of compressed air).
- Liquids are only slightly compressible (it is unlikely you've heard much about compressed water).

What is air? Air is a mixture of gases that constitutes the Earth's atmosphere. What is the Earth's atmosphere? The atmosphere is that thin shell, veil, envelope of gases that surrounds the planet like the skin of an apple—thin, very thin—but very, very vital. The approximate composition of dry air, by volume at sea level, is nitrogen 78%, oxygen 21% (necessary for life as we know it), argon 0.93%, and **carbon dioxide** 0.03%, together with very small amounts of numerous other constituents (see Table 9.1). Because of constant mixing by the winds and other **weather** factors, the percentages of each gas in the atmosphere are normally constant to 70,000 feet. However, it is important to point out that the water vapor content is highly variable and depends on atmospheric conditions. Air is said to be pure when none of the minor constituents is present in sufficient concentration to be injurious to the health of human beings or animals, damage vegetation, or cause loss of amenity (e.g., through the presence of dirt, dust, or odors or by diminution of sunshine).

Table 9.1. Composition of Air/Earth's Atmosphere

Gas	Chemical Symbol	Volume (%)
nitrogen	N_2	78.08
oxygen	O_2	20.94
carbon dioxide	CO_2	0.03
argon	Ar	0.093
neon	Ne	0.0018
helium	He	0.0005
krypton	Kr	trace
xenon	Xe	trace
ozone	O_3	0.00006
hydrogen	H_2	0.00005

Where does air come from? Genesis 1:2 states that the mighty hand of God separated the water environment into the atmosphere and surface waters on the second day of creation. Many scientists state that 4.6 billion years ago, a cloud of dust and gases forged the Earth and also created a dense, molten core enveloped in cosmic gases. This was the **proto-atmosphere** or **proto-air**, composed mainly of carbon dioxide, hydrogen, ammonia, and carbon monoxide, but it did not last long before it was stripped away by a tremendous outburst of charged particles from the sun. As the outer crust of the Earth began to solidify, a new atmosphere began to form from the gases pouring out of gigantic hot springs and volcanoes. This created an atmosphere of air composed of carbon dioxide, nitrogen oxides, hydrogen, sulfur dioxide, and water vapor. As the Earth cooled, water vapor condensed into highly acidic rainfall, which collected to form oceans and lakes.

For much of Earth's early existence (the first half), only trace amounts of free oxygen were present. But then green plants evolved in the oceans and began to add oxygen to the atmosphere as a waste gas; later oxygen increased to about 1% of the atmosphere, and with time to its present 21%.

How do we know for sure about the evolution of air on Earth? Are we just guessing, using "voodoo" science? There is no guessing or voodoo involved with the historical geological record. Consider, for example, geological formations that are dated to 2 billion years ago. In these early sediments, there is a clear and extensive band of red sediment ("red bed" sediments)—sands colored with oxidized (ferric) iron. Previously, ferrous formations had been laid down showing no oxidation. But there is more evidence. We can look at the time frame of 4.5 billion years ago, when carbon dioxide in the atmosphere was beginning to be lost in sediments. The vast amount of carbon deposited in limestone, oil, and coal indicate that carbon dioxide concentrations must once have been many times greater than it is today, where it stands at only 0.03%. The first carbonated deposits appeared about 1.7 billion years ago, the first sulfate deposits about 1 billion years ago. The decreasing carbon dioxide was balanced by an increase in the nitrogen content of the air. The forms of **respiration** practiced advanced from fermentation 4 billion years ago to anaerobic **photosynthesis** 3 billion years ago to aerobic photosynthesis 1.5 billion years ago. The aerobic respiration that is so familiar today only began to appear about 500 million years ago.

Fast-forward to the present. The atmosphere itself continues to evolve, but human activities—with their highly polluting effects—have now overtaken nature in determining the changes. And that is the overriding theme of this text: Human beings and their effectd on Earth's air.

Have you ever wondered where the air goes when we expel it from our lungs, or if, when we do so, it is still air? When we use air to feed our fires, power our machines, weld or braze our metals, vacuum our floors, spray our propellants—paints, insecticides, lubricants, etc.—do we change the nature of air? These questions and their answers are important in this text because it is about the science of air, thus all things that affect air are important here.

At this point you are probably asking yourself: What does all this have to do with anything? What it has to do with air is quite simple. We do not know as much as we need to know about air. Have you ever gone to the library and tried to find a text that deals exclusively and extensively with the science of air? Such texts are few and far between—there is a huge information gap in this area.

To start with, let's discuss air—breathing air in particular (this text discusses all aspects of air, both breathing air and working air), the air we need to survive, to sustain life, the air that probably concerns us the most.

When the average person takes in a deep breath of air, he or she probably gives little thought to what he or she is doing; that is, breathing life-sustaining air. Let's face it, taking a breath of air is something that usually requires little effort and even less thought. The situation could be different, however. For example, consider a young woman, a firefighter, an emergency services provider. On occasion she has to fight fires at which she must wear a self-contained breathing apparatus (SCBA) to avoid breathing smoke and the decreased oxygen levels created by the fire. The standard SCBA with a single bottle contains approximately 45 minutes of air (class D breathing air, which is not just oxygen, but regular air with 21% oxygen and associated gases, nitrogen etc.).

On this particular day, our firefighter responds to a fire at which she and another firefighter are required to enter a burning building to look for and rescue trapped victims. Before entering such a building, the firefighters don their SCBAs and activate their air supply. Normally, 45 minutes of air is plenty to make a quick survey of a house's interior, especially when it is on fire. However, sometimes (this was one of them) the best laid plans go awry, and things just don't go according to plan.

After having swept the first floor of the two-story house without discovering any victims, the two firefighters climb the stairs to the second floor to look there. But the fire, which started in the kitchen, is spreading fast—and the smoke and toxic vapors are spreading even faster. The firefighters know all this; they are well-trained professionals. They know that any people in this house without respiratory protection will not survive for long. The fire will not kill them, but the smoke and toxic vapors surely will.

At the landing upstairs, the firefighters are on their knees, crawling, looking for victims. The smoke and toxic vapors are intense and intensifying by the second. But the firefighters are not worried (not yet); they have all the air they need strapped to their backs.

By the time they reach the hallway, the visibility is zero, the heat intense, and the toxic vapors and smoke so thick they can't see them but can literally feel them. All is well until flames find their way up the stairs and quickly spread down the carpeted hallway to the backs of the firefighters. They have 15 minutes of air left.

But the flames are becoming intimate; they reach out and touch the firefighters. The situation has instantly changed from one of rescuing victims to one of fleeing for their own lives.

They have 12 minutes of air left.

They turn on their hands and knees and face the fire. Their only hope of escape is through the flames, but they are not too worried because they are well-equipped with fire protective clothing and have nine minutes of air left.

Nine minutes of air is a lot of air in most escape situations. But this is no normal situation. As the firefighters literally slide down the stairs to the first floor, their air supply registers two minutes. They have used more air in the last 30 seconds than in the previous 10 minutes. This excessive use of air should come as no surprise when we consider that with toxic vapors and smoke and flame all over the place, and the flames licking at their bodies, they have a tendency to get excited, to breath in and out copious amounts of air. Our two firefighters are no different than you or me—they are scared and breathe hard until they breathe their last. They fall unconscious right in front of the doorway—just one more breath of air with its 21% oxygen, and they would have escaped. But they do not. The irony is that the fire—well beyond its flashover state—has all the air, with its accompanying oxygen supply, it needs to continue its deadly destruction.

Did You Know?

Because of an actual incident similar to the one described above, in which two firefighters lost their lives fighting a structure fire, OSHA's Respiratory Protection Standard (29 CFR 1910.134) reemphasizes the requirement that firefighters abide by the standard. Specifically, OSHA stipulates the "two in/two out" rule. This rule assures that "two in" monitor each other and assist with equipment failure or entrapment or other hazards, and "two out" monitor those in the building, initiate rescue, or call for backup. One of the "two out" can be assigned another role, such as incident commander. Moreover, under this standard, firefighters (and anyone else using respirators) must check the condition of the respirator before donning it for use.

This example sheds light on a completely different view of air, a very basic truth: We cannot live without it. If we cannot live without air—if air is so precious, so necessary for sustaining life, then two questions arise: (1) Why do we ignore air? (2) Why do we abuse it (pollute it)? We ignore air (as we do water) because it is so common, so accessible (normally), so unexceptional (unless you're in a burning building and your life depends on it). We pollute for several reasons; many are discussed later in this text.

You might be asking: Is air pollution really that big of a deal? Isn't pollution relative? That is, isn't pollution dependent on one's point of view, a judgment call? Well, if you could ask the victims of the incidents listed in Table 9.2, the answer would be yes, it is.

Beyond the fact that air is one of our essential resources, sustaining life as it stimulates and pleases the senses—though invisible to the human eye, it makes possible such sights as beautiful and dazzling rainbows, heart-pinching sunsets and sun rises, the Northern Lights, and on occasion, a clear view of that high alpine meadow sprinkled throughout with the colors of spring.

But air is more than this. It is capable of many other wondrous things. For example, have you ever felt the light touch of a cool, soothing breeze against your skin? Air carries thousands of scents, both pungent and subtle: salty ocean breezes, approaching rain, fragrances from blooming flowers, and others. It is the "others" that concern us here: the sulfurous gases from industrial processes—that typical rotten egg odor; the stink of garbage, refuse, trash, all part of our throwaways—and the toxic poison

Table 9.2.   Mortality Occurring During Air Pollution Events

Location	Year	Deaths Reported as a Result of Pollution
Belgium	1930	63
Pennsylvania	1948	17
London	1948	700–800
London	1952	4,000
London	1956	1,000
London	1957	700–800
London	1959	200–250
London	1962	700
London	1963	700
New York	1963	200–400

Source: Committee on Public Works, 1968.

remnants from pesticides, herbicides, and all the other "cides." We are surrounded by air, but we seldom think about it until it displeases us (we can put up with just about anything until it displeases us). It is pollution, those discarded, sickening leftovers of the heavy hand of man, that causes the problem. As stated previously, we cover this life-threatening travesty of polluting our environment in greater detail later in the text.

As this text leads us down a path sometimes heavy with soot, chemicals, smoke, malodorous scents, and particulate matter, at all times we will progress with the sense of importance that such a simple substance as air, containing only a few gaseous elements and other products, has on our lives.

DEFINITION OF KEY TERMS

Every branch of science, including air science, has its own language. The terminology used herein is as different from that of aeronautical engineering as its is from agronomy. To work at even the edge of air science and the science disciplines closely related to it, the reader must acquire a familiarity with the vocabulary used in this text.

Although it is helpful and important for technical publications to include definitions or a glossary of key terms at the end of the work, for the reader's sake, it is more useful to include many of these key definitions early in the text to facilitate a more orderly, logical, step-by-step learning process. Thus, in the following section some of the key terms are listed and defined. Other terms not defined here are defined where they are used in the text.

Absolute pressure: the total pressure in a system, including both the pressure of a substance and the pressure of the atmosphere (about 14.7 psi at sea level).
Acid: any substance that releases hydrogen ions (H^+) when it is mixed into water.
Acid precipitation: rain, snow, or fog that contains higher than normal levels of sulfuric or nitric acid, which may damage forests, aquatic ecosystems, and cultural landmarks.
Acid surge: a period of short, intense acid deposition in lakes and streams resulting from the release (by rainfall or spring snowmelt) of acids stored in soil or snow.

Acidic solution: a solution that contains significant numbers of H^+ ions.

Airborne toxins: hazardous chemical pollutants that have been released into the atmosphere and are carried by air currents.

Albedo: reflectivity, or the fraction of incident light that is reflected by a surface.

Arithmetic mean: a measurement of average value, calculated by summing all terms and dividing by the number of terms.

Arithmetic scale: a series of intervals (marks or lines), usually made along the side or bottom of a graph, that represents the range of values of the data. When the marks or lines are equally spaced, it is called an arithmetic scale.

Atmosphere: a 500-kilometer thick layer of colorless, odorless gases known as air that surrounds the Earth and is composed of nitrogen, oxygen, argon, carbon dioxide, and other gases in trace amounts.

Atom: the smallest particle of an element that still retains the characteristics of that element.

Atomic number: the number of protons in the nucleus of an atom.

Atomic weight: the total number of protons and neutrons in the nucleus of an atom.

Base: any substance that releases hydroxyl ions (OH^-) when it dissociates in water.

Chemical bond: the force that holds atoms together within molecules. A chemical bond is formed when a chemical reaction takes place. Two types of chemical bond are ionic and covalent.

Chemical reaction: a process that occurs when atoms of certain elements are brought together and combine to form molecules, or when molecules are broken down into individual atoms.

Climate: the long-term weather pattern of a particular region.

Covalent bond: a type of chemical bond in which electrons are shared.

Density: the weight of a substance per unit of its volume (e.g., pounds per cubic foot).

Dew point: the temperature at which a sample of air becomes saturated, that is, has a relative humidity of 100%.

Element: any of more than 100 fundamental substances that consist of atoms of only one kind and that constitute all matter.

Emission standards: the maximum amount of a specific pollutant permitted to be legally discharged from a particular source in a given environment.

Emissivity: the relative power of a surface to re-radiate solar **radiation** back into space in the form of heat or long-wave infrared radiation.

Energy: the ability to do work, to move matter from place to place, or to change matter from one form to another.

1st Law of Thermodynamics: natural law that dictates that during physical or chemical change, energy is neither created not destroyed, but it may be changed in form and moved from place to place.

Global warming: the increase in global temperature predicted to arise from increased levels of carbon dioxide, methane, and other greenhouse gases in the atmosphere.

Greenhouse effect: the prevention of the re-radiation of heat waves to space by carbon dioxide, methane, and other gases in the atmosphere. The greenhouse effect makes possible the conditions that enable life to exist on Earth.

Ion: an atom or radical in solution carrying an integral electrical charge either positive (cation) or negative (anion).

Insolation: the solar radiation received by the Earth and its atmosphere (**in**coming **so**lar radia**tion**).

Lapse rate: the rate of temperature change with altitude. In the **troposphere**, the normal lapse rate is −3.5°F per 1,000 ft.

Matter: anything that exists in time, occupies space, and has mass.

Mesosphere: a region of the atmosphere between approximately 35 and 60 miles in altitude.

Meteorology: the study of atmospheric phenomena.

Mixture: two or more elements, compounds, or both, combined with no chemical reaction occurring.

Ozone: the compound O_3. It is found naturally in the atmosphere in the ozonosphere and is also a constituent of photochemical smog.

pH: a means of expressing hydrogen ion concentration in terms of the powers of 10; measurement of how acidic or basic a substance is. The pH scale runs from 0 (most acidic) to 14 (most basic). The center of the range (7) indicates the substance is neutral.

Photochemical smog: an atmospheric haze that occurs above industrial sites and urban areas, resulting from reactions, which take place in the presence of sunlight, between pollutants produced in a high temperature and pressurized combustion process (such as the combustion of fuel in a motor vehicle). The primary component of smog is ozone.

Photosynthesis: the process by which chlorophyll-containing plants use the sun's light energy to convert carbon dioxide (CO_2) and water (H_2O) into complex chemical bonds forming simple carbohydrates such as glucose and fructose.

Pollutant: a contaminant at a concentration high enough to endanger the environment.

Pressure: the force pushing on a unit area. Normally, in air applications, it is measured in atmospheres, pascals (Pa), or pounds per square inch (psi).

Primary pollutants: pollutants emitted directly into the atmosphere, where they exert an adverse influence on human and environmental health. The six primary pollutants are carbon dioxide, carbon monoxide, sulfur oxides, nitrogen oxides, hydrocarbons, and particulates. All but carbon dioxide are regulated in the United States.

Raleigh scattering: the preferential scattering of light by air molecules and particles that accounts for the blueness of the sky. The scattering is proportional to $1/\lambda^4$.

Radon: a naturally occurring radioactive gas, arising from the decay of uranium 238, which may be harmful to human health in high concentrations.

Rain shadow effect: the phenomenon that occurs as a result of the movement of air masses over a mountain range. As an air mass rises to clear a mountain, the air cools and precipitation forms. Often, both the precipitation and the pollutant load carried by the air mass will be dropped on the windward side of the mountain. The air mass is then devoid of most of its moisture; consequently, the lee side of the mountain receives little or no precipitation and is said to lie in the rain shadow of the mountain range.

Relative humidity: the concentration of water vapor in the air. It is expressed as the percentage that its moisture content represents of the maximum amount that the air could contain at the same temperature and pressure. The higher the temperature, the more water vapor the air can hold.

Secondary pollutants: pollutants formed from the interaction of primary pollutants with other primary pollutants or with atmospheric compounds such as water vapor.

2nd Law of Thermodynamics: natural law that dictates that with each change in form, some energy is degraded to a less useful form and given off to the surroundings, usually as low-quality heat.

Solute: the substance dissolved in a solution.

Solution: a liquid containing a dissolved substance.

Specific gravity: the ratio of the density of a substance to a standard density. For gases, the density is compared with the density of air (=1).

Stratosphere*:* an atmospheric layer extending from 6 or 7 miles to 30 miles above the Earth's surface.

Stratospheric ozone depletion: the thinning of the ozone layer in the stratosphere; occurs when certain chemicals (such as chlorofluorocarbons) capable of destroying ozone accumulate in the upper atmosphere.

Thermosphere*:* an atmospheric layer that extends from 56 miles to outer space.

Troposphere: the atmospheric layer that extends from the Earth's surface to six or seven miles above the surface.

Weather: the day-to-day pattern of precipitation, temperature, wind, barometric pressure, and humidity.

Wind: horizontal air motion.

The Atmosphere

We live at the bottom reaches of a virtual ocean of air. Extending upward approximately 1,000 miles, this massive, restless ocean is dynamic and far different from the watery oceans that cover most of Earth's surface. Humans and other creatures live at the bottom of our atmosphere (from the Greek *atmos*, vapor, and *sphaira*, sphere).

CHEMICAL COMPOSITION

Atmospheric air is a mixture of many gases that also holds many suspended liquid droplets and solid particles. Only two gases comprise about 99% of the volume of air near the Earth. In Figure 9.1, we see that air is primarily composed of a relatively constant mixture of nitrogen (78%) and oxygen (21%), with nitrogen being about four times as abundant as oxygen. The other main constituents are argon and carbon dioxide.

Many other gases are found in the atmosphere in minute quantities, along with dust, pollen, salt particles, and other constituents. Some of these, especially water vapor and carbon monoxide, vary in concentration, depending on conditions and locality. The amount of water vapor in the air depends to a great extent on the temperature (see

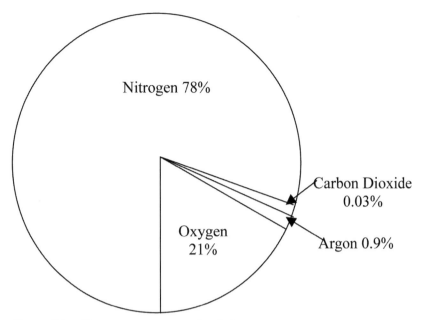

Figure 9.1. Gaseous components of air.

Chapter 10). Carbon monoxide and carbon dioxide, both by-products of incomplete combustion, are both present in abnormally high concentrations in populated areas.

In Figure 9.1 we see that nitrogen (N_2) is the most abundant gas in the atmosphere, but it has a relatively limited direct role in atmospheric or life processes. It serves as a precursor molecule for the formation of the nitrate nitrogen required by plants to make proteins, amino acids, chlorophyll, and nucleic acids, which are essential to all living things. The conversion of nitrogen to nitrate nitrogen is the result of chemical and biological processes in the atmosphere.

Approximately 21% of the atmosphere's mass is composed of molecular oxygen (O_2), which is vital to almost all living things. It is also important because it provides for the formation of the ozone layer (O_3), which protects all living things from the high-energy ultraviolet (UV) radiation incident (striking or falling upon) on the Earth's atmosphere.

The concentration of carbon dioxide (CO_2), in contrast to N_2 and O_2, in the atmosphere is relatively low—about 0.036% or 360 ppm by volume. Life is carbon-based, and carbon dioxide is the source of that carbon. Carbon dioxide is also a principal raw material from which green plants (photosynthesis) make the food that most living things need. Because of its thermal absorptivity, carbon dioxide works to maintain a favorable global **heat balance**. However, carbon dioxide is also a major contributor to the greenhouse effect (see Chapter 13).

The most visible constituent of the atmosphere is water vapor (H_2O). Like carbon dioxide, water vapor is a major greenhouse gas that absorbs thermal energy radiated from the Earth's surface. Because it readily changes phase, water vapor is significant in the atmosphere. On cooling, it condenses to form large masses of air that contain precipitation.

**Table 9.3.   Relative Proportions of
Gases in the Lower Atmosphere***

Gas	Percent by Volume
Nitrogen	78.08
Oxygen	20.95
Argon	0.93
Carbon dioxide	0.03
Neon	0.0018
Helium	0.00052
Methane	0.00015
Krypton	0.00010
Nitrous oxide	0.00005
Hydrogen	0.00005
Ozone	0.000007
Xenon	0.000009

*Water vapor excluded.

The other gaseous constituents of the atmosphere—hydrogen, helium, xenon, and krypton (see Table 9.3)—are inert and do not appear to have any major impact on, or role in, the atmosphere.

STRUCTURE

The structure of the atmosphere is characterized not only by the gases that comprise it, but also by physical phenomena that act on and within it. These include density and pressure, temperature, and solar and thermal radiation.

Density and Pressure

The atmosphere extends upward with continuously decreasing mass per volume (density); concentrations of the molecules that comprise the atmosphere decrease with altitude. The greater density near the Earth's surface is because of gravitational attraction and compression of the air. As a result, more than one-half of the mass of the atmosphere lies below an altitude of 7 miles (11 km), and almost 99% lies below an altitude of 19 miles (30 km). At higher altitudes, the air becomes quite thin.

Although no clear line of demarcation between Earth's atmosphere and outer space exists, because of a continuous decrease in density in the upper regions of the atmosphere, an outermost limit can roughly be placed at a range of about 300 to 600 miles (480 to 960 km) from the surface of the Earth.

Closely related to mass per volume or density is force per area, or atmospheric pressure. This can be seen in the direct relationship between density and pressure. As atmospheric density decreases with altitude, atmospheric pressure decreases as well. The pressure at a particular altitude is effectively a measure of the weight of gas above that location (an object on the Earth's surface literally supports a vertical column of air that overlays it).

Temperature

When measuring the temperature of the atmosphere versus altitude, distinct changes are apparent. These variations in temperature lead to distinguishing major divisions within the atmosphere. These major divisions or boundaries are not sharply defined, and they extend over appreciable distances, but they exist.

Near the Earth's surface, the temperature of the atmosphere decreases with increasing altitude at an average rate of about 3.5°F/1,000 feet (6.5°C/km), up to about 10 miles (16 km). This region is called the troposphere (see Figure 9.2). The atmospheric conditions of the lower troposphere are collectively called weather. Changes in the weather reflect the local variations in the atmosphere near the Earth's surface (see Chapter 10).

Above the troposphere, the temperature of the atmosphere increases nonuniformly up to an altitude of about 30 miles (50 km) (see Figure 9.2). This region of

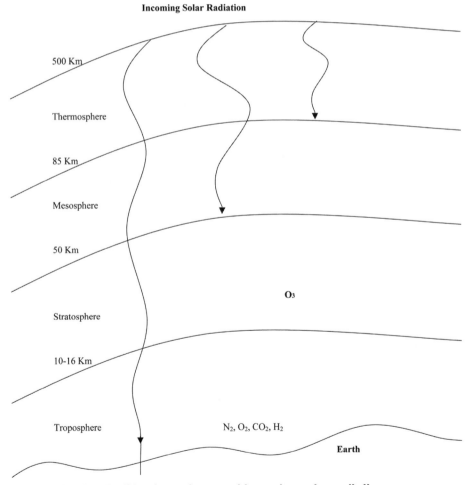

Figure 9.2. The Earth's atmosphere and incoming solar radiation.

the atmosphere, from approximately 10 to 30 miles (16 to 50 km) in altitude, is called the stratosphere.

Beyond the stratosphere, the temperature decreases uniformly to about −140°F (−95°C) at an altitude of 50 miles (80 km). This region of the atmosphere is called the mesosphere.

Above the mesosphere, the thin atmosphere is heated intensely by the sun's rays, and the temperature climbs to over 1,800°F (1,000°C). This region extending to the outer reaches of the atmosphere is called the thermosphere. The temperature of the thermosphere varies directly with solar activity.

Solar and Thermal Radiation

In reality more of a physical than a structural characteristic of the Earth's atmosphere, solar and thermal radiation still have a major influence on the overall character of Earth's atmosphere. The sun's radiated energy (**solar radiation**) literally showers the atmosphere with huge amounts of electromagnetic energy.

Energy from the sun in the form of radiation that is incident on the Earth's atmosphere is called **insolation—in**coming **sol**ar radi**ation**. Even though atmospheric gases such as oxygen, ozone, carbon dioxide, and water vapor absorb some incoming solar energy (radiation), a portion of solar energy does reach the Earth's surface.

If we assume that the sun generates incoming solar radiation at 100 percent, we can illustrate insolation distribution, as shown in Figure 9.3. We can see in Figure 9.3 that about 23% of solar radiation directly reaches ground level. About 5% is scattered by the atmosphere to the ground, and the atmosphere absorbs 15%. Some 22% is able to reach the Earth's surface indirectly by penetrating clouds. Approximately 2% is absorbed by clouds; 24% is reflected by clouds along with another 7% scattered by the atmosphere back into outer space (total = 33% reflected back to space).

Of the insolation received, 33% is returned to space with no appreciable effect on the atmosphere, as a result of reflection by clouds, scattering by particles in the atmosphere, and reflection from terrestrial surfaces (including water, ice, and variable ground surfaces), known as albedo (reflectivity; see Box 9.1).

The Earth and its atmosphere re-radiate solar radiation incident on the Earth's surface and atmosphere at longer wavelengths within a specific emission spectrum. This **thermal radiation** or thermal energy radiates to space from the surface and directly from the atmosphere within the infrared rage of 3 to 8 μm, with a peak of about 11 μm.

Earth's Heat Balance

Approximately 50% of the solar radiation entering the atmosphere reaches Earth's surface either directly or after being scattered by clouds, particulate matter, or atmospheric gases. The other 50% is either reflected directly back or absorbed in the atmosphere, its energy re-radiated back into space at a later time as infrared radiation. Most of the solar energy reaching the surface is absorbed and must be returned to space to maintain heat balance. The energy produced within the Earth's interior (from hot mantle area via **convection** and **conduction**) that reaches the Earth's surface (about 1% of that received from the sun) must also be lost (Figure 9.4).

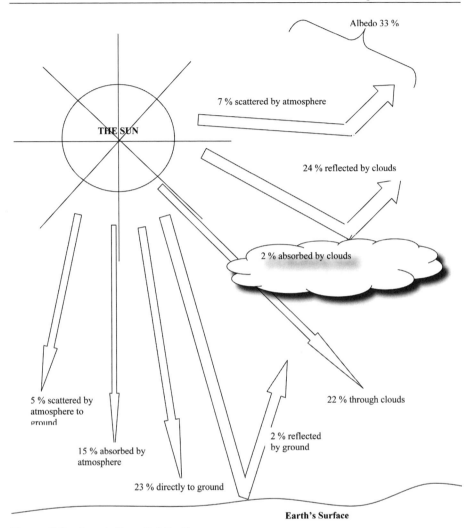

Albedo 33 %

7 % scattered by atmosphere

THE SUN

24 % reflected by clouds

2 % absorbed by clouds

5 % scattered by
atmosphere to
ground

22 % through clouds

2 % reflected
by ground

15 % absorbed by
atmosphere

23 % directly to ground

Earth's Surface

Figure 9.3.   Insolation distribution

Albedo

Albedo (the ratio of light reflected from a particle, planet, or satellite to that falling on it) always has a value less than or equal to 1. An object with a high albedo (near 1) is very bright, whereas a body with a low albedo (near 0) is dark. For example, freshly fallen snow typically has an albedo between 75 and 90+%; that is, 75 to 95% of the solar radiation that is incident on snow is reflected. At the other extreme, the albedo of a rough, dark surface, such as a green forest, may be as low as 5%. The albedos of some common surfaces are listed in Table 9.4. The portion of insolation not reflected is absorbed by the Earth's surface, warming it. This means Earth's albedo plays an important part in its radiation balance and influences the **mean annual temperature** and the climate, on both local and global scales.

Table 9.4.   Albedo of Surface Types

Surface	Albedo (percent reflected)
Water (low sun)	10–100
Water (high sun)	3–10
Grass	16–26
Glacier ice	20–40
Deciduous forest	15–20
Coniferous forest	5–15
Old snow	40–70
Fresh snow	75–95
Sea ice	30–40
Blacktopped tarmac	5–10
Desert	25–30
Crops	15–25

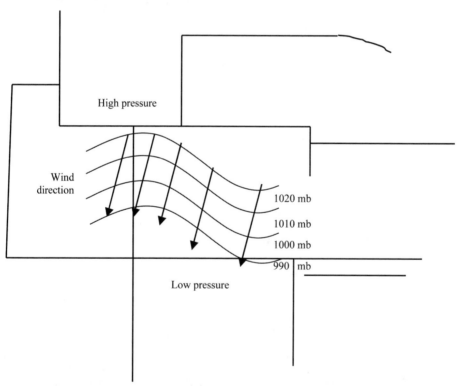

Figure 9.4.   Isobars drawn though locations having equal atmospheric pressures. The air motion, or wind direction, is at right angles to the isobars and movers form a region of high pressure to a region of low pressure.

Re-radiation of energy from the Earth is accomplished by three energy transport mechanisms: radiation, conduction, and convection. Radiation of energy occurs through electromagnetic radiation in the infrared region of the spectrum. The crucial importance of the radiation mechanism is that it carries energy away from Earth—on a much longer wavelength than the solar energy (sunlight) that brings energy to the Earth—and in turn, works to maintain the Earth's heat balance. This heat balance is of particular interest to us in this text because it is susceptible to upset by human activities.

Did You Know?

Note that although most people prefer an environment with "clean or fresh, pollution-free air" to live in, not all do. A good example is in the Los Angeles basin. Before Los Angeles became the mega-city it is today, local inhabitants named the basin area the "Valley of the Smokes" because of the emissions from campfires and settlements. This early warning about adverse climatic conditions did not stop settlement. Today, strangers to Los Angeles need only pull into the basin area, step out of their air-conditioned SUVs, place their feet on terra firma (the exception being during a quake), and take in one huge breathe of air—then let the coughing and gagging begin. Have you ever breathed in diesel fumes mixed with other motor vehicle and industry emissions? Welcome to the Los Angeles basin, home of super smog.

Because of the large numbers of people who decided to make the LA basin their homes, Los Angeles and California have enacted probably the most restrictive air pollution control requirements in the United States.

Air quality is impacted by those things we can see readily with the naked eye (smoke and smog), by things that can only be seen under the microscope (pollen, microbes, and dust), and by substances we can't see (ozone, carbon dioxide, and sulfur dioxide). These compounds are heavily regulated, and each passing day seems to bring some new regulation for a new or old compound from the U.S. Environmental Protection Agency (EPA) or other regulatory authority. On local television weather forecasts these days, we often hear references to the local "air quality index."

A comparatively smaller (but significant) amount of heat energy is transferred to the atmosphere by conduction from the Earth's surface. Conduction of energy occurs through the interaction of adjacent molecules with no visible motion accompanying the transfer of heat—for example, when the whole length of a metal rod is heated when one end is held in a fire. Because air is a poor heat conductor, conduction is restricted to the layer of air in direct contact with the Earth's surface. The heated air is then transferred aloft by convection, the movement of whole masses of air, which may be either relatively warm or cold. Convection is the mechanism by which abrupt temperature variations occur when large masses of air move across an area. Air temperature tends to be greater near the surface of the Earth and decreases gradually with altitude. A large amount of the Earth's surface heat is transported to clouds in the atmosphere by conduction and convection—before being lost ultimately by radiation—and this redistribution of heat energy plays an important role in weather and climate conditions.

The Earth's average surface temperature is maintained at about 15°C because of the atmospheric greenhouse effect. The greenhouse effect occurs when the gases of the lower atmosphere transmit most of the visible portion of incident sunlight in the same way as the glass of a garden greenhouse. The warmed Earth emits radiation in the infrared region, which is selectively absorbed by the atmospheric gases, whose absorption spectrum is similar to that of glass. This absorbed energy heats the atmosphere and helps maintain the Earth's temperature. Without this greenhouse effect, the surface temperature would average around –18°C.

Water molecules in the atmosphere perform most of the absorption of infrared energy. In addition to the key role played by water molecules, carbon dioxide, although to a lesser extent, is also essential in maintaining the heat balance. Environmentalists and others studying environmental issues are concerned that an increase in the carbon dioxide level in the atmosphere could prevent sufficient energy loss, causing damaging increases in the Earth's temperature. This phenomenon, commonly known as *anthropogenic greenhouse effect* (see Chapter 13), may occur from elevated levels of carbon dioxide caused by increased use of fossil fuels and the reduction in carbon dioxide absorption because of destruction of the rain forest and other forest areas.

MOTION

To state that Earth's atmosphere is constantly in motion is to state the obvious. Anyone observing constant weather changes is well aware of this phenomenon. The importance of the dynamic state of our atmosphere is much less obvious.

The constant motion of Earth's atmosphere (air movement) consists of both horizontal (wind) and vertical (**air currents**) dimensions. The atmosphere's motion is the result of thermal energy produced from the heating of the Earth's surface and the air molecules above it. Because of differential heating of the Earth's surface, energy flows from the equator toward the poles.

Even though air movement plays the critical role in transporting the energy of the lower atmosphere, bringing the warming influences of spring and summer and the cold chill of winter, the effects of air movements on our environment are often overlooked, despite wind and air currents being fundamental to how nature functions. All life on Earth has evolved with mechanisms dependent on air movement: pollen is carried by winds for plant reproduction; animals sniff the wind for essential information; and wind power was the motivating force that began the earliest stages of the Industrial Revolution. Now we see the effects of wind in other ways, too: wind causes weathering (erosion) of the Earth's surface; it influences ocean currents; and air pollutants and contaminants such as radioactive particles transported by the wind impact our environment.

Causes of Air Motion

In all dynamic situations, forces are necessary to produce motion and changes in motion—winds and air currents. The air (made up of various gases) of the atmosphere is subject to two primary forces: (1) **gravity** and (2) pressure differences from temperature variations.

Gravity (gravitational forces) holds the atmosphere close to the Earth's surface. Newton's law of universal gravitation states that every body in the universe attracts another body with a force equal to:

$$F = G\frac{m_1 m_2}{r2}$$ (9.1)

where:

F	= Force
m_1 and m_2	= the masses of the two bodies
G	= universal constant of 6.67×10^{-11} $N \times m^2/kg^2$
R	= distance between the two bodies

The force of gravity decreases as an inverse square of the distance between the bodies.

Thermal conditions affect density, which in turn cause gravity to affect vertical air motion and planetary air circulation. This affects how air pollution is naturally removed from the atmosphere.

Although forces in other directions often overrule gravitational force, the ever-present force of gravity is vertically downward and acts on each gas molecule, accounting for the greater density of air near the Earth.

Atmospheric air is a mixture of gases, so the gas laws and other physical principles govern its behavior. The pressure of a gas is directly proportional to its temperature. Pressure is force per unit area ($P = F/A$), so a temperature variation in air generally gives rise to a difference in pressure of force. This difference in pressure resulting from temperature variations in the atmosphere creates air movement—on both large and local scales. It corresponds to an unbalanced force, and when a pressure difference occurs, the air moves from a high- to a low-pressure region.

In other words, horizontal air movements (called **advective winds**) result from temperature gradients, which give rise to density gradients and subsequently, pressure gradients. The force associated with these pressure variations (**pressure gradient force**) is directed at right angles to (perpendicular to) lines of equal pressure (called **isobars**) and is directed from high to low pressure.

Look at Figure 9.4. The pressures over a region are mapped by taking barometric readings at various locations. Lines drawn through the points (locations) of equal pressure are called isobars. All points on an isobar are of equal pressure, which means no air movement along the isobar. The wind direction is at right angles to the isobar in the direction of the lower pressure. In Figure 9.4, notice that air moves down a pressure gradient toward a lower isobar like a ball rolls down a hill. If the isobars are close together, the pressure gradient force is large, and such areas are characterized by high wind speeds. If isobars are widely spaced (see Figure 9.4), the winds are light because the pressure gradient is small.

Localized air circulation gives rise to **thermal circulation** (a result of the relationship based on a law of physics wherein the pressure and volume of a gas are directly related to its temperature). A change in temperature causes a change in the pressure and/or volume of a gas. With a change in volume comes a change in density, since $P = m/V$, so regions of the atmosphere with different temperatures may have different air pressures and densities. As a result, localized heating sets up air motion and gives rise to thermal circulation. To gain understanding of this phenomenon, consider Figure 9.5.

Once the air has been set in motion, secondary forces (velocity-dependent forces) act. These secondary forces are (1) Earth's rotation (Coriolis force) and (2) contact with the rotating Earth (friction). The **Coriolis force**, named after its discoverer,

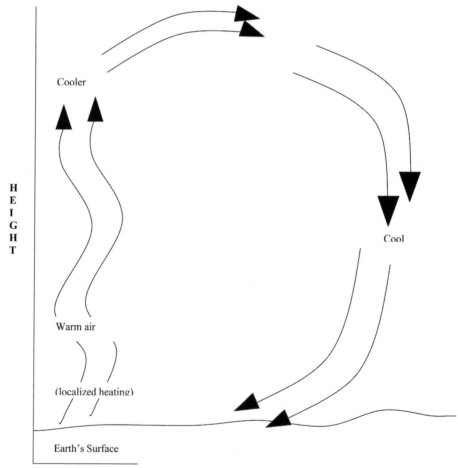

Figure 9.5. Thermal circulation of air. Localized heating, which causes air in the region to rise, initiates the circulation. As the warm air rises and cools, cool air near the surface moves horizontally into the region vacated by the rising air. The upper, still cooler, air then descends to occupy the region vacated by the cool air.

French mathematician Gaspard Coriolis (1772–1843), is the effect of rotation on the atmosphere and on all objects on the Earth's surface. In the Northern Hemisphere, it causes moving objects and currents to be deflected to the right; in the Southern Hemisphere, it causes deflection to the left, because of the Earth's rotation. Air, in large-scale north or south movements, appears to be deflected from its expected path. That is, air moving toward the pole in the Northern Hemisphere appears to be deflected toward the east; air moving southward appears to be deflected toward the west.

Friction (drag, resistance) can also cause the deflection of air movement. It is both internal and external. The friction of air's molecules generates internal friction. Friction is also generated when air molecules run into each other. External friction is caused by contact with terrestrial surfaces. The magnitude of the frictional force along a surface is dependent on the air's magnitude and speed, and the opposing frictional force is in the opposite direction of the air motion.

Local and World Air Circulation

Air moves in all directions, and these movements are essential for those of us on Earth: vertical air motion is essential in cloud formation and precipitation (see Chapter 10). Horizontal air movement near the Earth's surface produces winds.

Wind is an important factor in human comfort, especially affecting how cold we feel. A brisk wind at moderately low temperatures can quickly make us uncomfortably cold. Wind promotes the loss of body heat, which aggravates the chilling effect, expressed through **wind chill factors** in the winter and the **heat index** in the summer (see Tables 9.5 and 9.6). These two scales describe the cooling effects of wind on exposed flesh at various temperatures.

Local winds are the result of atmospheric pressure differences involved with thermal circulations because of geographic features. Land areas heat up more quickly than do water areas, giving rise to a convection cycle. As a result, during the day, when land is warmer than the water, we experience a lake or sea breeze.

At night, the cycle reverses. Land loses its heat more quickly than water, so the air over the water is warmer. The convection cycle sets to work in the opposite direction, and a land breeze blows.

In the upper troposphere (above 11 to 14 km, west to east flows) are very narrow, fast-moving bands of air called **jet streams**. Jet streams have significant effects on surface airflows. When jet streams accelerate, divergence of air occurs at that altitude. This promotes convergence near the surface and the formation of cyclonic motion. Deceleration causes convergence aloft and subsidence near the surface, causing an intensification of high-pressure systems. Jet streams are thought to result from the general circulation structure in the regions where great high- and low-pressure areas meet.

Table 9.5. Wind Chill Chart

Wind MPH	Temperature (°F)											
	30	25	20	15	10	5	0	-5	-10	-15	-20	-25
5	25	19	13	7	1	-5	-11	-16	-22	-28	-34	-40
10	21	15	9	3	-4	-10	-16	-22	-28	-35	-41	-47
15	19	13	3	0	-7	-13	-19	-26	-32	-39	-45	-51
20	17	11	4	-2	-9	-15	-22	-29	-35	-42	-48	-55
25	16	9	3	-4	-11	-17	-24	-31	-37	-44	-51	-58
30	15	8	1	-5	-12	-19	-26	-33	-39	-46	-53	-60
35	14	7	0	-7	-14	-21	-27	-34	-41	-48	-55	-62
40	13	6	-1	-8	-15	-22	-29	-36	-43	-50	-57	-64
45	12	5	-2	-9	-16	-23	-30	-37	-44	-51	-58	-65
50	12	4	-3	-19	-17	-24	-31	-38	-45	-52	-60	-67
55	11	4	-3	-11	-18	-25	-32	-39	-46	-54	-61	-68
60	10	3	-4	-11	-19	-26	-33	-40	-48	-55	-62	-69

Note: Gray cells indicate frostbite occurs in 15 minutes or less.

Source: Adapted from *USA Today,* http://www.usatoday.com/weather/resources/basics/windchill/wind-chill-chart.htm.

Table 9.6. Heat Index Chart (Temperature and Relative Humidity)

	Temperature (°F)															
RH (%)	90	91	92	93	94	95	96	97	98	99	100	101	102	103	104	105
90	119	123	128	132	137	141	146	152	157	163	168	174	180	186	193	199
85	115	119	123	127	132	136	141	145	150	155	161	166	172	178	184	190
80	112	115	119	123	127	131	135	140	144	149	154	159	164	169	175	180
75	109	112	115	119	122	126	130	134	138	143	147	152	156	161	166	171
70	106	109	112	115	118	122	125	129	133	137	141	145	149	154	158	163
65	103	106	108	111	114	117	121	124	127	131	135	139	143	147	151	155
60	100	103	105	108	111	114	116	120	123	126	129	133	136	140	144	148
55	98	100	103	105	107	110	113	115	118	121	124	127	131	134	137	141
50	96	98	100	102	104	107	109	112	114	117	119	122	125	128	131	135
45	94	96	98	100	102	104	106	108	110	113	115	118	120	123	126	129
40	92	94	96	97	99	101	103	105	107	109	111	113	116	118	121	123
35	91	92	94	95	97	98	100	102	104	106	107	109	112	114	116	118
30	89	90	92	93	95	96	98	99	101	102	104	106	108	110	112	114

Note: Exposure to full sunshine can increase HI values to increase by up to 15°F.

Source: Adapted from Weather Images, http://www.weatherimages.org/data/heatindex.html.

Response Scenario 9.1. Blowing in the Wind

Wind energy conversion—the leading mechanically based renewable energy for much of human history—has been around for thousands of years. It's a proven technology that has been reinvented numerous times, with many advantages for the consumer. Modern wind farms demonstrate that wind turbines are a viable alternative to fossil fuel energy production.

Cost and capacity factors are so different between wind-generated energy and fossil fuel–generated energy that low installed-cost-per-kilowatt figures for wind turbines are somewhat misleading, because of the low-capacity factor of wind turbines relative to coal and other fossil-fueled power plants. (*Note:* "Capacity factor" is the ratio of actual energy produced by a power plant to the potential energy produced if the plant operated at rated capacity for a full year.) Capacity factors of successful wind farm operations range from 0.20 to 0.35. Fossil-fuel power plants have factors of more than 0.50, and some of the new gas turbines reach over 0.60.

"Capacity factor" and the difference between low- and high-capacity production is also misleading. Wind conversion capacity is flexible; production levels vary with the density of the wind resource. More important, the wind resource is constant for the life of the machine, not subject to cost manipulation or cost increases. Fossil fuels as energy sources are popular with investors because many of the risks are passed on to consumers. When fossil fuel shortages occur, the investors can raise their prices—causing an *increase* in revenues for investors. In a nasty twist for the consumer, investors in fossil fuel energy production are *rewarded* for 1) speeding up the depletion of a nonrenewable resource or 2) not investing enough of their profits in support infrastructure, which drives up prices (think California in 2000–2001). This seeming advantage for wind conversion technology thus becomes a barrier to investment: if big oil, coal, or gas companies could charge consumers for the wind, wind power development would have been a done deal long ago.

The cost of energy from larger electrical output wind turbines used in utility-interconnected or wind farm applications dropped from more than $1.00 per kilowatt-hour (kWh) in 1978 to under $0.05 per kWh in 1998, and to $0.025 per kWh when new large wind plants came on line in 2001 and 2002. Hardware costs have dropped below $800 per installed kilowatt, lower than the capital costs of almost every other type of power plant.

Wind energy will soon be the most cost-effective source of electrical power, and perhaps has already achieved this status. The actual life cycle cost of fossil fuels (starting with coal mining and fuel extraction, including transport and use technology, and factoring in environmental impact and political costs) is not really known, but is certainly far higher than the current wholesale rates, and has been loaded squarely on the shoulders of consumers by the energy industry. From a strictly fuel-cost perspective, since fossil fuel resources are nonrenewable, the eventual depletion of these energy sources will entail rapid escalations in price. Add to this the environmental and political costs of fossil fuels use and the increased public awareness of these issues, and fossil fuels become even more expensive.

Wind energy experts are hopeful about the future of their industry. While infinite refinements and improvements are possible, the major technology developments that allow commercialization are complete. "At some point, a 'weather change' in the marketplace, or a "killer application" somewhere will put several key companies or financial organizations in a position to profit, and wind energy conversion investors will take advantage of public interest, the political and economic climate, and emotional or marketing factors to position wind energy technology (developed in a long lineage from the Chinese and the Persians to the present wind energy researchers and developers) for its next round of development."

Though wind energy production is generally considered unusually environmentally clean, serious environmental issues do exist. For species protection, wind farm placement should be carefully studied. Wind farms put stresses on already fragmented and reduced wildlife habitat. Another serious factor is the avian mortality rate. Just as high-rise buildings, power lines, towers, antennas, and other man-made structures are passive killers of many birds, badly positioned wind farms take a heavy toll on bird populations, especially on migratory birds. The Altamont Pass wind farms (near San Francisco) are badly placed, and since their construction in the 1980s, have killed many golden eagles and members of other species as well. Golden eagles lock on to a prey animal and dive for it, totally blocking out the threat of the wind turbine. They can see the propellers under normal circumstances, but their instinctive prey focus is so strong that when they stoop over a kill, they only see it.

Six to ten different companies, including U.S. Wind Power, Kenetech Windpower, and Green Mountain Energy, own the turbines at the Altamont Pass wind farms—over 7,000 of them. Another wind facility, in Tehachapi Pass near Los Angeles, poses little threat to bird populations.

In an interview with a reporter from the *San Francisco Chronicle*, conservationist Stan Moore stated:

> It is estimated that 40 to 60 golden eagles are killed annually, plus 200 red-tailed hawks and smaller numbers of American kestrels, crows, burrowing owls and other birds. Those numbers are conservative . . . .
>
> I'm in favor of renewable energy when it is sited appropriately, but Altamont Pass is one of the worst places to put a wind farm on planet Earth, because it is adjacent to one of the densest breeding populations of golden eagles in the world. It's a unique place for raptors because of the abundant food source in ground squirrels . . . .
>
> Altamont Pass is not an appropriate place for wind turbines. What we have there is world-class golden-eagle habitat.

The California Energy Commission financed a five-year study, conducted by Dr. Grainger Hunt, a world authority on birds of prey who works with the Santa Cruz Predatory Bird Research Group. The study detected no population-level impacts for golden eagles in Altamont Pass; however, the local eagles could provide source population for all of California, if the wind farm deaths were halted. Instead, the local eagles are an at-risk population: If other pressures disturbed the Altamont Pass golden eagle population—an outbreak of West Nile virus, for example—catastrophic population losses would occur, because the wind turbines have removed much of the buffer population.

Because control guidelines are voluntary, not mandatory, the energy industry essentially polices itself on this issue. When the U.S. Fish and Wildlife Service (practicing what officials themselves call "discretionary" law enforcement of FWS laws) chooses not to enforce the Migratory Bird Treaty Act and the Bald and

(continued)

Response Scenario 9.1. (*continued*)

Golden Eagle Protection Act, and when California officials fail to enforce their own decrees (a state designation of the golden eagle as a "fully protected species" and a "species of special concern"), the protections supposedly provided by federal and state laws become a farce.

RESPONSE

(i) Is the killing or injuring of birds a legitimate reason to not use wind turbines for energy production?
(ii) Will the day ever arrive when wind turbines replace our need for hydrocarbon energy sources?

REFERENCES

Pellissier, Hank. (2003, September 8). "Golden Eagle Eco-Atrocity at Altamont Pass." *San Francisco Chronicle*, special to SF Gate.
Xcel Energy Ponnequin wind farm in northeastern Colorado. http://telosnet.com/wind/

Chapter Summary

We have pointed out that pollutants in the air we breathe cause concern because of potential adverse effects on human health. These adverse health effects include acute conditions such as respiratory difficulties and chronic effects such as emphysema and cancer. Although health issues related to air pollution are usually at the top of any concerned person's list, we must keep in mind that air pollution has adverse impacts on other aspects of our environment that are important to us as well, such as vegetation, materials, and degradation of visibility.

In any discussion of air quality, specific areas must be addressed. Any such discussion that does not include types of air pollutants, air pollutant sources, the mechanics of air pollution (dispersion, transformation, and depletion), emission control devices, air quality regulations, and ambient air quality evaluation methods is an empty effort. We cover these topics in detail in Chapters 11–14.

Discussion Questions and Problems

1. Explain insolation.
2. State the forces that produce air motion.
3. There is a considerable difference between the amount of solar energy that strikes the outer atmosphere and that actually reaches the Earth's surface. Why?
4. For the entire planet, why must incoming solar radiation balance outgoing infrared radiation?
5. What are jet streams? How are they formed?

6. Distinguish between air currents and wind.
7. Discuss the advantages and disadvantages of wind energy conversion.
8. How does gravity affect the flow of air in the atmosphere?
9. What is the Coriolis effect? What is its impact on air motion?
10. Discuss wind chill and the heat index.

Suggested Research Topics and Projects

- Write an extended definition of air.
- Examine the diverse chemical elements that air is composed of and determine who what, when, where, why, and how organisms use them. Where do they go? What do they do? What functions do they serve?
- Examine why we don't seem to consider nitrogen as essential to "air" as oxygen is.
- Research solar radiation and how it affects our atmosphere. Compare it to how solar radiation affects other planetary bodies.
- Research solar radiation and how it affects our atmosphere. Examine how we could use its power to our benefit.
- Research the profits, costs, and drawbacks associated with various types of energy production and compare production costs, price per kilowatt, possible profits, environmental costs, and political costs.
- Examine atmospheric motion more fully.
- Examine the problems associated with smog in Los Angeles.

References and Recommended Reading

Anthes, R. A. (1996). *Meteorology*. 7th ed. Upper Saddle River, NJ: Prentice Hall.

Anthes, R. A., Cahir, J. J., Fraizer, A. B., & Panofsky, H. A. (1984). *The Atmosphere*. 3rd ed. Columbus, OH: Charles E. Merrill Publishing Company.

Committee on Public Works, Subcommittee on Air and Water Pollution, S. Rep. No. 94-411. (1968). Staff Report, Air Quality Criteria.

Ingersoll, A. P. (1983). 'The Atmosphere." *Scientific American* 249(33): 162–74.

Lutgens, F. K., & Tarbuck, E. J. (1982). *The Atmosphere: An Introduction to Meteorology*. Englewood Cliffs, NJ: Prentice-Hall.

Miller, G. R., Jr. (2004). *Environmental Science*. 10th ed. Australia: Thompson-Brooks/Cole

Moran, J. M., Morgan, M. D., & Wiersma, J. H. (1986). *Introduction to Environmental Science*. 2nd ed. New York: W. H. Freeman & Company.

NASA (2007). *The Water Planet*. Accessed December 25, 2007. http://rst.gsfc.nasa.gov/Sect14/Sect14_1b. html.

Shipman, J. T., Adams, J. L., & Wilson, J. D. (1987). *An Introduction to Physical Science*. 5th ed. Lexington, MA: D.C. Heath & Company.

Spellman, F. R. (1998). *Environmental Science and Technology: Concepts and Applications*. Lancaster, PA: Technomic Publishing Company.

Spellman, F. R., & Whiting, N. (2006). *Environmental Science and Technology: Concepts and Applications*. 2nd ed. Rockville, MD: Government Institutes.

U.S. EPA (2007). "Introduction to Air Pollution." Accessed December 25, 2007. http://www.epa.gov/air/oaqps/eog/course42/ap.html.

CHAPTER 10

Meteorology

Just as there are people with distorted, failing, or nonexistent senses of smell, there are those at the other end of the olfactory spectrum, prodigies of the nose, the most famous of whom is probably Helen Keller. "The sense of smell," she wrote, "has told me of a coming storm hours before there was any sign of it visible. I notice first a throb of expectancy, a slight quiver, a concentration in my nostrils. As the storm draws near my nostrils dilate, the better to receive the flood of Earth odors which seem to multiply and extend, until I feel the splash of rain against my cheek. As the tempest departs, receding farther and farther, the odors fade, become fainter and fainter, and die away beyond the bar of space." Other individuals have been able to smell changes in the weather, too, and, of course, animals are great meteorologists (cows, for example, lie down before a storm). Moistening, misting, and heaving the Earth breathes like a great dark beast. When barometric pressure is high, the Earth holds its breath and vapors lodge in the loose packing and random crannies of the soil, only to float out again when the pressure is low and the Earth exhales. The keen-nosed, like Helen Keller, smell the vapors rising from the soil, and know by that signal that there will be rain or snow. This may also be, in part, how farm animals anticipate earthquakes—by smelling ions escaped from the Earth.

—D. Ackerman, 1990, 44–45

Chapter Objectives

After studying this chapter, you should be able to:

- Define, describe, and discuss the evolution of the National Weather Service.
- Define, describe, and discuss weather.
- Define, describe, and discuss climate.

391

- Define and describe microclimates.
- Define, describe, and discuss El Nino.
- Describe and explain how the sun is the weather generator.
- Define, describe humidity and relative humidity.
- Define, describe, and discuss air masses, fronts, and cold and warm fronts.
- Define, describe, and discuss thermal inversions.
- Define, describe, and discuss air pollution.

Chapter Outline

- Discussion: evolution of National Weather Service
- Discussion and definition: weather
- Discussion and definition: climate
- Discussion and definition: microclimates
- Discussion and definition: meteorology
- Discussion and definition: El Nino
- Discussion and definition: the sun
- Discussion and definition: winds
- Discussion: air currents
- Discussion definition: humidity
- Discussion and definition: air masses
- Discussion and definition: thermal inversions
- Discussion and definition: air pollution

Key Terms

air currents

air mass

climate

cold front

convection

El Niño

front

humidity

meteorology

relative humidity

thermal inversion

warm front

weather

winds and breezes

Introduction[1]

The U.S. National Weather Service (1849–1994), according to the National Oceanic and Atmospheric Administration (NOAA 2010), has its beginning in the early history of the United States. **Weather** always has been important to the citizenry of this country, and this was especially true during the 17th and 18th centuries. Weather also was important to many of the Founding Fathers. Colonial leaders who blazed the trail to independence for our country also were avid weather observes. Thomas

Jefferson bought his first thermometer while writing the Declaration of Independence and his first barometer a few days after the signing of the document. (Incidentally, he noted that the high temperature in Philadelphia, Pennsylvania, on July 4, 1776, was 76 degrees.) Jefferson made regular observations at Monticello for 1772–1778 and participated in taking the first known simultaneous weather observations in America. George Washington also made regular observations; the last weather entry in his diary was the day before he died.

During the early and mid-1800s, weather observation networks began to grow and expand across the Unites States. Although most basic meteorological instruments had existed for more than 100 years, it was the telegraph that was largely responsible for the advancement of operational **meteorology** during the 19th century. With the advent of the telegraph, weather observations from distant points could be "rapidly" collected, plotted, and analyzed at one location.

Following is a chronology of the development of official weather observation in the United States:

- **1849:** The Smithsonian Institution supplies weather instruments to telegraph companies and establishes extensive observation network. Observations are submitted by telegraph to the Smithsonian, where weather maps are created.

    By the end of the year, 150 volunteers throughout the United States are reporting weather observations to the Smithsonian regularly.

- **1860:** 500 stations are making regular observations and telegraphing them to the *Washington Evening Star*, but work is interrupted by the Civil War. As the network grows, other existing systems are gradually absorbed, including several state weather services.

- **1869:** Telegraph service, instituted in Cincinnati, begins collecting weather data and producing weather charts.

    The ability to observe and display simultaneously observed weather data through the use of the telegraph quickly leads to initial efforts in the next logical advancement, the forecasting of weather. However, the ability to observe and forecast weather over much of the country requires considerable structure and organization—a government agency.

- **1870:** A joint congressional resolution is introduced requiring the Secretary of War "to provide for taking meteorological observations at the military stations in the interior of the continent and at other points in the States and Territories . . . and for giving notice on the northern (Great) Lakes and on the seacoast by magnetic telegraph and marine signals, of the approach and force of storms." The resolution is passed by Congress and signed into law on February 9, 1870, by President Ulysses S. Grant. An agency has been born that will affect the daily lives of most of the citizens of the United States through forecasts and warnings.

- **1870–1880:** Ben. Albert J. Meyer serves as the first director of the Weather Bureau. Gen. William Babcock serves as the director of the Weather Bureau.

- **1887–1891:** Maj. Gen. Adolphus Greely takes over as director of the Weather Bureau.

- **May 30, 1889:** An earthen dam breaks near Johnstown, Pennsylvania. The flood kills 2,209 people and wrecks 1,880 homes and businesses.
- **October 1, 1890:** The Weather Service is first identified as a civilian enterprise when Congress, at the request of President Benjamin Harrison, passes an act creating the Weather Bureau in the Department of Agriculture.

  A weather-sensitive sports event in this first year is 15th running of the Kentucky Derby.
- **1891:** The secretary of agriculture directs R. G. Dyrenforth to carry out rain-making experiments by setting off explosions from balloons in the air; the Weather Bureau becomes responsible for issuing flood warnings to the public; telegraphic reports of stages of rivers are made at 26 places on the Mississippi and its tributaries, the Savannah and Potomac Rivers.
- **1891–1895:** Professor Mark W. Harrington replaces Maj. Gen. Greely as director of the Weather Bureau.
- **1894:** William Eddy, using five kites to fly a self-recording thermometer, makes the first observations of temperatures aloft.
- **September 30, 1895:** The first daily Washington weather map is published by the Weather **Bureau.**

Did You Know?

The weather map is the most valuable tool that the meteorologist uses to forecast the weather. Without this tool, it would be very difficult to predict changes in the weather. Weather maps summarize what is happening in the atmosphere at a certain time. By looking at weather maps from different heights in the atmosphere, meteorologists can envision a three-dimensional picture of what is happening in the atmosphere. They can tell whether a particular area has high or low pressure, whether it may rain, and many other things, just by looking at a weather map (NOAA 2007).

- **1895–1913:** Secretary of Agriculture J. Sterling Morton appoints Professor Willis Luther Moore chief of the Weather Bureau.
- **1898:** President William McKinley orders the Weather Bureau to establish a hurricane warning network in the West Indies.
- **1900:** Cable exchange with Europe of weather warnings and other weather information begins.
- **September 1900:** Hurricane strikes Galveston, Texas, killing over 6,000 people. The wife of the Galveston official in charge and one Weather Bureau employee and his wife are killed in the associated flooding. The Weather Bureau forecasts the storm four days ahead, but not the high tide.
- **1901:** Official three-day forecasts begin for the North Atlantic. At a Weather Bureau Conference in Milwaukee, Wisconsin, Willis Moore reports that the Post Office Department is delivering slips of paper on which are daily forecasts and frost

and cold-wave warnings to everyone's door with the mail. The one disadvantage to the system is that the mail carriers start their routes about 7:00 a.m., and each day's forecast is not issued until 10:00 a.m., so the previous night's forecasts are used.

- **1902:** The Marconi Company begins broadcasting Weather Bureau forecasts by wireless telegraphy to Cunard Line steamers; the bureau begins collecting flood damage statistics nationally.
- **1903:** The United States and Panama sign the Canal Treaty; the first automobile trip across the United States is completed, from San Francisco to New York City; Orville Wright makes the first powered airplane flight at Kill Devil Hill, North Carolina, after consultation with the Weather Bureau.
- **1904:** Government begins using airplanes to conduct upper air atmospheric research.
- **1905:** The SS *New York* transmits the first wireless weather report received on ship at sea.
- **1907:** Round-the-world cruise of the U.S. "Great White Fleet," including 16 battleships and 12,000 men, is made.
- **1909:** The Weather Bureau begins its program of free-rising balloon observations.
- **1910:** The Weather Bureau begins issuing generalized weekly forecasts for agricultural planning; the River and Flood Division begins assessment of water available each season for irrigating the Far West.
- **1911:** The first transcontinental airplane flight is made, from New York City to Pasadena, California, by C. P. Rogers, in 87 hours and 4 minutes air time, over a period of 18 days.
- **1912:** As a result of the *Titanic* disaster, an international ice patrol is established, conducted by the Coast Guard; the first fire weather forecast is issued; Dr. Charles F. Marvin is appointed chief of the Weather Bureau.
- **1913–1934:** Professor Charles F. Marvin serves as the new chief of the Weather Bureau, replacing Professor Moore.
- **1914:** An aerological section is established within the Weather Bureau to meet the growing needs of aviation; the first daily radiotelegraphy broadcast of agricultural forecasts is made by the University of North Dakota.
- **1916:** The Fire Weather Service is established, with all district forecast centers authorized to issue fire weather forecasts; the bureau's fire district forecast center is started at Medford, Oregon.
- **1917:** Norwegian meteorologists begin experimenting with **air mass** analysis techniques, which will revolutionize the practice of meteorology.

Did You Know?

Today, weather observations are taken from thousands of locations. These data are then sent to Washington, D.C., to be analyzed. Computers are the main tool for creating weather maps, because they can handle large amounts of data quickly. Forecasts have become much more accurate because meteorologists have better weather maps than in the past (NOAA 2007).

- **1918:** The Weather Bureau begins issuing bulletins and forecasts for domestic military flights and for new air mail routes.
- **1919:** The Navy Aerological Service is established on a permanent basis; the first transatlantic flight is made by a U.S. Navy sea plane, with stops in Newfoundland, Azores, and Lisbon.
- **1920**: Meteorologists form a professional organization, the American Meteorological Society.
- **1921:** The University of Wisconsin makes a radiotelephone broadcast of weather forecasts, the first successful use of the new medium for weather advisories.
- **1922:** Histories of 500 river stations are completed.
- **1926:** The Air Commerce Act directs the Weather Bureau to provide for weather services to civilian aviation; the fire weather service formally inaugurated when Congress provides funds for seven fire weather districts.
- **1927:** The Weather Bureau establishes a West Coast prototype for an Airways Meteorological Service; Charles A. Lindbergh flies alone from Long Island, nonstop, to Paris. The 3,610-mile trip is completed in 33.5 hours. As on his earlier transcontinental flight, he consults the bureau in planning this flight. However, Lindbergh does not wait for the final confirmation of good weather over the Atlantic. When Weather Bureau officials in New York hear that Lindberg has left, they express surprise because the forecasts indicate the flight should have been delayed by at least 12 hours. Indeed, Lindbergh runs into problems with fog and rain—as the Weather Bureau had predicted.
- **1928:** The teletype replaces telegraph and telephone service as the primary method for communicating weather information.
- **1931:** The Weather Bureau begins regular 5:00 a.m. EST aircraft observations at Chicago, Cleveland, Dallas, and Omaha, at altitudes reaching 16,000 feet. This program spells the demise of the "kite stations."
- **1933:** A science advisory group apprizes President Franklin D. Roosevelt that the volunteer cooperative Earth observer network is one of the most extraordinary services ever developed, netting the public more information per dollar expended than any other government service in the world. (By 1990, the 25-mile radius network will encompass nearly 10,000 stations.)
- **1934–1938:** Dr. Willis L. Gregg is named bureau chief, replacing Professor Marvin.
- **1934:** The bureau establishes Air Mass Analysis Section; from 1934 to 1937, the Dust Bowl drought in the southern Plains causes severe economic damage.
- **1935:** A hurricane warning service is established; the Smithsonian Institution begins making long-range weather forecasts based on solar cycles; floating automatic weather instruments mounted on buoys begin collecting marine weather data.
- **1936:** Hoover Dam is completed, a weather-sensitive engineering feat.
- **1937:** The first official Weather Bureau radio meteorograph or radiosonde sounding is made at East Boston, Massachusetts. This program spells the end for aircraft soundings, because balloons average only 50,000 feet altitude. Twelve pilots die flying weather missions. The January flood on the Ohio River is the greatest ever experienced, with the water levels exceeding all previous. (Cincinnati's 80-foot crest and Louisville's 81.4-foot crest have never been exceeded.) Seventy percent of Louisville

is under water; 175,000 of its residents flee their homes; the entire city of Paducah, Kentucky (population 40,000) is evacuated.

- **1938–1963:** President Franklin D. Roosevelt appoints Dr. Francis W. Reichelderfer chief of the Weather Bureau.

Did You Know?

A meteorologist must convey a lot of information without using a lot of words. When looking at a weather map, a meteorologist needs to know where the cola air is, where the warm air is, where it is raining, what type of clouds are in the area, and many more things. Forecasts need to be accurate, but they also need to be timely (NOAA 2007).

- **1939:** The bureau initiates automatic telephone weather service in New York City; radio meteorographs, or radiosondes, replace all military and Weather Bureau aircraft observations.
- **1940:** The Weather Bureau is transferred to the Department of Commerce; the Army and Navy establish weather centers; President Roosevelt orders the U.S. Coast Guard to man ocean weather stations.
- **1941:** Dr. Helmut Landsberg, "the Father of Climatology," writes the first edition of his elementary textbook, *Physical Climatology*. Two women are listed as observer and forecaster in the Weather Bureau.
- **1942:** A Central Analysis Center, forerunner of the National Meteorological Center, is created to prepare and distribute master analyses of the upper atmosphere; the Joints Chiefs of Staff establish a Joint Meteorological Committee to coordinate wartime civilian and military weather activities; the Navy gives the Weather Bureau 25 surplus aircraft radars to be modified for ground meteorological use, marking the start of a weather radar system; in the U.S. Navy aerologists play a key role as U.S., carrier-based Navy planes decimate the Japanese fleet in the Pacific Battle of Midway Island in early June 1942, turning the tide in World War II. A cooperative thunderstorm research effort is undertaken by the bureau, military services, and the University of Chicago.
- **1944:** The decision to invade Normandy on June 6 is based on weather forecasts, which indicate the correct combination of tides and winds.

Did You Know?

If too much time is spent making the forecast, it will be late. Not many people want to know what the weather was doing 20 minutes ago. Most want to know what the weather is going to do in the near future. Because of this, weather symbols were invented so that weather maps could be looked at quickly (NOAA 2007).

- **1945:** More than 900 women are employed by the Weather Bureau as observers and forecasters, as a result of filling positions during World War II.
- **1946:** The U.S. Weather Bureau selects Cincinnati, Ohio, and Kansas City, Missouri, as locations for the nation's first hydrologist-staffed river forecast centers. Eventually, 13 RFCs will be established to serve the United States.
- **1948:** USAF Air Weather Service meteorologists issue the first tornado warnings from a military installation. Princeton's Institute for Advanced Studies begins research into use of a computer for weather forecasting; the Chicago Weather Bureau office demonstrates use of facsimile for map transmission; truck-mounted campers areused as mobile forecast stations in major forest fires for the first time.
- **1950:** The Weather Bureau begins issuing 30-day weather outlooks and authorizes release of "tornado alerts" to the public.
- **1951:** The Severe Weather Warning center begins operation at Tinker Air Force Base, Oklahoma, the forerunner of the National Severe Storms Center; the World Meteorological Organization is established by the United Nations; Bureau Chief Reichelderfer is elected its first head; the bureau's New Orleans data tabulation unit moves to Asheville, North Carolina, to become the National Weather Records Center and later the National Climatic Data Center.
- **1952:** The bureau organizes the Severe Local Storms Forecasting Unit in Washington, D.C., and begins issuing tornado forecasts.
- **1954:** The Weather Bureau, Navy, Air Force, MIT's Institute for Advanced Study, and the University of Chicago form a Joint Numerical Weather Prediction Unit at Suitland, Maryland. The first radar specifically designed for meteorological use, the AN/CPS-9, is unveiled by the Air Weather Service, USAF.
- **1955:** Hurricane Diane floods the Northeast and 187 people die. Regularly scheduled operational computer forecasts are begun by the Joint Numerical Forecast Unit. The Weather Bureau becomes a pioneer civilian user of computers along with the Census Bureau; it begins development of the barotropic model, a first for numerical predictions.
- **1956:** The bureau initiates the National Hurricane Research Project.
- **1957–1958:** The International Geophysical Year provides the first concerted, worldwide sharing of meteorological research data. Dr. Reichelderfer accepts a proposal by Dr. James Brantly of Cornell Aeronautical Laboratories to modify surplus Navy Doppler radars for several storms observation—the first endeavor to measure the motion of precipitation particles by radar.
- **1958:** *Explorer I* is launched into space by an Army Redstone rocket from Cape Canaveral, Florida. This satellite discovers the Van Allen radiation belts; the National Meteorological Center is established; the first commercial jet passenger flight from New York to Miami is made by National Airlines.
- **1959:** The Army launches *Vanguard II* from Cape Canaveral, carrying two photocell units to measure sunlight reflected from clouds, a demonstration of the feasibility of a weather satellite. The bureau's first WSR-57 weather surveillance radar is commissioned at the Miami Hurricane Forecast Center. (The same model, now obsolete, is still in service in New York City, although replacement parts must be machined by hand.) The Naval Aerological Service becomes the Naval Weather Service.

The Thomas Jefferson and John Campanius Holm awards are created by the Weather Bureau to honor volunteer observers for unusual and outstanding accomplishments in the field of meteorological observation.

- **1960:** The world's first weather satellite, solar orbiting TIROS I, successfully launches from the Air Force Missile Test Center at Cape Canaveral; the bureau and the National Aeronautics and Space Administration (NASA) invite scientists from 21 nations to participate in the analysis of weather data gathered by TIROS II. In cooperation with the Department of Health, Education and Welfare, Weather Bureau meteorologists issue the first advisories on air pollution potential over the eastern United States.

- **1961:** President Kennedy, in his State of the Union address, invites all nations to join the United States in developing an International Weather Protection Program. The bureau assumes full responsibility for severe weather forecasting, establishing the National Severe Storms Center in Kansas City; special training begins for Federal Aviation Authority employees to equip them to brief pilots as part of a joint FAA–Bureau program; the USAF Air Weather Service issues the first official forecast of clear air turbulence; scientists from 27 countries attend a NASA–Weather Bureau sponsored internal workshop on techniques to interpret weather satellite data.

- **1963–1965:** Dr. Robert M. White succeeds Dr. Reichelderfer as chief of the Weather Bureau.

Did You Know?

Because a large part of the United States was not well populated in the late 1800s and early 1900s, the weather maps of the day were missing observations from most of the central Plains states. Also, meteorologists did not always understand what the maps they were analyzing meant. Many of the theories used today in forecasting had not yet been developed (NOAA 2007).

- **1963:** The Commerce Department's polar orbiting weather satellite TIROS III is launched with automatic picture transmission (APT) capability, eventually to provide continuous cloud images to over 100 nations.

- **1964:** The secretary of commerce establishes the office of the federal coordinator for meteorology; the National Severe Storms Laboratory is established in Norman, Oklahoma; the American Meteorological Society writes to the Taiwanese ambassador to the United States deploring the treatment accorded Mr. Kenneth T. C. Cheng, head of the Taiwan Weather Service, who had been indicted for an incorrect typhoon forecast. The AMS points out that if forecasters were indicted for an incorrect forecast, there could soon be a total lack of forecasters (NOAA (1964); Evolution of the National Weather Service. Minutes from AMS Council. Accessed 1/10/2011 @ www.erh.noaa.gov/er/gyx/timeline/html).

- **1965:** The Environmental Science Services Administration is created in the Department of Commerce, incorporating the Weather Bureau and several other agencies; Dr. White is appointed administrator.

- **1965–1979:** Dr. George Cressman is named bureau director.
- **1966:** Weather officials from 25 nations meet in London for the First International Clean Air Congress; the National Meteorological Center introduces a computer numerical model capable of making sea level predictions as accurate as those made manually.
- **1967:** Responsibility for issuing air pollution advisories is assigned to the Weather Bureau's National Meteorological Center; fire weather forecasts are extended to cover the contiguous United States.
- **1969:** Neil Armstrong, commander of the spacecraft *Apollo 11*, becomes the first person to set foot on the moon.
- **1970:** The Environmental Science Services Administration (ESSA) becomes the National Oceanic and Atmospheric Administration (NOAA), with Dr. White as administrator. The U.S. Weather Bureau becomes the National Weather Service.
- **1972:** Rainfall from Hurricane Agnes floods the East Coast, killing 105 people; a flash flood in the Black Hills of South Dakota kills 237 people.
- **1973:** the National Weather Service purchases its second generation radar (WSR-74).
- **1975:** The first "hurricane hunter" Geostationary Operational Environmental Satellite (GOES) is launched into orbit; these satellites, with their early and close tracking of hurricanes, will greatly reduce the loss of life from such storms.
- **1976:** Real-time operational forecasts and warnings using Doppler radar are evaluated by the Joint Doppler Operational Project, spawning a third-generation Weather Radar (WSR 889). The Big Thompson Canyon, Colorado, flood kills 139 people.
- **1977:** The success of weather satellites results in the elimination of the last U.S. weather observation ship; real-time access to satellite data by national centers advances hurricane, marine, and coastal storm forecasts.
- **1979–1988:** Dr. Richard Hallgren is appointed NOAA assistant administrator for the Weather Services.
- **1979:** The Nested Grid Model (NGM) becomes operational; the Global Data Assimilation System (GDA) is developed; the AFOS computer system is deployed, connecting all Weather Service forecast offices. AFOS is the most ambitious computer network yet created, setting records for volume of data and number of entry points while supporting a full range of word processing and other capabilities.
- **1980:** Mt. St. Helens, a dormant volcano in Washington State, erupts; weather satellites spot the eruption and alert the Federal Aviation Administration.
- **1980:** "Dean of the Cooperative Weather Observers," Mr. Edward H. Stoll of Elwood, Nebraska, is honored at the nation's capital and meets President Jimmy Carter in the While House. Mr. Stoll had faithfully served as a cooperative observer since October 10, 1905.

    Various "hot weather topics" become of general public concern, such as global warming and the role of El Niño/Southern Oscillation (ENSO) in U.S. weather.
- **1981:** The world's first reusable space shuttle, *Columbia*, is launched, completing its mission three days later.
- **1982:** El Chicon erupts in Mexico; NOAA polar weather satellites track movement of its cloud around the Earth as a possible global climate impact.

Did You Know?

Outside of normal seasonal variation, ENSO is one of the main sources of year-to-year variability in Earth's weather and **climate**, with significant socioeconomic implications for many regions around the world. In normal years, trade winds push warm water and its associated heavy rainfall westward from the central Pacific toward Indonesia. During an El Niño period, the winds die down and can even reverse direction, pushing the rains toward South America instead. This is why people in Indonesia and Australia typically associate El Niño with drought, while people in Peru connect it with floods.

- **1984:** The National Weather Service provides a special forecast for the Olympic Games in Los Angeles; the first successful solo balloon crossing of the Atlantic is made by pilot Joe Kittinger, taking 83 hours and 45 minutes.

- **September 11–13, 1984:** The first official Air Transportable Mobile Unit (ATMU) is dispatched to the Shasta-Trinity National Forest wildfire by plane from Redding, California, while the forecaster is flying from Sacramento, California. These mobile fire units are deployed nationwide in 1987. ATMUs permit NWS forecasters to set up remote observing and forecasting offices anywhere in the world within hours of a request for on-site fire weather support.

- **1985:** Harvard's Blue Hill Observatory celebrates 100 years of continuous monitoring of the atmosphere.

  President Ronald Regan awards Dr. Helmet Landsberg the National Medal of Science, the most prestigious service award a civilian can receive.

- **1986:** An eight-day, nonstop, around-the-world flight by a balloon called *Voyager* is completed with the assistance of continuous weather support from retired, volunteer, and current Weather Service employees.

- **1988:** The Weather Service operates several remote forecast operations in Yellowstone Park to assist in fighting a weeklong wildfire; the National Hurricane Center provides continuous advisories and early forecasts on the movement of giant hurricane Gilbert to assist Caribbean and U.S. coastal areas with evacuation plans; a major drought is experienced in 1987–1988 by the nation's midsection, with some of the lowest river levels in 50 years observed on the Mississippi; Dr. Hallgren retires to become president of the AMS.

- **1988:** Dr. Elbert W. Friday Jr. is appointed NOAA assistant administrator for the Weather Service.

- **1989:** The United States assists clean-up efforts in the San Francisco earthquake area with a mobile forecast unit; the Miami Hurricane Center plays a central role in limiting loss of life from gigantic storm Hugo, which causes $7 billion in damage.

  An eight-year national plan for the modernization and restructuring of the National Weather Service is announced.

- **1990:** The Cray Y-MP8 supercomputer is procured and installed at the National Meteorological Center to run higher resolution and more sophisticated numerical weather production models.

The National Weather Service exercises the contract option for full-scale production with the Unisys Corporation for 165 Next Generation Radar (NEXRAD) units and over 300 display subsystems. The explosive growth of technology has led to this joint project of the Departments of Commerce, Transportation, and Defense to meet their common radar needs.

Development and planning continue for the Automated Surface Observing System (ASOS). In 2012, routine surface observations are collected manually each hour at 260 Weather Service facilities, with 1,200 people working at least part time on the task. By freeing them of manual observation, the ASOS helps free up vital time.

(A joint effort of NOAA and the Federal aviation Administration, the ASOS program will produce as many as 1,700 units—installation at U.S. airports began in the mid-1990s. Operating automatically 24 hours a day, they alert forecasters to significant weather changes. As of June 2010, 900 ASOS had been installed.)

- **1991:** The ASOS contract, a key element in NOAA's modernization of the NWS, is awarded to AAI Corporation of Hunt Valley, Maryland.
- **1992:** Twenty-two of the planned 115 modernized Weather Forecast Offices (WFO) are built or remodeled during the year, with 12 NWS radars installed. Of a programmed 1,700 ASOS units, 151 are installed and 13 commissioned. Hurricane Inki strikes the Hawaiian island of Kauai, killing seven, and Hurricane Andrew devastates Florida and Louisiana.
- **1993:** The "Year of Water": record floods inundate the Midwest; the National Weather Service earns the U.S. Commerce Department's highest award, a gold medal, for performance during the flooding. The Advanced Weather Interactive Processing System (AWIPS) contract is awarded to PRC, Inc., of McLean, Virginia. AWIPS rapidly analyzes weather data and distributes it nationwide. The 100th new Doppler weather radar is installed; the blizzard of 1993 deposits enough precipitation in one weekend to drastically change the spring hydroponic outlook; an international training facility is dedicated at the National Meteorological Center.

  Two scientists develop a new method of processing atmospheric data needed for global forecasting, and five meteorologists from Alaska design a state-of-the-art computer network used to improve forecasting capabilities in Alaska.
- **1994:** Dr. Elbert W. Friday Jr. is honored as Federal Executive of the Year; tornadoes plow through the Southeast United States, killing 40; the new GRAY C90 supercomputer is dedicated, providing for faster and more accurate forecasts; NOAA and the EPA launch an experimental Ultraviolet Exposure Index.
- **1995–2012:** Technological upgrades are ongoing.

Weather

Weather is a constant minor, and occasionally major, concern for most of us. Do you know anyone who (like Helen Keller) claims to be able to smell changes in the weather, or who says he or she "senses" a change in the weather brewing? You have heard people talk about the weather—have you heard anyone ask (in ordinary conversation) what the weather is like in someone else's locale? Or whether you have heard the weather forecast for the weekend? Ever gotten a letter discussing how the weather in the writer's area had been, or been asked how the weather in your area was? Did you know London Victorians' affinity for dark-tinted wallpaper was weather related?

Because weather affects us all, physically and emotionally, we are often concerned with what changes weather is going to bring us on a day-to-day and season-to-season basis. Whether or not you know anyone who can smell or sense weather change, people discuss the weather in conversation daily. We're interested in the weather conditions in other people's cities (especially bad weather), and people move to one locale or another because of that area's weather conditions. Or do they? Do they move because of the weather there—or because of the climate?

Let's look at climate for a moment. Have you ever asked someone how his or her climate is, when you really wanted to know what the weather was? We don't often confuse the two. When we talk about weather, we are generally referring to the transient changes in temperature, precipitation, and wind that affect whether we take an umbrella along or wear a heavy coat. Most people rely heavily on the local meteorologist and the daily weather forecasts, so much so that an entire (and very visible) branch of science is dedicated to the effort of trying to predict the weather—a difficult task, because of the extensive variables in any prediction.

Try to define *climate* and *weather*. Most people do not have a good feel for the exact meanings of and differences between these terms. Their specific meanings and differences, and the elements that comprise them, are the subject of this chapter. The fundamentals of how weather affects air pollution are essential to a basic study of pollution and how it affects our environment.

Meteorology: The Science of Weather

Meteorology is the science concerned with the atmosphere and its phenomena; the meteorologist observes the atmosphere's temperature, density, winds, clouds, precipitation, and other characteristics, and endeavors to account for its observed structure and evaluation (weather, in part) in terms of external influence and the basic laws of physics. Meteorological phenomena affect the chemical properties of the atmosphere.

Weather is the state of the atmosphere, mainly with respect to its effect on human life and activities; as distinguished from climate (long-term manifestations of weather), weather consists of the short-term (minutes to months) variations of the atmosphere. Weather is defined primarily in terms of heat (temperature), pressure, clouds, **humidity**, wind, and moisture—the elements of which weather is made. At high levels above the Earth, where the atmosphere thins to near vacuum, weather does not exist. Weather is a near-surface phenomenon. We see this clearly, daily, as we observe the ever-changing, sometimes dramatic, and often violent weather display that travels through our environment.

In the study of environmental science, and in particular the study of air quality (especially regarding air pollution in a particular area), the determining factors are directly related to the dynamics of the atmosphere—local weather. These factors include strength of winds, the direction they are blowing, temperature, available sunlight

Response Scenario 10.1.
Shenk's Ferry: A Microclimate in Action

In southern Lancaster County, Pennsylvania, in a sheltered valley that ends at a low ridge and a railroad line at the Susquehanna River, lies the Shenk's Ferry Wildflower Preserve. Fifty acres owned by Pennsylvania Power and Light and maintained as a conservation project, Shenk's Ferry is protected in several ways, by law and by nature. Bisected by Grubb Run Creek, which enters the valley through what used to be a natural passage in the hillside, but is now a stone underpass, the valley begins a mile or two from the Susquehanna, its perimeter marked by high, steep ridges; entrance to the valley at the river is accessible only by trespassing along train tracks or on unimproved dirt and gravel roads.

The high ridges that form the barricade to this valley cycle the prevailing winds around Shenk's Ferry, and the southern exposure warms the air, forming an isolated niche that is 7 to 10°F warmer on the valley slopes than the outside areas in early spring, when the tree cover is thin. Any wildflower that occurs naturally in southern Lancaster County is apt to grow there, and chances are that it will bloom earlier there and reproduce itself in greater quantities. Yet the creek, with the tunnel that allows flow into the upper end of the valley, provides air circulation into the valley as well, so breezes do flow—and heavy shade and breezes make it 10 to 15°F cooler than the surrounding areas in the summer.

A low-impact hiking trail runs along a ridge above the creek; the land inclines steeply upward and downward, and a more gradual incline is visible on the creek's opposite side, an open forest glade. Occasional paths invite exploration up into the higher points of the preserve or investigation down to the level of the creek itself. The trail isn't very long, about a mile and a half; it follows the creek until the upper end of the valley climbs steeply into bramble, brush, and poison ivy. To get to the other side of the hill, hikers brave the brambles or wade the creek through that stony-bottomed underpass. The trail vanishes, and going beyond this point becomes hiking, up steep, boulder-strewn terrain.

The biological diversity is astounding. Over 130 varieties of Pennsylvania wildflowers grow in this sheltered, sunny, shady valley, benefiting from the microclimate, seeding and reseeding themselves naturally. There are common ones—sheets of spring beauties, daylilies, wild geranium, isolated patches of Solomon's seal, hillside after hillside of Virginia bluebells, spontaneous spreadings of Dutchman's breeches, clumps of white violets, yellow violets, blue violets, dog's tooth violets, squirrel corn, wild blue phlox—and varieties more rare: bloodroot, lady's slippers, blue cohosh, three kinds of trillium, and ferns.

RESPONSE

(i) Describe a local microclimate that you are familiar with or know about.

(needed to trigger photochemical reactions, which produce smog), and the length of time since the last weather event (strong winds and heavy precipitation) cleared the air.

Nondestructive weather events (including strong winds and heavy precipitation) that work to clean the air we breathe are obviously beneficial. However, few people would categorize weather events such as tornadoes, hurricanes, and typhoons as beneficial. Other weather events can have both positive and negative effects. One such event is **El Niño**, discussed in Response Scenario 10.2.

THE SUN: THE WEATHER GENERATOR

> All living creatures and all plants derive their life from the sun.
> If it were not for the sun, there would be darkness and nothing
> could grow—the Earth would be without life.
>
> —Okute, Teton Sioux

The sun is the driving force behind weather. Without the distribution and re-radiation to space of solar energy, weather (as we know it) would not exist. The sun is the source of most of the Earth's heat. Of the gigantic amount of solar energy generated by the sun, only a small portion bombards the Earth. Most of the sun's solar energy is lost in space. A little over 40% of the sun's radiation that reaches Earth hits the surface and is changed to heat. The rest stays in the atmosphere or is reflected back into space.

Like a greenhouse, the Earth's atmosphere admits most of the solar radiation. When solar radiation is absorbed by the Earth's surface, it is re-radiated as heat waves, most of which are trapped by carbon dioxide and water vapor in the atmosphere, which work to keep the Earth warm.

By now you are aware of the many functions performed by the Earth's atmosphere, and you know that the atmosphere plays an important role in regulating the Earth's heating supply. The atmosphere protects the Earth from too much solar radiation during the day and prevents most of the heat from escaping at night. Without the filtering and insulating properties of the atmosphere, the Earth would experience severe temperature extremes similar to those on other planets in our solar system.

On bright, clear nights, the Earth cools more rapidly than on cloudy nights, because cloud cover reflects a large amount of heat back to Earth, where it is reabsorbed again. The Earth's air is heated primarily by contact with the warm ground. When air is warmed, it expands and becomes lighter. Air warmed by contact with Earth rises and is replaced by cold air that flows in and under it. When this cold air is warmed, it too rises and is replaced by cold air. This cycle continues and generates a circulation of warm and cold air called **convection**.

At the Earth's equator, the air receives much more heat than the air at the poles. This warm air at the equator is replaced by colder air flowing in from north and south. The warm, light air rises and moves poleward high above the Earth. As it cools, it sinks, replacing the cool surface air that has moved toward the equator.

The circulating movement of warm and cold air (convection) and the differences in heating cause local **winds** and **breezes**. Different amounts of heat are absorbed by different land and water surfaces. Soil that is dark and freshly plowed absorbs much

Response Scenario 10.2. El Niño

El Niño is a natural phenomenon that occurs every two to nine years on an irregular and unpredictable basis. A warming of the surface waters in the tropical eastern Pacific, El Niño causes fish to disperse to cooler waters, which in turn causes adult birds that feed upon them to fly off in search of new food sources elsewhere.

Through a complex web of events, El Niño (which means "the child" in Spanish because it usually occurs during the Christmas season off the coasts of Peru and Ecuador) can have a devastating impact on all forms of marine life.

During a normal year, equatorial trade winds pile up warm surface waters in the western Pacific. Thunderheads unleash heat and torrents of rain. This heightens the east–west temperature difference, sustaining the cycle. The jet stream blows from north Asia to California. During an El Niño year, trade winds weaken, allowing warm waters to move east. This decreases the east–west temperature difference. The jet stream is pulled farther south than normal and picks up storms it would usually miss, carrying them to Canada or California. The warm waters eventually reach South America.

One of the first signs of El Niño's appearance is a shifting of winds along the equator in the Pacific Ocean. The normal easterly winds reverse direction and drag a large mass of warm water eastward toward the South American coastline. The large mass of warm water basically forms a barrier, which prevents the upwelling of nutrient-rich cold water from the ocean bottom to the surface. As a result, the growth of microscopic algae that normally flourish in the nutrient-rich upwelling areas diminishes sharply, limiting food supply for many marine life-forms, affecting more and more creatures up the food chain. This decrease has further repercussions: El Niño has been linked to patterns of subsequent droughts, floods, typhoons, and other costly weather extremes around the globe. Take a look at El Niño's affects on the West Coast of the United States, where it has been blamed for hurricanes, floods, and early snowstorms. On the positive side, El Niño typically brings good news to those who live on the East Coast of the United States: a reduction in the number and severity of hurricanes.

Not quite yet completely understood by scientists, El Niño is a phenomenon that causes both positive and negative results, depending upon where you live.

RESPONSE

(i) For years, people have been pointing to El Niño as the culprit behind floods, droughts, famines, economic failures, and record-breaking global heat. Can a single climate phenomenon really cause all these events?

(ii) Is the world just a step away from disaster when El Niño conditions develop?

(iii) "El Niño is a normal part of Earth's climate system and has likely been occurring for millions of years. Global climate change may affect ENSO cycles, but the research on this connection is still underway." Do you agree with this statement?

more than grassy fields, for example. Land warms faster than does water during the day and cools faster at night. Consequently, the air above such surfaces is warmed and cooled, resulting in production of local winds.

Winds should not be confused with **air currents**. Wind is primarily oriented toward horizontal flow, whereas air currents are created by air moving upward and downward. Both wind and air currents have a direct impact on air pollution, which is carried and dispersed by wind. An important factor in determining the areas most affected by an air pollution source is wind direction. Since air pollution is a global problem, wind direction on a global scale is important (see Figure 10.1).

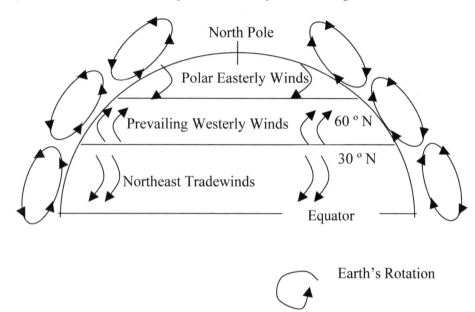

Figure 10.1. Global wind directions in the Northern Hemisphere.

Another constituent associated with Earth's atmosphere is water, which is always present in the air. It evaporates from the Earth, two-thirds of which is covered by water. In the air, water exists in three states: solid, liquid, and invisible vapor.

The amount of water in the air is called humidity. The **relative humidity** is the ratio of the actual amount of moisture in the air to the amount needed for saturation at the same temperature. Warm air can hold more water than cold. When air with a given amount of water vapor cools, its relative humidity increases; when the air is warmed, its relative humidity decreases.

AIR MASSES

An **air mass** is a vast body of air (so vast that it can have global implications) in which the conditions of temperature and moisture are much the same at all points in a horizontal direction. An air mass is affected by and takes on the temperature and moisture characteristics of the surface over which it forms, though its original characteristics tend to persist.

When two different air masses collide, a **front** is formed. A **cold front** marks the line of advance of a cold air mass from below as it displaces a warm air mass. A **warm front** marks the advance of a warm air mass as it rises up over a cold one.

Thermal Inversion and Air Pollution

We have said that during the day the sun warms the air near the Earth's surface. Normally, this heated air expands and rises during the day, diluting low-lying pollutants and carrying them higher into the atmosphere. Air from surrounding high-pressure areas then moves down into the low-pressure area created when the hot air rises (see Figure 10.2A). This continual mixing of the air helps keep pollutants from reaching dangerous levels in the air near the ground.

Sometimes, however, a layer of dense, cool air is trapped beneath a layer of less dense, warm air in a valley or urban basin. This is called a **thermal inversion** (see

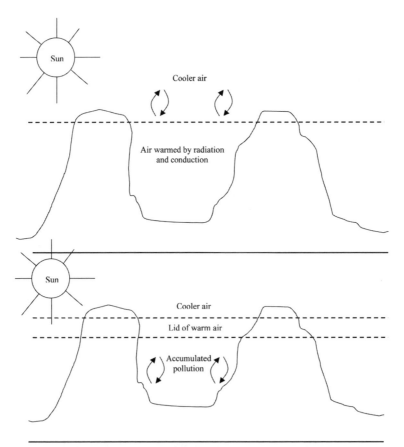

Figure 10.2. Normal conditions (A): Air at Earth's surface is heated by the sun and rises to mix with the cooler air above it. In thermal inversion (B), a layer of warm air forms a lid above the Earth, and the cooler air at the surface is unable to mix with the warm air above. Pollutants are trapped.

Figure 10.2B). In effect, a warm-air lid covers the region and prevents pollutants from escaping in upward-flowing air currents. Usually these inversions trap air pollutants at ground level for a short period of time. However, sometimes they last for several days, when a high-pressure air mass stalls over an area, trapping air pollutants at ground level, where they accumulate to dangerous levels.

The best-known location in the United States where thermal inversions occur almost on a daily basis is in the Los Angeles basin, a valley with a warm climate and light winds, surrounded by mountains located near the Pacific Coast. Los Angeles is a large city with a large population of people and automobiles and possesses the ideal conditions for smog—conditions worsened by frequent thermal inversions.

✓ **Interesting Point**: Earlier we stated that the affinity in Victorian-era London for dark-tinted wallpaper was weather related—in fact, it was a clever attempt to limit the visual impact of the dirty deposits left by air pollution.

Chapter Summary

One of the primary reasons people are so intensely interested in weather is our lack of control over it. We are intimately affected by weather in our lives. We dress as we do because of it; we plan our lives around it. We work because of it—shoveling snow, raking leaves, planting gardens around it. We go places because of it, or move away from it. We even make it the first topic of conversation after "how do you do?" We joke about it (If you don't like the weather in [your town's name here], just stick around—it'll change). But we can't change it. And it can change us.

Of course this sometimes terrifies us, chiefly because in its extremes of temperature, velocity, and precipitation, we know that weather can destroy us. Tornadoes, hurricanes, too much or too little rain, heavy snows, extreme cold and extreme heat damage, wreck, and kill. All we can do is take shelter from the adverse conditions and rebuild when they pass or plant our crops again and hope for better.

The only important way that we can affect our weather is one that is harmful to us: We can pump pollutants into our air, so that even nonextreme weather can affect us adversely as well.

Discussion Questions and Problems

1. Identify the various ways in which heat is added to or removed from the atmosphere.
2. For the entire Earth, why must incoming solar radiation balance outgoing infrared radiation?
3. In your own words, explain the following statement: The sun drives the atmosphere.
4. How is excess heat transported from the Earth's surface?
5. Why is air pollution such a large problem in urban areas?
6. What forces affect horizontal air movements?
7. Is the composition of the atmosphere changing? Explain your answer.
8. Why do winds differ in nature near the ground as compared to those aloft?

Possible Research Topics

- Create an extended definition of weather/climate.
- Research site-specific locations where terrain affects and weather together impact air quality and air pollution.
- Compare the media coverage of El Niño to the scientific views.
- Research El Niño's causes and effects.
- Research El Niño's effect on specific ocean biota.
- Research El Niño's effects on the U.S. East Coast as opposed to the U.S. West Coast.
- Research El Niño's effect on other geographic areas—e.g., South America.
- Research El Niño and weather pattern history.
- Examine what researchers believe is happening with El Niño.
- Research the history of smog in LA.
- Examine scientific research into theories and the study of long-term climate patterns.
- What would the effects be of a return to a once-common climate condition (e.g., glaciation)?

Note

1. From NOAA, 2010, *Evolution of the National Weather Service.*

References and Recommended Reading

Ackerman, D. (1990). *A Natural History of the Senses.* New York: Random House, 1990.
Anthes, R. A., Cahir, J. J., Frasier, A. B., & Panofsky, H. A. (1984). *The Atmosphere.* 3rd ed. Columbus, OH: Charles E. Merrill Publishing Co.
Battan, L. J. (1983). *Weather in Your Life.* New York: W. H. Freeman.
Budyko, M. I. (1982). *The Earth's Climate.* New York: Academic Press.
Gates, D. M. (1962). *Energy Exchange in the Biosphere.* New York: Harper & Row Monographs.
Ingersoll, A. P. (1983). "The Atmosphere." *Scientific American* 249(3): 162–74.
Kondratyev, K. Y. (1969). *Radiation in the Atmosphere.* New York: Academic Press.
Moran, J. M., & Morgan, M. D. (1994). *Essentials of Weather.* Upper Saddle River, NJ: Prentice-Hall.
National Research Council (1975). *Understanding Climatic Change: A Program for Action.* Washington, DC: National Academy of Sciences.
National Research Council (1982). *Solar Variability, Weather, and Climate.* Washington, DC: National Academy Press.
NOAA (1976). *U.S. Standard Atmosphere.* NOAA S/T 76-1562.
NOAA (2007). *Weather Maps.* Accessed May 22, 2011. http://www.nssl.noaa.gov/edu/ lessons/ lesson_mpa.html.
NOAA (2010). *Evolution of the National Weather Service.* Public Affairs Office Publication. Accessed May 20, 2011. http://www.nws.noaa.gov/pa/history/timeline.php.

CHAPTER 11

Atmospheric Pollutants

When we are asked to define pollution, we have little trouble doing so. We have witnessed it firsthand—up close and personal, you might say. We can come up with an answer that satisfied a momentary need, through a description of its obvious effects, usually. But is pollution really that easy to definitively define?

No. It is not. Pollution is complicated. It cannot be easily defined.

Why?

Because pollution is and isn't a judgment call. And because in nature, even the minutest elements are intimately connected with every other element, so are pollution's effects.

—Frank R. Spellman, 2006

Poverty is hierarchic, smog is democratic.

—Ulrich Beck

Turning the corner on air pollution requires moving beyond patchwork, end-of-pipe approaches to confront pollution at its source. This will mean reorienting energy, transportation, and industrial structures toward prevention.

—Hilary F. French

LONG-TERM IMPACT OF
INCREASED ATMOSPHERIC CO_2

If current patterns of carbon dioxide (CO_2) emission continue over the next century, the world's climate may heat up for several hundred years. Recent findings indicate that profound changes could occur in deep-ocean circulation, with the result that the Earth's carbon cycle would be altered. The findings suggest that if the present trends of greenhouse gas emissions prevail over the next century, atmospheric concentrations of CO_2 or equivalent gases would quadruple. Atmospheric temperatures would continue to increase, rising as much as 7 degrees C in 500–600 years. Sea levels would rise by about 2 meters from the thermal expansion of oceans alone. Most alarming, the ocean would settle into a stable pattern, its surface and deep waters no longer mixing. This could conceivably compromise marine biological activity, and by greatly reducing the ocean's ability to absorb CO_2, alter the Earth's carbon cycle.

—Manabe & Stouffer, 1993, 215–18

Chapter Objectives

After reading this chapter, you should be able to:

- Identify the chief primary and secondary types of atmospheric pollutants and their sources, their chemical composition, and their effects on human health and the environment.
- Define and discuss the National Ambient Air Quality Standards and their purpose, impact, and limits.
- Define, describe, and discuss in detail sulfur dioxide, its natural and anthropogenic sources, and its effects on human health and the environment.
- Define, describe, and discuss in detail the nitrogen oxide compounds important to atmospheric pollution and their natural and anthropogenic sources and effects on human health and the environment.
- Define, describe, and discuss in detail carbon monoxide, its natural and anthropogenic sources, and its effects on human health and the environment.
- Define, describe, and discuss in detail volatile organic compounds, their natural and anthropogenic sources, and their effects on human health and the environment.
- Define, describe, and discuss in detail photochemical smog, its relationship to ozone, ozone's positive and negative manifestations and the environmental and health problems associated with each, and photochemical smog and ozone's natural and anthropogenic sources.
- Define, describe, and discuss the importance of the tropospheric ozone budget.
- Define, describe, and discuss in detail carbon dioxide, its natural and anthropogenic sources, and the changes in its absorption cycle.
- Define and describe the nine categories of particulate matter and their configurations, sources, and effects.
- Define, describe, and discuss lead from human sources and its effects on human health and the environment.
- Describe and discuss in detail the enormous role that the automobile plays in the causes and sources of atmospheric pollution.

Chapter Outline

- Discussion: air pollution and long-term impact
- Discussion: the major air pollutants and their sources
- Definition and discussion: the history and importance of the National Ambient Air Quality Standards; primary and secondary pollutants
- Definition and discussion: sulfur dioxide, its sources, and the associated harm it causes environmentally
- Definition and discussion: nitrogen oxides, the dangers they present, and problems with source control
- Definition and discussion: the health problems caused by carbon monoxide and its natural and artificial origins
- Definition and discussion: VOC sources and the problems they cause
- Definition and discussion: ozone, its sources, its associated pollution and depletion problems, and pollutant gas patterns of concentration for photochemical smog
- Definition and discussion: how increased combustion affects carbon dioxide levels
- Definition and discussion: particulate matter, its composition, and its diverse sources and description
- Definition and discussion: lead, its affects on plants and humans, and emission standards

Key Terms

acid precipitation
carbon monoxide
Clean Air Act
hydrocarbons
lead
methane
National Ambient Air-Quality Standards
nitrogen dioxide
nitrogen oxide
ozone
ozone holes

particulate matter
photochemical reaction
photochemical smog
primary pollutants
primary standards
secondary pollutants
secondary standards
smog
sulfur dioxide
sulfurous smog
volatile organic compounds (VOCs)

Introduction

In the past, and to a lesser degree today, the sight of belching smokestacks has been comforting to many people: more smoke equaled more business, indicating a healthy economy. But many of us are now troubled by evidence that polluted air adversely affects our health (many toxic gases and fine particles entering the air pose health hazards—cancer, genetic defects, and respiratory disease). Nitrogen and sulfur oxides, ozone, and other air pollutants from fossil fuels are inflicting damage on our forests, crops, soils, lakes, rivers, coastal waters, and buildings. Chlorofluorocarbons (CFCs) and other pollutants entering the atmosphere are depleting the Earth's protective ozone layer, allowing more harmful ultraviolet radiation to reach the surface. As pointed out in the opening of this chapter, fossil fuel combustion is increasing the amount of *carbon dioxide* in the atmosphere, which can have severe long-term environmental impacts. Historically, many felt that the air renewed itself (through interaction with vegetation and the oceans) in sufficient quantities to make up for the influx into our atmosphere of anthropogenic pollutants. Today, however, this kind of thinking is challenged by clear evidence that the increased use of fossil fuels, expanding industrial production, and growing use of motor vehicles have a detrimental affect on atmosphere, air, and the environment. In this chapter, we examine the types and sources of air pollutants related to these concerns. In Chapter 12, we examine how these pollutants are dispersed throughout the atmosphere.

Major Air Pollutants

The most common and widespread anthropogenic pollutants currently emitted are **sulfur dioxide** (SO_2), **nitrogen oxide**s (NO_x), **carbon monoxide** (CO), carbon dioxide (CO_2), **volatile organic compounds** (**hydrocarbon**s), particulates, **lead**, and several toxic chemicals. Table 11.1 lists important air pollutants and their sources.

Table 11.1.   Pollutant Sources

Pollutant	Source
Sulfur & nitrogen oxides	From fossil fuel combustion
Carbon monoxide	Mostly from motor vehicles
Volatile organic compounds	From vehicles and industry
Ozone	From atmospheric reactions between nitrogen oxides and organic compounds

Source: Adapted from U.S. EPA, 1988a, 13.

NATIONAL AMBIENT AIR QUALITY STANDARDS

We lay the groundwork for our discussion of air pollutants with some of the history behind current air quality regulations. In the United States, the Environmental Protection Agency (EPA) regulates air quality under the **Clean Air Act** (CAA) and amendments that charged the federal government to develop uniform **National Ambient Air Quality Standards** (NAAQS). These included a dual requirement of **primary standards** (covering criteria pollutants), designed to protect health, and **secondary standards** to protect public welfare. Primary standards were slated for achievement by July 1975 and secondary standards in "a reasonable period of time." Pollutant levels protective of public health take priority (and are more stringent) than those for public welfare; achievement of the primary health standard had immediate priority. In 1971, the EPA promulgated National Ambient Air Quality Standards (NAAQS) for six classes of air pollutants. Later, in 1978, an air-quality standard was also promulgated for lead, and the photochemical oxidant standard was revised to an ozone (O_3) standard (the ozone permissible level was increased). The PM (**particulate matter**) standard was revised and redesignated PM_{10} standard in 1987. This revision reflected the need for a PM standard based on particle sizes (≤ 10 μm) that have the potential for entering the respiratory tract and affecting human health. We summarize the National Ambient Air Quality Standards in Table 11.2.

Table 11.2.   National Ambient Air Quality Standards*

Pollutant	Averaging Time	Primary Std	Secondary Std
Carbon monoxide	8 hour	10 mg/m³ (9 ppm)	Same
	1 hour	40 mg/m³ (35 ppm)	
Nitrogen dioxide	Annual average	100 μg/m³ (0.05 ppm)	Same
Sulfur dioxide	Annual average	80 μg/m³ (0.03 ppm)	Same
	24 hour	365 μg/m³ (0.14 ppm)	
	3 hour	1300 μg/m³ (0.5 ppm)	
PM_{10} (= μm)	Annual arithmetic mean	50 μg/m³	Same
	24 hour	150 μm/m³	50 μg/m³
Hydrocarbons (corrected for methane)	3 hour	160 μg/m³ (0.24 ppm)	Same
Ozone	1 hour	235 μg/m³ (0.12 ppm)	Same
Lead	3 month avg.	1.5 μg/m³	Same

*Standards, other than those based on the annual average, are not to be exceeded more than once a year.
Source: U.S. EPA, 1990.

Thus, air pollutants were categorized into two groups: primary and secondary. **Primary pollutants** are emitted directly into the atmosphere, where they exert an adverse influence on human health or the environment. Of particular concern are primary pollutants emitted in large quantities: carbon dioxide, carbon monoxide, sulfur dioxide, **nitrogen dioxide**s, hydrocarbons, and particulate matter (PM). Once in the atmosphere, primary pollutants may react with other primary pollutants or atmospheric compounds such as water vapor to form **secondary pollutants**. A secondary pollutant with a lot of press and attention is **acid precipitation**, formed when sulfur or nitrogen oxides react with water vapor in the atmosphere.

WRI & IIED (1988–1989) report that NO_x rose in several countries, then leveled off or declined during the 1970s. During this same time frame (see Figure 11.1), levels of nitrogen oxide did not drop as dramatically as those of sulfur dioxide, primarily because a large part of total NO_x emissions comes from millions of motor vehicles, while most sulfur dioxide is released by a relatively small number of emission-controlled, coal-burning power plants.

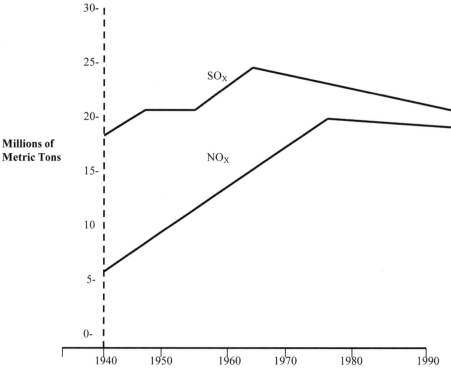

Figure 11.1. Annual emissions of SO2 and NOx in the United States, 1940–1987. EPA. National Air Pollutant Emissions Estimate, 1989.

CARBON MONOXIDE (CO)

Carbon monoxide is a colorless, odorless, tasteless gas and by far the most abundant of the primary pollutants. The principal source of carbon monoxide from human activities is motor vehicle exhaust, which contributes up to about 70 percent of all CO emissions in the United States (see Figure 11.2).

Volatile Organic Compounds (VOCs—Hydrocarbons)

Volatile organic compounds (VOCs) (also listed under the general heading of hydrocarbons) encompass a wide variety of chemicals that contain exclusively hydrogen and carbon. Emissions of volatile hydrocarbons from human resources are primarily the result of incomplete combustion of fossil fuels. Fires and the decomposition of matter are the natural sources. Of the VOCs that occur naturally in the atmosphere, **methane** (CH_4) is present at highest concentrations (approximately 1.5 ppm). But even at relatively high concentrations, methane does not interact chemically with other substances and causes no ill health effects. However, in the lower atmosphere, sunlight causes

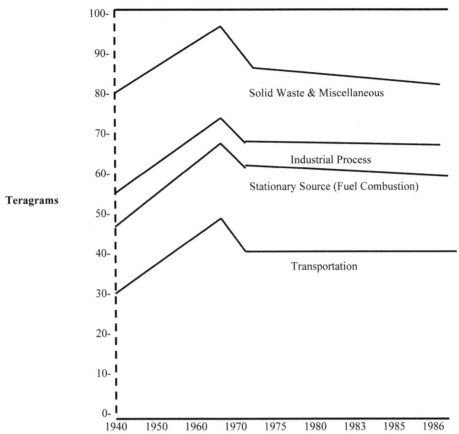

Figure 11.2.   Trends in carbon monoxide emissions, 1940–1986. Adapted from EPA, National Air Pollution Emission Estimates 1940–1986, 1988.

VOCs to combine with other gases (e.g., NO_2, oxygen, and CO) to form secondary pollutants such as formaldehyde, ketones, ozone, peroxyacetyl nitrate (PAN), and other types of photochemical oxidants. These active chemicals can irritate the eyes and damage the respiratory system, as well as damage vegetation.

Ozone and Photochemical Smog

By far the most damaging photochemical air pollutant is **ozone** (each ozone molecule contains three atoms of oxygen and thus is written O_3). Other photochemical oxidants (peroxyacetyl nitrate [PAN], hydrogen peroxide [H_2O_2], and aldehydes) play minor roles. All of these are secondary pollutants because they are not emitted, but are formed in the atmosphere by photochemical reactions involving sunlight and emitted gases, especially NO_x and hydrocarbons.

Ozone is a bluish gas, about 1.6 times heavier than air, and relatively reactive as an oxidant. It is present in a relatively large concentration in the stratosphere and is formed naturally by ultraviolet radiation. At ground level, ozone is a serious air pollutant; it has caused serious air pollution problems throughout the industrialized world, posing threats to human health and damaging foliage and building materials.

How serious is the problem with ozone pollution? Very. According to MacKenzie and El-Ashry (1988), ozone concentrations in industrialized countries of North America and Europe were up to three times higher than the level at which damage to crops and vegetation begins. Ozone harms vegetation by damaging plant tissues; inhibiting photosynthesis; and increasing susceptibility to disease, drought, and other air pollutants.

In the upper atmosphere, good (vital) ozone is produced. However, at the same time, anthropogenic emission of ozone-depleting chemicals has increased on the ground. With this increase, concern has been raised over a potential upset of the dynamic equilibria among stratospheric ozone reactions, with a consequent reduction in ozone concentration, a serious situation because stratospheric ozone absorbs much of the incoming solar ultraviolet (UV) radiation. As a UV shield, ozone helps to protect organisms on the Earth's surface from some of the harmful effects of this high-energy radiation. If not interrupted, UV radiation could cause serious damage, such as disruption of genetic material, which could lead to increased rates of skin cancers and inheritable problems.

In the mid-1980s, a serious problem with ozone depletion became apparent. A springtime decrease in the concentration of stratospheric ozone (**ozone holes**) has been observed at high latitudes, most notably over Antarctica between September and November. Scientists strongly suspect that chlorine atoms or simple chlorine compounds may play a key role in this ozone depletion problem (see Chapter 13).

On rare occasions, upper stratospheric ozone (good ozone) enters the lower atmosphere (troposphere). Generally, this phenomenon only occurs during an event of great turbulence in the upper atmosphere. On these rare incursions, atmospheric ozone reaches ground level for a short period of time. Most of the tropospheric ozone is formed and consumed by endogenous **photochemical reactions** (first described in the 1950s), the result of the interaction of hydrocarbons, oxides of nitrogen, and sunlight, which produces Los Angeles–type **smog**.

Did You Know?

[A]s he handed me into a fly after superintending the removal of my boxes, I asked him whether there was great fire anywhere? For the streets were so full of dense brown smoke that scarcely anything was to be seen. "Oh, dear no, miss," he said. "This is a London particular." I had never heard of such a thing. "A fog, miss," said the young gentleman.

—Charles Dickens, *Bleak House* (1853)

The word "smog" is a portmanteau of smoke and fog. Modern smog is a type of air pollution derived from vehicular emissions from internal combustion engines and industrial fumes that react in the atmosphere with sunlight to form secondary pollutants that also combine with the primary emissions to form **photochemical smog**. Smog is also caused by large amounts of coal burning in an area caused by a mixture of smoke, sulfur dioxide, and other components.

What is the best way to describe Los Angeles–type smog? We like a quote by Michael J. Cohen (1999, Pacific Institute, Oakland, California): "I thought I saw a blue jay this morning. But the smog was so bad that it turned out to be a cardinal holding its breath."

Although the incursion of stratospheric ozone into the troposphere can cause smog formation, the actual formation of Los Angeles–type smog involves a complex group of photochemical interactions. These interactions are between anthropogenically emitted pollutants (NO and hydrocarbons) and secondarily produced chemicals (PAN, aldehydes, NO_2, and ozone). The concentrations of these chemicals exhibit a pronounced diurnal pattern, depending on their rate of emission and on the intensity of solar radiation and atmospheric stability at different times of the day (Freedman, 1989). The most important pollutant gases that contribute to LA-type smog, and their diurnal pattern, are illustrated in Figure 11.3.

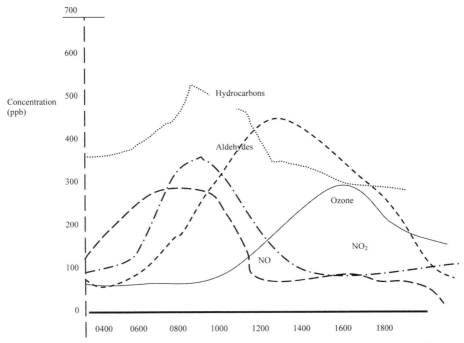

Figure 11.3. Shows average concentration of various air pollutants in the atmosphere of Los Angeles during days of eye irritation. Adaptation from Haagen-Smit, A. J., & Wayne, L. G. (1976), Atmospheric reactions and scavenging processes. Air Pollution, (A. C. Stern, ed.). 3rd ed., Vol. 1, pp. 235–288. New York: Academic Press

If we look at Figure 11.3 and follow the timeline for the presence of various air pollutants in the atmosphere of Los Angeles, we see that NO (emitted as NO_x) has a morning peak of concentration at 0600–0700, largely because of emissions from morning rush-hour vehicles. Hydrocarbons are emitted from both vehicles and refineries. They display a pattern similar to that of NO, except that their peak concentration is slightly later. In bright sunlight the NO is photochemically oxidized to NO_2, resulting in a decrease in NO concentration and a peak of NO_2 at 0700–0900. Photochemical reactions involving NO_2 produce O atoms, which react with O_2 to form O_3. These result is a net decrease in NO_2 concentration and an increase in O_3 concentration, peaking between 1200 and 1500. Aldehydes (also formed photochemically) peak earlier than O_3. As the day proceeds, the various gases decrease in concentration as they are diluted by fresh air masses or are consumed by photochemical reactions. This cycle is typical of an area that experiences photochemical smog and is repeated daily (Urone, 1976).

A tropospheric ozone budget for the Northern Hemisphere in shown in Table 11.3. The considerable range of the estimates reflects uncertainty in the calculation of the ozone fluxes. On average, stratospheric incursions account for about 18% of the total ozone influx to the troposphere, while endogenous photochemical production accounts for the remaining 82%. About 31% of the tropospheric ozone is consumed by oxidative reactions at vegetative and inorganic suffocates at ground level, while the other 69% is consumed by photochemical reactions in the atmosphere (Freedman, 1989).

Table 11.3. Tropospheric Ozone Budget (Northern Hemisphere) (kg/ha-year)

Transport from stratosphere	13–20
Photochemical production	48–78
Destruction at ground	18–35
Photochemical destruction	48–55

Source: Adapted from Hov, 1984.

Carbon Dioxide

Carbon-laden fuels, when burned, release carbon dioxide (CO_2) into the atmosphere. Although much of this carbon dioxide is dissipated and then absorbed by ocean water, some is taken up by vegetation through photosynthesis, and some remains in the atmosphere. Today, the concentration of carbon dioxide in the atmosphere is approximately 350 parts per million (ppm) and is rising at a rate of approximately 20 ppm every decade. The increasing rate of combustion of coal and oil has been primarily responsible for this occurrence, which may eventually have an impact on global climate (see Chapter 13).

Particulate Matter

Atmospheric particulate matter is defined as any dispersed matter, solid or liquid, in which the individual aggregates are larger than single small molecules, but smaller than about 500 μm. Particulate matter is extremely diverse and complex, because size and chemical composition, as well as atmospheric concentrations, are important characteristics (Masters, 1991).

A number of terms are used to categorize particulates, depending on their size and phase (liquid or solid). These terms are described in Table 11.4.

Response Scenario 11.1.
Snowmobiling in Yellowstone National Park

Near the end of the Clinton administration, a three-year phaseout of snowmobiling in the park was put into place. Because extensive research shows that any level of snowmobiling undermines the park's primary mission of conserving wildlife and natural habitat, environmental groups began litigation that forced the National Park Service to stop ignoring essential conservation laws.

Upon taking office, President George W. Bush suspended the ban; the Interior Department's new leaders argued that new engines and new management approaches could preserve some access without damage to the park environment.

The Bush plan, announced in October 2003, however, potentially allowed even more snowmobile access. The proposed plan relied on management and improved engine regulations for control, rather than evaluating how much air and noise pollution the park's natural resources could reasonably handle and setting limits based on the resources.

In December 2003, Judge Emmet Sullivan's federal court decision threw out the Interior Department's plan. Judge Sullivan's move was strongly supported by REP America, the national grassroots organization of Republicans for environmental protection.

"Nothing else has a higher priority—not insistent demands to expand motorized recreation to the farthest reaches of America's unsullied wild lands, not the never-ending pressures to commercialize special public places, and not political calculations," said Jim DiPeso, REP America policy director. "The law, public sentiment, and our obligation to be good stewards of America's heritage are clear—the incomparable natural wonders of national parks must be maintained, unimpaired for future generations."

Shortly after Judge Sullivan's ruling, though, and roughly a month before the season ended, a federal judge in Wyoming, in a parallel case, found that reinstating the Clinton rules would irrevocably harm Yellowstone's gateway communities, and ordered the Park Service to devise yet another policy. The Park Service made minor changes to the Bush plan and immediately reissued it.

Snowmobiling in Yellowstone National Park is still in limbo; the battle is not yet resolved.

RESPONSE

(i) Should snowmobiling be prohibited in Yellowstone National Park?

REFERENCE

"Yellowstone Decision a Breath of Fresh Air," December 18, 2003, http://www.repamerica .org/opinions/pressreleases/release12-18-03.html.

"Yellowstone/Snowmobiling Can't Continue," *Minneapolis Star-Tribune*, March 7, 2004, http://news.greateryellowstone.org/article.php?article_id=33.

Table 11.4. Atmospheric Particulates

Term	Description
Aerosol	General term for particles suspended in air
Mist	Aerosol consisting of liquid droplets
Dust	Aerosol consisting of solid particles that are blown into the air or are produced from larger particles by grinding them down
Smoke	Aerosol consisting of solid particles or a mixture of solid and liquid particles produced by chemical reactions such as fires
Fume	Generally means the same as smoke, but often applies specifically to aerosols produced by condensation of hot vapors, especially of metals
Plume	The geometrical shape or form of the smoke coming out of a stack or chimney
Fog	Aerosol consisting of water droplets
Haze	Any aerosol, other than fog, that obscures the view through the atmosphere
Smog	Popular term originating in England to describe a mixture of smoke and fog; implies photochemical pollution

Dust, spray, forest fires, and the burning of certain types of fuels are among the sources of particulates in the atmosphere. Even with the implementation of stringent emission controls that have worked to reduce particulates in the atmosphere, the U.S. Office of Technology Assessment (Postel, 1987) estimates that current levels of particulates and sulfates in ambient air may cause the premature death of 50,000 Americans every year.

Lead

Lead is emitted to the atmosphere primarily from human sources (e.g., burning leaded gasoline) in the form of inorganic particulates. In high concentrations, lead can damage human health and the environment. Once lead enters an ecosystem, it remains there permanently. In humans and animals, lead can affect the neurological system and cause kidney disease. In plants, lead can inhibit respiration and photosynthesis, as well as block the decomposition of microorganisms. Since the 1970s, stricter emission standards have caused a dramatic reduction in lead output.

Chapter Summary

Those who live in highly developed, heavily populated, wealthy, industrialized countries have to pay in many ways for their luxuries and high standard of living. On a personal level, two-income family groups allow people to buy what they want while suffering from the effects of stress and overwork. On a national scale, economically, we encourage more and more growth, while wringing our hands and weeping as industry alters our essential resources in harmful ways. Industry grows and advances, and environmental science improves and advances, cleaning up industry's messes and

Response Scenario 11.2.
Take a Deep Breath . . . and Hold It

REP America, the national grassroots organization of Republicans for Environmental Protection, has strong opinions about the August 2003 rule change adopted by the EPA that loosened pollution control requirements for old power plants and industrial facilities. This new rule takes advantage of a loophole to handle issues of "routine maintenance" for about 17,000 "grandfathered" industrial facilities.

"The rule change allows old, dirty plants to continue using people's lungs as free garbage cans. In addition, the change biases the market by giving preferential treatment to old, dirty plants, which puts cleaner facilities at a competitive disadvantage. The administration should level the playing field, enforce the law, and stop coddling irresponsible companies whose pollution causes sickness, death, and environmental damage," said REP America policy director Jim DiPeso.

Under the Clean Air Act's "New Source Review" provisions, any of roughly 17,000 power plants and other industrial facilities must install modern pollution controls only if plant modifications result in increased pollution. If changes cost less than 20 percent of the value of an essential production unit, they fall under the "routine maintenance" clause and do not have to meet more stringent Clean Air Act provisions, even if the changes result in pollution increases.

"Thanks to this Orwellian definition of routine maintenance, plants can extend their lives indefinitely and increase harmful emissions without installing modern pollution control equipment. Old, outdated facilities won't have to clean up after themselves, they won't have to comply with standards that newer facilities must obey, and they can shift their pollution costs onto innocent bystanders, including children, senior citizens, and people who suffer from respiratory diseases," DiPeso said.

REP America supports full enforcement of the Clean Air Act and legislation that requires all grandfathered facilities to comply with current pollution control requirements by a definite deadline.

"New legislation that requires cleanup of old facilities by a date-certain, and which sets tough caps for sulfur dioxide, nitrogen oxides, mercury, and carbon dioxide emissions from power plants would result in cleaner air, reduced greenhouse gas emissions, more cost-effective cleanup, and greater regulatory certainty. In the meantime, the existing Clean Air Act must be enforced rigorously," DiPeso said (http://www.repamerica.org/opinions/pressreleases/release8-27-03.html).

RESPONSE

(i) Should existing clean air regulations be grandfathered whenever they are changed in the future to require new compliance guidelines?

constantly and consistently issuing warnings about what will happen to our Earth if we don't think about what we are doing before we start. Some of the problems facing us in the future will be at the critical stage before our children reach adulthood. Atmospheric pollutants are the cause of several of those problems. And we will all have to pay for solving them.

Discussion Questions and Problems

1. When can peak levels of CO and hydrocarbons be expected in an urban area?
2. Describe the differences among smoke, fume, dust, and plume.
3. What is PAN? How is it produced?
4. Why is NO_2 such an important atmospheric pollutant?
5. Why are air pollution levels so high in Los Angeles?
6. Distinguish between primary and secondary air pollution and provide examples of each.
7. What is photochemical smog? What causes it?
8. List five pollutants commonly released into the atmosphere and their sources.
9. What factors are contributing to the destruction of the stratospheric ozone layer? What effects could this destruction have?
10. What do you think is the most pressing concern with respect to air pollution? Explain.

Suggested Research Topics and Projects

- Examine current findings on changes in deep ocean circulation, greenhouse gas emissions, atmospheric temperature increases, sea level rise, and ocean movement stability.
- Examine the Industrial Revolution in the light of environmental damage.
- Look at the EPA's Clean Air Act NAAQS primary and secondary standards and what they mean environmentally.
- Examine SO_2's role in the formation of **sulfuric smog** and acid deposition.
- Examine the role of auto emissions in NO_x formation.
- What has the media response to some sources of CH_x been?
- Examine how VOCs react with sunlight.
- Research current findings on ozone and chlorine's relationship.
- Look at LA's peak pollution patterns in the light of society's work patterns and chemical reaction time frames.
- Examine the concept of tropospheric ozone budget.
- Look at carbon dioxide increases from combustion of coal and oil.
- How do particulates cause health problems? Who is affected, with what, when, and how?
- Research the auto industry's use of lead as a fuel additive.

References and Recommended Reading

Bridgman, H. A. (1994). *Global Air Pollution*. New York: John Wiley & Sons.

Brownell, F. W., & Zeugin, L. B. (1991). *Clean Air Handbook*. Rockville, MD: Government Institutes.

Colls, J. (1997). *Air Pollution*. London: Chapman & Hall.

Cooper, C. D., & Alley, F. C. *Air Pollution Control: A Design Approach*. Boston: PWS, 1986.

Dutsch, H. V. (1981). "Ozone Research—Past-Present-Future." *Bulletin of the American Meteorological Society* 62: 213–17.

Elsom, D. M. (1992). *Atmospheric Pollution—A Global Problem*. 2nd ed. Oxford, England: Blackwell Publishers.

Flagan, R. C., & Seinfeld, J. H. (1988). *Fundamentals of Air Pollution Engineering*. Englewood Cliffs, NJ: Prentice Hall.

Freedman, B. (1989). *Environmental Ecology*. New York: Academic Press.

Haagen-Smit, A. J., & Wayne, L. G. (1976). "Atmospheric Reactions and Scavenging Processes." In Stern, A. C., ed., *Air Pollution*, Vol. 1, 3rd ed. New York: Academic Press.

Hov, O. (1984). "Ozone in the Troposphere: High Level Pollution." *Ambio* 13: 73–79.

MacKenzie, J. J., & El-Ashry, T. (1998). *Ill Winds: Airborne Pollutant's Toll on Trees and Crops*. Washington, DC: World Resource Institute.

Manabe, B., & Stouffer, R. (1993). "Century-Scale Effects of Increased Atmospheric CO_2 on the Ocean-Atmosphere System." *Nature* 364, no. 6434: 215–18.

Postel, S. (1984). *Air Pollution, Acid Rain, and the Future of the Forests*. Washington, DC: Worldwatch Institute.

Postel, S. (1987). "Stabilizing Chemical Cycles." In Brown, Lester R., ed., *State of the World*. New York: Norton.

Urone, P. (1976). "The Primary Air Pollutants—Gaseous: Their Occurrence, Sources, and Effects." In Stern, A. C., ed., *Air Pollution*, Vol. 1. New York: Academic Press.

U.S. EPA (1988a). *Environmental Progress & Challenges*. Washington, DC: Environmental Protection Agency.

U.S. EPA (1988b). *National Air Pollution Emission Estimates 1940–1986*. Washington, DC: Environmental Protection Agency.

U.S. EPA (1989). *National Air Pollution Emission Estimates*. Washington, DC: Environmental Protection Agency.

U.S. EPA (1990). *The CAA Amendments of 1990*. Washington, DC: Environmental Protection Agency.

CHAPTER 12

Atmospheric Air Dispersion

The air motions in the atmosphere transport pollutants that are released in the atmosphere. The smaller time and space scales of motion serve to disperse pollutants in the air by mixing these pollutants with air having lower pollution levels and thus lowering the air pollutant concentrations with time after release from a particular source.

—D. B. Turner, 1994

Chapter Objectives

After studying this chapter, you should be able to:

- Describe and discuss how weather affects pollution levels mechanically and chemically.
- Define, describe, and discuss how turbulence and air movement's stability class affect the state of the atmosphere.
- Define, describe, and discuss adiabatic lapse rate and how it affects stability.
- Describe why air mixing is important and discuss how it works.
- Describe how three topographical features affect wind movement and discuss how that affects transport.
- Define the two types of temperature inversions and explain their effects on the concentration of pollution at ground level.
- Identify the seven types of plume rise behaviors, describe their formation, and discuss how plume rise affects air pollution dispersal on single stack and city scale.
- Define and discuss the effects transport has on air pollution.
- Define dispersion modeling and describe its purpose.

Chapter Outline

- Definition and discussion: air pollutants, sources, dispersal, and processes
- Discussion: how weather conditions and patterns affect pollutants in the atmosphere, dispersal patterns, and local conditions
- Discussion and definition: how differing levels of turbulence affect local conditions and pollution levels
- Discussion and definition: how altitude affects air temperature and air movement
- Discussion: how vertical air movement affects dispersal
- Discussion: how topography affects local weather conditions and air movement
- Definition and discussion: radiant and subsidence inversions, how they function, and their effects on local conditions
- Definition and discussion: plume behaviors under specific air movement patterns on single stack and city scale
- Discussion: how, through transport processes, specific single airborne pollutants can travel long distances
- Discussion: air dispersion modeling

Key Terms

adiabatic
adiabatic lapse rate
anticyclones
building downwash
dry adiabatic lapse rate
fumigation
lapse rate
neutrally stable atmosphere
normal lapse rate
plume
radiation inversions

slope wind
stability
stability class
stable atmosphere
subadiabatic
subsidence inversion
superadiabatic
temperature inversion
turbulence
unstable atmosphere
valley winds

Introduction

The *air pollutants* discussed in Chapter 11 are released from both stationary and mobile sources. Scientists have gathered much information on the sources, quantity, and toxicity levels of these pollutants. The measurement of air pollution is an important scientific skill, and practitioners are usually well-grounded in the pertinent related sciences and modeling aspects applicable to their studies and analyses of air pollutants in the ambient atmosphere. However, to get at the very heart of air pollution, the air pollution practitioner must also be well-versed in how to determine the origin of the pollutants, the dispersal process in the atmosphere, the impact on new sources, and the benefits of controls.

Air pollution practitioners must constantly deal with one fact: Air pollutants rarely remain still at their release locations. Instead, various atmospheric wind flow conditions and **turbulence**, local topographic features, and other physical conditions work to disperse these pollutants. So, along with having a thorough knowledge and understanding of the pollutants in question, the practitioner has a definite need for detailed knowledge of the atmospheric processes that govern their subsequent dispersal and fate. To this point we have discussed wind and its formation (Chapter 10), elements essential to air pollutant dispersion. In this chapter, we discuss atmospheric dispersion of air pollutants in greater detail and the factors associated with this phenomenon, including dispersion modeling.

The Atmosphere and Meteorology

In Chapter 10, we discussed the basics of meteorology, setting the stage for providing a comprehensive presentation of air pollution. In this section, we expand and build on that information to emphasize the natural associations among our atmosphere, air pollution, and meteorology.

WEATHER

As stated previously, the air in Earth's atmosphere is not still. Constantly in motion, air masses warmed by solar radiation rise at the equator and spread toward the colder poles, where they sink, and flow downward, eventually returning to the equator. Near the Earth's surface, as a result of its rotation, major wind patterns develop. During the day, the land warms more quickly than the sea; at night, the land cools more quickly. Local wind patterns are driven by this differential warming and cooling between the land and adjacent water bodies. Normally, onshore breezes bring cooler, denser air from over the landmasses out over the waters during the night. Precipitation is also affected by wind patterns. Warm, moisture-laden air rising from the oceans is carried inland, where the air masses eventually cool, causing the moisture to fall as rain, hail, sleet, or snow.

Even though pollutant emissions may remain relatively constant, air quality varies tremendously from day to day. The determining factors have to do with weather.

Weather conditions have a significant impact on air quality and air pollution, both favorable and unfavorable, especially on local conditions. For example, on hot, sun-filled days when the weather is calm with stagnating high-pressure cells, air quality suffers, because these conditions allow the buildup of pollutants on the ground level. When local weather conditions include cool, windy, stormy weather with turbulent low pressure cells and cold fronts, these conditions allow the upward mixing and dispersal of air pollutants.

Weather has a direct impact on pollution levels, in both mechanical and chemical ways. Mechanically, precipitation works to cleanse the air of pollutants (transferring the pollutants to rivers, streams, lakes, or the soil). Winds transport pollutants from one place to another. Winds and storms often dilute pollutants with cleaner air, making pollution levels less annoying in the area of their release. Air and its accompanying pollution (in a low-pressure cell) are also carried aloft by air heated by the sun. When wind accompanies this rising air mass, the pollutants are diluted with fresh air. In a high-pressure cell, the opposite occurs, with air and the pollutants it carries sinking toward the ground. When no wind blows, these pollutants are trapped and concentrated near the ground, where serious air pollution episodes may occur.

Weather can also affect pollution levels chemically. Winds and turbulence mix pollutants together in a giant chemical broth in the atmosphere. Energy from the sun, moisture in the clouds, and the proximity of highly reactive chemicals may cause chemical reactions, which lead to the formation of secondary pollutants. Many of these may be more dangerous than the original ones.

Initially, dispersion of air pollutants from point or area sources depends on meteorological phenomena such as wind. Other factors (turbulence, **adiabatic lapse rate**, turbulent mixing, topography, **temperature inversions**, **plume** rise, and transport) also affect air contaminant dispersion.

Turbulence

The amount of **turbulence** in the ambient atmosphere has major effects on the dispersion of air pollution plumes, because it increases the entrainment and mixing of unpolluted air into the plume and thereby acts to reduce the concentration of pollutants there. In the atmosphere, the degree of turbulence (resulting from wind speed and convective conditions related to the change of temperature with height above the Earth's surface) is directly related to **stability** (a function of vertical distribution of atmospheric temperature). The stability of the atmosphere refers to the susceptibility of rising air parcels to vertical motion; consideration of atmospheric stability or instability is essential in establishing the dispersion rate of pollutants. When specifically discussing the stability of the atmosphere, we refer to the lower boundary of the Earth where air pollutants are emitted. **Stability class** usually indicates the degree of turbulence in the atmosphere. Ambient and adiabatic lapse rates are a measure of atmospheric stability.

In 1961, Frank Pasquill developed a method of classifying atmospheric stability using six classes: very unstable, unstable, slightly unstable, neutral, slightly stable, and stable. In this text we are concerned—for explanatory purposes, and because these classifications are not generally used in advanced models—with just three principal classes. (1) A **stable atmosphere** is marked by air cooler at the ground than aloft, low wind speeds, and consequently, a low degree of turbulence. A plume of pollutants released into a stable lower layer of the atmosphere can remain relatively intact for long distances. Thus, we can say that stable air discourages the dispersion and dilution of pollutants. (2) An **unstable atmosphere** is marked by a high degree of turbulence. A plume of pollutants released into an unstable atmosphere may exhibit a characteristic looping appearance produced by turbulent eddies. (3) A **neutrally stable atmosphere** is an intermediate class between stable and unstable conditions. A plume of pollutants released into a neutral stability condition is often characterized by a coning appearance as the edges of the plume spread out in a V-shape.

The "state of the atmosphere" and stability's effects are critical. Since the ease with which pollutants can disperse vertically into the atmosphere is mainly determined by the rate of change of air temperature with height (altitude), air stability is a primary factor in determining where pollutants travel and how long they remain aloft. Stable air discourages the dispersion and dilution of pollutants. Conversely, in unstable air conditions, rapid vertical mixing takes place, encouraging pollutant dispersal that increases air quality.

Did You Know?

Many of the more advanced models used today do not categorize atmosphere turbulence using the simple meteorological parameters found in the six Pasquill classes. Instead, surface roughness length and the Monin-Obukhov length are used.

Adiabatic Lapse Rate

With an increase in altitude in the troposphere, the temperature of the ambient air usually decreases. The rate of temperature change with height is called the **lapse rate**. On average, temperature decreases –0.65°C/100m or –6.5°C/km. This is known as the **normal lapse rate**.

In a dry environment, when a parcel of warm, dry air is lifted in the atmosphere, it undergoes adiabatic expansion and cooling. This adiabatic cooling results in a lapse rate of –1°C/100m or 1-10°C/km, the **dry adiabatic lapse rate**. The term "adiabatic" means that no heat exchange occurs between the rising parcel of air under consideration and the surrounding air; that is, the dry adiabatic lapse rate is a function only of elevation.

When the ambient lapse rate exceeds the adiabatic lapse rate, the ambient rate is **superadiabatic**, and the atmosphere is highly unstable. When the two lapse rates are exactly equal, the atmosphere is neutral. When the ambient lapse rate is less than the dry adiabatic lapse rate, the ambient lapse rate is termed **subadiabatic,** and the atmosphere is stable (Peavy, Rowe, & Tchobanglous, 1985).

The cooling process within a rising parcel of air is assumed to be **adiabatic** (occurring without the addition or loss of heat). A rising parcel of air (under adiabatic conditions) behaves like a rising balloon, with the air in that distinct parcel expanding as it encounters air of lesser density until its own density is equal to that of the atmosphere that surrounds it. This process is assumed to occur with no heat exchange between the rising parcel and the ambient air.

Turbulent Mixing

For effective pollutant dispersal to occur within the atmosphere, turbulent mixing is important. Turbulent mixing, the result of the movement of air in the vertical dimension, is enhanced by vertical temperature differences. The steeper the temperature gradient and the larger the vertical air column in which the mixing takes place, the more vigorous the convective and turbulent mixing of the atmosphere.

Topography

Near point and area sources (on a local scale with a geographical area encompassing less than 100 miles), topography may affect air motion. In the United States, most large urban centers are located along sea and lake coastal areas. Contained within these large urban centers is much heavy industry. Local airflow patterns in these urban centers have a significant impact on pollution dispersion processes. Topographic features also affect local weather patterns, especially in large urban centers located near lakes, seas, and open land. Breezes from these topographical features affect vertical mixing and pollutant dispersal. Seasonal differences in heating and cooling of land and water surfaces may also precipitate the formation of inversions near the sea or lakeshore.

River valley areas also routinely suffer from industry-related pollution. Many early settlements began in river valleys because of the readily available water supply and the ease of transportation afforded to settlers by river systems. Along with settlers came industry—the type of industry that invariably produces air pollutants. Because of terrain and physical configuration of the valley, these air pollutants are not easily removed from the valley.

Winds that move through a typical river valley are called **slope winds**. Like water, these winds flow downhill to the valley floor. At valley floor level, slope winds transform into **valley winds**, which flow down-valley with the flow of the river. Down-valley winds are lighter than slope winds. The valley floor becomes flooded with a large volume of air that intensifies the surface inversion normally produced by radiative cooling. As the inversion deepens over the course of the night, it often reaches its maximum depth just before sunrise, with the height of the inversion layer dependent on the depth of the valley and the intensity of the radiative cooling process.

Hills and mountains can also affect local airflow. These natural topographical features tend to decrease wind speed (because of their surface roughness) and form physical barriers preventing the air movement.

Temperature Inversions

Temperature inversions (extreme cases of atmospheric stability) create a virtual lid on the upward movement of atmospheric pollution (see Chapter 10). Two types of inversions are important from an air quality standpoint: radiation and subsidence.

Radiation inversions prompt the formation of fog and simultaneously trap gases and particulates, creating a concentration of pollutants. They are characteristically a nocturnal phenomenon caused by cooling of the Earth's surface. On a cloudy night, the Earth's radiant heat tends to be absorbed by water vapor in the atmosphere. Some of this is re-radiated back to the surface. However, on clear winter nights, the surface more readily radiates energy to the atmosphere and beyond, allowing the ground to cool more rapidly. The air in contact with the cooler ground also cools, and the air just above the ground becomes cooler than the air above it, creating an inversion close to the ground that lasts for only a matter of hours. These radiation inversions usually begin to form at the worst time of the day for human activities in large urban areas: when early evening traffic begins to build up, trapping automobile exhaust at ground level and causing elevated concentrations of pollution for commuters. During evening hours, photochemical reactions cannot take place, so the biggest problem can be the accumulation of carbon monoxide. At sunrise, the sun warms the ground, and the inversion begins to break up. Pollutants that have been trapped in the stable air mass are suddenly brought back to Earth, in a process known as **fumigation**. Fumigation can cause a short-lived, high concentration of pollution at ground level (Masters, 1991).

Subsidence inversions are usually associated with a high-pressure system. Known as **anticyclones**, they may significantly affect the dispersion of pollutants over large regions. A subsidence inversion is caused by the characteristic sinking motion of air in a high-pressure cell. Air in the middle of a high-pressure zone descends slowly, becoming compressed and heated. It forms a blanket of warm air over the cooler air below, thus creating an inversion (located anywhere from several hundred meters to several thousand meters above the surface) that prevents further vertical movement of air.

Plume Rise

There are three primary types of air pollution emission plumes. *Buoyant plumes* are lighter than air, because they are at a higher temperature and lower density than the surrounding ambient air or at about the same temperature but have a lower molecular weight and hence lower density. Plumes that are heavier than air because they are denser than the surrounding ambient air are called *dense gas plumes*. Plumes that are neither lighter nor heavier than air are called *neutral* or *passive plumes*.

In regard to the efficacy of plume formation related to atmospheric air dispersion, one way to quickly determine the stability of the lower atmosphere is to view the shape of a smoke trail or plume from a tall stack located on flat terrain. Visible plumes usually consist of pollutants emitted from a smokestack into the atmosphere. The formation and fate of the plume itself depends on a number of related factors: (1) the nature of the pollutants; (2) meteorological factors; (3) source obstructions; and (4) local topography, especially downwind. Overall, maximum ground level concentrations occur in a range from the vicinity of the smokestack to some distance downwind.

When the atmosphere is slightly stable, a typical plume "cones." When the atmosphere is highly unstable, a "looping" plume forms. In the looping plume, the stream of emitted pollutants undergoes rapid mixing, and the wind causes large eddies that may carry the entire plume down to the ground, causing high concentrations close to the stack before dispersion is complete. In an extremely stable atmosphere, a "fanning" plume spreads horizontally, with little mixing. When an inversion layer occurs a short distance above the plume source, the plume is said to be "fumigating." When inversion conditions exist below the plume source, the plume is said to be "lofting." When conditions are neutral, the plume issuing from a smokestack tends to rise directly into the atmosphere. When an inversion layer prevails both above and below the plume source, the plume issuing from a smokestack tends to be "trapped."

The types of air pollutant emission sources are commonly characterized as point, line, area, or volume sources. A *point source* is a single, identifiable source of emissions (gas stack). *Line sources* are one-dimensional sources of emissions (vehicular traffic). An *area source* is a two-dimensional source of diffuse emissions (forest fires, large soil of volatile liquid, etc.). A *volume source* is a three-dimensional source of diffuse emissions (e.g., fugitive gas emissions from piping flanges, valves and other equipment).

Pollutant dispersion rarely comes from a single point source (smokestack plume). In large urban areas, many plumes are generated and collectively combine into a large plume (city plume), whose dispersion presents a huge environmental challenge: The high pollutant concentrations from the city plume frequently affect human health and welfare.

Air quality problems associated with dispersion of city plumes are compounded by an already contaminated environment. Even though conventional processes that normally work to disperse emissions from point sources occur within the city plume, because of micro-climates within the city and the volume of pollutants they must handle, they are usually less effective. Other compounding conditions present in areas where city plumes are generated (topographical barriers, surface inversions, and stagnating anticyclones) work to intensify the city plume and result in high pollutant concentrations.

Did You Know?

When an air pollution plume flows over nearby buildings or other structures, turbulent eddies are formed on the downwind side of the building. Those eddies cause a plume from a stack source located within about five times the height of a nearby building or structure to be forced down to the ground much sooner than it would be if a building or structure were not present. This phenomenon is referred to as **building downwash** effect (U.S. EPA, 1996).

Transport

Those people living east of the Mississippi River would be surprised to find out that they are breathing air contaminated by pollutants from various sources many miles away. Most people view pollution under the old cliché "out of sight, out of mind"; as far as they are concerned, if they don't see it, it doesn't exist. But weather and air transport patterns send midwestern pollutants far to the north and east: pollutants from the Ohio Valley affect Maine ecosystems.

Assume that a person on a farm in rural Arkansas heaps up a huge pile of assorted rubbish to be burned. The person preparing this huge bonfire probably gives little thought to the long-range transport (and consequences) of any contaminants that might be generated from that bonfire. This person simply has trash to get rid of, and burning seems like a low-cost, easy disposal solution.

This particular massive pile of rubbish contains various elements: discarded rubber tires, old compressed gas bottles, assorted plastic containers, paper, oils and greases, wood, and old paint cans. The person burning it doesn't consider this hazardous material—it's just household trash. When the pile of rubbish is ignited and allowed to burn, the fire-starter stands clear and watches as a huge plume of smoke forms and is carried away by a westerly flow of wind. He or she looks far off to the right, downwind, and notices that the smoke disappears (or is out of view) just a few miles over the property line. Obviously, for this person the dilution processes and the enormous size of the atmosphere dissipated the smoke plume. The fire-starter doesn't give it a second thought. However, elevated levels of pollutants from many such fires may occur hundreds to thousands of miles downwind of the combination point sources producing such plumes, with the result that people living many miles away end up breathing contaminated air, transported over a large distance to their location. Of course, the plumes produced by industrial and energy-generating sources are of far greater significance than the pollution from individuals.

DISPERSION MODELS

Air quality models are used to predict or describe the fate of airborne gases, particulate matter, and ground-level concentrations downwind of point sources. To determine the significance of air quality impact for a particular area, the first consideration is normal background concentrations, those pollutant concentrations from natural sources and/or distant, unidentified man-made sources. Each particular geographical area has a "signature" level of contamination, considered an annual mean background concentration level of certain pollutants—an area, for example, might normally have a particulate matter reading of 30–40 $\mu g/m^3$ over a particular area. If particulate matter readings are significantly higher than the background level, this suggests an additional source. To establish background contamination for a particular source under consideration, air quality data related to that site and its vicinity must be collected and analyzed.

The U.S. EPA recognized that in calculating the atmospheric dispersion of air pollutants, some means by which consistency could be maintained in air quality analysis had to be established. Therefore, the EPA promulgated two guidebooks to assist in modeling for air quality analysis: *Guidelines on Air Quality Models* (1978) and *Industrial Source Complex (ISC) Dispersion Models User's Guide* (1986).

When performing dispersion calculations, particularly for health effect studies, the EPA and other recognized experts in the field recommend following a four-step procedure:

1. Estimate the rate, duration, and location of the release into the environment.
2. Select the best available model to perform the calculations.
3. Perform the calculations and generate downstream concentrations, including lines of constant concentration (*isopleths*) resulting from the source emission(s).
4. Determine what effect, if any, the resulting discharge has on the environment, including humans, animals, vegetation, and materials of construction. These calculations often include estimates of the so-called vulnerability zones—that is, regions that may be adversely affected because of the emissions (Holmes, Singh, & Theodore, 1993).

Before beginning any dispersion determination activity, the practitioner must first determine the acceptable ground-level concentration of the waste pollutant(s). Local meteorological conduits and local topography must be considered, and an accurate knowledge of the constituents of the waste gas and its chemical and physical properties is paramount (U.S. EPA, 1986).

Air quality models are a relatively inexpensive means of determining compliance and predicting the degree of emission reduction necessary to attain ambient air quality standards. Under the 1977 Clean Air Act amendments, the use of models is required for the evaluation of permit applications associated with permissible increments under the so-called prevention of significant deterioration (PSD) requirements, which require localities "to protect and enhance" uncontaminated air (Godish, 1997).

Several dispersion models have been developed. Really equations, these models are mathematical descriptions of the meteorological transport and dispersion of air contaminants in a particular area, which permit estimates of contaminant concentrations, in plume from either a ground-level or an elevated source (Carson & Moses, 1969). User-friendly modeling programs are now available that produce quick, accurate results from the operator's pertinent data.

There are five types of air pollution dispersion models, as well as some hybrids of the five types:

- The **box model** is the simplest of the model types. It assumes the airshed is in the shape of a box, containing air pollutants that are homogeneously distributed. Because of this assumption (which is too simple), this model is limited in its ability to accurately predict dispersion of air pollutants (Atkins, 2011).
- The **Gaussian model** is the oldest (1936) and most commonly used air pollution dispersion model. It assumes that the air pollutant dispersion has a normal probability Gaussian distribution. Gaussian models are most often used on continuous buoyant air pollution plumes originating from ground-level or elevated sources (Bosanquet and Pearson, 1936; Beychok, 2005, 124).
- The **Lagrangian model** mathematically follows pollution plume parcels (aka particles) as they move in the atmosphere; they model the motion of the parcels as a random walk process using a moving frame of reference (JRC, 2011).
- The **Eulerian model** is similar to the Lagrangian model in that it also tracks the movement of a large number of pollution plume parcels as they move away from their initial location. The most important difference between the two models is that the Eulerian model uses a fixed, three-dimensional Cartesian grid as a frame of reference rather than a moving frame of reference (JRC, 2011).
- The **dense gas model** simulates the dispersion of dense gas (plumes heavier than air) pollution plumes. The three most commonly used dense gas models are the
  ○ *DEGADIS model,* developed by Havens and Spicer at the University of Arkansas under commission by the U.S. Coast Guard and EPA (U.S. EPA, 2010);
  ○ *SLAB model,* developed by the Lawrence Livermore National Laboratory and funded by the U.S. Department of Energy, the U.S. Air Force, and the American Petroleum Institute (U.S. EPA, 2010); and
  ○ *HEGADAS model,* developed by Shell Oil (Britter, 1991).

This chapter's intent is not to develop each dispersion model in detail, but rather to recommend those with the greatest present-day applicability. Probably the best atmospheric dispersion workbook for modeling published to date is Turner's (1970), developed for the EPA, and most of the air dispersion models used today are based on the **Pasquill-Gifford Model**.

Chapter Summary

Breathing is automatic—so automatic we cannot stop it voluntarily for a time long enough to hurt us. Because breathing is one of our most unconscious actions, most people don't pay attention to the air unless they sense something wrong with how it smells or feels. But as testing devices for pollutants, our noses are not very sensitive. Environmentally, wishful thinking lets us believe that our air is okay and will remain so, that our atmosphere is self-cleaning and capable of absorbing the abuse we heap on it. We ignore the truth—that often the air we breathe contains elements we would be surprised and alarmed to find out we had inhaled. Those pollutants, carried by a variety of routes and methods, enter our environments, lives, and bodies. They affect our world, our lives, and our health.

Fortunately, to some extent air pollution episodes can now be predicted on the basis of meteorological data. The EPA and many local air pollution control agencies have implemented early warning systems and are acting to curtail emissions.

Discussion Questions and Problems

1. Name and define two types of thermal inversions.
2. What meteorological factors affect the dispersion of pollutants from a city source?
3. Explain why lake and land breezes occur.
4. Explain why valleys are more susceptible to inversions than is flat terrain.
5. What is the level of stability of the atmosphere when looping, coning, and fanning occur?
6. What atmospheric conditions produce fumigation?

Suggested Research Topics and Projects

- Explore the reasons air movement creates advantages and disadvantages in the treatment of air pollutants.
- Examine the natural association among the atmosphere, air pollution, and meteorology.
- Examine how weather affects pollution mechanically.
- Examine how weather affects pollution chemically.
- Examine specific locations in your state for geographical/geological features that affect air movement.
- Research dispersion models, how they work, and what they are meant to accomplish.

References and Recommended Reading

Atkins, N. (2011). "Air Pollution Dispersion: Ventilation Factor." Accessed May 30, 2011, http://apollo.lsc.vsc.edu/classes/met130/notes/capater18/dispersion_intro.html.

Britter, R. E. (1991). *Assessment of HEGADAS Model Technical Report BP Engineering*. Boston: University of Cambridge.

Beychok, M. R. (2005). *Fundamentals of Stack Gas Dispersion*. 4th ed. n.p.: Author.

Bosanquet, C. H., & Person, J. L. (1936). "The Spread of Smoke and Gases from Chimney." *Transactions of the Friday Society* 32: 1249.

Brown, M. H. (1987). *The Toxic Cloud*. New York: Harper & Row.

Carson, J. E., & Moses, H. (1969). "The Validity of Several Plume Rise Formulas." *Journal of the Air Pollution Control Association* 19, no. 11: 862.

Godish, T. (1997). *Air Quality*. 3rd ed. Boca Raton, FL: Lewis Publishers.

Holmes, G., Singh, B. R., & Theodore, L. (1993). *Handbook of Environmental Management & Technology*. New York: John Wiley & Sons.

JRC (2011). "Features of Dispersion Models." European Union Joint Research Center (JRC). Accessed May 30, 2011. http://rem.jrc.cec.ue.int/etex/37.htm.

Masters, G. M. (1991). *Introduction to Environmental Engineering and Science*. Englewood Cliffs, NJ: Prentice-Hall.

Peavy, H. S., Rowe, D. R., & Tchobanglous, G. (1985). *Environmental Engineering*. New York: McGraw-Hill.

Turner, D. B. (1970). *Workbook of Atmospheric Dispersion Estimates*. Washington, DC: Environmental Protection Agency.

Turner, D. B. (1994). *Workbook of Atmospheric Dispersion Estimation: Second Edition*. Boca Raton, FL: CRC Press.

U.S. EPA (1978). *Guidelines on Air Quality Models*. Washington, DC: Environmental Protection Agency.

U.S. EPA (1986). *Industrial Source Complex (ISC) Dispersion Models User's Guide*. Washington, DC: Environmental Protection Agency.

U.S. EPA (1996). *Development and Evaluation of the Prime Plume Rise and building Downwash Model*. Accessed May 29, 2011, www.epa.gov/scram001/7thconf/iscprime/tepapri.pdf.

U.S. EPA (2010). *DEGADIS Technical Manual and User's Guide*. Accessed May 30, 2011, http://www.epa.gov/scram001/dispersion_alt.htm.

U.S. EPA (2011). "Alternative Models." Accessed May 29, 2011, http://www.epa.gov/scram00l/dispersion.

CHAPTER 13

Atmospheric Change

> Some of the scientists, I believe, haven't they been changing their opinion a little bit on global warming? There's a lot of differing opinions and before we react I think it's best to have a full accounting, full understanding of what's taking place.
>
> —George W. Bush, Presidential Debate, October 11, 2000

Chapter Objectives

After studying this chapter, you should be able to:

- Identify some of the practices that alter our atmosphere and describe the effects of each on our air.
- Define and describe global warming and identify the problems inherent in proving that global warming is or is not occurring.
- Describe and discuss the relationship between global warming and changes in the greenhouse effect. Identify and define the major contributors.
- Discuss the counterarguments used to refute the possibility of global warming.
- Describe and discuss the six factors scientists have identified as possibly involved in long-term global warming.
- Describe and discuss the tests scientists are using to determine greenhouse signature or footprint and how these tests could indicate long-term global warming.
- Discuss the probability of sea-level rise related to global warming and identify the important factors involved.
- Discuss how sea level rise will affect human populations.
- Discuss precipitation pH levels and the processes that produce acid precipitation. Define the causes at work in producing decreased pH levels in precipitation.
- Describe how some soils act as a buffer to acid precipitation and the effects acidic precipitation has on lakes.

- Discuss stratospheric ozone depletion, identify the compounds that contribute to it, and describe the effects continuing depletion will have.

Chapter Outline

- Definition and discussion: the human activities that alter Earth's environment in dangerous ways
- Definition and discussion: the nature and causes of global warming
- Definition and discussion: changes in the greenhouse effect
- Definition and discussion: how global warming and the greenhouse effect are related and current counterarguments
- Definition and discussion: the factors at work in the changes in Earth's average surface temperature
- Definition and discussion: global signs of advancing long-term surface temperature change
- Definition and discussion: probable consequences of global warming—sea-level rise
- Definition and discussion: how sea-level rise would affect coastal areas: the Bruun Rule
- Discussion: how rising sea level would affect human populations
- Definition and discussion: the causes and effects of acid precipitation
- Definition and discussion: how human activities are affecting stratospheric ozone and what steps for change are in progress

Key Terms

acid rain
buffer
chlorofluorocarbons (CFCs)
global warming
greenhouse effect
greenhouse gases
heat islands

heavy metals
infrared radiation
Montreal Protocol
ozone
regulation and control technology
sea level rise

Introduction

How serious is environmental air pollution? Simply answered: You can literally bet your life on its seriousness. And that is exactly what we are doing—betting our lives, all of us. Remember, environmental pollution transcends national boundaries and threatens the global ecosystem.

Should we panic? Should we join some fanatical, radical "green" organization and shove our environmental concerns down people's throats? Not exactly. Should we be concerned about environmental problems? Yes.

Just how serious is the problem?

Very serious. Humans are altering the environment in dramatic ways, especially over the past 200 years. In this chapter, we focus on human activities that profoundly affect the environment. These activities are not secret or mysterious; they are obvious, and most of us take part in some of these activities, in some way, daily. As Graedel and Crutzen (1989) point out, the activities of people are changing our atmosphere: (1) Our industrial activities emit a variety of atmospheric pollutants; (2) our practice of burning large quantities of fossil fuel introduces pollutants into the atmosphere; (3) our transportation practices emit pollutants into the atmosphere; (4) our mismanagement and alteration of land surfaces (deforestation) lead to atmospheric problems; (5) our practice of clearing and burning massive tracts of vegetation produces atmospheric contaminants; and (6) our agricultural practices, which produce chemicals such as methane, impact the atmosphere. These alterations to the Earth's atmosphere have produced profound effects, including increased acid precipitation, localized smog events, **greenhouse gases**, ozone depletion, and increased corrosion of materials induced by atmospheric pollutants.

What exactly should we do?

We should understand the human-made mechanisms at work destroying our environment and what we are collectively doing to our environment—and we must be aware that our environment is finite, not inexhaustible or indestructible. It can be destroyed. We must also clearly identify and understand both the causal and the remedial factors involved. Recognizing one particular salient point is absolutely essential: Life on Earth and the nature of Earth's atmosphere are connected—literally chained together. The atmosphere drives the climate and ultimately determines its suitability for life. We must work to preserve the quality of our atmosphere.

Only through a cool-headed, scientifically intellectual, informed mindset will we be able to solve our environmental dilemma. To save our environment (and ourselves), we must develop a vision of an environmentally healthy world—a vision that can be realized. And this is something we can accomplish.

In this chapter, we discuss issues relevant to environmental pollution of our atmosphere and air quality on Earth: **global warming**, acid precipitation, and stratospheric ozone depletion.

Global Warming

> Humanity is conducting an unintended, uncontrolled, globally pervasive experiment whose ultimate consequences could be second only to nuclear war. The Earth's atmosphere is being changed at an unprecedented rate by pollutants resulting from human activities, inefficient and wasteful fossil fuel use and the effects of rapid population growth in many regions. These changes are already having harmful consequences over many parts of the globe.
>
> —Toronto Conference Statement, June 1988

The preceding quotation clearly states the issue. But what is global warming? It has been defined as a long-term rise in the average temperature of Earth. This appears to be the case, even though the geological record shows that abrupt climate changes have occurred from time to time (Crowley & North, 1988). There is a second question that many people use to question the validity of the concept of global warming as an environmental hazard: Is global warming actually occurring? The answer is of enormous importance to all life on Earth and is the subject of intense debate throughout the world. All the debate about global warming can't dispute the historical record: Measurements made in central England, Geneva, and Paris from about AD 1700 until the present indicate a general downward trend in surface temperature (Thompson, 1995).

Did You Know?

Climate change can have broad effects on biodiversity (the number and variety of plant and animal species in a particular location). Although species have adapted to environmental change for millions of years, a quickly changing climate could require adaption on larger and faster scales than in the past. Those species that cannot adapt are at risk of extinction. The loss of even a single species can have cascading effects, because organisms are connected through food webs and other activities (U.S. EPA, 2010).

For the sake of discussion, let's assume that global warming is occurring. With this assumption in place, we must ask other questions, which deal with why, how, and what. (1) Why is global warming occurring? (2) How can we be sure it is occurring? (3) What will be its ultimate effects? (4) What can we do/are we going to do about it? These questions are difficult to answer. There is a real danger that we may be unable to definitively answer them before it is too late, when we have reached the point that the process has progressed beyond our ability to prevent or mitigate the damage. This situation raises a red flag—a huge red flag—and additional questions. Are we to stand by and do nothing? Are we to simply ignore the potential impact of this problem? Are we to take the consequences of global warming lightly? Are we not to take precautionary actions now instead of later—much later, when it is too late? Indeed, a red flag has been raised (a cause-and-effect relationship to the **greenhouse effect**), but there is still time before it signifies that climate change is inevitable—when mitigation becomes harder, more expensive, and impossible to effect.

Did You Know?

Oceans and the atmosphere are constantly interacting: exchanging heat, water, gases, and particles. As the atmosphere warms, the ocean absorbs some of this heat. The amount of heat stored by the ocean affects the temperature of the ocean both at the surface and at great depths. Warming of the Earth's oceans can change the habitat and food supplies of many kinds of marine life—from plankton to polar bears. The oceans also absorb carbon dioxide from the atmosphere. Once it dissolves in the ocean, carbon dioxide reacts with sea water to form carbonic acid. As people put more carbon dioxide into the atmosphere, the oceans absorb some of it, which leads to more carbonic acid. An increasingly acidic ocean can have negative effects on animal life, such as coral reefs (U.S. EPA, 2010).

Exactly what is the nature of the problem of global warming? We may not be able to provide all the answers here, but we are about to launch a discussion of the entire phenomena and its potential impact on Earth.

Did You Know?

Although some forests may derive near-term benefits from an extended growing season, climate change is also expected to encourage wildfires by extending the length of the summer fire season. Larger periods of hot weather could stress trees and make them more susceptible to wildfires, insect damage, and disease. Climate change has likely already increased the size and number of forest fires, insect outbreaks, and tree deaths, particularly in Alaska and the West. The area burned in western U.S. forests from 1987 to 2003 is almost seven times larger than the area burned from 1970 to 1986. In the last 30 years, the length of the wildfire season in the West has increased by 78 days (U.S. EPA, 2010).

GREENHOUSE EFFECT AND GLOBAL WARMING

Those who support the theory of global warming base their assumptions on humankind's altering of the Earth's normal greenhouse effect, which provides necessary warmth for life. They blame human activities (burning of fossil fuels, deforestation, and use of certain aerosols and refrigerants) for the increased quantities of greenhouse gases. These gases have increased the amounts of heat trapped in the Earth's atmosphere, gradually increasing the temperature of the whole globe.

Taking a long-term view, scientists look at temperature variations over thousands or even millions of years. Having done this, they cannot definitively show that global warming is anything more than a short-term variation in Earth's climate. They base this assumption on historical records that show the Earth's temperature does vary widely, growing colder with ice ages and then warming again. On another side of the argument, some people point out that in the 1980s, nine of the twelve warmest temperatures ever recorded occurred, and the Earth's average surface temperature has risen approximately 0.6°C (1°F) in the last century (U.S. EPA, 1995). But at the same time, others offer as evidence the fact that the same decade also saw three of the coldest years: 1984, 1985, and 1986. So what is really going on? We are not certain. But let's assume that we are indeed seeing long-term global warming. If this is the case, we must determine what is causing it. But here we face a problem. Scientists cannot be sure of the greenhouse effect's causes. The global warming may simply be part of a much longer trend of warming since the last ice age. Though much has been learned in the past two centuries of science, little is actually known about the causes of the worldwide global cooling and warming that have carried the Earth through a succession of major ice ages and smaller ones. We simply don't have the enormously long-term data needed to support our theories.

HOW IS CLIMATE CHANGE MEASURED?

Worldwide, scientists are trying to establish ways to test or measure whether or not greenhouse-induced global warming is occurring. They are currently looking for signs that collectively are called a greenhouse "signature" or "footprint." If it is occurring, eventually it will be obvious to everyone—but what we really want is clear advance warning. Thus, scientists are currently attempting to collect and then decipher a mass of scientific evidence to find those signs that will give us clear advance warning. According to Franck and Brownstone (1992), these signs are currently believed to include changes in the following:

- **Global temperature patterns**, with continents being warmer than oceans; lands near the Arctic warming more than the tropics; and the lower atmosphere warming, while the higher stratosphere becomes cooler.
- **Atmospheric water vapor**, with increasing amounts of water evaporating into the air as a result of the warming, more in the tropics than in the higher latitudes. Since water vapor is a "greenhouse gas," this would intensify the warming process.
- **Sea surface temperature**, with a fairly uniform rise in the temperature of oceans at their surface and an increase in the temperature differences among oceans around the globe.
- **Seasonality**, with changes in the relative intensity of the seasons, with the warming effects especially noticeable during the winter and in higher latitudes (143).

In a measured, scientific way, these signs give a general overview of some of the changes that would be expected to occur with global warming. Note, however, that from the viewpoint of life on Earth, changes resulting from long-term global warming would be drastic—profoundly serious. Probably the most dramatic—and the effect with the most far-reaching results—would be **sea level rise**.

Global Warming and Sea Level Rise

In the past few decades, human activities (burning fossil fuels, leveling forests, and producing synthetic chemicals such as CFCs) have released into the atmosphere huge quantities of carbon dioxide and other greenhouse gases. These gases are warming the Earth at an unprecedented rate. If current trends continue, Earth's average surface temperature is expected to rise by at least 1.5°to 4.5°C in the next century, with warming at the poles perhaps two to three times as high as warming at the middle latitudes (Wigley et al., 1986).

If we assume global warming is inevitable and is already under way, what, then, must we do? Obviously we cannot jump off the planet and head for greener pastures. We live on Earth and are stuck here. (We have no effective method or technology to allow us to leave, or a convenient place to go even if we did have the technology.) Understanding the dynamics of change that are evolving around us and taking whatever prudent actions we can to mitigate the situation makes good sense.

We must also take this approach to the effect that global warming is having on the rise in sea level. It is already under way, and with it will come increased storm damage, pollution, and subsidence of coastal lands.

"Rise in sea level is already underway?" Absolutely. Consider the following information from the EPA's 1995 report, *The Probability of Sea Level Rise*:

1. Global warming is most likely to raise sea levels 15 cm by the year 2050 and 34 cm by the year 2100. There is also a 10 percent chance that climate change will contribute 30 cm by 2050 and 65 cm by 2100. These estimates do not include sea level rise caused by factors other than greenhouse warming.

2. There is a 1 percent chance that global warming will raise sea level 1 meter in the next 100 years and 4 meters in the next 200 years. By the year 2200, there is also a 10 percent chance of a 2-meter contribution. Such a large rise in sea level could occur either if Antarctic ocean temperature warms 5 degrees C and Antarctic ice streams respond more rapidly than most glaciologists expect, or if Greenland temperatures warm by more than 10 degrees C. Neither of these scenarios is likely.

3. By the year 2100, climate change is likely to increase the rate of sea level rise by 4.1 mm/yr. There is also a 1-in-10 chance that the contribution will be greater than 10 mm/yr, as well as a 1-in-10 chance that it will be less than 1 mm/yr.

4. Stabilizing global emissions in the year 2050 would be likely to reduce the rate of sea level rise by 28 percent by the year 2100, compared with what it would be otherwise. These calculations assume that we are uncertain about the future trajectory of greenhouse gas emissions.

5. Stabilizing emissions by the year 2025 could cut the rate of sea level rise in half. If a high global rate of emissions growth occurs in the next century, sea level is likely to rise 6.2 mm/yr by 2100; freezing emissions in 2025 would prevent the rate from exceeding 3.2 mm/yr. If less emissions growth were expected, freezing emissions in 2025 would cut the eventual rate of sea level rise by one-third.

6. Along most coasts, factors other than anthropogenic climate change will cause the sea to rise more than the rise resulting from climate change alone. These factors include compaction and subsidence of land, groundwater depletion, and natural climate variations. If these factors do not change, global sea level is likely to rise 45 cm by the year 2100, with a 1 percent chance of a 112 cm rise. Along the coast of New York, which typifies the United States, sea level is likely to rise 26 cm by 2050 and 55 cm by 2100. There is also a 1 percent chance of a 55 cm rise by 2050 and a 120 cm rise by 2100 (iii).

Additional evidence corroborates the assertion that global mean sea level has been rising during at least the last 100 years. According to Broecker (1987), this evidence is apparent in tide gauge records, erosion of 70% of the world's sandy coasts and 90% of America's sandy beaches, and the melting and retreat of mountain glaciers. Edgerton (1991) points out that the correspondence between the two curves of rising global temperatures and rising sea levels during the last century appears to be more than coincidental.

Major uncertainties are present in estimates of future sea level rise. The problem is further complicated by our lack of understanding of the mechanisms contributing to relatively recent rises in sea level. In addition, different outlooks for climatic warming dramatically affect estimates. In all this uncertainty, one thing is sure: Estimates of sea level rise will undergo continual revision and refinement as time passes and more data are collected.

Major Physical Effects of Sea Level Rise

With increased global temperatures, global sea level rise will occur at a rate unprecedented in human history (Edgerton, 1991). Changes in temperature and sea level will be accompanied by changes in salinity levels. For example, a coastal freshwater aquifer is influenced by two factors: pumping and mean sea level. In pumping, if withdrawals exceed recharge, the water table is drawn down, and saltwater penetrates inland. With mean sea level, the problem occurs if sea level rises and the coastline moves inland, reducing aquifer area. Additional problems brought about by changes in temperature and sea level are seen in tidal flooding, oceanic currents, biological processes of marine creatures, runoff and landmass erosion patterns, and saltwater intrusion.

Major Direct Effects of Sea Level Rise on Humans

Along with the physical effects of sea level rise, in one way or another, directly or indirectly, accompanying effects have a human side, especially concerning human settlements and the infrastructure that accompanies them: highways, airports, waterways, water supply and wastewater treatment facilities, landfills, hazardous waste storage areas, bridges, and associated maintenance systems. Sea level rise could also cause intrusion of saltwater into groundwater supplies (Edgerton, 1991).

To point out that the infrastructure will be placed under tremendous strain by a rising sea level coupled with other climatic change is to understate the possible consequences. Indeed, the impact on infrastructure is only part of the direct consequences to humans. For example, there is widespread agreement among scientists that any significant change in world climate resulting from warming or cooling will (1) disrupt world food production for many years, (2) lead to a sharp increase in food prices, and (3) cause considerable economic damage.

Just how much of a rise in sea level are we talking about? According to the EPA, "if the experts on whom we relied fairly represent the breadth of scientific opinion, the odds are fifty-fifty that greenhouse gases will raise sea level at least 15 cm by the year 2050, 25 cm by 2100, and 80 cm by 2200" (1995, 123).

Response Scenario 13.1.
The 411 on Global Climate Change

Is global warming a hoax? Is Earth's climate changing? Are warmer times or colder times on the way? Is the greenhouse effect going to affect our climate, and if so, do we need to worry about it? Will the tides rise and flood New York? Does the ozone hole portend disaster right around the corner?

We are all aware of these and many other questions related to climate change. We are inundated by a constant barrage of newspaper headlines, magazine articles, and television news reports on these topics. In recent decades, we have seen report after report on El Niño and its devastation of the West Coast of the United States (and Peru and Ecuador) and reduction in the number, magnitude, and devastation of hurricanes that blasted the East Coast of the United States.

To illustrate the barrage of newspaper headlines, we have listed below a sample of the climate change news and global warming headlines published in various locations in April 2008 (Carbonify.com, 2009).

April 1, 2008—GLOBAL WARMING AWARENESS AND APATHY
April 2, 2008—OCEANS UNDER STRESS FROM GLOBAL WARMING
April 7, 2008—AUSTRALIAN DROUGHT AFFECTED AREAS GROW
April 13, 2008—FOSSIL FUEL CARBON EMISSIONS OVER 8 GIGATONS
April 22, 2008—UK MIGRATING BIRDS NUMBERS DROP
April 28, 2008—MARCH WARMEST ON RECORD GLOBALLY

Scientists have been warning us of the catastrophic harm that can be done to the world by atmospheric warming. One view states that we could see record droughts, record heat waves, record smog levels, and an increasing number of forest fires.

Another warning is that the increasing atmospheric heat could melt the world's ice caps and glaciers, causing ocean levels to rise to the point where some low-lying island countries would disappear, while the coastlines of other nations would be drastically altered for ages—or perhaps for all time.

What's going on? We hear plenty of theories put forward by doomsayers, but are they correct? If they are, what does it all mean? Does anyone really know the answers? Should we be concerned? Should we invest in waterfront property in Antarctica? Should we panic?

Although no one really knows the answers—the "we don't know what we don't know syndrome"—and we should be concerned, no real cause for panic exists.

Should we take some type of decisive action—come up with quick answers and put together a plan to fix these problems? What really needs to be done? What can we do? Is there anything we can do?

The key question to answer here is, "What really needs to be done?" We can study the facts, issues, and possible consequences, but the key to successfully combating these issues is to stop and seriously evaluate the problems. Scientific fact, common sense, and cool-headedness must prevail. Shooting from the hip is not called for, makes little sense, and could have *Titanic* consequences for us all.

(continued)

Response Scenario 13.1. (*continued*)

Another question that has merit here is, "Will we take the correct actions before it is too late?" The key words here are "correct actions." Eventually, we may have to take some action (beyond hiding in a cave somewhere). But we do not yet know what those actions could or should be.

From our perspective, one thing is certain: In our college-level environmental health courses, sooner or later, we address global warming and/or global climate change. Through time and experience we have learned that whether we call it global warming, global climate change (humankind-induced global warming), or an inconvenient truth, the topic is a conundrum (a riddle, the answer to which is a pun). Before diving into the many emotionally charged, heated discussions about this "hot" topic (pun intended), we are reminded by two familiar conundrums just how complicated they can be:

What is black and white and read all over? A newspaper.

"Why is a man in jail like a man out of jail?" (There is no answer to this.) (Charles Dickens, *Martin Chuzzlewit*, 1843).

Any damage we do to our atmosphere affects the other environmental media: water, soil, and biota (all living things, including us). Thus, the endangered atmosphere (if it is endangered) is a major concern (a life and death concern) to all of us.

THE PAST

Before we begin our discussion of the past, we need to define what we mean by "the past." Table 13.1 covers the entire expanse of time from Earth's beginning to the present. Table 13.2 provides the sequence of geological epochs over the past 65 million years, as dated by modern methods. The Paleocene through Pliocene epochs together make up the Tertiary period; the Pleistocene and the Holocene compose the Quaternary period.

Table 13.1. Geological Eras and Periods

Era	Period	Millions of Years before Present
Cenozoic	Quaternary	2.5–present
	Tertiary	65–2.5
Mesozoic	Cretaceous	135–65
	Jurassic	190–135
	Triassic	225–190
Paleozoic	Permian	280–225
	Pennsylvanian	320–280
	Mississippian	345–320
	Devonian	400–345
	Silurian	440–400
	Ordovician	500–440
	Cambrian	570–500
Precambrian		4,600–570

Table 13.2. Geological Epochs

Epoch	Million Years before Present
Holocene	01–0
Pleistocene	1.6–0.01
Pliocene	5–1.6
Miocene	24–5
Oligocene	35–24
Eocene	58–35
Paleocene	65–58

When we think about climatic conditions in the prehistoric past, two things generally come to mind—ice ages and dinosaurs. Of course, in the immense span of time that prehistory covers, those two eras represent only a brief moment in time. So let's look at what we know or think we know about the past and about Earth's climate and conditions. Geological history shows us that the normal climate of the Earth was so warm that subtropical weather reached to 60°N and S, and polar ice was entirely absent.

Glaciers have advanced and reached as far south as what is now the temperate zone of the northern hemisphere during less than 1% of the Earth's history. The latest such advance, which began about one million ago, was marked by geological upheaval and (perhaps) the advent of human life on Earth. During this time, vast ice sheets advanced and retreated, grinding their way over the continents.

A Time of Ice

The oldest known glacial epoch occurred nearly two billion years ago. A series of deposits of glacial origin in southern Canada, extending east to west about 1,000 miles, shows us that within the last billion years or so, apparently at least six major phases of massive, significant climatic cooling and consequent glaciation occurred at intervals of about 150 million years. Each lasted perhaps as long as 50 million years.

Examination of land and oceanic sediment core samples clearly indicates that in more recent times (the Pleistocene epoch to the present), many alternating episodes of warmer and colder conditions occurred over the last two million years (during the middle and early Pleistocene epochs). In the last million years, at least eight such cycles have occurred, with the warm part of the cycle lasting a relatively short time.

During the Great Ice Age (the Pleistocene epoch), ice advances began, at times covering over one-quarter of the Earth's land surface. Great sheets of ice thousands of feet thick, these glaciers moved across North America over and over, reaching as far south as the Great Lakes. An ice sheet thousands of feet thick spread over northern Europe, sculpting the land and leaving behind lakes, swamps, and terminal moraines as far south as Switzerland. Each succeeding glacial advance was apparently more severe than the previous one. Evidence indicates that the most severe began about 50,000 years ago and ended about 10,000 years ago. Several interglacial stages separated the glacial advances, melting the ice. Average temperatures were higher than ours today.

(continued)

Response Scenario 13.1. (*continued*)

Wait a minute! Temperatures were higher than today? Yes, they were. Think about that as we proceed.

Because one-tenth of the globe's surface is still covered by glacial ice, scientists consider the Earth to be still in a glacial stage. The ice sheet has been retreating since the climax of the last glacial advance, and world climates, although fluctuating, are slowly warming.

From our observations and from well-kept records, we know that the ice sheet is in a retreating stage. The records clearly show that a marked world-wide retreat of ice has occurred over the last hundred years. World famous for its 50 glaciers and 200 lakes, Glacier National Park in Montana does not present the same visual experiences it did a hundred years ago. In 1937, a 10-foot pole was put into place at the terminal edge of one of the main glaciers. The sign is still in place, but the terminal end of the glacier has retreated several hundred feet back up the slope of the mountain. Swiss resorts built during the early 1900s to offer scenic glacial views now have no ice in sight. Theoretically, if glacial retreat continues, melting all of the world's ice supply, sea levels would rise more than 200 feet, flooding many of the world's major cities. New York and Boston would become aquariums.

Scientists still grapple with what causes ice ages. Theories range from changing ocean currents to sunspot cycles. Of one fact we are absolutely certain, however: An ice age event occurs because of a change in Earth's climate. But what could cause such a drastic change?

Climate results from uneven heat distribution over the Earth's surface. It is caused by the Earth's tilt—the angle between the Earth's orbital plane around the sun and its rotational axis. This angle is currently 23.5 degrees, but it has not always been that way. The angle, of course, affects the amount of solar energy that reaches the Earth and where it falls. The heat balance of the Earth, which is driven mostly by the concentration of carbon dioxide (CO_2) in the atmosphere, also affects long-term climate. If the pattern of solar radiation changes or if the amount of CO_2 changes, climate change can result. Abundant evidence that the Earth does undergo climatic change exists, and we know that climatic change can be a limiting factor for the evolution of many species.

Evidence (primarily from soil core samples and topographical formations) tells us that changes in climate include events such as periodic ice ages characterized by glacial and interglacial periods. Long glacial periods lasted up to 100,000 years, temperatures decreased about 9°F, and ice covered most of the planet. Short periods lasted up to 12,000 years, with temperatures decreasing by 5°F and ice covering 40° north latitude and above. Smaller periods (e.g., the "Little Ice Age," which occurred from about AD 1000 to 1850) involved about a 3°F drop in temperature. (**Note:** Despite its name, the Little Ice Age was a time of severe winters and violent storms, not a true glacial period. These ages may or may not be significant, but consider that we are presently in an interglacial period and that we may be reaching its apogee. What does that mean? No one knows for sure.)

Let's look at the effects of ice ages (i.e., the effects we think we know about). Changes in sea levels could occur. Sea level could drop by about 100 meters in a full-blown ice age, exposing the continental shelves. Increased deposition during melt would change the composition of the exposed continental shelves. Less evaporation would change the hydrological cycle. Significant landscape changes could occur, on the scale of the formation of the Great Lakes. Drainage patterns and topsoil characteristics throughout most of the world would change. Flooding on a massive scale could occur. How these changes would affect you depends on whether you live in northern Europe, Canada, Seattle, or Washington; around the Great Lakes; or near a seashore.

We are not sure what causes ice ages, but we have some theories. Scientists point out that certain periodic or cyclic events or happenings must occur to generate a full-blown ice age (a massive ice sheet covering most of the globe). Periodic fluctuations would have to affect the solar cycle, for example; however, we have no definitive proof that this has ever occurred.

Another theory posits that periods of volcanic activity could generate masses of volcanic dust that would block or filter heat from the sun, thus cooling down the Earth. Some speculate that the carbon dioxide cycle would have to be periodic or cyclic to bring about periods of climate change. The so-called Factor 2 reduction would cause a 7°F temperature drop worldwide. Some speculate that another global ice age could be brought about by increased precipitation at the poles due to changing orientation of continental land masses. Others theorize that a global ice age would result if the mean temperatures of ocean currents decreased. But the question is, how? By what mechanism? Are these plausible theories? No one is sure—this is speculation. Some would say it is feel-good speculation; others say it is real, honest speculation. So, which one is it? We are not sure.

Speculation aside, what are the most probable causes of ice ages on Earth? According to the Milankovitch hypothesis, ice age occurrences are governed by a combination of factors: (1) the Earth's change of altitude in relation to the sun (the way it tilts in a 41,000-year cycle and at the same time wobbles on its axis in a 22,000-year cycle), making the time of its closest approach to the sun occur at different seasons; and (2) the 92,000-year cycle of eccentricity in its orbit round the sun, changing from an elliptical to a near circular orbit, the most severe period of an ice age coinciding with the approach to circularity.

So, what does all this mean? We have a lot of speculation about ice ages and their causes and their effects. This is the bottom line: We know that ice ages occurred and that they caused certain things to occur (e.g., formation of the Great Lakes), and although there is a lot we do not know, we recognize the possibility of recurrent ice ages. Currently, no single theory is completely sound, and undoubtedly many factors are involved. Keep in mind that it is possibile we are still in the Pleistocene ice age. It may reach another maximum in another 60,000 years or so.

Warm Winter

The headlines we see in the paper sound authoritative: "1997 Was the Warmest Year on Record"; "Scientists Discover Ozone Hole Is Larger Than Ever"; "Record Quantities of Carbon Dioxide Detected in Atmosphere." Or maybe you saw this one: "January 1998 Was The Third Warmest January on Record." Other reports indicate we are undergoing a warming trend, but conflicting reports abound. This section discusses what we think we know about climate change.

Two environmentally significant events took place late in 1997: El Niño's return and the Kyoto Conference on Global Warming and Climate Change.

(continued)

Response Scenario 13.1. (*continued*)

News reports blamed El Niño for just about anything that had to do with weather conditions throughout the world. Some incidents were indeed El Niño–related or –generated: the out-of-control fires, droughts, floods, stretches of dead coral with no sign of fish in the water, and few birds around certain Pacific atolls. The devastating storms that struck the west coasts of South America, Mexico, and the United States were also probably El Niño related. El Niño's effects on the 1997 hurricane season, one of the mildest on record, is not in question, either.

Does a connection exist between El Niño and global warming or global climate change? On December 7, 1997, the Associated Press reported that while delegates at the global climate conference in Kyoto haggled over greenhouse gases and emission limits, a compelling question had emerged: "Is global warming fueling El Niño?" Nobody knows for sure, because we need more information than we have today. The data we do have, however, suggest that El Niño is getting stronger and more frequent.

Some scientists fear that the increasing frequency and intensity of El Niños (records show that two of the last century's three worst El Niños were in 1982 and 1997) may be linked to global warming. At the Kyoto Conference, experts said the hotter atmosphere is heating up the world's oceans, setting the stage for more frequent and extreme El Niños. Weather-related phenomena seem to be intensifying all over the globe. Can we be sure that this is related to global warming? No. Without more data, more time, and more science (real science), we cannot be sure.

According to the Associated Press coverage of the Kyoto Conference, scientist Richard Fairbanks reported that he had found startling evidence of a need for concern. During two months of scientific experiments conducted in autumn 1997 on Christmas Island, the world's largest atoll in the Pacific Ocean, he witnessed a frightening scene. The water surrounding the atoll was 7°F warmer than average for the time of year, which upset the balance of the environmental system. According to Fairbanks, 40% of the coral was dead, the warmer water had killed off or driven away fish, and the atoll's plentiful bird population was almost completely gone.

No doubt El Niños are having an acute impact on the globe; however, we do not know if these events are caused by or intensified by global warming. What do we know about global warming and climate change? An article in *USA Today* (1997) discussed the results of a report issued by the Intergovernmental Panel on Climate Change, interviewing Jerry Mahlman of the National Oceanic and Atmospheric Administration and Princeton University and presenting the following information about what most scientists agree on:

- There is a natural greenhouse effect, and scientists know how it works; without it, Earth would freeze.
- The Earth undergoes normal cycles or warming and cooling on grand scales. Ice ages occur every 20,000 to 100,000 years.
- Globally, average temperatures have risen 1°F in the past 100 years, within the range that might occur normally.
- The level of man-made carbon dioxide in the atmosphere has risen 30% since the beginning of the Industrial Revolution in the 19th century, and is still rising.

- Levels of man-made carbon dioxide will double in the atmosphere over the next 100 years, generating a rise in global average temperatures of about 3.5°F (larger than the natural swings in temperature that have occurred over the past 10,000 years).
- By 2050, temperatures will rise much higher in northern latitudes than the increase in global average temperatures. Substantial amounts of northern sea ice will melt, and snow and rain in the northern hemisphere will increase.
- As the climate warms, the rate of evaporation will rise, further increasing warming. Water vapor also reflects heat back to Earth.

Global Warming

What is global warming? To answer this question, we need to first discuss the "greenhouse effect." Water vapor, carbon dioxide, and other atmospheric gases (greenhouse gases) help warm the Earth. Earth's average temperature would be closer to 0° than its actual 60° without the greenhouse effect. But as gases are added to the atmosphere, the average temperature could increase, changing orbital climate.

How does the greenhouse effect actually work? Earth's greenhouse effect, of course, was so named because of the similarity in effects to a greenhouse. Because the glass walls and ceilings of a greenhouse are largely transparent to shortwave radiation from the sun, surfaces and objects inside the greenhouse absorb the radiation. The radiation, once absorbed, transforms into longwave (infrared) radiation (heat), which radiates back from the greenhouse interior, but the glass prevents the longwave radiation from escaping again, and the warm rays are absorbed (Figure 13.1). The interior of the greenhouse becomes much warmer than the air outside, because of the heat trapped inside.

Earth and its atmosphere undergo a process very similar to this. Shortwave and visible radiation reaching Earth is absorbed by the surface as heat. The long heat waves radiate back out toward space, but the atmosphere absorbs many of them, trapping them. This natural and balanced process is essential to supporting our lives on Earth. Changes in the atmosphere can radically change the amount of absorption and therefore the amount of heat the atmosphere retains. In recent decades, scientists have speculated that various air pollutants have caused the atmosphere to absorb more heat. At the local level, with air pollution, the greenhouse effect causes heat islands in and around urban centers, a widely recognized phenomenon.

The main contributors to this effect are the greenhouse gases: water vapor, carbon dioxide, carbon monoxide, methane, volatile organic compounds (VOCs), nitrogen oxides, chlorofluorocarbons (CFCs), and surface ozone. These gases cause a general climatic warming by delaying the escape of infrared radiation from the Earth into space. Scientists stress that this is a natural process. Indeed, as noted previously, if the normal greenhouse effect did not exist, the Earth would be far cooler than it currently is (Hansen et al., 1986).

However, human activities are rapidly intensifying the natural phenomenon, which may lead to problems of warming on a global scale. There is much debate, confusion, and speculation about this potential consequence, because scientists cannot yet agree about whether the recently perceived worldwide warming trend is attributable to greenhouse gases or some other cause, or is simply a wider variation in the normal heating and cooling trends

(continued)

Response Scenario 13.1. (*continued*)

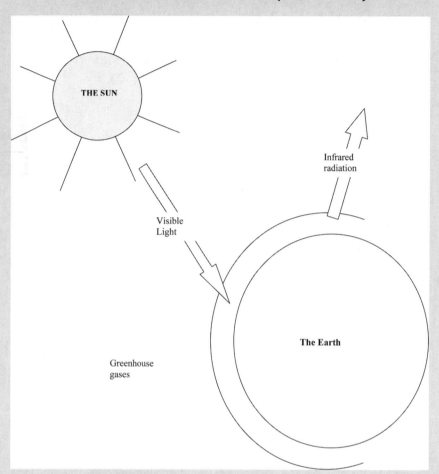

Figure 13.1.   Greenhouse effect.

of the Earth. Unchecked, the greenhouse effect may lead to significant global warming, with profound effects on our lives and environment. Human impact on greenhouse effect is real; it has been measured and detected. The rate at which the greenhouse effect is intensifying is now more than five times what it was during the last century (Hansen et al., 1989).

Supporters of the global warming theory assume that human activities are significantly altering the Earth's normal and necessary greenhouse effect. The human activities they blame for this increase of greenhouse gases include burning of fossil fuels, deforestation, and use of certain aerosols and refrigerants. From information based on recent or short-term observations, many scientists have concluded that the last decade has been the warmest since temperature recordings began in the late 19th century. They can see that the general rise in temperature coincides with the Industrial Revolution and its accompanying increase in fossil fuel use. Other evidence supports the global warming theory.

In places that are synonymous with ice and snow—the Arctic and Antarctica, for example—we see evidence of receding ice and snow cover.

Trying to pin down definitively whether or not changing our anthropogenic activities could have any significant effect on lessening global warming, however, is difficult. Scientists look at temperature variations over thousands and even millions of years, taking a long-term view of Earth's climate. The variations in climate are wide enough that they cannot definitively show that global warming is anything more than another short-term variation. Historical records show that the Earth's temperature does vary widely, growing colder with ice ages and then warming again. Because we cannot be certain of the causes of those climate changes, we cannot be certain what is causing the current warming trend.

Still, debate abounds over whether our climate is warming and our activities are part of the equation. The 1980s saw 9 of the 12 warmest temperatures ever recorded, and the Earth's average surface temperature has risen approximately 0.6°C (1°F) in the last century (USEPA, 2009). An article in *Time Magazine* (1998) reported that scientists are increasingly convinced that the Earth is getting hotter because of the buildup in the atmosphere of carbon dioxide and other gases, produced in large part by the burning of fossil fuels. Each month from January through July 1998, for example, set a new average global temperature record, and if that trend continues, the surface temperature of the Earth could rise by about 1.8° to 6.3°F by 2100. At the same time, others offer as evidence that the 1980s also saw three of the coldest years: 1984, 1985, and 1986. The debate does not end there, however. For example, ever since NASA's Goddard Institute for Space Studies made a correction to data that seemed to show 9 of the 10 hottest years in U.S. history had occurred since 1995 (the correct number was 3), the global warming deniers have become more vocal, using this error to prove that the entire issue of global warming–induced climate change is a hoax. Others argue that this one faux pas does not undermine the credibility of the global warming theory.

What is really going on? We cannot be certain. Assuming that we are indeed seeing long-term global warming, we must determine what causes it. But again, we face the problem that scientists cannot be sure of precise causes of the greenhouse effect. The current possible trend in global warming may simply be part of a much longer trend of warming since the last ice age. We have learned much in the past two centuries, but little is actually known about the causes of the worldwide global cooling and warming that sent the Earth through major and smaller ice ages. The data we need reach back over millennia. We simply do not possess enough long-term information to support our theories.

Currently, scientists point to six factors they think could be involved in long-term global warming and cooling:

1. Long-term global warming and cooling could result if changes in the Earth's position relative to the sun occur (i.e., the Earth's orbit around the sun), with higher temperatures resulting when the two are closer together and lower ones when they are farther apart.
2. Long-term global warming and cooling could result from major catastrophes (meteor impacts or massive volcanic eruptions) throwing pollutants into the atmosphere that can block out solar radiation.

(continued)

Response Scenario 13.1. (*continued*)

3. Long-term global warming and cooling could result if changes in albedo (reflectivity of Earth's surface) occur. If the Earth's surface were more reflective, for example, the amount of solar radiation radiated back toward space instead of absorbed would increase, lowering temperatures on Earth.
4. Long-term global warming and cooling could result if the amount of radiation emitted by the sun changes.
5. Long-term global warming and cooling could result if the shape and relationship of the land and oceans change.
6. Long-term global warming and cooling could result if the composition of the atmosphere changes.

"If the composition of the atmosphere changes"—this final factor, of course, defines our present concern: Have human activities had a cumulative impact large enough to affect the total temperature and climate of Earth? Right now, we cannot be sure. The problem concerns us, and we are alert to it, but we are not certain. Because, again, we do not know what we do not know about global warming or climate change.

However, if global warming is occurring, we can expect that summers will be hotter. Over the next 100 years, sea level will rise a foot or so. Is this bad? The answer depends on where you live. Keep in mind, however, that not only could sea level rise 1 foot over the next 100 years, it could continue to do so for many hundreds of years. Another point to consider is that we have routine global temperature measurements for only about 100 years. Even these are unreliable, because instruments and methods of observation changed over time.

The only conclusion we can safely draw about climate and climate change is that we do not know if drastic changes are occurring. We could be at the end of a geological ice age. Evidence indicates that during interglacials, temperatures increase before they plunge. Are we ascending the peak temperature range? We have no way to tell. To what extent does our human activity impact climate? Have anthropogenic effects become so marked that we have affected the natural cycle of ice ages (which have occurred for roughly the last 5 million years)? Maybe we are just experiencing a breathing spell of a few centuries before the next advance of the glaciers. If this is the case, if we are at the apogee of the current interglacial, then we have to ask ourselves: Is global warming the lesser of two evils when compared to the alternative, global cooling? If we are headed into another glacial freeze, in this era of expanding population and decreasing resources, where will we get the energy (fuel) to keep all of us warm?

RESPONSE

(i)   Is global warming or global climate change real?
(ii) Are humans responsible for global climate change?
(iii) Is global climate change cyclical or human driven?

Acid Precipitation

When you stand on your porch during a light evening rain and look out on your terraced lawn and that flourishing garden of perennials, you probably feel a sense of calm and relaxation hard to describe—but not hard to accept. The sound of raindrops against the roof of the house and porch, the foliage and lawn, the sidewalk, and the street, and that light wind through the boughs of the evergreens soothe you. Whatever it is that makes you feel this way, rainfall is a major ingredient.

But someone knowledgeable and/or trained in environmental science might take another view of such a seemingly welcome and peaceful event. We might wonder whether the rainfall is as clean and pure as it should be. Is this actually rainfall—or is it rain carrying acids as strong as lemon juice or vinegar with it, capable of harming both living and nonliving things like trees, lakes, and structures? This might seem to some folks to be an off-the-wall attitude.

Such thoughts may have been off-the-wall before the Industrial Revolution, but today the purity of rainfall, especially the level of acidity, is a major concern for many people. Most rainfall is slightly acidic because of decomposing organic matter, the movement of the sea, and volcanic eruptions, but the principal factor is atmospheric carbon dioxide, which causes carbonic acid to form. **Acid rain** (pH<5.6) (in the pollution sense) is produced by the conversion of the primary pollutants sulfur dioxide and nitrogen oxides to sulfuric acid and nitric acid, respectively (see Figure 13.2 for an explanation of pH). These processes are complex and depend on the physical dispersion processes and the rates of the chemical conversions. The basic cycle is shown in Figure 13.3.

Contrary to popular belief, acid rain is not a new phenomenon, nor does it result solely from industrial pollution. Natural processes such as volcanic eruptions and forest fires produce and release acid particles into the air. The burning of forest areas to clear land in Brazil, Africa, and other countries also contributes to acid rain. However, the rise in manufacturing that began with the Industrial Revolution literally dwarfs all other contributions to the problem.

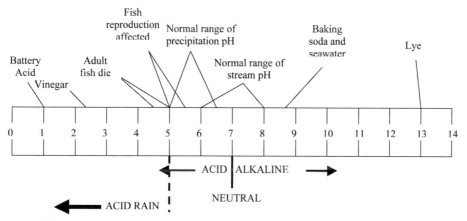

Figure 13.2.   Measuring activity: pH scale. Adapted from: Water Fact Sheet, U.S. Geological Society, U.S. Department of Interior, 1987

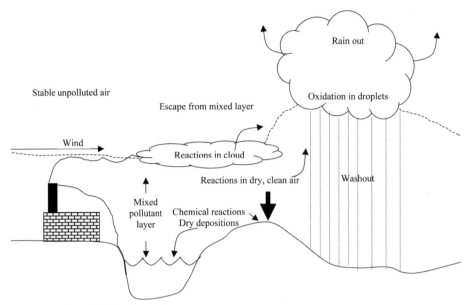

Figure 13.3. Acid rain cycle.

The main culprits are emissions of sulfur dioxide from the burning of fossil fuels, such as oil and coal, and nitrogen oxide, formed mostly from internal combustion engine emissions, which is readily transformed into nitrogen dioxide. These mix in the atmosphere to form sulfuric acid and nitric acid.

The Earth's ecosystems are not completely defenseless in dealing with atmospheric acid deposition; they can handle a certain amount of acid through natural alkaline substances in soil or rocks that **buffer** and neutralize acid. The American Midwest and southern England are areas with highly alkaline soil (limestone and sandstone) that provide some natural neutralization. Areas with thin soil and those laid on granite bedrock, however, have little ability to neutralize acid rain.

Scientists continue to study how living beings are damaged and/or killed by acid rain. This complex subject has many variables. We know from various episodes of acid rain that pollution can travel over very long distances. Lakes in Canada, Maine, and New York feel the effects of coal burning in the Ohio Valley. For this and other reasons, the lakes of the world are where most scientific studies have taken place. In lakes, the smaller organisms often die off first, leaving the larger animals to starve to death. Sometimes the larger animals (fish) are killed directly; as lake water becomes more acidic, it dissolves **heavy metals**, leading to concentrations at toxic and often lethal levels. Have you ever wandered up to the local lakeshore and observed thousands of fish belly-up? Not a pleasant sight or smell, is it? Loss of life in lakes also disrupts the system of life on the land and the air around them.

In some parts of the United States, the acidity of rainfall has fallen well below 5.6. In the northeastern United States, for example, the average pH of rainfall is 4.6, and rainfalls with a pH of 4.0, which is 100 times more acidic than distilled water, are not unusual (see Figure 13.4).

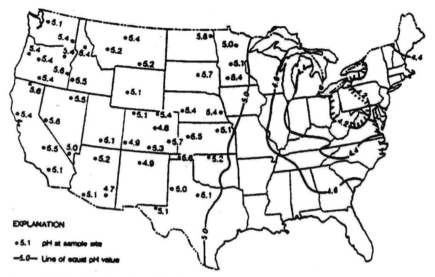

Figure 13.4.   Profile of acid rain deposition in the United States. U.S. Geological Survey, U.S. Department of Interior Water Fact Sheet, 1987.

Despite intensive research into most aspects of acid rain, there are still many areas of uncertainty and disagreement among scientists. That is why the progressive, forward-thinking countries emphasize the importance of further research into acid rain.

Stratospheric Ozone Depletion

Ozone (discussed previously) is formed in the stratosphere by radiation from the sun and helps to shield life on Earth from some of the sun's potentially destructive ultraviolet (UV) radiation.

In the early 1970s, scientists suspected that the ozone layer was being depleted. By the 1980s, it was clear that the ozone shield was indeed thinning in some places, and at times it even has a seasonal hole in it, notably over Antarctica. The exact causes and actual extent of the depletion are not yet fully understood, but most scientists believe that various chemicals in the air are responsible.

Most scientists identify the family of chlorine-based compounds, most notably chlorofluorocarbons (CFCs) and chlorinated solvents (carbon tetrachloride and methyl chloroform), as the primary culprits in ozone depletion. In 1974, Molina and Rowland hypothesized that CFCs, containing chlorine, were responsible for ozone depletion. They pointed out that chlorine molecules are highly active and readily and continually break apart the three-atom ozone into the two-atom form of oxygen generally found close to Earth in the lower atmosphere.

The Interdependent Committee for Atmospheric Sciences (1975) estimates that a 5% reduction in ozone could result in nearly a 10% increase in cancer. This already disturbing scenario became even more frightening in 1987, when evidence showed that CFCs destroy ozone in the stratosphere above Antarctica every spring. The ozone hole

Response Scenario 13.2.
Ozone: The Jekyll and Hyde of Chemicals

In Robert Louis Stevenson's classic horror novel, *Dr. Jekyll and Mr. Hyde*, Jekyll and Hyde are different aspects of the same person. Dr. Jekyll's kind, compassionate character is countered by Mr. Hyde's evil, dispassionate nature. The chemical ozone has the same potential for good and evil within a single entity.

Ozone (O_3) is a molecule containing three atoms of oxygen. In the Earth's stratosphere, about 50,000 to 120,000 feet high, ozone molecules band together to form a protective layer that shields the Earth from some of the sun's potentially destructive UV radiation. Stratospheric ozone (ozone in its kindly Dr. Jekyll incarnation), formed in the atmosphere by radiation from the sun, performs an enormously beneficial function for us. Life as we know it on Earth could have evolved only with the protective ozone shield in place.

The Centers for Disease Control in Atlanta look at ozone more critically, however. They point out that ozone (in its evil Mr. Hyde form) is an extraordinarily dangerous pollutant. Only two-hundredths of a gram of ozone is a lethal dose. A single 14-ounce aerosol can filled with ozone could kill 14,000 people. Ozone is nearly as effective at destroying lung tissue as mustard gas. Not only is ozone a poisonous gas for us on Earth, it is a main contributor to air pollution, especially smog.

RESPONSE

(i) Is this description hyperbole or an accurate depiction of ozone?

had become larger, with more than half of the total ozone column wiped out and essentially all ozone gone from some regions of the stratosphere (Davis & Cornwell, 1991).

In 1988, Zurer reported that on a worldwide basis, the ozone layer had shrunk approximately 2.5% in the preceding decade. This obvious thinning of the ozone layer, with its increased chances of skin cancer and cataracts, is also implicated in suppression of the human immune system and damage to other animals and plants, especially aquatic life and soybean crops. The urgency of the problem spurred the 1987 signing of the **Montreal Protocol** by 24 countries, which required signatory countries to reduce their consumption of CFCs by 20% by 1993 and by 50% by 1998, marking a significant achievement in solving a global environmental problem.

Air Pollution Control Technology

Good air quality depends on pollution prevention and on limiting what is emitted. Now that you have a clear picture of the problems that air pollution control is trying to solve, the time has come to introduce the various measures used to control it. At this point you should understand that limiting emissions into the air is expensive and technically difficult.

Two important factors in pollution control are **regulation** and **control technology**. Neither is more important than the other—in fact, in many ways, they drive each other.

Air pollution control begins with regulation. Regulations (e.g., to clean up, reduce, or eliminate a pollutant emission source) in turn, are generated because of certain community concerns. Buonicore, Theodore, and Davis point out that regulation usually evolves around three considerations:

1. Legal limitations imposed for the protection of public health and welfare.
2. Social limitations imposed by the community in which the pollution source is or is to be located.
3. Economic limitations imposed by marketplace constraints (1992, 1).

An environmental science practitioner assigned to mitigate an air pollution problem tries to ensure the design control methodology used will bring the source into full compliance with applicable regulations. To accomplish this feat, environmental practitioners must first understand the problem(s), then rely heavily on technology for solutions. Various air pollution control technologies are available to mitigate air pollution source problems. By analyzing the problem carefully and applying the most effective method for the situation, the scientist or technician can ensure that a particular pollution source is brought under control and the responsible parties are in full compliance with regulations.

AIR POLLUTION CONTROL: CHOICES

Assuming that the design engineer has a complete knowledge of the contaminant and the source, all available physical and chemical data on the effluent from the source, and the regulations of the control agencies involved, he or she must then decide which control methodology to employ. Since only a few control methods exist, the choice is limited. Control of atmospheric emissions from a process will generally consist of one of four methods, depending on the process, types, fuels, and availability of control equipment: (1) elimination of the process in part or entirely, (2) modification of the operation to a fuel that will give the desired level of emission, (3) installation of control equipment between the pollutant source and the receptor, and (4) relocation of the operation.

Because of the tremendous costs involved in eliminating or relocating a complete process or operation, which makes the first and last methods choices of last resort, let's begin by taking a look at them. Eliminating a process is no easy undertaking, especially when the "process" to be eliminated is the reason the facility exists. Relocation is not always an answer, either. Consider the real-life situation presented in Response Scenario 13.3.

Response Scenario 13.3. Cedar Creek Composting

Cedar Creek Composting (CCC) Facility was built in 1970. A 44-acre site designed to receive and process to compost wastewater biosolids from six local wastewater treatment plants, CCC composted biosolids at the rate of 17.5 dry tons per day. It employed the aerated static pile (ASP) method to produce a pathogen-free, humus-like material that could be beneficially used as an organic soil amendment. The final compost product was successfully marketed under a registered trademark name.

Today, CCC is no longer in operation. The site was shut down in early 1997. From an economic point of view, CCC was highly successful. When a fresh pile of compost had completed the entire composting process (including curing), dump truck after dump truck would line the road outside the main gate, waiting to buy loads of the popular product. Economics was not the problem. In fact, CCC could not produce enough compost fast enough to satisfy the demand.

What was the problem? The answer to this is twofold. The first problem was the social limitations imposed by the community where the compost site was located. In 1970, the 44 acres CCC occupied were located in an out-of-town, rural area. Its only neighbor was a regional one-plane airport on its eastern border. There were woods on the other three sides. The nearest town was two miles away. But in the mid-1970s, things started to change. Population growth and its accompanying urban sprawl quickly turned forested lands into housing complexes and shopping centers. CCC's western border soon became the site of a two-lane road that was upgraded to four and then six lanes. Its northern fence separated it from a mega-shopping mall. On the southern end of the facility, acres of houses, playgrounds, swimming pools, tennis courts, and a golf course were built. CCC became an island surrounded by urban growth. Further complicating the situation was the airport; it expanded to the point that by 1985, three major airlines were using the facility.

CCC's ASP composting process was not a problem before the neighbors moved in. Let's face it—we all know dust and odor control problems are not problems until the neighbors complain—and complain they did. CCC was attacked from all four sides. The first complaints came from the airport that dust from the static piles of compost was interfering with air traffic control.

The new, expanded highway brought several thousand new commuters right up alongside CCC's western fence line. Commuters complained any time the compost process was in operation, primarily about the odor; that thick, earthy smell does permeate everything. A handful of commuters actually liked the smell; they thought it comforting, bringing them thoughts of gardens, farms, and nature. But a handful of admirers do not offset a stadium full of complainers—and they wouldn't have thought about writing or calling to say they did like it, anyway.

After the enormous housing project was completed and people took up residence there, complaints were raised on a daily basis. The new homeowners complained about the earthy odor and the dust that blew from the compost piles onto their properties when the wind shifted to make them downwind from the site.

Then (of course) the shoppers spoke up. They drove into the mall, got out of their cars, breathing normally—and got a hit of that heavy, earthy air and gagged. "What is that horrendous smell?" they asked. When they found out what it was—and where it emanated from—the phone lines at City Hall rang off the hook.

City Hall received several thousand complaints over a few months before taking any action. The city environmental engineer was told to approach CCC's management and see if some resolution of the problem could be effected. CCC management listened to the engineer's concerns, but stated that there wasn't a whole lot that the site could do to rectify the problem.

As you might imagine, this was not the answer the city fathers were hoping to get. Feeling the increasing pressure from local inhabitants, commuters, shoppers, and airport management, the city brought the local state representatives into the situation.

The two state representatives for the area immediately began a campaign to close down the CCC facility. Their reasoning was that 44 acres is a lot of land for new homes, which meant more local inhabitants, thus more voters.

CCC was not powerless in this struggle—after all, it was there first, right? After all, the developers, those people in those new houses didn't HAVE to buy land right next to the facility—right? Besides, CCC had the EPA on its side. The company was taking a waste product no one wanted, one that traditionally ended up in the local landfill (taking up valuable space), and turning it into a beneficial reuse product. It was helping Mother Nature conserve and protect her local environment. Can there be a nobler goal?

The city leaders didn't really care about noble goals, but they did care about the concerns of their constituents, the voters. They continued their assault through the press, electronic media, legislatively, and by any other means they could bring to bear.

Management at CCC understood the problem and felt the pressure. They had to do something, and they did. Their environmental engineering division was assigned the task of coming up with a plan to mitigate not only CCC's odor problem, but also its dust problem. After several months of research and a pilot study, CCC's environmental engineering staff came up with a solution. It included enclosing the entire facility within a self-contained structure. The structure would be equipped with a state-of-the-art ventilation system and two-stage odor scrubbers. The engineers estimated that the odor problem could be reduced by 90% and the dust problem by 98.99%. CCC management thought they had a viable solution to the problem and were willing to spend the $5.2 million to retrofit the plant.

After CCC presented its mitigation plan to the city council, the council members made no comment, but said that they needed time to study it. Three weeks later, CCC received a letter from the mayor stating that CCC's efforts to come up with a plan to mitigate the odor and dust problems were commendable and to be applauded, but were unacceptable. From the mayor's letter, CCC could see that the focus of attack had now changed from a social to a legal issue. The mayor pointed out that he and the city fathers had a legal responsibility to ensure the good health and well-being of local inhabitants, and that certain legal limitations would be imposed and placed on the CCC facility to protect their health and welfare.

Compounding the problem was the airport. Airport officials also rejected CCC's plan to retrofit the composting facility. Their complaint (written on official FAA paper) stated that the dust generated at the compost facility was a

(continued)

Response Scenario 13.3. Cedar Creek Composting

hazard for flight operations, and even though the problem would be reduced substantially by engineering controls, the chance of control failure was always possible, and then an aircraft could be endangered; from the airport's point of view, this was unacceptable.

Several years went by, with local officials and CCC management contesting the plight of the compost facility. In the end, CCC management decided they had to shut down the operation and move to another location. So they closed the facility.

Both before and after shutdown, CCC management staff searched for another site to build a new wastewater biosolids-to-compost facility. They are still looking. To date, their search has located several pieces of property relatively close to the city (but far enough away to preclude any dust and odor problems), but they have had problems finalizing any deal. Buying the land is not the problem; getting the required permits from various county agencies to operate the facility is. CCC officials were turned down in each and every case. The standard excuse? Not in my backyard. Have you heard this phrase before? It's so common now, it's usually abbreviated—NIMBY. CCC officials are not all that optimistic about their chances of finding another site for their facility.

RESPONSE

(i) Do you think it was fair and justified to shut down the CCC facility?

The second control method often looks favorable to those who have weighed the high costs associated with air pollution control systems. Modifying a process to eliminate as much of the pollution problem as possible at the source is generally the first approach to be examined.

Often, the easiest way to modify a process for air pollution control is to change the fuel. If a power plant emits large quantities of sulfur dioxide and fly ash, conversion to cleaner-burning natural gas is cheaper than installing the necessary control equipment to reduce the pollutant emissions to permitted values.

But changing from one fuel to another causes its own problems related to costs, availability, and competition. Today's fuel prices are high, and no one counts on the trend reversing. Finding a low-sulfur fuel isn't easy, especially since many industries own their own dedicated supplies (not available for use in other industries). Facing the threat of regulatory compliance, everyone wants a share of any available low-cost, low-sulfur fuel. Because supplies are limited, the law of supply and demand takes over, and prices go up.

Some industries employ other process modification techniques. These may include evaluation of alternative manufacturing and production techniques, substitution of raw materials, and improved process control methods (Buonicore, Theodore, & Davis, 1992).

When elimination of the process entirely or in part, relocation of the operation, and modification of the operation to a fuel that gives the desired level of emission are not possible, the only alternative control method left is the third one listed above. The purpose of installing pollution control equipment or a control system, obviously, is to remove the pollution from the polluted carrier gas. To accomplish this, the polluted carrier gas must pass through a control device or system that collects or destroys the pollutant and releases the cleaned carrier gas to the atmosphere (Boubel et al., 1994).

AIR POLLUTION CONTROL EQUIPMENT AND SYSTEMS

Several considerations must be factored into any selection decision about air pollution control equipment or systems. Careful consideration must be given to costs. No one ever said air pollution equipment/systems were inexpensive—they are not. Obviously, the equipment/system must be designed to comply with applicable regulatory emission limitations. The operational and maintenance history/record (costs of energy, labor, and repair parts should also be factored in) of each equipment/system must be evaluated. Remember, emission control equipment must be operated on a continual basis, without interruptions, because any interruption could be subject to severe regulatory penalty, which could again be quite costly.

Probably the major factor to consider in the equipment/system selection process is what type of pollutant or pollutant stream is under consideration. If the pollutant is conveyed in a carrier gas, for example, factors such as carrier gas pressure, temperature, viscosity, toxicity, density, humidity, corrosiveness, and inflammability must all be considered before any selection is made.

Other important factors that must also be considered when selecting air pollution control equipment are listed in Table 13.3.

Table 13.3. Factors in Selecting Air Pollution Control Equipment/Systems

1. Best available technology (BAT)
2. Reliability
3. Lifetime and salvage value
4. Power requirements
5. Collection efficiency
6. Capital cost, including operation and maintenance costs
7. Track record of equipment/system and manufacturer
8. Space requirements and weight
9. Power requirements
10. Availability of space, parts, and manufacturer's representatives

In addition, process considerations dealing with gas flow rate and velocity, pollutant concentration, allowable pressure drop, and the variability of gas and pollutant flow rates (including temperature) must all be considered. The type of pollutant is also an important factor; is it gaseous or particulate? If, for example, the pollutant is gaseous, how corrosive, inflammable, reactive, and toxic is it? After these factors have been evaluated, the focus shifts to the selection of the best air pollution control equipment/system—affordable, practical, and permitted by regulatory requirements.

Chapter Summary

People in general often react to difficult-to-deal-with information emotionally, not logically, and news of pending environmental crisis is no exception. Those reactions cover a wide range of conditions, from denial, to hysteria, to indifference, to obsession, to anger, to activism, to foolhardiness, and none of those reactions—or the people behind them—does much toward bringing us closer to a solution.

By the time our societal and political systems get through with the information our scientists provide us with, public evaluation by anything close to scientific methodology is impossible, because the information the public receives is distorted and incomplete—chopped up and twisted to provide a good sound bite and tipped to suit the political beliefs of those in power and the financial concerns of the owners.

Little doubt exists that we are putting our environment—and thus ourselves—at serious risk. Although we are not sure (yet) of the exact causes—or all the causes—the changes we observe in our world are measurable. As active members of an increasingly global economy, we increase our risk by pretending these problems will go away. Sooner or later, we will have to face them—and technology will be how we solve them.

Discussion Questions and Problems

1. Several factors are pushing environmental air quality concerns increasingly into the international area. What are some of these concerns? Explain.
2. What are the unique factors responsible for the Antarctic ozone hole?
3. What effect, if any, does acidic deposition have on forests and crops?
4. What are the potential environmental effects associated with global warming?

Suggested Research Topics and Projects

- *The ozone hole:*
  - Ozone hole depletion and skin cancer.
  - Ozone hole depletion—the current state of scientific research and theory.
  - Ozone hole depletion as media hype.
  - Ozone hole depletion and U.S. politics.
  - Ozone hole depletion and world politics.
  - Ozone hole depletion and CFCs.
  - Ozone hole depletion and long-term climate history.
- *Global warming:*
  - Current state of scientific research and theory.
  - Global warming as media hype.

- ◦ Global warming and U.S. politics.
- ◦ Global warming and world politics.
- ◦ Global warming and CFCs.
- ◦ Global warming and long-term climate history.
- *Greenhouse effect:*
  - ◦ Current state of scientific research and theory.
  - ◦ Greenhouse effect as media hype.
  - ◦ Greenhouse effect and U.S. politics.
  - ◦ Greenhouse effect and world politics.
  - ◦ Greenhouse effect and CFCs.
  - ◦ Greenhouse effect and long-term climate history.
  - ◦ How global warming and the greenhouse effect are interrelated.
- *Acid rain:*
  - ◦ How have regulations affected acid rain levels?
  - ◦ Research air pollutant travel patterns.
  - ◦ Long-range and short-range transportation patterns in the United States: use of cars and/or public transportation and air quality.
  - ◦ How effective are car pool laws at reducing emissions?
  - ◦ State of research on acid rain's health effects.
  - ◦ State of research on acid rain's effects on crops.
- *Sea level rise:*
  - ◦ How sea level rise will affect U.S. coastal areas.
  - ◦ How sea level rise will affect other countries.
  - ◦ History of sea level rise.
  - ◦ What effect will significant sea level rise have on economics?
  - ◦ On commerce?
  - ◦ On tourism?
  - ◦ On wildlife?
  - ◦ On agriculture?
  - ◦ On local communities?
  - ◦ On infrastructure?
- *The Industrial Revolution*
  - ◦ The Industrial Revolution and the dying agrarian society: economic history.
  - ◦ Social history.
  - ◦ Political history.
  - ◦ Environmental history

References and Recommended Reading

Associated Press. (1997, December 7). "Does Warming Feed El Niño?" *Virginian-Pilot* (Norfolk, VA), A-15.

Associated Press. (1998b, September 28). "Ozone Hole over Antarctica at Record Size." *Lancaster New Era* (Lancaster, PA).

Associated Press. (1998a, September 25). "Tougher Air Pollution Standards Too Costly, Midwestern States Say." *Lancaster New Era* (Lancaster, PA).

Black-Covilli, L. L. (1992). "Basic Air Quality." In Knowles, Porter-C., ed., *Fundamentals of Environmental Science and Technology.* Rockville, MD: Government Institutes, Inc.

Boubel, R. W., Fox, D. L., Turner, D. B., & Stern, A. C. (1994). *Fundamentals of Air Pollution.* New York: Academic Press.

Broecker, W. (1987). "Unpleasant Surprises in the Greenhouse?" *Nature* 328: 123–26.

Bruun, P. (1962). "Sea Level Rise as a Cause of Shore Erosion." *Proceedings of the American Society of Engineers and Journal Waterways Harbors Division* 88: 117–30.

Bruun, P. (1986). "Worldwide Impacts of Sea Level Rise on Shorelines." In *Effects of Changes in Stratospheric Ozone and Global Climate*, Vol. 4, 99–128. New York: UNEP/EPA.

Buonicore, A. J., & Davis, W. T., eds. (1992). *Air Pollution Engineering Manual.* New York: Van Nostrand Reinhold.

Carbonify.com. (2009). "Global Warming—a Hoax?" Accessed November 7, 2009, http://www.carbonify. Com/articles/global-warming-hoax.htm.

"Contrails Reduce Daily Temperature Range." (2002). *Nature* 418. Accessed March 2, 2009, www.nature.com/nature.

Crowley, T. J., & North, G. R. (1988). "Abrupt Climate Change and Extinction Events in Earth's History." *Science* 240.

Davis, M. L., & Cornwell, D. A. (1991). *Introduction to Environmental Engineering.* New York: McGraw-Hill.

Dolan, E. F. (1991). *Our Poisoned Sky.* New York: Cobblehill Book.

Edgerton, L. (1991). *The Rising Tide: Global Warming and World Sea Levels.* Washington, DC: Island Press.

Franck, I., & Brownstone, D. (1992). *The Green Encyclopedia.* New York: Prentice-Hall.

Graedel, T. E., & Crutzen, P. J. (1989, S). "The Changing Atmosphere." *Scientific American*, 58–68.

Hansen, J. E., et al. (1986). "Climate Sensitivity to Increasing Greenhouses Gases." In Barth, M. C., & Titus, J. G., eds., *Greenhouse Effect and Sea Level Rise: A Challenge for This Generation.* New York: Van Nostrand Reinhold.

Hansen, J. E., et al. (1989, November). "Greenhouse Effect of Chlorofluorocarbons and Other Trace Gases." *Journal of Geophysical Research* 94: 16, 417–421.

Hegerl, G. C., Zwiers, F. W., Braconnot, P., Gillett, N. P., Luo, Y., Marengo Orsini, J. A., Nicholls, N., Penner, J. E., et al. (2007). "Understanding and Attributing Climate Change— Section 9.2.2 Spatial and Temporal Patterns of the Response to Different Forcings and Their Uncertainties, in Solomon; Quin, D.; Manning, M. et al. *Climate Change 2007: The Physical Science Basis. Contribution of Working Group I to the Fourth Assessment Report of the Intergovernmental Panel on Climate Change*, Intergovernmental Panel on Climate Change, Cambridge, UK: Cambridge University Press.

Interdependent Committee for Atmospheric Sciences. (1975, May). *The Possible Impact of Fluorocarbons and Hydrocarbons on Ozone.* Washington, DC: U.S. Government Printing Office, 3.

Ladurie, E. L. (1971). *Times of Feast, Times of Famine: A History of Climate since the Year 1000.* New York: Doubleday.

Masters, G. M. (1991). *Introduction to Environmental Engineering and Science.* Englewood Cliffs, NJ: Prentice-Hall.

Molina, M. J., & Rowland, F. S. (1974). "Stratospheric Sink for Chlorofluoromethanes: Chlorine Atom Catalyzed Destruction of Ozone." *Nature* 248: 810–12.

Ramanathan, V. (2006). "Atmospheric Brown Clouds: Health, Climate and Agriculture Impacts." *Pontifical Academy of Sciences Scripta Varia* 106: 47–60.

Spellman, F. R., & Whiting, N. (2006). *Environmental Science and Technology: Concepts and Applications*. Boca Raton, FL: CRC Press.

Stanhill, G., & Moreshet, S. (2004). "Global Radiation Climate Changes in Israel." *Climatic Change* 22: 121–38.

Thompson, D. J. (1995). "The Seasons, Global Temperature, and Precession." *Science* 268: 59.

Time Magazine. (1998, August 24). "Global Warming: It's Here . . . and Almost Certain to Get Worse."

USA Today. (1997, December 1). "Global Warming: Politics and Economics Further Complicate the Issue," A-1, 2.

USA Today. (2009). "Your Eyes Aren't Deceiving You: Skies Are Dimmer." Accessed March 13, 2009, http://www.usadtodya.com/weaterh/environment.

U.S. EPA. (1995). *The Probability of Sea Level Rise*. Washington, DC: Environmental Protection Agency.

U.S. EPA. (2005). *Basic Air Pollution Meteorology*. Accessed January 15, 2008, www.epa.gov/apti.

U.S. EPA. (2007). *National Ambient Air Quality Standards (NAAQS)*. Accessed January 12, 2008, www.epa.gov/air/criteria/html.

U.S. EPA. (2009). *Regulatory Atmospheric Modeling*. Accessed March 2, 2009, http://www.epa.gov/scram001/.

U.S. EPA. (2010). *Climate Change and Ecosystems*. Accessed June 2, 2011, www.epa.gov/climate change.

U.S. Geological Survey (USGS). (2009). *Hydroelectric Power Water Use*. Accessed November 11, 2009, http://ga.water.usgs.bof/ edu/suhy.html.

Wigley, T. M., Jones, P. D., & Kelly P. M. (1986). "Empirical Climate Studies: Warm World Scenarios and the Detection of Climatic Change Induced by Radioactively Active Gases." In Bolin, B., et al., eds., *The Greenhouse Effect, Climatic Change, and Ecosystems*. New York: Wiley.

WMO. (2009). *Manual of Codes*. Accessed March 2, 2009, http://www.wmo.ch/pages/prog/www/WMOCodes/Manual/WMO306_vol-1-2-PartB.pdf.

Wood, R., et al. (2007). "Climate Models and Their Evaluation." In Solomon, S. Qin, D., Manning, M., Chen, Z., Marquis, M., Averyt, K. B., Tignor, M., & Miller, H. L., *Climate Change 2007: The Physical Science Basins*. Cambridge, UK: Cambridge University Press.

Zurer, P. S. (1988, May). "Studies on Ozone Destruction Expand Beyond Antarctic." *C & E News*, 18–25.

Part III

WATER QUALITY

Perhaps the profession of doing good may be full, but everybody should be kind, at least to himself. Take a course in good water and air, and in the eternal youth of Nature you may renew your own. Go quietly, alone; no harm will befall you. Some have strange, morbid fears as soon as they find themselves with Nature, even in the kindest and wildest of her solitudes, like very sick children afraid of their mother—as if God were dead and devil were King.

—John Muir, 1888

CHAPTER 14

All about Water: Earth's Blood

The watery environment in which single-cell organisms live provides them food and removes their wastes, a function that the human circulatory system provides for the 60–100 trillion cells in a human body. The circulatory system brings each cell its daily supply of nutritive amino acids and glucose, and carries away waste carbon dioxide and ammonia, to be filtered out of our systems and flushed away through micturition and excretory functions. The heart, the center of our circulatory system keeps blood moving on its predetermined circular path, so essential that if the pump fails, we quickly fail as well—we die.

As single-celled organisms no longer, humans sometimes assume they no longer need a watery environment in which to live—but they aren't paying close attention to the world around them. Actually, those of us who live on Earth are as dependent upon the Earth's circulatory system as we are on our own circulatory system. As our human hearts pump blood, circulating it through a series of vessels, and as our lives are dependent upon that flow of blood, so life on Earth is, and our own lives are dependent on the Earth's water cycle, and on water, in every aspect of our lives.

This cycle is so automatic that we generally ignore it until we are slapped in the face by it. Just as we don't control or pay attention to the beating of our hearts unless the beat skips or falters, unless we are confronted by flood or drought, unless our plans are disrupted by rain, we ignore the water cycle, preferring to believe that the water we drink comes out of the faucet, and not from deep within the belly of the Earth, placed there by a process we only dimly comprehend. But water is as essential to us and to the Earth as blood is in our bodies, and the constant cycle water travels makes our lives possible.

Earth's blood, water, is pumped, not by a heart, but by the hydrological cycle—the water cycle. A titanic force of nature, the water cycle is beyond our control—a fact that we ignore until weather patterns shift and suddenly inundated rivers flow where they will and not within human-engineered banks, floodwalls, dikes and levees. In the water cycle, water evaporated from the oceans falls as rain, hail, sleet, or snow and it strikes the Earth again; the cycle continues.

In cities, in summer, rain strikes hot cement and asphalt and swiftly evaporates, or runs into storm drains, swiftly rejoining the cycle. In fields, rain brings essential moisture to crops, and sinking deeper into the Earth, ends as groundwater. If water strikes a forested area, the forest canopy breaks the force of the falling drops. The forest floor, carpeted in twigs, leaves, moss, dead and decaying vegetation, keeps the soil from splashing away in erosion as the water returns to the depths of the Earth, or runs over the land to join a stream.

Whenever water strikes the Earth, it flows along four pathways, which carry water through the cycle as our veins, arteries and capillaries carry our blood to our cells.

It may evaporate directly back into the air.

It may flow overland into a stream as runoff.

It may soak into the ground and be taken up by plants for evapotranspiration.

It may seep down to groundwater.

Whatever pathway water takes, one fact is certain: water is dynamic, vital, constantly on the move. And like human blood, which sustains our lives, Earth's blood, to sustain us as well, must continue to flow.

—Frank R. Spellman (1996)

Chapter Objectives

After studying this chapter, you should be able to

- Discuss how human activity has affected the pathways water takes through the landscape and what results that has on water quality.
- Discuss the effects of 1972's Clean Water Act on American water supplies and the current condition of our water supply.
- Describe needed characteristics of water.
- Discuss how water supply affects population.
- Identify the key locations of water and the percentages each location has in global water distribution.
- Define the two general sources of water.
- Describe surface water's place in the water cycle and identify its major sources.
- Discuss surface water's advantages and disadvantages as a freshwater source.
- Describe the various factors that influence surface water's flow.
- Describe and discuss groundwater's place in the water cycle and the effects of soil and rock.
- Discuss groundwater's advantages and disadvantages as a water source.

- Identify the major users of water in the United States and determine the percentages of available freshwater they consume.
- Describe and discuss domestic, commercial and industrial, and public use of water.
- Identify, describe, and discuss the physical, chemical, and biological substances that affect water characteristics.
- Discuss the differences between volatile and nonvolatile solids.
- Define turbidity and describe the factors that affect water clarity.
- Describe the conditions and factors that affect water color.
- Discuss consumer expectations of color, taste, and odor for water.
- Describe the organic and inorganic contaminants that affect water's smell and taste.
- Discuss palpability and temperature.
- Describe the effect temperature has on water treatment.
- Discuss the definition of water as the universal solvent.
- Identify the chemical constituents commonly found in water and describe how they affect water quality.
- Define total dissolved solids, discuss their sources, and describe how they are controlled.
- Discuss the problems created by high alkalinity.
- Identify the range and description classifications for water hardness and discuss the advantages and disadvantages of both hard and soft water.
- Discuss fluoride's importance in drinking water and describe how it affects teeth.
- Identify and discuss the metals, both toxic and nontoxic, commonly found in water supplies, and describe their effects on water quality.
- Identify the primary effects organic matter has on water quality.
- Discuss biodegradable and nonbiodegradeable organic matter in terms of BOD and COD.
- Identify the essential nutrients water carries and discuss how excessive or deficient quantities of these nutrients affect the environment.
- Discuss how biological water characteristics can affect human health and well-being and describe how pathogens are transported by the water system.
- Discuss how the presence or absence of biological organisms works as an indicator of water quality to water specialists.
- Identify the ways organisms extract nutrients and energy from their waste environment.
- Describe the role oxygen plays in organism metabolism.
- Define the types of aquatic organisms (bacteria, viruses, protozoa, worms, rotifers, crustaceans, fungi, and algae) that can inhabit aquatic environments and identify the physical, chemical, and biological factors necessary for their existence.

Chapter Outline

- Description: the water cycle
- Discussion: water and the relationship between supply and quality, the Clean Water Act, and possible options for maintaining and improving water quality

- Discussion: U.S. history and water—transportation, industry, and population
- Identification: global water distribution
- Definition and discussion: advantages and disadvantages of surface water sources; runoff problems, influences, and variables
- Definition and discussion: advantages and disadvantages of groundwater sources
- Discussion: U.S. water consumption by domestic, commercial, industrial, and public customers
- Definition and discussion: why the physical, chemical, and biological characteristics and contaminants of water are important indicators of water quality
- Definition and discussion: why water is wet, and how the physical characteristics of water (solids, turbidity, color, taste and odor, and temperature) affect water quality
- Definition and discussion: water as a universal solvent, and how chemical water perimeters (total dissolved solids, alkalinity, hardness, fluorides, metals, organics, and nutrients) affect water quality
- Definition and discussion: the factors that affect a watery environment, and how the biological inhabitants of water—bacteria, viruses, protozoa, worms, rotifers, crustaceans, fungi, and algae—extract their needs from the water environment and affect water quality

Key Terms

aerobic
algae
alkalinity
anaerobic
autotrophs
bacteria
best available technology (BAT)
biodegradable
biological oxygen demand (BOD)
biostimulant
brackish water
carbonate hardness
catchment
chemical oxygen demand (COD)
colloidal material
color
crustaceans
drainage basin
eutrophication
fluoride
freshwater
fungi

groundwater
hardness
heterotrophs
laxative effect
limiting nutrient
metals
noncarbonate hardness
nonbiodegradable
nonvolatile
nutrients
organic matter
oxidation
pathogens
protozoa
recharge area
reduction
rotifers
saline water
scaling
soft water
surface water
taste and odor

temperature	turbidity
total dissolved solids	virus
toxic metals	volatile

Introduction

Although we pursue the second environmental medium in Part III of this text, we are only shifting among related concepts. Air, water, and soil are interrelated, and we must not lose sight of these essential connections.

Water is an essential compound in the maintenance of all forms of life on Earth. This fact has resulted in the development of direct relationships between the abundance of water and the quality of the water—remember, having mega-gallons of water in storage, readily available, is of little use if the water is unsuitable for human use and reuse.

In the pre-Columbian era, on the North American continent, the natural water cycle was able to deliver clean water to the landscape. Today, the natural water cycle has been changed, tainted in a number of ways. We have dredged, drained, dammed, channeled, tampered with, and sometimes eliminated the ecological niches where water cleans itself. We have simplified the pathways that water takes through the American landscape. As a result, water that is no longer able to clean itself naturally must be regulated and cleaned using various advanced technologies.

In the United States, in response to a national crisis in water quality, water has been regulated since 1972. The purpose of these water regulations is to restore and maintain the chemical, physical, and biological integrity of the waterways. The discharge of pollutants into streams, rivers, and lakes was supposed to cease by 1995. The goal was to make these freshwater bodies fishable and swimmable. The means to accomplish this goal was to be provided by technology. Every U.S. city was required to build a wastewater treatment plant with secondary treatment capability. Every industry had to incorporate the **best available technology** (BAT) to decrease the discharge of pollutants into waterways.

In the years since then, the stranglehold that pollutant wastes had on the nation's **surface water** bodies has eased. However, the task is far from complete. A generation after the Clean Water Act was promulgated, about 30% of the stream miles and lake acres in the United States are still polluted (Outwater, 1997). A great deal must still be done. Despite our best legislative efforts, our waterways are still impaired. The question has become: Will our waterways ever return to their natural state, as they were in pre-Columbian times?

The answer is simple: No, they will not.

A mindset pervades regulatory and environmental activist circles, professing the hope that by changing the way we manage our vast public lands—by restoring those elements of the natural world that made the water pristine in pre-Columbian times—we can have clean water again. Much can be said in favor of this mindset. We have to start somewhere—we have to learn to respect water for what it really is: the land's blood.

But more is required. With the explosive growth of populations and the accompanying increased need for more natural resources and habitable land, we will have to work at restoring and maintaining water quality. The authors of this text take the view that this can only be accomplished by the correct and judicial use of technology to clean our water. Water must be available for human use and in abundant supply. Available water must have specific characteristics, and water quality is defined in terms of those characteristics (Tchobanoglous & Schroeder, 1987).

Did You Know?

According to the U.S. Geological Survey (2011), if all of Earth's water (oceans, ice caps and glaciers, lakes, rivers, **groundwater**, and water in the atmosphere) were put into a sphere, the diameter of that water ball would be about 860 miles (about 1,385 kilometers) across, a bit more than the distance between Salt Lake City, Utah, and Topeka, Kansas.

- A cubic mile of water equals more than 1.1 trillion gallons.
- A cubic kilometer of water equals about 264 billion gallons.

Water Resources

Note: Much of the information contained in the following sections is based on Spellman (2007).

Where on planet Earth is potable (drinkable) water readily found for human consumption? First, we must define potable water:

> Potable water is water fit for human consumption and domestic use, which is sanitary and normally free of minerals, organic substances, and toxic agents in excess of reasonable amounts for domestic usage in the area served, and normally adequate in quantity for the minimum health requirements of the persons served (Spellman, 2003).

For a potential potable water supply, the key words are *quality* and *quantity*. If we have a water supply that is unfit for human consumption, we have a quality problem. If we do not have an adequate supply of quality water, we have a quantity problem (Spellman, 2003).

Look at a map of the world, one that clearly indicates the world's population centers (cities). Take a look at the United States, for example. The first American settlers built their settlements along rivers, which provided the water settlers needed to sustain life and were the principal source of power for early industry and an easy means of transportation.

Most of the earliest settlements in the United States occurred on its East Coast. In most cases (the early Jamestown, Virginia, settlement is an exception—potable water quality there was poor), settlers along this eastern seaboard area were lucky. They had found river systems of excellent quality. These rivers were ideally suited for paper and textile manufacturing, which were among the earliest industries established.

As more settlers arrived in North America, they began to branch out inland (westward, where there was more elbow room) from the earliest settlements, and in many cases, they discovered that finding potable water was not so easy. The farther west they traveled, the higher the salinity of rivers and streams was, especially long rivers and streams that flowed through and over areas of relatively soluble rock formations.

In western regions of the United States (especially in desert regions), the U.S. map shows only sparse settlement, because those arid areas lack water to support a larger population. These regions are occupied by fewer people and different (more tolerant of water shortage) species than other biomes. A real estate saying emphasizes that location is "everything." Although we may not think of it that way, for the beginnings of human settlements, "Location, Location, Location!" really meant, "Water! Water! Water!" To be suitable as a living place, a new location had to have potable water (Spellman, 1998).

On land, the availability of a regular supply of potable water is the most important factor affecting the presence—or absence—of many life forms. Most people (and other living things) are found in regions of the United States and other parts of the world where potable water is readily available.

WHAT ARE THE MAJOR SOURCES OF DRINKING WATER?

Approximately 326 million cubic miles of water cover much of the planet, but only about 3% of this total is freshwater. Most of it is locked up in polar ice caps, glaciers, lakes, flows through soil, and river and stream systems. Out of this 3%, only 0.027% is available for human consumption.

Table 14.1 shows where the world's water is distributed. From Table 14.1, it should be obvious that the major sources of drinking water are surface water, groundwater, and groundwater that is under the direct influence of surface water (GWUDISW; a spring or a shallow well).

Table 14.1. World Water Distribution

Location	Percent of Total
Land areas	
Freshwater lakes	0.009
Saline lakes and inland seas	0.008
Rivers (average instantaneous volume)	0.0001
Soil moisture	0.005
Groundwater (above depth of 4000 m)	0.61
Ice caps and glaciers	2.14
Subtotal	**2.8**
Atmosphere (water vapor)	**0.001**
Oceans	**97.3**
Total of all locations (rounded)	**100.0**

Source: Adapted from Peavy, Rowe, & Tchobanoglous, 1985, 12.

Surface Water

Surface water (water on the Earth's surface, as opposed to subsurface water—ground-water) is mostly a product of precipitation: rain, snow, sleet, or hail. Surface water is exposed or open to the atmosphere and results from the movement of water on and just under the Earth's surface (overland flow). This overland flow is the same thing as surface runoff, which is the amount of rainfall that passes over the Earth's surface. Specific sources of surface water include the following:

Rivers
Streams
Lakes
Impoundments (lakes created by humans damming a river or stream)
Very shallow wells that receive input via precipitation
Springs affected by precipitation (their flow or quantity is directly affected by precipitation)
Rain **catchment**s (drainage basins)
Tundra ponds or muskegs (peat bogs) and other wetlands (swamps)

As a source of potable water, surface water does have some advantages:

1. Surface water is usually easy to locate—you do not have to be (or hire) a geologist or hydrologist to find it.
2. Normally, surface water is not tainted with chemicals precipitated from the Earth's strata.

Surface water also has its disadvantages. The biggest disadvantage of using surface water as a source of potable water is that it is easily contaminated (polluted) with microorganisms that can cause waterborne diseases and chemicals from surrounding runoff and upstream discharges. Problems can also occur with water rights.

If you are familiar with the battles that took place (some are still being waged) in the western United States when cattle folks were fighting homesteaders over rangeland, you know the cause: the rights to surface water. Today, in most places in the United States, significant removal of water from a river, stream, spring, or lake requires a legal permit (Spellman, 1998).

Most surface water is the result of surface runoff. The amount and flow rate of surface runoff is highly variable. This variability comes into play for two main reasons: (1) human interference (influences) and (2) natural conditions. In some cases, surface water runs quickly off land. Generally, quick runoff is undesirable (from a water resources standpoint) because water needs time to infiltrate into the ground and recharge aquifers. Other problems associated with quick surface water runoff are erosion and flooding. Probably the only good thing that can be said about surface water that quickly runs off land is that it does not have enough time (usually) to become contaminated with high mineral content. Surface water running slowly off land may be expected to have all the opposite attributes.

Surface water travels over the land to what amounts to a predetermined destination. What factors influence how surface water moves? Its journey over the Earth typically begins at a **drainage basin**, sometimes referred to as its drainage area, catchment, or watershed. For a groundwater source, this is known as the **recharge area**—the area from which precipitation flows into an underground water source. A surface water drainage basin is usually measured in square miles, acres, or sections, and if a city takes water from a surface water source, the size of and what lies within the drainage basin are essential information for water quality assessment.

Water doesn't run uphill. Surface water runoff (like the flow of electricity) follows the path of least resistance. Generally speaking, water in a drainage basin will naturally (by the geological formation of the area) be shunted toward one primary watercourse (a river, stream, creek, or brook) unless some man-made distribution system diverts the flow.

Various factors directly influence the surface water's flow over land. The principal factors are rainfall duration, rainfall intensity, soil moisture, soil composition, vegetation cover, ground slope, and human interference.

Rainfall duration: Rainstorm length affects runoff amount. Even a light, gentle rain eventually saturates the soil if it lasts long enough. Once the saturated soil can absorb no more water, rainfall builds up on the surface and begins to flow as runoff.

Did You Know?

About 3,100 mi³ (12,900 km³) of water, mostly in the form of water vapor, is in the atmosphere at any one time. If it all fell as precipitation at once, the Earth would be covered with only about 1 inch of water (USGS, 2011).

Rainfall intensity: The harder and faster it rains, the more quickly soil becomes saturated. With hard rains, the surface inches of soil quickly become inundated, and with short, hard storms, most of the rainfall may end up as surface runoff, because the moisture is carried away before significant amounts of water are absorbed into the Earth.

Did You Know?

The 48 contiguous states receives a total of about 4 mi³ (17.7 km³) of precipitation each day. Each day, 280 m³ (1,170 k m³) of water evaporates or transpires into the atmosphere. If all the world's water was poured on the United States, it would cover the land to a depth of 90 miles (145 kilometers) (USGS, 2011).

Soil moisture: Obviously, if the soil is already laden with water from previous rains, the saturation point is reached sooner than with dry soil. Frozen soil also inhibits water absorption: up to 100% of snowmelt or rainfall on frozen soil ends as runoff, because frozen ground is impervious.

Did You Know?

Of the freshwater on Earth, much more is stored in the ground than is available in lakes and rivers. More than 2,000,000 m³ (8,400,000 km³) of freshwater is stored in the Earth, most within one-half mile of the surface. Contrast that with the 60,000 mi³ (250,000 km³) of water stored as freshwater in lakes, inland seas, and rivers (USGS, 2011).

Soil composition: Runoff amount is directly affected by soil composition. Hard rock surfaces shed all rainfall, obviously, but so will soils with heavy clay composition. Clay soils possess small void spaces that swell when wet. When the void spaces close, they form a barrier that does not allow additional absorption or infiltration. On the opposite end of the spectrum, course sand allows easy water flow-through, even in a torrential downpour.

Vegetation cover: Runoff is limited by groundcover. Roots of vegetation and pine needles, pine cones, leaves, and branches create a porous layer (a sheet of decaying natural organic substances) above the soil. This porous "organic" sheet (ground cover) readily allows water into the soil. Vegetation and organic waste also act as a cover to protect the soil from hard, driving rains. Hard rains can compact bare soils, close off void spaces, and increase runoff. Vegetation and groundcover work to maintain the soil's infiltration and water-holding capacity. Note that vegetation and groundcover also reduce evaporation of soil moisture.

Ground slope: Flat-land water flow is usually so slow that large amounts of rainfall can infiltrate the ground. Gravity works against infiltration on steeply sloping ground; up to 80% of rainfall may become surface runoff.

Human Interference: Various human activities have a definite impact on surface water runoff. Most human activities tend to increase the rate of water flow. For example, canals and ditches are usually constructed to provide steady flow, and agricultural activities generally remove groundcover that would work to retard the runoff rate. On the opposite extreme, human-made dams are generally built to retard the flow of runoff.

Human habitations, with their paved streets, tarmac, paved parking lots, and buildings, create surface runoff potential, because so many of these surfaces are impervious to infiltration. Because all these surfaces hasten the flow of water, they also increase the possibility of flooding, often with devastating results. Moreover, water running off impervious areas, such as roads and parking lots, can contain a lot of contaminants, such as oil and garbage. This runoff often goes directly into streams. In addition, following summer storms, runoff from heated roads and parking lots causes rapid increases in stream **temperatures**, which can produce thermal shock and death in many fish. Because of urban increases in runoff, a whole new field (industry) has developed: stormwater management.

Paving over natural surface acreage has another serious side effect. Without enough area available for water to infiltrate the ground and percolate into the soil to eventually reach and replenish/recharge groundwater sources, those sources may eventually fail, with devastating impacts on local water supplies.

Response Scenario 14.1.
Real and Artificial Wetlands

Former common land use practices placed little or no value on natural wetlands. Wetland areas were commonly filled in, the water channeled and drained away, and the land "reclaimed" for agriculture or building.

Gradually, however, we began to realize the value of natural wetland areas. We finally figured out that nature, as usual, knew exactly what she was doing. Wetlands are an essential part of the hydrogeologic cycle, and we tamper with them at our peril. They provide a natural buffer for stormwater runoff, flood control, a natural filtration system for pollutants and sedimentation, and important habitat for specialized species.

Now we are attempting to copy natural wetlands protection zones ourselves. Artificial wetlands in the Bayswater area of Perth, Australia, have proven effective in containing the most damaging kind of runoff—the first heavy flush of water after dry weather. Designed to act as traps for low drainage flows and as filters for higher water levels, these artificial wetlands are preventing runoff damage and providing sediment and nutrient control. These designed wetlands hold water for an average seven-day detention period. The slow infiltration of stormwater into the soil and native vegetation is estimated to filter out 50% of the pollutants from average flows.

Artificial wetlands require long development time for vegetation to mature. Even at its early stages, however, this artificial wetlands is performing effectively at what it was designed to accomplish. It is also aesthetically pleasing and provides habitat for birds and native fish.

RESPONSE

(i) Are artificial wetlands the answer for replacing the natural wetlands we have destroyed or modified?

Groundwater

Approximately three feet of water falls each year on every square foot of land. About six inches of this goes back to the sea. Evaporation takes up about two feet. What remains, approximately six inches, seeps into the ground, entering and filling every interstice, each hollow and cavity, like an absorbent. Although comprised of only 1/6 of the total (1,680,000 miles of it), if it could be ladled up and spread out over the Earth's surface, it would blanket all land to a depth of one thousand feet.

This gigantic water source (literally an ocean beneath our feet) forms a reservoir that feeds all the natural fountains and springs of Earth. Eventually, it works its way to the surface. Some comes out clean and cool, a liquid blue-green phantom; and some, occupying the deepest recesses, pressurizes and shots back to the surface in white, foamy, wet chaos, as geysers.

Fortunately, most of the rest lies within easy reach, just beneath the surface.

This is groundwater.

—Spellman (1998 22–23)

Water falling to the ground as precipitation normally follows three courses. Some runs off directly to rivers and streams, some infiltrates to ground reservoirs, and the rest evaporates or transpires through vegetation. The water in the ground (groundwater) is "invisible" and may be thought of as a temporary natural reservoir (ASTM, 1969). Almost all groundwater is in constant motion toward rivers or other surface water bodies.

Groundwater is defined as water below the Earth's crust, but above a depth of 2,500 feet. Thus, if water is located between the Earth's crust and the 2,500-foot level, it is considered usable (potable) freshwater. In the United States, "at least 50% of total available fresh water storage is in underground aquifers" (Kemmer, 1979, 17).

Groundwater is usually obtained from wells or from springs that are not influenced by surface water or local hydrologic events. Groundwater has several advantages over surface water:

1. Unlike surface water, groundwater is not easily contaminated.
2. Groundwater sources are usually lower in bacteriological contamination than surface water.
3. Groundwater supply usually remains stable throughout the year.
4. In the United States, for example, groundwater is available in most locations.

When comparing groundwater with surface water sources, groundwater does have some disadvantages:

1. Contamination is usually hidden from view in groundwater.
2. Groundwater is usually loaded with minerals (has an increased level of **hardness**) because it is in contact with minerals longer.
3. Removing contaminants from groundwater supplies is very difficult.
4. Because groundwater must be pumped from the ground, operating costs are usually higher.
5. Groundwater sources near coastal areas may be subject to saltwater intrusion.

Water Use

In the United States, rainfall averages approximately $4,250 \times 10^9$ gallons a day. About two-thirds of this returns to the atmosphere through evaporation from the surface of rivers, streams, and lakes or from transpiration from plant foliage. This leaves approximately $1,250 \times 10^9$ gallons a day to flow across or through the Earth to the sea (Kemmer, 1979).

Water is currently used in the United States at a rate of 1.6×10^{12} liters per day, which amounts to almost a tenfold increase since the turn of the 19th century. Where is this water used? The National Academy of Sciences (1962) estimates that approximately (1) 310 billion gallons per day (bgd) are withdrawn; (2) 142 bgd are used for irrigation; (3) 142 bgd are used for industry (principally utility cooling water—100 bgd); (4) 26 bgd are used in municipal applications; (5) 90 bgd are consumed (principally irrigation, loss to ground, and evaporation); and (6) 220 bgd are returned to streams. That much of the increase is accounted for by high agricultural and industrial use is evident; each accounts for more than 40% of total consumption. Municipal use consumes 10–12% (Manahan, 1997).

How Much Water Does It Take to . . . ?

- drink: ½ gallon per person, per day
- shower with a low-flow showerhead: 9–12 gallons per person, per day
- fill the bathtub: about 36 gallons
- cook: 5–10 gallons per person, per day
- wash cloths or the car: 50 gallons per wash
- water the lawn/yard: 300 gallons per watering
- flush the toilet: 3.5–7 gallons, or 1.5 gallons with a water-saving toilet

(USDA, 2011)

We are primarily concerned with water use for municipal applications (demand). Municipal water demand is usually classified according to the nature of the user. These classifications are the following:

- *Domestic.* Domestic water is supplied to houses, schools, hospitals, hotels, restaurants, and so forth, for culinary, sanitary, and other purposes. Use varies with the economic level of the consumer, the range being 20–100 gallons per capita per day. Note that these figures include water used for watering gardens and lawns and washing cars.
- *Commercial and industrial.* Commercial and industrial water is supplied to stores, offices, and factories. The importance of commercial and industrial demand is based on whether large industries use water supplied from the municipal system, because large industrial facilities can make heavy demands on a municipal system. Large industries demand a quantity directly related to the number of persons employed, the actual floor space or area of each establishment, and the number of units manufactured or produced.
- *Public use.* Public use water is furnished to public buildings and used for public services. This includes water for schools, public buildings, fire protection, and flushing streets.
- *Loss and waste.* Water that is lost or wasted (unaccounted for) is attributable to leaks in the distribution system, inaccurate meter readings, and unauthorized connections. Loss and waste of water can be expensive. Reducing these costs requires a regular program that includes maintenance of the system and replacement and/or recalibration of meters (McGhee, 1991).

Manahan (1997) points out that water is not destroyed, but it can be lost for practical use. The three ways in which this may occur are

- **Evaporative losses** that occur during spray irrigation, and when water is used for evaporative cooling;
- **Infiltration** of water into the ground, often in places and ways that preclude its later use as water source groundwater; and
- **Degradation** from pollutants, such as salts picked up by water used for irrigation (1997, 133).

Characteristics of Water

Note: To understand water's properties, it is important to recognize its characteristics. Water is more than just plain old water—it actually has some very unusual properties. Let us first describe water's major characteristics and then take a brief USGS quiz on water's properties to test your knowledge about real water facts.

When we attempt to characterize water, we normally jump on the obvious features available: appearance, taste, and smell. These physical attributes are important, but so are chemical and biological characteristics.

The chemical characteristics of water are important because even though water may appear, smell, and even taste okay, that doesn't necessarily mean some chemical contaminant is not present. Today, with all the pesticides used in agriculture and various other industrial activities, chemical contamination is a very real possibility.

The biological characteristics of water are extremely important to anyone who might drink it. As stated previously, even before Typhoid Mary, people suspected there was a relationship between microorganisms and disease. Today, we know with certainty that waterborne diseases are a real threat to human health.

We also know that contaminated water (whether physically, chemically, or biologically contaminated) does not start out contaminated. Precipitation in the form of rain, snow, hail, or sleet (aside from what we contaminate ourselves) contains very few (if any) impurities. It may pick up trace amounts of mineral matter, gases, and other substances as it forms and falls through the Earth's atmosphere, but the precipitation has virtually no bacterial content—no waterborne disease.

When precipitation reaches the Earth's surface, many opportunities for the introduction of mineral and organic substances, microorganisms, and other forms of pollution (contamination) are presented. When water runs over and through the ground surface, it may pick up particles of soil. This attaches a physical property to water that can be readily seen—cloudiness or **turbidity**. Water, as it courses its inexorable way along the Earth's surface, also picks up **organic matter** and **bacteria**. As water seeps down into the soil and through the underlying material to the water table, most of the suspended particles are filtered out. This natural filtration may be a two-edged sword: It can be partially effective in removing bacteria and other particulate matter, but it may also change the chemical properties of water as it comes in contact with mineral deposits.

Substances that alter the quality of water or its characteristics as it moves over or below the surface of the Earth are of major concern to environmental practitioners. Thus, in the following sections we discuss water's physical, chemical, and biological characteristics.

PHYSICAL CHARACTERISTICS OF WATER

What makes water wet? Why is it wet? David Clary (1997), a chemist at University College London, points out that water does not start to behave like a liquid until at least six molecules form a cluster. He found that groups of five water molecules or fewer have planar structures, forming films one molecule thick. However, when a sixth molecule is added, the cluster switches to a three-dimensional, cagelike structure, and suddenly it has the properties of water—it becomes wet.

Beyond wetness, other physical characteristics of interest to us are water's solids; turbidity; **color**; **taste** and **odor**; and temperature—all of which are apparent to our senses of smell, taste, sight, and touch.

Solids

Other than gases, all contaminants of water contribute to water's total solids (filterable + nonfilterable solids) content. *Solids* are classified by size and state, chemical characteristics, and size distribution. Solids can be dispersed in water in both suspended and dissolved forms. They are also size classified as suspended, settleable, colloidal, or dissolved, depending on their behavioral attributes. **Colloidal material** in water is sometimes beneficial and sometimes harmful. Beneficial colloids are those that provide a dispersant effect by acting as protective colloids. Some colloids (silica-based types) can be troublesome, forming very hard scale when it deposits on heat transfer surfaces (Kemmer, 1988). Chemically, solids are also characterized as being **volatile** (volatize at 550°C) or **nonvolatile**.

In determining the distribution of solids, we compute the percentage of solids by size range. Typically, solids include inorganic solids (silt and clay from riverbanks) and organic matter such as plant fibers and microorganisms from natural or man-made sources. In flowing water, many of these contaminants result from the erosive action of water flowing over surfaces. Suspended material is not normally found in groundwater because of the filtering effect of the soil.

Suspended material present in water is objectionable because it provides adsorption sites for biological and chemical changes. These sites provide attached microorganisms a protective barrier against the chemical action of chlorine used in the disinfection process. Suspended solids in water may also be objectionable because they can be degraded biologically into unwanted by-products. Obviously, the removal of these solids is of primary concern in the production of clean, safe drinking water.

In the water treatment process, the most effective means of removing solids from water is by filtration. However, not all solids (colloids and other dissolved solids) can be removed by filtration.

Turbidity

As mentioned previously, one of the first conditions we notice about water is its clarity—which we measure by turbidity, an assessment of the extent to which light is either absorbed or scattered by suspended material in water. Both the size and surface characteristics of the suspended material influence absorption and scattering.

In surface water, most turbidity results from the erosion of very small colloidal material (rock fragments, silt, clay, and metal oxides from the soil). Microorganisms and vegetable material may also contribute to turbidity. In running waters, turbidity interferes with light penetration and photosynthetic reactions critical to aquatic plants. In water treatment, turbidity is a useful indicator of water quality.

Color

Water color is a physical characteristic often used to judge its quality. Pure water is colorless. Water takes on color when foreign substances—organic matter from soils, vegetation, minerals, and aquatic organisms—are present. For the most part, color in water is a mixture of colloidal organic compounds that represent breakdown products of high molecular weight substances produced by living cells. Consider, for example, water with a yellowish or tea color. The source of this yellow color is decayed vegetation leached from the watershed by runoff. These organic materials are broadly classified as humic substances (Kemmer, 1988). Color can also be contributed to water by municipal and industrial wastes.

Color in water is classified as either *true color* or *apparent color*. Color that is partly due to dissolved solids that remain after removal of suspended matter is known as true color. Color contributed by suspended matter is said to be apparent color. In water treatment, true color is the most difficult to remove (Spellman, 1998).

Colored water is generally unacceptable to the general public. People tend to prefer clear, uncolored water. Another problem with colored water is the affect it has on manufacturing, textiles, food preparation/processing, papermaking, and laundering. The color of water has a profound effect on its marketability for both domestic and industrial use. In water treatment, color is not usually considered unsafe or unsanitary, but is a treatment problem related to exerting chlorine demand, which reduces the effectiveness of chlorine as a disinfectant. Some of the processes used in treating colored water are filtration, softening, **oxidation**, chlorination, and adsorption.

Taste and Odor

Taste and *odor* are used jointly in the vernacular of freshwater science. In drinking water, odor and taste are usually not a consideration until the consumer complains. The problem is, of course, that most consumers find any taste and odor in water aesthetically displeasing. Taste and odor do not normally present a health hazard; however, they can cause the customer to seek out water that might taste and smell better, but may also be unsafe to drink. The fact is, consumers expect that water should be tasteless and odorless—and if it isn't, they consider it substandard. If a consumer can taste or smell the water, he or she automatically assumes it is contaminated (Spellman, 1998).

Water contaminants are attributable to contact with natural substances (rocks, vegetation, soil, etc.) or human use. Taste and odor are caused by foreign matter: organic compounds, inorganic salts, or dissolved gases. Again, these substances may come from domestic, agricultural, or natural sources. Some substances found naturally in groundwater, though not necessarily harmful, may impart a disagreeable taste or undesirable property to the water. Magnesium sulfate, sodium sulfate, and sodium chloride are a few of these (Corbitt, 1990).

When water has a taste but no accompanying odor, the cause is usually inorganic contamination. Water that tastes bitter is usually alkaline, while salty water is commonly the result of the salts mentioned previously. However, when water has both taste and odor, the likely cause is organic materials. The list of possible organic contaminants is too long to record here; however, petroleum-based products lead the list of offenders. Taste- and odor-producing liquids and gases in water are produced by biological decomposition of organics. A prime example is hydrogen sulfide, known best for its characteristic "rotten-egg" taste and odor. Table 14.2 lists a number of other distinct smells that are commonly encountered.

Table 14.2. Categories of Offensive Odors Often Encountered in Water

Compound	Descriptive Quality
Amines	Fishy
Ammonia	Ammoniacal
Diamines	Decayed flesh
Hydrogen sulfide	Rotten egg
Mercaptans	Skunk secretion
Organic sulfides	Rotten cabbage
Skatole	Fecal

Source: Adapted from Moncrief, 1967.

Objectionable tastes and odors caused by biological activity also include those from various **algae** species (e.g., *Diatomaceae:* Asterionella, Synerdra; *Protozoa:* Synura, Dionbyron; *Cyanophyceae*: Anabaea, Aphanizomenon; and *Chlorophyceae*: Volvox, Staurastrum), diatoms, and actinomycetes, which produce organic by-products, such as essential oils, that can be observed by microscopic examination. The release of these materials into water, particularly when large populations of organisms die, produces objectionable tastes and odors (Kemmer, 1988).

One of the common water treatment methods used to remove taste and odor is oxidation (usually with potassium permanganate and chlorine) of the problem material. Another standard treatment method is to feed powdered activated carbon to the flow prior to filtration. The activated carbon has numerous small openings that adsorb the components that cause the odor and tastes.

Temperature

Most consumers prefer drinking water that is consistently cool and does not have temperature fluctuations of more than a few degrees. Groundwater from mountainous areas generally meets these criteria. Water with a temperature between 10° and 15°C (50° and 60°F) is generally the most palatable (Corbitt, 1990).

Heat is added to surface and groundwater in many ways, some natural, some artificial. A problem associated with heat or excessive temperature in surface water is that it affects the solubility of oxygen in water, the rate of bacterial activity, and the rate at which gases are transferred to and from the water.

In the actual evaluation of water (for its suitability for consumption), temperature is not normally a parameter used. However, temperature is one of the most important parameters in natural surface-water systems, which are subject to great temperature variations. It affects a number of important water quality parameters. Temperature has an effect on the rate at which chemicals dissolve and react. When water is cold, more chemicals are required for efficient coagulation and flocculation to take place. When water temperature is high, the result may be a higher chlorine demand because of increased reactivity, and an increased level of algae and other organic matter in raw water. Temperature also has a pronounced effect on the solubility of gases in water.

Ambient temperature (temperature of the surrounding atmosphere) has the most profound and universal effect on the temperature of shallow natural water systems. When water is used by industry to dissipate process waste heat, the discharge points into surface water may experience dramatic localized temperature changes. Other sources of increased temperatures in running water systems result are clear-cutting practices in forests (where protective canopies are removed) and irrigation flows returned to a body of running water.

Many people harbor a misconception about water temperature. Although the temperature of groundwater seems relatively "cool" in summer and warm in winter, its temperature remains nearly constant throughout the year. Human perception of temperature is relative to air temperature—the slight temperature fluctuation is not usually detectable. Contrary to popular belief, colder water is not obtained by drilling deeper wells. Beyond the 100-foot depth mark, the temperature of groundwater actually increases steadily at the rate of about 0.6°C (1°F) for each 100 feet or so of depth. This rate may increase dramatically in volcanic regions.

CHEMICAL CHARACTERISTICS OF WATER

Other parameters used to define water quality are its chemical characteristics. Water's chemical composition is changed by the nature of the rocks that form the Earth's crust. As surface water seeps down to the water table, it dissolves and carries portions of the minerals contained in/by soils and rocks. Because of this, groundwater usually is heavier in dissolved mineral content than surface water. Each chemical constituent that water may contain affects water use in some manner, by either restricting or enhancing specific uses (see Table 14.3 for principal constituents).

Water, commonly called the *universal solvent*, is a solvent because of its chemical characteristics. Water analysts test a water supply to determine the supply's chemical characteristics; whether other harmful substances are present; if substances are present that will enhance corrosion (e.g., of metals in water heaters); and if the chemicals re-

Table 14.3. Chemical Constituents Commonly Found in Water

Calcium	Fluorine
Magnesium	Nitrate
Sodium	Silica
Potassium	TDS
Iron	Hardness
Manganese	Color
Bicarbonate	pH
Carbonate	Turbidity
Sulfate chloride	Temperature

sponsible for staining fixtures and clothing are present in the water. The exact analyses to be conducted on a municipal water supply are mandated by Public Health Service Drinking Water Standards promulgated by the U.S. Department of Health, Education, and Welfare.

Along with the elements listed in Table 14.3 and toxic substances, water-quality managers are concerned with the presence of **total dissolved solids** (TDS), **alkalinity**, hardness, **fluorides**, **metals**, organics, and **nutrients** that might be present in a water supply. We discuss these chemical parameters in the following sections.

Total Dissolved Solids (TDS)

Total dissolved solids (TDS) come from the minerals dissolved in water from rocks and soil as water passes over and through them. TDS is the residue remaining in a water sample after filtration or evaporation and is expressed in mg/L.

TDS is an important water quality parameter, commonly used to measure salinity. Roughly, **freshwater** has a TDS of less than 1,500 mg/L (drinking water has a recommended maximum TDS level of 500 mg/L), **brackish water** has a TDS up to 5,000 mg/L, and **saline water** has a TDS above 5,000 mg/L. Seawater has 30,000–34,000 mg/L TDS (Tchobanoglous & Schroeder, 1987).

Dissolved solids may be organic or inorganic. Water may come into contact with these substances within the soil, on surfaces, or in the atmosphere. The organic dissolved constituents of water come from degradation (decay) of products of vegetation, organic chemicals, and organic gases.

These dissolved solids can be removed from water by distillation, electrodialysis, reverse osmosis, or ion exchange. Removing these dissolved minerals, gases, and organic constituents is desirable, because they may cause physiological effects and produce aesthetically displeasing color, taste, and odor.

You might think removing all these dissolved substances from water is desirable, but this is not a prudent move. Pure, distilled water tastes flat. Also, water has an equilibrium state with respect to dissolved constituents. If water is out of equilibrium or undersaturated, it aggressively dissolves materials it comes into contact with. Because of this particular problem, substances that are readily dissolvable are sometimes added to pure water to reduce its tendency to dissolve plumbing fixtures.

Alkalinity

As pointed out in Chapter 3, alkalinity, imparted to water by bicarbonate, carbonate, or hydroxide components, is a measure of water's ability to absorb hydrogen ions without significant pH change. Stated another way, alkalinity is a measure of the buffering capacity of water. Alkalinity measures the ability of water to neutralize acids and is the sum of all titratable bases down to about pH 4.5. The bicarbonate, carbonate, and hydroxide constitutes of alkalinity originate from carbon dioxide (from the atmosphere and as a by-product of microbial decomposition of organic material) and from their mineral origin (primarily from chemical compounds dissolved from rocks and soil).

Highly alkaline water has no known significant impact on human health, but is unpalatable. The principal problem with alkaline water is the reactions that occur between alkalinity and certain substances in the water. The resultant precipitate can foul water system appurtenances. Alkalinity levels also affect the efficiency of certain water treatment processes, especially the coagulation process.

Hardness

Water hardness is familiar to those individuals who have washed their hands with a bar of soap and found that they needed more soap to "get up a lather." For this reason, originally hardness referred to the soap-consuming power of water. Hardness is the presence in water of multivalent cations, most notably calcium and magnesium ions. It is classified as **carbonate hardness** and **noncarbonate hardness**. The carbonate that is equivalent to the alkalinity is termed carbonate hardness. Hardness is either temporary or permanent. Carbonate hardness (temporary hardness) can be removed by boiling. Noncarbonate hardness cannot be removed by boiling and is classified as permanent.

Hardness values are expressed as an equivalent amount or equivalent weight of calcium carbonate (equivalent weight of a substance is its atomic or molecular weight divided by n). Water with a hardness of less than 50 ppm is **soft**. Above 200 ppm, domestic supplies are usually blended to reduce the hardness value. The U.S. Geological Survey uses the classification shown in Table 14.4.

Table 14.4. Hard/Soft Water Classification

Range of Hardness (mg/liter [ppm] as $CaCo_3$)	Descriptive Classification
1 to 50	Soft
51 to 150	Moderately hard
151 to 300	Hard
Above 300	Very Hard

Hardness has an economic impact, in soap consumption as well as on tanks and pipes. When using a bar of soap in hard water, you work the soap until the lather is built up. When lathering does occur, the water has been "softened" by the soap. However, the precipitate formed by hardness and soap (soap curd) adheres to just about anything (tubs, sinks, dishwashers) and may stain clothing, dishes, and other items. Hardness also affects people in personal ways: residues of the hardness-soap precipitate may remain in skin pores, causing skin to feel rough and uncomfortable. Today these problems have been largely reduced by the development of synthetic soaps and detergents that do not react with hardness. However, hardness still leads to other problems, including **scaling** and **laxative effect**. Scaling, of course, occurs when carbonate hard water is heated and calcium carbonate and magnesium hydroxide are precipitated out of solution, forming a rock-hard scale that clogs hot water pipes and reduces the efficiency of boilers, water heaters, and heat exchangers. Hardness, especially with the combined presence of magnesium sulfates, can lead to the development of a laxative effect on new consumers.

Rowe & Abdel-Magid (1995) point out that using hard water has some advantages, including that (1) hard water aids in growth of teeth and bones; (2) hard water reduces toxicity of poisoning by lead oxide from pipelines made of lead; and (3) **soft water** is suspected to be associated with cardiovascular disease.

Fluoride

Fluoride, seldom found in appreciable quantities in surface water, appears in groundwater in only a few geographical regions, though it is sometimes found in a few types of igneous or sedimentary rocks. Fluoride is toxic to humans in large quantities and toxic to some animals. Some plants used for fodder can store and concentrate fluoride. Animals that consume this forage ingest an enormous overdose of fluoride. Their teeth mottle, they lose weight, give less milk, grow bone spurs, and become so crippled they must be destroyed (Koren, 1991).

Fluoride in small concentrations is beneficial for controlling dental caries. Water containing the proper amount of fluoride can reduce tooth decay by 65% in children between ages 12 and 15. Adding fluoride to provide a residual of 1.5 to 2.5 mg/L has become common practice among municipal water plants. Concentrations above 5 mg/L are detrimental and limited by drinking water standards.

How does the fluoridation of a drinking water supply actually work to reduce tooth decay? Fluoride combines chemically with tooth enamel when permanent teeth are forming. The result, of course, is harder, stronger teeth that are more resistant to decay. Adult teeth are not affected by fluoride.

The EPA sets the upper limit for fluoride based on ambient temperatures, because people drink more water in warmer climates. Fluoride concentrations should be lower in those areas.

Metals

Iron and manganese are commonly found in groundwater, but surface water may also contain significant amounts. Metals in water are classified as either toxic or nontoxic. Only those metals that are harmful in relatively small amounts are labeled toxic; other metals fall into the nontoxic group. In natural water, sources of metals include dissolution from natural deposits and discharges of domestic, agricultural, or industrial wastewater.

Nontoxic metals commonly found in water include the hardness ions (calcium and manganese), iron, aluminum, copper, zinc, and sodium. Sodium (abundant in the Earth's crust and highly reactive with other elements) is by far the most common nontoxic metal found in natural water. Sodium salts (in excessive concentrations) cause a bitter taste in water and are a health hazard for kidney and cardiac patients. The usual low-sodium diet allows for 20 mg/L of sodium in drinking water. Sodium in large concentrations is toxic to plants.

Although iron and manganese in natural water (in very small quantities) may cause color problems, they frequently occur together and present no health hazards at normal concentrations. Some bacteria, however, use manganese compounds as an energy source, and the resulting slime growth may produce taste and odor problems. The recommended limit for iron is 0.3 mg/L, and it is 0.05 mg/L for manganese.

Very small quantities of other nontoxic metals are found in natural water systems. Most of these metals cause taste problems well before they reach toxic levels.

Fortunately, **toxic metals** are present in only minute quantities in most natural water systems. However, even in small quantities, these toxic metals can be especially harmful to humans and other organisms. Arsenic, barium, cadmium, chromium, lead, mercury, and silver are toxic metals that dissolve in water. Arsenic, cadmium, lead, and mercury—all cumulative toxins—are particularly hazardous to human health. Concentrated in organisms' bodies, these toxins are passed up the food chain and pose the greatest threat to organisms at the top of the chain.

Organic Matter

Organic matter (a broad category) includes both natural and synthetic molecules containing carbon, and usually hydrogen. All living matter is made up of organic molecules. Some organics are extremely soluble in water (alcohol and sugar are good examples); others may be quite insoluble (plastics).

Tchobanoglous and Schroeder point out that the presence of organic matter in water is troublesome for the following reasons: "(1) color formation, (2) taste and odor problems, (3) oxygen depletion in streams, (4) interference with water treatment processes, and (5) the formation of halogenated compounds when chlorine is added to disinfect water" (1987, 94).

The main source of organic matter in water—although total amounts in water are low—is decaying vegetation (leaves, weeds, and trees). The general category of "organics" in natural water includes organic matter whose origins could be both natural sources and human activities. Distinguishing natural organic compounds from solely human-made compounds (e.g., pesticides and other synthetic organic compounds) is critical.

Natural water-soluble organic materials are generally limited to contamination of surface water only. Dissolved organics are usually divided into two categories: **biodegradable** and **nonbiodegradable**.

Biodegradable (tends to break down) material consists of organics that can be used as nutrients (food) by naturally occurring microorganisms within a reasonable length of time. These materials usually consist of alcohols, acids, starches, fats, proteins, esters, and aldehydes. They may result from domestic or industrial wastewater discharges, or they may be end products of the initial decomposition of plant or animal tissue. The principal problem associated with biodegradable organics is the effect resulting from the action of microorganisms. Secondary problems include color, taste, and odor problems.

For microorganisms to use dissolved organic material effectively requires oxidation and **reduction**. In oxidation, oxygen is added to, or hydrogen is deleted from, elements of the organic molecule. Reduction occurs when hydrogen is added to or oxygen is deleted from elements of the organic molecule. The oxidation process is by far more efficient and is predominant when oxygen is available. In **aerobic** (oxygen-present) environments, the end products of microbial decomposition of organics are stable and acceptable compounds. **Anaerobic** (oxygen-absent) decomposition results in unstable and objectionable end products.

The quantity of oxygen-consuming organics in water is usually determined by measuring the **biological oxygen demand (BOD)**: the amount of dissolved oxygen needed by aerobic decomposers to break down the organic materials in a given volume of water over a five-day incubation period at 20°C (6°F).

Nonbiodegradable organics (resistant to biological degradation and thus considered refractory) include constituents of woody plants (tannin and lignic acids, phenols, and cellulose) and are found in natural water systems. Some polysaccharides with exceptionally strong bonds, and benzene with its ringed structure, are essentially nonbiodegradable.

Some organics are toxic to organisms and thus are nonbiodegradable. These include organic pesticides and compounds that have combined with chlorine.

Pesticides and herbicides have found widespread use in agriculture, forestry, and mosquito control. Surface streams are contaminated via runoff and washoff by rainfall. These toxic substances are harmful to some fish, shellfish, predatory birds, and mammals. Some compounds are toxic to humans.

Certain nonbiodegradable chemicals can react with oxygen dissolved in water. The **chemical oxygen demand (COD)**—the amount of oxygen needed to chemically oxidize a waste—is a more complete and accurate measurement of the total depletion of dissolved oxygen in water.

Nutrients

Nutrients are elements (carbon, nitrogen, phosphorous, sulfur, calcium, iron, potassium, manganese, cobalt, and boron) essential to the growth and reproduction of plants and animals. Aquatic species depend on their watery environment for their nutrients. In water quality terms, however, nutrients can be considered pollutants when their concentrations are sufficient to encourage excessive growth of aquatic plants such as algal blooms. The nutrients required in most abundance by aquatic species are carbon, nitrogen, and phosphorous. Plants, in particular, require large amounts of each of these three nutrients, or their growth will be limited.

Carbon is readily available from a number of natural sources, including alkalinity, decaying products of organic matter, and dissolved carbon dioxide from the atmosphere. Because carbon is usually readily available, it is seldom a **limiting nutrient** (the nutrient least available relative to the plant's needs) (Masters, 1991). The limiting nutrient concept is important, because it suggests that identifying and reducing the supply of a particular nutrient can control algal growth. In most cases, nitrogen and phosphorous are essential growth factors and are the limiting factors in aquatic plant growth. According to Welch (1980), seawater is most often limited by nitrogen, whereas freshwater systems are most often limited by phosphorous.

Nitrogen gas (N_2), which is extremely stable, is the primary component of the Earth's atmosphere. Major sources of nitrogen in water include runoff from animal feedlots, fertilizer runoff from agricultural fields, municipal wastewater discharges, and certain bacteria and blue-green algae that obtain nitrogen directly from the atmosphere. Certain forms of acid rain can also contribute nitrogen to surface waters.

In water, nitrogen is frequently found in the form of nitrate (NO_3). Nitrate in drinking water can lead to serious problems, most notably nitrate poisoning. Human and animal infants can be affected by nitrate poisoning, which can cause serious illness and even death, if bacteria commonly found in the infant's intestinal tract convert nitrates to highly toxic nitrites (NO_2). Nitrite can replace oxygen in the bloodstream and result in oxygen starvation, which causes a bluish discoloration of the infant ("blue baby" syndrome).

In aquatic surface water systems, nitrogen (and phosphorous in the form of phosphate) can stimulate biological growth and is classified as a **biostimulant**. As biostimulants, nitrogen and phosphates (derived from fertilizers and detergents) are impurities that can result in greatly increased **eutrophication** (or slow death) of the body of water. Eutrophication of water systems, especially lakes, is usually a natural phenomenon that occurs over time. Increases in biostimulants (any growth-stimulating nutrient) speed up eutrophication, affecting the natural process.

Eutrophication can result when algal blooms get a large supply of nitrogen or phosphorous (or both) and grow out of control. When natural processes get out of control, nature steps in and lowers the boom. Algal blooms die off at the end of the growing season, then degrade and provide a rich source of organic material for bacteria. With an ample food supply, bacteria may grow exponentially, consuming dissolved oxygen in the process. As food supplies are consumed, waste products accumulate, and the process slows.

BIOLOGICAL CHARACTERISTICS OF WATER

Along with the physical and chemical parameters of water quality, the environmental science practitioner is also concerned with the biological characteristics of water. This concern is well warranted when the health and well-being of the people who receive and use the product from the "end of the pipe" or "at the spigot" is at stake. In this context, remember that water may serve as a medium in which thousands of biological species spend part, if not all, of their lives. Note that, to some extent, all members of the biological aquatic community serve as parameters of water quality, because their presence or absence may indicate in general terms the characteristics of a given body of water.

The biological characteristics of water directly impact water quality. To a lesser degree, this impact includes the development of tastes and odors in surface water and

USGS Quiz—What Are Some of the Physical and Chemical Properties of Water?

The answers are provided in a box near the end of the chapter.

___ True   ___ False   (1) Water contracts (gets smaller) when it freezes.
___ True   ___ False   (2) Water has a high surface tension.
___ True   ___ False   (3) Condensation is water coming out of the air.
___ True   ___ False   (4) More things can be dissolved in sulfuric acid than in water.
___ True   ___ False   (5) Rainwater is the purest form of water.
___ True   ___ False   (6) It takes more energy to heat water at room temperature to 212°F than it does to change 212°F water to steam.
___ True   ___ False   (7) If you evaporate an eight-inch glass full of water from the Great Salt Lake (with a salinity of about 20% by weight), you will end up with about one inch of salt.
___ True   ___ False   (8) Seawater is slightly more basic (the pH value is higher) than most natural water.
___ True   ___ False   (9) Raindrops are tear-shaped.
___ True   ___ False   (10) Water boils at a lower temperature in Denver, Colorado, than at the seashore.

groundwater and the corrosion of and biofouling of heat transfer surfaces in cooling systems and water supply treatment facilities. However, the presence or absence of particular biological organisms is of paramount importance to the water specialist. These organisms are the **pathogens**, capable of infecting or transmitting diseases to humans and animals. These organisms are not native to aquatic systems and usually require an animal host for growth and reproduction. They can be—and are—transported by natural water systems. Waterborne pathogens include species of bacteria, **viruses**, **protozoa**, and parasitic worms (helminths). In the following subsections, we provide a brief "basic" description of each of these species, along with a brief description of **rotifers**, **crustacean**s, **fungi**, and algae, which are also microorganisms of concern in water. For those who are not well-grounded in the basic microbiology of aquatic systems or would like a refresher in this area, additional details on the microorganisms of concern in water may be found in the text *Microbiology for Water/Wastewater Operators* (Spellman, 1997).

Before we begin a discussion of the basics of aquatic microorganisms of concern in environmental science, note that having some knowledge of the environmental factors that affect their environment is also important. For example, the environmental practitioner who specializes in water quality must be familiar with the nutritional requirements of aquatic organisms.

To grow in an aquatic environment, organisms must be able to extract the nutrients they need for cell synthesis and for the generation of energy from their water environment. Some organisms obtain their energy from photosynthetic light, others from organic or inorganic matter. Carbon is a critical ingredient for all aquatic microorganisms (actually, carbon is critical to all organisms). Some aquatic organisms (higher plants, algae, and photosynthetic bacteria) get their carbon from carbon dioxide. Others (bacteria, fauna, protozoa, animals) get it from organic matter. Oxygen also plays a critical role in the growth of cells. Many organisms (aerobes) require molecular oxygen (O_2) for their metabolism. Other organisms (anaerobes) do not require molecular oxygen and derive the oxygen they need for synthesis of cells from chemical compounds.

Consider also the effects of environmental factors covered previously in the text, including chemical composition, pH, temperature, and light. The environmental practitioner must not only be familiar with the types of aquatic organisms that can inhabit water systems, but also must understand the physical, chemical, and biological environmental factors required for their existence. To refresh and reinforce the reader's memory of the important biological characteristics of water, they are briefly summarized below.

Bacteria

As discussed previously, the word *bacteria* (singular, bacterium) comes from the Greek word meaning "rod" or "staff," a shape characteristic of many bacteria. Bacteria are single-celled microscopic organisms that multiply by splitting in two (binary fission). To multiply, they need carbon either from carbon dioxide (if they are **autotrophs**, which synthesize organic substances from inorganic molecules by using light or chemical energy) or from organic compounds (dead vegetation, meat, sewage) (if they are **heterotrophs**). Their energy comes from sunlight if they are photosynthetic or from chemical reaction if they are chemosynthetic. Bacteria are present in air, water, Earth, rotting vegetation, and the intestines of animals. Gastrointestinal disorders are common symptoms of most diseases transmitted by waterborne pathogenic bacteria.

Viruses

A virus is an infectious particle consisting of a core of nucleic acid (DNA and RNA) enclosed in a protein shell. It carries the information needed for its replication, but does not possess the machinery to carry it out. Thus, viruses are *obligate* parasitic particles that require a host in which to live. They are the smallest biological structures known and can only be seen with the aid of an electron microscope. Waterborne viral contaminants that are known to cause poliomyelitis and infectious hepatitis are usually indicated by disorders of the nervous system rather than of the gastrointestinal tract.

Protozoa

Protozoa (singular, protozoan) are mobile, single-celled, complete, self-contained organisms that can be free-living or parasitic, pathogenic or nonpathogenic, microscopic or macroscopic. Protozoa range in size from two to several hundred microns in length. They are highly adaptable and widely distributed in natural water, although only a few are parasitic. Most protozoa are harmless. Only a few cause illness in humans—*Entamoeba histolytica* (amebiasis) and *Giardia lamblia* (giardiasis) being two of these. Giardiasis (typically contracted by drinking surface water contaminated by wild animals or humans) is the most widespread protozoan disease occurring throughout the world (Tchobanoglous & Schroeder, 1987). Unless properly treated, giardiasis can be chronic. Symptoms usually include diarrhea, nausea, indigestion, flatulence, bloating, fatigue, and appetite and weight loss.

Worms (Helminths)

Worms are also important in water quality assessment from the standpoint of human disease. Normally, worms inhabit organic mud and organic slime. They have aerobic requirements, but can metabolize solid organic matter not readily degraded by other microorganisms. Water contamination may result from human and animal waste that contains worms. Worms pose hazards primarily to those persons who come into direct contact with untreated water. Thus swimmers in surface water polluted by sewage or stormwater runoff from cattle feedlots are at particular risk. The *Tubifix* worm is a common organism used as an indicator of pollution in streams.

Rotifers

Rotifers (the name derives from the apparent rotating motion of the cilia located on the head) make up a well-defined group of the smallest, simplest multicellular microorganisms and are found in nearly all aquatic habitats. Strict aerobes, rotifers range in size from about 0.1 to 0.8 nm. Bacteria are rotifers primary food source.

Crustaceans

Microscopic crustaceans are important members of freshwater zooplankton and are thus of interest to water specialists. Characterized by a rigid shell structure, they are multicellular, strict aerobes, and primary producers that feed on bacteria and algae. They are important as a source of food for fish.

Fungi

Fungi (singular, fungus) constitute an extremely important and interesting group of aerobic microbes, ranging from the unicellular yeasts to the extensively mycelial molds. Fungi are not considered plants, but are instead a distinctive life form of great practical and ecological importance. Like bacteria, fungi metabolize dissolved organic matter. As the principal organisms responsible for decomposition of carbon in the biosphere, fungi are essential. They are unique (compared to bacteria), in that they can grow in low moisture areas and in low pH solutions, which aids in the breakdown of organic matter in aquatic environments.

Algae

Algae are a diverse group of autotrophic, photosynthetic, eucaryotic microorganisms containing chlorophyll. The feature that distinguishes algae from fungi is the chlorophyll. Algal microorganisms impact water quality by shifting the balance between oxygen and carbon dioxide in the water, affecting pH levels, and contributing to odor and taste problems.

USGS Quiz Answers and Explanations

(1)   Water contracts (gets smaller) when it freezes.   **False**

Explanation: Actually, water expands (gets less dense) when it freezes, which is unusual for liquids. Think of ice—it is one of the few items that floats as a solid. If it didn't, lakes would freeze from the bottom up (that would mean we'd have to wear wetsuits when ice skating!), and more lakes in the far north would be permanent blocks of ice.

(2)   Water has a high surface tension.   **True**

Explanation: Water has the highest surface tension among common liquids (mercury is higher). Surface tension is the ability of a substance to stick to itself (cohere). That is why water forms drops and also why when you look at a glass of water, the water "rises" where it touches the glass (the "meniscus"). Plants are happy that water has a high surface tension, because they use capillary action to draw water from the ground up through their roots and stems.

(3)   Condensation is water coming out of the air.   **True**

Explanation: This is actually true—water that forms on the outside of a cold glass or on the inside of a window in winter is liquid water condensing from water vapor in the air. Air contains water vapor (humidity). In cold air, water vapor condenses faster than it evaporates. So, when the warm air touches the outside of your cold glass, the air next to the glass gets chilled, and some of the water in that air turns from water vapor to tiny liquid water droplets. Clouds in the sky and the "cloud" you see when you exhale on a cold day are condensed water vapor particles. (It is a myth that clouds form because cold air cannot hold as much water vapor as warm air!)

(4)   More things can be dissolved in sulfuric acid than in water.   **False**

Explanation: Sulfuric acid might be able to dissolve a car, but water isn't known as the "universal solvent" for nothing! It can dissolve more substances than any other liquid. This is lucky for us; what if all the sugar in your soft drink ended up as a pile at the bottom of the glass? The water you see in rivers, lakes, and the ocean may look clear, but it actually contains many dissolved elements and minerals, and because these elements are dissolved, they can easily move with water over the surface of the Earth.

(5)   Rainwater is the purest form of water.   **False**

Explanation: Distilled water is "purer." Rainwater contains small amounts of dissolved minerals that have been blown into the air by winds. It also contains tiny particles of dust and dissolved gases, such as carbon dioxide and sulfur dioxide (acid rain). That doesn't mean rainwater isn't very clean—normally only about 1/100,000th of the weight of rain comes from these substances. In a way, the distillation process is responsible for rainwater. Distilled water comes from water vapor condensing in a closed container (such as a glass jar). Rain is produced by water vapor evaporating from the Earth and condensing in the sky. Both the closed jar and the Earth (via its atmosphere) are "closed systems," where water is neither added nor lost.

(6) **It takes more energy to heat water at room temperature to 212°F than it does to change 212°F water to steam.**   **False**
Explanation: First, water at boiling temperature (212°F at sea level) is not really the same as boiling water. When water first reaches boiling, it has not yet begun to turn to steam. More energy is needed to begin turning the boiling liquid water into gaseous water vapor. The bonds holding water molecules as a liquid are not easily broken. It takes about seven times as much energy to turn boiling water into steam as it does to heat water at room temperature to the boiling point.

(7) **If you evaporate an eight-inch glass full of water from the Great Salt Lake (with a salinity of about 20% by weight), you will end up with about one inch of salt.**   **True**
Explanation: They don't call it the Great Salt Lake for nothing. Water in the Great Salt Lake varies in salinity both by location and in time. In this example, we are assuming about a 20% salt concentration. In other words, about one-fifth of the weight of the water comes from salt. And how much saltier is Great Salt Lake water than seawater? Quite a bit. Seawater has a salt concentration of about 3.5%.

(8) **Seawater is slightly more basic (the pH value is higher) than most natural water.**   **True**
Explanation: Neutral water (such as distilled water) has a pH of 7, which is in the middle of being acidic and alkaline. Seawater happens to be slightly alkaline (basic), with a pH of about 8. Most natural water has a pH of between 6 and 8, although acid rain can have a pH as low as 4.

(9) **Raindrops are tear-shaped.**   **False**
Explanation: When you think of a drop of falling water, you probably think it looks a like a tear. When a drop of water comes out of a faucet, it does have a tear shape. That is because the back end of the water drop sticks to the water still in the faucet until it can't hold on anymore. But using high-speed cameras, scientists have found that falling raindrops look more like a small hamburger bun! Gravity and surface tension come into play here. As rain falls, the air below the drop pushes up from the bottom, causing the drop to flatten out somewhat. The strong surface tension of water holds the drop together, resulting in a bun shape.

(continued)

Chapter Summary

One of the blessings of modern life that we enjoy (but usually ignore) is readily available, clean, safe, potable water. As anyone knows who has carried water along for camping or backpacking or who has traveled or lived in a country without safe drinking water, just being able to turn on the tap to get water is an enormous boon that modern technology has given us. We don't have to carry water in pails from the village well, the river, or our own well or spring. We don't have to boil it or chemically treat it to drink or cook with it. We don't have to brush our teeth with bottled water. We take our safe water for granted, even if we buy spring water to drink because we don't like the taste of the treated water from the faucet.

We also forget that even when our water supplies were relatively unspoiled, unsafe water killed many people, because technology to test the water was not available. The physical, chemical, and biological characteristics of water, and our understanding of the forces at work on groundwater and surface water, allow us to control the quality of the water we rely on so absolutely.

Discussion Questions and Problems

1. The range of water quality problems encountered in the field is extremely diverse. List the physical, chemical, and biological characteristics of water in outline form.
2. Explain eutrophication.
3. How do human activities accelerate the rate of eutrophication?
4. One of the major objectives of water quality management is to reduce or mitigate the effects of human activities on eutrophication. Give a few examples of how this may be accomplished.
5. Briefly explain the differences in water quality problems.

6. Should all dumping of wastes worldwide in surface water be banned? What exceptions, if any, would you permit? Explain why banning surface water dumping alone will not stop surface water pollution.
7. What are the major nonpoint sources of pollution of surface water and groundwater in your area?
8. Write a definition in your own words of each of the terms that are boldfaced in this chapter. Compare your definitions with those in the glossary.
9. How is water pollution related to agricultural activities?
10. What is thermal pollution?

Suggested Research Topics and Projects

- Explore the four possible pathways water may take when it strikes the Earth.
- Examine the ways people have altered the hydrogeologic system and their consequences.
- Research the history of water pollution in America.
- What's the current research in water reclamation and reuse?
- Map how water quality and availability controls human population expansion.
- Which do you think makes a better water supply, surface or groundwater? Why? Support your opinion.
- Examine groundwater as "the ocean beneath our feet."
- Examine the environmental outlook on our current water supply and water usage.
- Research what makes water wet.
- Examine the waterborne diseases that pose a serious threat to human health.
- Do you drink the tap water in your area? Do you feel safe doing so? Do you like the taste, color, smell? Does water in another community taste different to you? What is your community's opinion of its water supply?
- Examine how temperature affects water quality.
- Extended definition—water as the universal solvent.
- Explore the problems associated with undersaturation or out-of-equilibrium water.
- Examine public and fringe group opinions of fluoridation.
- Research the history of fluoride use in water for control of dental caries.
- Examine why seawater is limited by nitrogen and freshwater by phosphorus.
- Examine how the members of the aquatic biological community serve as parameters of water quality.

References and Recommended Reading

ASTM. (1969). *Manual of Water*. Philadelphia: American Society for Testing and Materials.
Clary, D. (1997). "What Makes Water Wet." *Geraghty & Miller Newsletter* 39: 4.
Corbitt, R. A. (1990). *Standard Handbook of Environmental Engineering*. New York: McGraw-Hill.
Kemmer, F. N. (1979). *Water: The Universal Solvent*. 2nd ed. Oak Brook, IL: Nalco Chemical Company.

Kemmer, F. N. (1988). *The Nalco Water Handbook*. 2nd ed. New York: McGraw-Hill.

Koren, H. (1991). *Handbook of Environmental Health & Safety: Principles and Practices*. Chelsea, MI: Lewis Publishers.

Manahan, S. E. (1997). *Environmental Science and Technology*. Boca Raton, FL: Lewis Publishers.

Masters, G. M. (1991). *Introduction to Environmental Engineering and Science*. Englewood Cliffs, NJ: Prentice-Hall.

McGhee, T. J. (1991). *Water Supply and Sewerage*. New York: McGraw-Hill.

Moncrief, R. W. (1967). *The Chemical Senses*. 3rd ed. London: Leonard Hill.

Outwater, A. (1996). *Water: A Natural History*. New York: Basic Books.

Peavy, H. S., Rowe, D. R., & Tchobanoglous, G. (1985). *Environmental Engineering*. New York: McGraw-Hill.

Rowe, D. R., & Abdel-Magid, I. M. (1995). *Handbook of Wastewater Reclamation and Reuse*. Boca Raton, FL: Lewis Publishers.

Spellman, F. R. (1997). *Microbiology for Water/Wastewater Operators*. Lancaster, PA: Technomic.

Spellman, F. R. (2003). *Handbook of Water and Wastewater Treatment Plant Operations*. Boca Raton, FL: Lewis Publishers.

Spellman, F. R. (2007). *The Science of Water: Concepts and Applications*. 2nd ed. Boca Raton, FL: CRC Press.

Tchobanoglous, G., & Schroeder, E. D. (1987). *Water Quality*. Reading, MA: Addison-Wesley.

U.S. Department of Agriculture (USDA). (20110. *Water Use Facts*. Accessed June 6, 2011, http.www.fs.fed.us/r5/publications/water_resources/html/water_uaw_facts.html.

U.S. Geological Survey (USGS). (2011). *Water Science for Schools*. Accessed June 5, 2011, http://ga.water.usgs.gov/edu/edu/sc#.html.

"U. S Watersheds Have Water Quality Problems." (1997, November/December). *Environmental Technology*, 10.

Welch, E. G. (1980). *Ecological Effects of Waste Water*. Cambridge, UK: Cambridge University Press.

CHAPTER 15

Freshwater: Surface and Ground Sources

I am well again, I came to life in the cool winds and crystal waters of the mountains.

—John Muir, 1868

Freshwater ecosystems are aquatic systems which contain drinkable water or water of almost no salt content. Freshwater resources include lakes and ponds, rivers, and streams, reservoirs, wetlands, and groundwater. The United States derives many benefits from these freshwater resources. They provide the majority of our nation's drinking water resources, water resources for agriculture, industry, sanitation, as well as food including fish and shellfish. They also provide recreational opportunities and a means of transportation. In addition, freshwater ecosystems are home to numerous organisms (e.g., fish, amphibians, aquatic plants, and invertebrates).

—U.S. EPA, 2011a

Chapter Objectives

After studying this chapter, you should be able to:

- Identify and discuss what percentage of the total supply each major source of freshwater provides and discuss the possibilities of use for water supply.
- Define limnology, lentic systems, and lotic systems and discuss their components.
- Identify and discuss the types of ponds and their characteristics, stages, habitats, and zones.
- Identify and discuss the types of lakes and their classification, characteristics, stages, habitats, and zones.
- Discuss lake succession and how eutrophication can affect it.
- Identify lake characteristics by eutrophication state.

505

- Identify lake characteristics by special types.
- Discuss lake thermal stratification and turnover in terms of the relationship between temperature and density. Identify the effects stratification and turnover have on water quality.
- Discuss the advantages lotic systems have over lentic systems in terms of water quality and self-purification.
- Describe the life span stages of river systems and the changes in river bottom and turbidity.
- Describe the dissolved oxygen (DO) levels common in river flow variations and how they differ from DO in still water bodies.
- Discuss rivers and land–water interchange and how this reflects river inhabitant food supply.
- Define the two river zones related to currents and pools and discuss how the two different habitats support their specialized organisms.
- Describe the factors that can individually or collectively lead to flooding, and the human activities that affect runoff and infiltration.
- Compare and contrast the differences between landlocked (still) water bodies and flowing water bodies. Describe how water quality in each system is affected by pollutants.
- Describe the self-purification capabilities and system for rivers and the relationship among DO, biochemical oxyden demand (BOD), and river organisms.
- Identify the natural processes at work in lentic self-purification.
- Identify and describe the zones present in the self-purification process.
- Describe the related chain of events inherent in stream purification, the concentrations of DO and BOD, and organisms and how they work to remove organic matter from the stream.
- Define groundwater and discuss its usefulness in terms of availability, accessibility, and potability as a water supply.
- Discuss groundwater's advantages and disadvantages as a water supply source.
- Define water table, confined and unconfined aquifers, vadose water, and unsaturated zone and discuss how they affect groundwater flow.
- Identify hydraulic gradient and discuss the concept that drives it.
- Describe how groundwater is cleaned during infiltration.

Chapter Outline

- Description and discussion: the view from a distance and water's presence on Earth; percentages and distribution of marine and freshwater
- Definition: freshwater source categories available for potable water: surface water and groundwater
- Definition and discussion: important properties of surface water
- Definition and discussion: lentic water systems, cycles, zones, characteristics, and habitat in transitory and permanent ponds

- Definition and discussion: lentic water systems, classifications, cycles, zones, characteristics, and habitats in lakes and their advantages and disadvantages related to water supply; thermal stratification and turnover
- Definition and discussion: lotic water systems, classifications, cycles, zones, characteristics, and habitat in rivers; flooding; temperature and DO levels; their advantages and disadvantages related to water supply; the self-purification abilities inherent in lotic systems; DO and BOD levels and their impact on river pollutants; general biological succession
- Definition and discussion: groundwater supplies, uses, sources, and condition: the water table and confined and unconfined aquifers; groundwater movement

Key Terms

aquifer	plankton
benthic	pond
biochemical oxygen demand (BOD)	pond succession
clean zone	pool zone
confined aquifer	profundal
cultural eutrophication	rapids zone
dissolved oxygen (DO)	recovery zone
drainage	reservoir
dystrophic	runoff
emergent vegetation	saturated zone
emergents	self-purification
epilimnion	senescent pond
euphotic	septic zone
eutrophic	spring overturn
eutrophic lake	stratification
floating leaf vegetation	submerged vegetation
general biological succession	summer stagnation
groundwater	surface water
hydraulic gradient	thermocline
hypolimnion	turnover
impoundment	unconfined aquifer
lentic	unsaturated zone
limnetic	vadose water
limnology	vernal ponds
littoral	water table
lotic	watershed
meromictic	watershed divide
mesotrophic lake	winter kill
nekton	winter stratification
neustons	zonation
oligotrophic lake	zone of recent pollution
permanent pond	

Introduction

From the space shuttle circling 150 miles above Earth, we could see our world in a way very few people have experienced and could view it with a sense of unity and completeness, of interconnection difficult to comprehend from our usual position on the ground. Our eyes might first be drawn to the circulating cloud masses and patterns of Earth's weather as it passes over the globe. Then the intense, deep blues would attract our attention through the cloud cover and thin haze, broken here and there by the brown, green, and tan landmasses that float on the oceans of blue.

This view serves to verify on a visceral visual level what most Earth-dwellers know only intellectually: that the Earth is literally shrouded in water. But the sight of so much water drives home another point that most of us land-dwellers don't contemplate, don't realize, don't understand: Water not only shrouds Earth, covering roughly 71% of its surface mass, but controls, predominates, dominates—it is everywhere. We occupy landmasses that are nothing more than islands.

Our most abundant resource, water covers almost three-quarters of Earth's surface, yet it is only a thin film, of which almost 97% is saltwater. This veil of water performs many functions: It helps maintain climate, works to dilute environmental pollution, and of course, is essential to life. Without freshwater, agriculture, manufacturing, transportation, and life as we know it would not exist.

From our space ship high above Earth, we would also notice that freshwater is not evenly distributed. Some areas have too little water and others too much. Human beings, with varying degrees of success, have attempted to correct these imbalances by capturing freshwater in **reservoirs** behind dams; transferring it in rivers and streams from one area to another; tapping underground supplies; and endeavoring to reduce water use, waste, and contamination. In some of these efforts we have been successful, in others we are still learning—we have a lot more to learn.

Our focus in this chapter is on the characteristics of "freshwater" bodies. We pointed out previously that most of the Earth's water supply is salty, and only a small portion (less than 3%) is fresh. Three-quarters of freshwater is found in polar ice caps and glaciers, unavailable for human use, and nearly all of the remaining one-quarter (**groundwater**) is found under the Earth's crust in water-bearing rock or sand and gravel formations. Only a small proportion (about 0.5%) of all freshwater on Earth is found in lakes, rivers, streams, or the atmosphere. Obviously, this seems a small amount relative to Earth's total water supply. But it is more than enough; even this small amount, if it were kept free of pollution and distributed evenly, could provide for the drinking, food preparation, and agricultural needs of all Earth's people. We simply need to learn how to better manage and conserve the freshwater readily available to us.

Water is classified as either marine (salt) or fresh, depending on its salt content. The salt content of marine water is fairly consistent, about 35 parts per thousand (ppt). On average the salt content of freshwater is 0.5 part per thousand. Freshwater's salt content tends to vary more than that of marine water, because lakes, rivers, and streams are much more dominated by local environmental conditions, including the rate of evaporation and the mineral content of soils they drain.

In the following sections, we discuss freshwater found in two basic forms: **surface water** and groundwater. Precipitation that does not infiltrate into the ground or return to the atmosphere is known as surface water and becomes runoff—water that flows into nearby lakes, wetlands, streams, rivers, and reservoirs.

Precipitation, under the influence of gravity, infiltrates and percolates slowly through porous ground material deep into the Earth. It completely saturates water-bearing layers of the Earth's crust (**aquifers**) and eventually becomes a part of groundwater stores. Although classified separately, surface water and groundwater are not entirely distinct. Some water from lakes, streams, and rivers may percolate downward to groundwater supplies. Springs feed into surface water bodies, returning to the water cycle. During dry seasons, when surface **runoff** is minimal, groundwater sources help to maintain the flow of rivers and streams and the water level of lakes.

Before we continue our discussion of surface water and groundwater bodies, review the basic concepts of the water or hydrological cycle (see Figure 6.2).

The water cycle, which is actually a manifestation of an enormous heat engine, raises water from the oceans in warmer latitudes by a prodigious transformation of solar energy. Transferred through the atmosphere by the winds, the water is deposited far away over sea or land. Figure 6.2 depicts this ongoing natural circulation of water through the atmosphere. It shows water taken from the Earth's surface to the atmosphere (either by evaporation from the surface of lakes, rivers, streams, and oceans or through transpiration of plants), where it forms clouds that condense to deposit moisture on the land and sea as rain or snow. The water that collects on land flows back to the oceans in streams and rivers.

The water that we see is surface water. The U.S. EPA (1989) defines surface water as all water open to the atmosphere and subject to runoff. Surface water can be broken down into five components: oceans, lakes, rivers and streams, estuaries, and wetlands. Each category of surface water is important. However, the water contained in surface water bodies and available for human consumption is the focus of the next section.

Surface Water

The study of surface or open freshwater bodies is known as **limnology**. More specifically, limnology is the study of the plant and animal biology and physical properties of bodies of open freshwater (lakes, rivers, and streams). Limnology divides freshwater systems into groups or classes, **lentic** and **lotic**. Examples of *lentic* (*lenis* = calm) or standing water systems are lakes, **ponds**, **impoundments**, reservoirs, and swamps. Examples of *lotic* (*lotus* = washed) or running water systems are rivers, streams, brooks, and springs. On occasion, these two different systems are not well differentiated. This can be seen in the case of old, wide, and deep rivers where water velocity is quite low, and the system becomes similar to that of a pond.

On its journey over Earth's landscape, surface water produced by melting snow or ice or from rainstorms follows the path of least resistance. A series of droplets, rills, rivulets, brooks, creeks, streams, and rivers carries water from an area of elevated land surface that slopes down toward one primary watercourse. This **drainage** area is known as a **watershed** or **drainage basin**. A watershed is a basin surrounded by a ridge of high ground called the **watershed divide**, which separates one drainage area from another (Fig. 15.1).

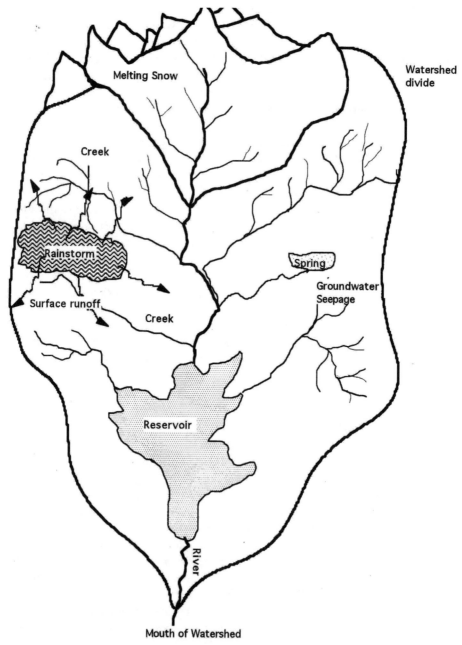

Figure 15.1.   An example of a lotic water system.

LENTIC (STANDING OR STILL) WATER SYSTEMS

Natural lentic water systems consist of lakes, ponds, bogs, marshes, and swamps. The other standing freshwater bodies, such as reservoirs, oxidation ponds, and holding basins, are usually human-made. In this section we focus on lakes (major sources of freshwater) and reservoirs (used to hold freshwater in reserve), primarily because these two bodies of standing water are widely used as sources of potable water. However, there probably is no better or easier way to gain an understanding of lentic water systems than by studying the pond—thus, we begin our discussion of lentic water systems with ponds.

Ponds

Simply defined, a pond is a still body of water smaller than a lake, often of artificial construction. A pond may be ancient ("permanent") or transitory. Those of the shortest duration are known as **vernal ponds** (pertaining to spring) and are generally only formed in early spring or late winter by meltwater or heavy rains. At the start of summer, they begin to shrink, and they usually dry up completely before summer's end. Ponds are shallow, and the quality of their water is strongly influenced by the soils that form their basins. Pond water temperature is closely related to, and usually closely follows, ambient air temperature.

Though transitory or vernal ponds are usually short-lived, they often exist long enough to support basic aquatic life-forms such as branchiopod crustaceans (fairy shrimp), which hatch out and swarm in the early season (cold) water. Ponds also normally contain various cysts and spores from which rotifers, protozoans, nematodes, and algae emerge. Frogs usually become the next residents of the pool—the perfect setting for mating and egg laying. The eggs hatch quickly and produce rapidly developing tadpoles in short order.

Vernal or transitory ponds are not used for freshwater supplies. Because they lack permanence and stability, they aren't suitable for the permanent potable water supply municipal water systems require. Their transitory nature also causes water problems. Because they are of short duration and subject to contamination from soils and surface runoff, they do not provide water of a quality suitable for human consumption.

Generalizing about **permanent ponds** is difficult, because ponds are not permanent. Remember, although the water itself is permanent (we have the same amount of water today as the early Greeks and Roman did, the same amount that has been on Earth since it was formed), the location is not permanent—water cycles continuously. We cannot even generalize about so-called permanent ponds—if you were to examine dozen of these ponds, even if they were placed closely in the same geographical location, they would all differ.

A permanent pond is usually defined by any of the following characteristics: (1) It is shallow enough to permit aquatic plants to penetrate the surface anywhere over its entire mass; (2) its mass is not so great as to allow formation of large waves, which could erode the shoreline; and (3) it has no temperature layering, rather a gradient of temperatures extending from surface to bottom (Amos, 1969). Its age and productivity can also characterize a pond. For example, if a pond has no planktonic life or rooted plant life, it will not support animal life. Such ponds are nutrient poor; **oligotrophic**. Usually oligotrophic ponds are clear and fairly new. A highly productive pond, one that contains large populations of plants and animals, is nutrient rich: **eutrophic**. Eutrophic ponds can become unhealthy if too much enrichment occurs (usually by phosphorus). The nutrients are decomposed by bacteria and chemical processes that use large amounts of oxygen from the water, killing aerobic organisms and causing pond stagnation.

Because ponds have a life span (normally ranging from decades to a century or two), which is actually a transformation period from one phase to another, they can also be classified according to their age: young, mature, and **senescent** (old). Their age can be measured with a fair amount of accuracy according to their physical appearance and by the different organisms resident during each phase of the transformation process. This transformation process is well studied and well documented and is known as **pond succession**.

Once a land depression fills with water, a *young pond* forms. Characterized by their lack of sediment, young ponds produce pioneer plants along the shoreline, and their water contains plankton, invertebrates, and fish. As plants grow and decay within the pond, along with sediment accumulating from land, the young pond becomes a *mature pond*. The mature pond is carpeted with rich sediment; has aquatic vegetation extending out into open water; and has a great diversity of plankton, invertebrates, and fish. As the pond continues to fill with sediment, it transforms from mature to senescent. At this point, so much sediment exists within the depression that it fills, and the bottom rises close to the surface. Vegetation grows and covers the entire area. Obviously, in this environment the pond can't support fish or plankton, or even many invertebrates. The pond has transformed from a water to a land environment.

Pond Habitat

Many of the characteristics and conditions described for ponds also apply to lakes, which we will discuss in detail later in this chapter.

Ponds contain a number of quite distinct habitats, each inhabited by specifically adapted organisms. Freely swimming organisms are **nektons**. Floating organisms that move with water movement are called **plankton**. Plants and animals living on or near the pond bottom are called **benthic** organisms. Plants and animals living on the surface are **neustons**. Each of these populations can be graded into small subdivisions, often as the result of biotic **zonation** in the pond (Amos, 1969).

Large ponds normally consist of four distinct zones: **littoral, limnetic, profundal,** and benthic (see Figure 15.2A & B). Each zone provides a variety of ecological niches for different species of plant and animal life.

The most obvious (and easiest to observe) zonation is found along the shoreline, the littoral zone. In the littoral zone (the outermost shallow-water region), light penetrates to the bottom (see Figure 15.2A). It provides an interface zone between the land and the open water of ponds. The littoral zone contains rooted vegetation (grasses, sedges, rushes, water lilies, and waterweeds) that grows in the moist, saturated soil of

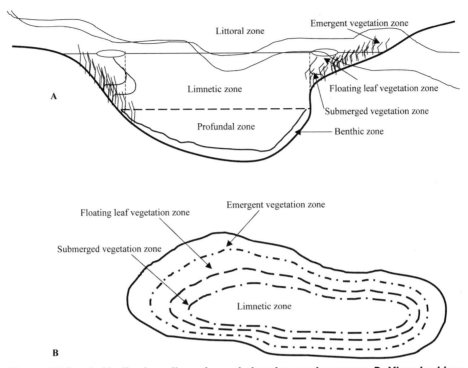

Figure 15.2.   A. Vertical section of pond showing major zones. B. View looking down on concentric zones that make up the littoral zone.

the pond bank, and a large variety of organisms. The littoral zone is further divided into concentric zones, with one group replacing another as the depth of water changes. Figure 15.2B shows these concentric zones: **emergent vegetation**, **floating leaf vegetation**, and **submerged vegetation** zones, proceeding from shallow to deeper water.

The **emergents** rise through shallow water before producing foliage and flowers, and thus invade the pond a yard or more from the shoreline. Floating-leaf plants begin where the emergents stop. Rooted in the bottom, floating-leaf plants have long, flexible stems anchoring their buoyant leaves in place. Beyond the floating-leaf plants is the open water of the limnetic zone. Given enough time, however, the floating-leaf plants will literally work their way across the surface of the pond and cover it completely. Below and never quite penetrating the pond surface, the submerged plants grow where light can penetrate and reach them. However, if the pond becomes covered with floating-leaf plants (thus preventing light penetration), submerged plants may be totally absent.

The open water portion of the pond that remains shallow enough for effective light penetration is the limnetic zone. The community in this zone is comprised of minute suspended organisms, plankton, and some insects and fish. The species population density is quite low. The rate of photosynthesis is equal to the rate of respiration; thus, the limnetic zone is at compensation level.

Small, shallow ponds do not have this zone; they have a littoral zone only. When all lighted regions of the littoral and limnetic zones are discussed as one, the term *euphotic* is used for both, describing these zones as having sufficient light for photo-synthesis and the growth of green plants to occur (Spellman, 1996).

The portion of the pond not penetrated by light is called the profundal zone. It contains darker water with lower oxygen levels, and only specially adapted aquatic organisms occupy this zone.

The final zone (the benthic zone) is the bottom of the pond. This zone supports scavengers and decomposers that live on sludge. The decomposers are mostly larger numbers of bacteria, fungi, and worms, which live on dead plant and animal debris and other wastes that find their way to the bottom.

Lakes

Much of the material covered above about ponds also applies to lakes, especially to their shorelines and shallows. However, lakes are distinct and separate entities (see Table 15.1). They are accurately described as arbitrary flow reactors with long hy-draulic residence times. That lakes are an important source of freshwater is nowhere more apparent and important than in North America, where the United States and Canada share the Great Lakes, considered the largest supply of freshwater in the world. Another huge supply of available freshwater is Lake Baikal in Siberia; it contains about the same volume of water as the entire Great Lakes system. Together, the Great Lakes and Lake Baikal contain 40% of the world's available freshwater (NALCO, 1988). Another 15% of the world's available freshwater is contained in several lakes that dot the landscape in Canada.

Table. 15.1.   The Differences Between a Lake and a Pond

Lakes	Ponds
Larger	Smaller
Deeper	Shallower
May have dramatically different temperatures from the surface to the bottom waters.	Top and bottom waters generally have the same temperature.
Light generally does not reach the bottom at deeper points.	Light generally will reach the bottom in all areas of the pond.
Lakes are natural.	Ponds are usually man-made.
Can affect local climate if large enough.	Tend to be greatly affected by local climate.

Source: U.S. EPA, 2011b.

Lakes are especially sensitive to pollution, much more so than rivers. Rivers, with their moving waters, have the ability, within limits, to self-purify (this process is explained in detail later). Lakes are still bodies of water that, with the exception of **stratification** and turnover, do not generally flow and self-purify. Oxygen-demanding wastes are one of the most prevalent lake pollutants. Phosphorus is generally the pol-lutant that most seriously affects overall water quality in lakes (Davis & Cornwell, 1991). Pathogenic organisms can also thrive in lakes and cause serious health problems for swimmers and others who participate in lake recreational activities.

You must have a basic knowledge of lake systems to understand the role of contaminants in lake pollution. This section is essentially a short course in limnology or lake science as it relates to contaminant pollution.

CLASSIFICATION OF LAKES

Odum (1971) points out that lakes can be classified in three ways: by eutrophication, by special types of lakes, and by impoundments. *Eutrophication* is a normal aging process that results from recycling and accumulation of organic material over long periods of time. As the sediments continue to accumulate, the lakebed fills until it is transformed into a bog and eventually into a terrestrial ecosystem. In its natural phase, eutrophication is the result of the natural lake succession process. This process is usually slow and sometimes can take up to tens of thousands of years to complete. However, lake succession via accelerated eutrophication can occur when massive amounts of organic material are dumped into the lake over time. This accelerated process is called **cultural eutrophication**.

Classification of Lakes Based on Eutrophication

Lakes can be classified into three types based on their eutrophication state:

1. **Oligotrophic lakes** (few foods). These are young, deep, nutrient-poor lakes with crystal-clear water, usually more aesthetically pleasing, but with little biomass productivity. The water quality is usually more suitable for a wider range of uses. Lake Superior is an oligotrophic lake, as is Lake Tahoe. Both of these lakes will eventually turn eutrophic; this process is inevitable.
2. **Mesotrophic lakes**. To draw a distinct line between oligotrophic and eutrophic lakes is hard, and often the term *mesotrophic* is used to describe a lake that falls somewhere between the two extremes. Mesotrophic lakes develop with the passage of time. Nutrients and sediments are added through runoff, and the lake becomes more biologically productive. Mesotrophic lakes hold a greater diversity of species with very low populations at first, but shift toward higher and higher populations with fewer and fewer species. Sediments and solids contributed by runoff and organisms make the lake shallower. At an advanced mesotrophic stage, lakes may have undesirable odors and colors in certain areas. Turbidity increases, and organic deposits accumulate on the bottom. Lake Ontario has reached this stage.
3. **Eutrophic lakes** (good foods). These are lakes with large or excessive supplies of nutrients. As nutrients continue to enter the lake system, large, unsightly algal blooms develop, fish populations increase, types of fish change from sensitive to more pollution-tolerant species, and biomass productivity becomes very high. The lake takes on undesirable characteristics, including offensive odors, very high turbidity, and a blackish color. This high level of turbidity can be seen in studies of Lake Washington in Seattle. Laws (1993) reports that Secchi (a device used to measure turbidity; shown in Figure 15.3) depth measurements made in Lake

Figure 15.3. A Secchi Disk, used to measure turbidity or water clarity. The disk is lowered into the water until it can no longer be seen from surface. The depth of visual disappearance becomes the Secchi Disk Transparency Extinction Coefficient, which will range from a few centimeters in very turbid waters to 35 m in a very clear lake.

Washington from 1950 to 1979 show an almost fourfold reduction in water clarity. Along with an increase in turbidity, a eutrophic lake becomes very shallow. Lake Erie and Green Lake (Seattle, Washington) are at this stage.

Special Types of Lakes

Odum (1971) and Spellman (1996) refer to several special lake types:

1. **Dystrophic lakes** (bog lakes) have low pH, and water color ranges from yellow to brown. Dissolved solids, nitrogen, phosphorus, and calcium are low, and humic matter is high. These lakes are sometimes void of fish fauna; other organisms are limited. When fish are present, production is poor (Welch, 1983).
2. **Deep ancient lakes** are specialized environments found in only a few places (endemic fauna)—for example, Lake Baikal in Russia.
3. **Desert salt lakes** are specialized environments like the Great Salt Lake, Utah, where evaporation rates exceed precipitation rates, resulting in salt accumulation.
4. **Volcanic lakes** form on volcanic mountain peaks, as in Japan and the Philippines.
5. **Chemically stratified lakes** include the Big Soda Lake in Nevada. These lakes are stratified because various dissolved chemicals have altered water supplies. They are **meromictic**, which means partly mixed.

Eutrophication

Why, in archaeology, is the site under study and exploration called a dig? Because, literally, the ground must be removed to reveal what time and Earth have covered.

Soil is formed constantly—wind carries soil particles into minute cracks and crevices, which help support plant life, which sheds tissues and decays, adding enriching matter to the soil, trapping more dirt particles, until eventually, over the course of hundreds and thousands of years, a particular location is buried under foot upon foot of earth. Think about this: Each year, over 100 tons of dust are deposited on each square mile of Earth. Time works as a leveler—using the materials at hand, it fills in the hollows and grinds down the mountains, in a constant, unconscious effort to even out the world.

Time also works on surface water bodies as well, but those hollows fill differently from those on land. The accumulation of decaying material from the water environment itself, as well as soil and other particles carried by the wind, gradually age a lake, slowly filling it in. In the process, the environmental conditions change, promoting the growth of a different set of plants and altering the habitat for living organisms.

Over the course of time, surface water bodies gradually fill in, becoming more and more shallow. Lakes and ponds can turn to marsh and eventually can disappear completely. Rivers and streams age, too, altering flow speed, habitat, and watercourse, and changing the terrain they travel through.

This process is generally very gradual, and in nature, without human intervention, occurs very slowly. Humans, of course, alter the natural eutrophication life cycle of water bodies in several ways. Fertilizers speed up the process, sometimes enormously. Humans also build levees, dams, floodwalls, channels, bridges, canals, and locks, any or all of which affect the conditions of the body of water involved. They build, divert, and dredge, in attempts to control where water goes, when, and how fast, in the process disrupting the physical, biological, and environmental cycles of nature.

Nature, though, is far from helpless in this process. Water goes where nature wills, eventually. The point is, in the natural balance of our world, nothing is exempt from the hand of nature; thus, on Earth, nothing is ever safe from change, which occurs and continues always.

6. **Polar lakes** exist in polar regions, with surface water temperature mostly below 4°C.

7. **Terminal lakes** are lakes with an incoming water source, but no exit—a terminal resting place for water flow. The mineral content of terminal lakes is extreme—to the extent that lake waters are mined for their mineral content. Utah's Great Salt Lake and the Dead Sea in Israel are terminal lakes.

8. **Glacial lakes** occur where basins have been excavated by moving ice or where drainage patterns have been altered by deposition of glacial till.

9. **Oxbow lakes** are formed when river meanders are cut off from the main channel and are therefore generally found in the immediate vicinity of rivers.

10. **Levee lakes** are formed when the water levels of rivers become too high and/or flood and deposit enough sediment to form a completely separate body of water.

Levees may also be human-made obstructions along the edge of a body of water used to restrain the flow of water out of a riverbank.

11. **Barrier lakes** occur behind sandbars in coastal regions, and have characteristically high levels of salinity. Water of this type, a mixture of fresh and saltwater, is referred to as **brackish** water. Brackish water may result from tidal flow or sea spray.

Classification of Lakes by Impoundments (Shut-ins)

Impoundments or *shut-ins* are artificial, human-made lakes formed by trapping water from rivers and watersheds. They vary in characteristics according to the region and nature of drainage. They have high turbidity and a fluctuating water level. The biomass productivity, particularly of benthos (bottom dwellers), is generally lower than that of natural lakes. Impoundments also include human-made enclosed pits and Earth-embankments filled artificially to form artificial lakes, reservoirs, or holding basins. Some of these structures may be spring fed, and all are subject to infiltration by runoff.

A reservoir is a special type of impoundment. Reservoirs used for storage of raw water are generally lakes, ponds, or basins that are either naturally formed or constructed. The term reservoir also applies to aboveground and underground storage and ground-level tanks designed to store treated or finished water. Some reservoirs (both raw and finished water types) are large and deep enough that they exhibit many of the characteristics of natural lake systems, in particular the characteristics of stratification and turnover, which only occur in lake-type water bodies.

Lake Thermal Stratification and Turnover

Water's temperature–density relationship is unique and especially important for lakes (only those located in some tropical and all temperate regions, because of their depth and long-term residence time). This relationship in temperate lakes (of more than 25 feet in depth) leads to lake stratification and subsequent **turnover**.

Water has its greatest density at 4°C (39.2°F); in the spring, a temperate lake's water may be this temperature throughout its entire depth. One result of this density characteristic (which is specific to the liquid water only) is that ice floats, because the surrounding water is slightly warmer and denser. For the biota occupying a lake, this fact of nature is good—otherwise their watery environment (and they) would freeze solid.

During summer, the **epilimnion** (upper levels; see Figure 15.4) of the lake warm up, while the **hypolimnion** (deepest portions) retain their 4°C temperature. The epilimnion is heated directly by the sun and indirectly by contact with warm air, forming a narrow band of warm water. When water is warm, it is less dense than colder water and tends to remain near the surface until mixed downward by turbulence. The epilimnion layer of warm water floats on the lower, colder water of the hypolimnion. A rather narrow horizontal zone of abrupt temperature change known as the **thermocline** separates these two layers. You may experience the thermocline while swimming in a temperate lake. When you swim horizontally on the surface, the water is warm. But tread water with your body vertical, and you experience the colder layers underneath.

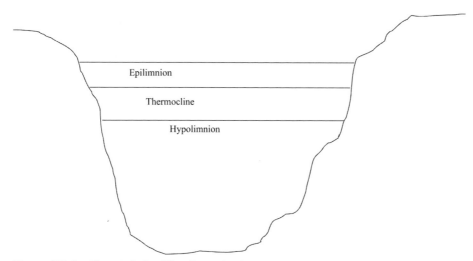

Figure 15.4.   Thermal stratification of a temperate lake.

In the summer, most of the plankton and nekton are found in the epilimnion, where sufficient **dissolved oxygen** exists, rather than below the thermocline (in the hypolimnion), where oxygen levels are very low. In each of these layers are differences in viscosity. Because the water viscosity changes between each level, the epilimnion, on top of the colder water, is circulated by wind action (wind-induced lake water circulation), while the hypolimnion is quiet and almost lifeless. These conditions remain fairly stable, or stability actually increases with increased temperatures in the epilimnion throughout the summer season, while the hypolimnion remains at a fairly constant temperature. This leads to a very stable layering effect known as *thermal stratification*. When thermal stratification occurs in a lake, it causes turnover.

During summer, stratification occurs because the top layer, warmer than the bottom, results in layers of different density: the top light, the bottom heavy. With increased rise in temperature, the top layer becomes even lighter, and the thermocline (medium density) forms. From top to bottom, we now have the lightest and warmest on top, medium weight and relatively warm in the middle, and heaviest and coldest below, with a sharp drop in temperature at the thermocline. The water in these three layers does not circulate. If the thermocline is below the range of effective light penetration, which is quite common, the oxygen supply becomes depleted in the hypolimnion, because both photosynthesis and the surface source of oxygen are cut off. This state is known as **summer stagnation**.

In the fall, as air temperature drops, so does the temperature of the epilimnion. The marked stratification of summer begins to disappear, until the epilimnion temperature is the same as that of the thermocline. At this point, these two layers mix. The temperature of the whole lake is now the same, with complete mixing. As the temperature of the surface water reaches 4°C, it becomes more dense than the water below, which is not in direct contact with the air and does not cool as rapidly at the lower levels. The denser, oxygen-rich surface layer stirs up organic matter as the water sinks, causing overturning; this is known as *fall turnover*.

During winter, the epilimnion, which is icebound, is at the lowest temperature and thus lightest; the thermocline is at medium temperature and medium weight; and the hypolimnion is at about 4°C and heaviest. This is **winter stratification**. In winter, the oxygen supply is usually not greatly reduced, as the low temperature solubility of oxygen is higher, and bacterial decomposition (along with other life activities) is operating at a low rate. When too much ice with heavy snow accumulates, light penetration is reduced. This reduces the rate of photosynthesis, which in turn causes oxygen depletion in the hypolimnion, resulting in **winter kill** of fish.

As the ambient temperatures rise in spring, the ice of the epilimnion melts and the top two layers mix. As the epilimnion reaches 4°C, it sinks down, causing **spring overturn**. Odum (1971) describes this spring overturn phenomenon as being analogous to the lake taking a "deep breath."

Lake turnover is important to water quality in two ways: (1) It causes changes in distribution of nutrients and temperature, and (2) it causes movement of bottom sediments throughout the volume. Normally, nutrient materials accumulate in the lower depths, either as sediments or because biological activity is lower. When turnover occurs, these sediments are brought to the surface, exposed to sunlight, higher temperatures, and oxygen concentrations, and eutrophication rates increase (Tchobanoglous & Schroeder, 1987).

LOTIC (FLOWING) WATER SYSTEMS

Consider the following information about flowing or running waters. Early in the spring on a snow- and ice-covered high alpine meadow is the time and place the water cycle continues. The cycle's main component, water, has been held in reserve, literally frozen for the long, dark winter months, but with longer, warmer spring days, the sun is higher, more direct, and out longer, and the frozen masses of water respond to the increased warmth. The melt begins with a single drop, then two, then more and more. As the snow and ice melt, the drops join a chorus that continues unending; they fall from their ice-bound lip to the bare rock and soil terrain below. The terrain the snowmelt strikes is not like glacial till, the unconsolidated, heterogeneous mixture of clay, sand, gravel, and boulders, dug-out, ground-out, and exposed by the force of a huge, slow, and inexorably moving glacier. Instead, this soil and rock ground is exposed to the falling drops of snowmelt because of a combination of wind and the tiny, enduring force exerted by drops of water as season after season, they collide with the thin soil cover, exposing the intimate bones of the Earth.

Gradually, the single drops increase to a small rush—they join to form a splashing, rebounding, helter-skelter cascade, many separate rivulets that trickle, then run their way down the face of the granite mountain. At an indented ledge halfway down the mountain slope, a pool forms whose beauty, clarity, and sweet iciness provide the visitor with an incomprehensible, incomparable gift—a blessing from the Earth.

The mountain pool fills slowly, tranquil under the blue sky, reflecting the pines, snow and sky around and above it, an open invitation to lie down and drink and to peer into the glass-clear, deep water, so clear that it seems possible to reach down over 50 feet and touch the very bowels of the mountain. The pool has no transition from shallow margin to depth; it is simply deep and pure. As the pool fills with more meltwater, we wish to freeze time, to hold this place and this pool in its perfect state forever, it is such a rarity to us in our modern world. But this cannot be—Mother Nature calls, prodding, urging—and for a brief instant, the water laps in the breeze against the outermost edge of the ridge, then a trickle flows over the rim. The giant hand of gravity reaches out and tips the overflowing melt onward, and it continues the downward journey, following the path of least resistance to its next destination, several thousand feet below.

When the overflow meets violently with the angled, broken rocks below, it bounces, bursts, and mists its way against steep, V-shaped walls that form a small valley, carved out over time by water and the forces of the Earth, still high in altitude, but its rock-strewn bed bent downward, toward the sea.

Within the valley confines, the meltwater has grown from drops, to rivulets, to a small mass of flowing water. And flow it does, through what is at first a narrow opening, then, gaining strength, speed, and power as the V-shaped valley widens to form a U-shape. But the journey still continues, as the water mass picks up speed and tumbles over massive boulders, then slows again.

At a larger but shallower pool, water from higher elevations has joined the main body, from the hillsides, crevices, springs, rills, and mountain creeks. At the influent poolsides, all appears peaceful, quiet, restful—but not far away, at the effluent end of the pool, gravity takes control again. The overflow is flung over the jagged lip and cascades downward several hundred feet, where the waterfall again brings its load to a violent, mist-filled meeting.

The water separates and joins again and again, forming a deep, furious, wild stream that calms gradually as it continues to flow over lands that are less steep. The waters widen into pools overhung by vegetation, surrounded by tall trees. The pure, crystalline waters have become progressively discolored on their downward journey, stained brown with humic acid and literally filled with suspended sediments; the once-pure stream is now muddy.

The mass divides and flows in different directions, over different landscapes. Small streams divert and flow off into open country. Different soils work to retain or speed the waters, and in some places the water spreads out into shallow swamps, bogs, marshes, fens, or mires. Other streams pause long enough to fill deep depressions in the land and form lakes. For a time, the water remains and pauses in its journey to the sea. But this is only a short-term pause, because lakes are only a short-term resting place in the water cycle. The water will eventually move on, by evaporation or seepage into groundwater, but move it will. Other portions of the water mass stay with the main flow, and the speed of the flow changes to form a river, which braids its way through the landscape, heading for the sea. As it changes speed and slows, the river bottom changes from rock and stone to silt and clay. Plants begin to grow, stems thicken, and leaves broaden. The river is now full of life and the nutrients needed to sustain life. But the river courses onward to its destination, where the flowing, rich mass slows at last and finally spills into the sea (Spellman, 2007).

In Chapter 14, we compared the human circulatory system to the Earth's water circulation system, pointing out that water (analogous to blood) is pumped by the hydraulic cycle and continuously circulated through air, water bodies, and various vessels. Like vessels in the human circulatory system, water vessels (rivers) are essential to Earth's circulatory system. Capillary creeks, brooks, streams, rills, and rivulets feed the Earth's rivers like arteries. In the next subsection, we discuss how this part of the Earth's circulatory system works with the complete system: how rivers/streams (for this text's purposes, the terms are interchangeable) carry water through the terrestrial part of the hydrological cycle.

Rivers

What exactly is a river? Several standard characteristics help define exactly what elements and parameters fit—massive flows of moving water, braided flows of moving water, white-water rapids, riffles, river pools, riparian areas—but definitions are slippery things, and for something as elemental as a river, unsatisfactory. Most people would have no difficulty in recognizing a river when they see one, even though rivers can be described in many different ways. This description by Watson (1988) may help illustrate the degree and depth of this dilemma:

> A river, almost by definition, is a body of moving water large enough to occupy one's mind. Something redolent of distant and legendary origins, filled with news of the sources from which it takes its strength. Rivers are metaphors for change, dreams of history. They move by, tangling the threads of time, braiding their waters into mixtures of the moment, open systems hinting at a single destiny—a predetermined and overwhelming need for the sea.
>
> On the same slope, large rivers flow faster than smaller ones, because there is less friction with their banks and beds. And, because even the air has a braking effect, the speed of any river's flow is greatest at a point somewhere between one-tenth and four-tenths of its depth below the surface. In addition, every bend and shift in direction, every rock and ledge below, produces whirls and upwellings which create random turbulence. The result is an environment where nothing is certain but change. A place for opportunists. (104–106)

For our purposes, we simplify the process by defining a river as a large, natural body of water, the movement of which erodes land surfaces and transports and deposits materials along its course, eventually emptying into an ocean, lake, or other body of water, and usually fed along its course by converging tributaries. The origination of this converging of tributaries (it looks like the branching of a tree) is best understood by examining a network analysis for a typical river system. In 1930, Robert E. Horton, a famous engineer, devised such a network analysis model (see Figure 15.7, later in the chapter, for an example).

Rivers are fed by precipitation that does not infiltrate into the ground or evaporate. Rivers, like lakes, pass through various stages. The life span can be divided into four stages:

1. **Establishment of a river:** Beginning as an outlet of lakes or ponds, arising from seepage areas or springs, or from runoff in a watershed, a river may be a dryrun or a headwater riverbed before it is eroded to the level of groundwater.

2. **Young rivers:** A youthful river becomes permanent as its bed is eroded below the groundwater level and it begins to receive runoff and spring water.

3. **Mature rivers:** A river reaches maturity as it becomes wider, deeper, and more turbid. Its velocity slows, and water temperature rises. Sand, silt, mud, and/or clay form the bottom.

4. **Old rivers:** Old rivers have reached their geologic base level. The flood plain may be very broad and flat. During normal flow periods, the channel refills and many shifting bars develop.

Remember that runoff affects rivers—varying amounts of runoff affect the rate and volume of flow—and that runoff is dependent, in part, upon the condition of the watershed soil. River channels are designed to handle normal river flow; contrary to popular belief, they are not designed to handle flow during all weather events, such as flooding.

Response Scenario 15.1. Why Do Rivers Flood?

If we had asked this question in 2004, the answer we would have received would probably have had something to do with El Niño: "El Niño's causing it, that's what's causing all the strange weather—including this flood right now."

But is El Niño responsible for the flooding events that occurred in the United States in 1973 and 1993, when gauging stations on the Mississippi River at St. Louis, Missouri, measured 43 feet and 49 feet peak above flood level, respectively? If you ask this question of a scientist who studies weather-related flooding events, he or she might reply "maybe." If you ask this same question of a scientist who knows weather (climatology), geology, and geophysics and who is an expert on flooding events, he or she might reply "possibly."

No one is absolutely certain of the exact impact El Niño, or its lesser known associated phenomenon, southern oscillation (together, ENSO), has on global weather patterns. The jury is still out on the exact impact of ENSO. However, enough historical evidence is available to accurately state why most rivers flood their basins.

Based on actual observation and measurement, we know for certain that all river systems naturally experience high discharge at a time of heavy precipitation. Flow alternates with time and is a consequence of the fluctuation of low and high precipitation periods. In short, when it rains, the river rises.

We are also certain that no river system in the world forms a channel that would convey without overflow all possible overflow events. You might pause for a moment and think to yourself that this last statement is strange or maybe inaccurate. That, deep incomparable canyon is on your mind; namely, the Grand Canyon in Arizona. "The Colorado River certainly has a steep enough channel to convey just about any type of flood event that is imaginable, right? Isn't the Grand Canyon itself evidence that during geologic time some great event carved out what we see today?"

The Grand Canyon is over one mile deep in places (dwarfing the Colorado River with walls that tell of at least two billion years of history), probably deep enough to convey just about any flood event short of Noah's Ark. But what about the river system itself? The Grand Canyon area is just a small section of

(continued)

Response Scenario 15.1. Why Do Rivers Flood?

the landscape the river courses through in a large river system that flows through hundreds and thousands of miles of widely diverse landscape.

Did some mammoth event occur in the distant geologic past to carve the Grand Canyon as we know it today? No—this is also a misconception. Geologic evidence indicates that the Grand Canyon and other similar formations were actually carved out by modest—but frequent—flows that carved, deepened, shaped, and altered the channel structure we see today.

Contrary to popular belief, a river system usually contains a channel that can contain within its banks only a discharge of modest size—its normal flow. But nature has not overlooked the fact that rivers do overflow; it handles such significant events by providing room for greater overflow discharges onto the valley floor. But humans tend to forget (at great cost, both financially and in terms of human life) that a river system consists not only of its channel, but also its valley floor—the floodplain. When humans use this part of the river for agriculture or construction, they encroach upon the river. The result? When floods occur, roads, homes, buildings, and crops may be destroyed—along with whatever else is in the river's path.

At this point we understand that (1) floods are of such magnitude that the channel cannot handle peak discharge, (2) a flood is a flow in excess of channel capacity, and (3) a flood is a normal and expected characteristic of rivers (on average, most rivers experience discharges in excess of channel capacity about twice a year). But what causes a river to flood?

When a river discharges enough water to overtop its banks and flow over the floodplain, many factors are involved. Precipitation combined with snowmelt is often enough to cause a river to flood, but other factors can easily enhance the runoff. If the landscape is already wet (saturated), infiltration is prevented or decreased, so runoff increases. Reduced or zero infiltration can also result if the landscape is frozen.

Human activities also affect runoff and, subsequently, flooding. Small-scale floods are affected by such activities as grazing by animals, surface paving, agricultural practices, and deforestation, which decrease infiltration. Human-made alterations in surface conditions that come with urbanization of an area, including street gutters, stormwater drains, and even roof downspouts, speed the movement of surface water downslope and prevent soil infiltration as well. The river channel alterations that communities put into place to prevent flooding in town also alter river flow, forcing greater masses of water farther downstream by preventing local infiltration. This can cause flood levels to increase for communities downriver as the water collects and moves onward. Large-scale (or great) floods (those caused by extraordinary total amounts of rainfall [great storms] or widespread rapid snow/icemelt) are not normally influenced by urbanization, deforestation, and agricultural practices.

RESPONSE

(i)   Do you think El Niño was actually responsible for the severe weather and flooding that occurred in 2011 in the United States?

(ii) Do you think it is wise to build in a floodplain?

(iii) Do you think those who reside in a floodplain who are flooded out and lose everything should be compensated by the government?

CREEKS, URBAN FLOODING, ENVIRONMENTAL CHANGE, AND WATER MANAGEMENT

River temperature and dissolved oxygen (DO) levels follow different rules than those of still bodies of water. In rivers, temperature and DO are generally evenly distributed, though some variations in DO exist between rapidly flowing, turbulent areas and deeper, quiet river pools because of physical aeration. The amount of oxygen in aquatic systems is controlled by the solubility of gaseous oxygen in water. Since the DO is usually high and evenly distributed (the amount of DO in rivers and lakes is generally eight to ten parts per million), river organisms are adapted to this environment and have a narrow range of tolerance for DO. Organisms residing in aquatic systems depend on the exact amount of oxygen present, which is controlled by the solubility of gaseous oxygen in water. The best example of this type of dependence is the fishkill level. Trout are adapted to high-oxygen rivers and cannot survive in rivers with DO levels below 5 mg/L. River systems that receive large amounts of organic pollution are especially susceptible to fish-kill because of the corresponding reduction in oxygen levels.

Rivers have a large area for land–water interchange (this can be clearly seen in Figure 15.7). Most rivers are primarily detritus-based food chains—their primary source of energy is not green plants, as in most ecosystems, but organic matter from the surrounding land, which is used as food by decomposers. Nutrients and waste products are transported by the flowing water to and away from many aquatic organisms, which helps to maintain a productivity level many times greater than that in standing waters (Smith, 1974).

Current is the outstanding feature of rivers and the major factor limiting the distribution of organisms. The current is determined by the steepness of the bottom gradient, the roughness of the streambed, and the depth and width of the streambed. Current in rivers has promoted many special biological adaptations by stream organisms.

River Habitat

Rivers typically have two types of zones: rapids and pools. In **rapids zones**, the current velocity is great enough to keep the bottom clear of silt and sludge, providing a firm bottom for organism growth. Organisms living in rapids zones are adapted for life in running water. Trout, for example, have streamlined bodies to help respiration and in obtaining food. River organisms that live under rocks to avoid the strong current have flat or streamlined bodies. Others have hooks or suckers to cling or attach to a firm substrate to avoid being carried away by the strong current.

River **pool zones** are usually deeper water regions where reduced water velocity allows silt and other settling solids to provide a soft bottom, unfavorable for sensitive bottom dwellers. Decomposition of these solids causes lower levels of dissolved oxygen (DO). Some river organisms spend part of their time in the rapids and part in the pool zone.

River Water Quality

Lakes are separate, isolated entities, typically landlocked, and they usually lack a separate freshwater feed system (with the exception of precipitation, infiltration, and runoff) to replenish total water supply. When contaminants run off land into such a body of water, or when people dispose of rubbish, garbage, and other unwanted items into the lake, the contaminants must remain within it. They have no place to go, and no transport system to take them elsewhere. Systems like lakes do not have self-purifying capabilities. Although lake water in temperate lakes may turn over twice each year, mixing its water and replacing surface water with bottom water, this process only works to exacerbate a contaminated lake's pollution problem. If highly toxic pesticides are dumped into a lake system, they will eventually sink to the bottom sediments and accumulate. During lake turnover, these toxins and any others present in the lake will be brought up from the bottom and redistributed throughout the lake system. Lakes have a distinct disadvantage: They lack the physical capability to maintain acceptable water quality on their own.

River systems don't have this problem. Rivers, because of their main characteristic—current, or flow—have the built-in capability to self-purify themselves, to a point. Ever since humans began to settle near rivers, they have used the rivers as transportation for themselves and their belongings, to provide waterpower, and to provide drinking and irrigation water; they have used the fish and other organisms in the river as a food source and used the river as the local garbage dump.

The local garbage dump? Absolutely. Remember, people only want those items that have some benefit or use to them. When an item is no longer beneficial or useful, becomes unsightly, boring, or wears out, they throw it away. Out of sight, out of mind. And rivers effectively took people's trash out of sight quickly—it was a convenient place to dispose of unwanted items.

When civilization was in its infancy, humans' river disposal practices were not terribly damaging to the local area they inhabited. They could simply walk over to the river, throw their unwanted items into it, and stand there and watch them sink or stream off down the river—either way, the unwanted items disappeared, and this is what people wanted.

As civilization advanced and settlements along river systems turned into cities, people continued to dispose of an increasing number of unwanted items in the river, but now the unwanted items included human sewage, organic waste, and chemical runoff. The river continued to carry what it could downstream—out of sight.

People seemed to think that because rivers flow and water in the river seemed to be only momentarily filthy (or otherwise contaminated), the rivers could continue to carry their unwanted items away indefinitely—out of sight.

But more and more people moved in, and along with more people, the production of more unwanted items accelerated, and dumping in the river increased. The river did its best to self-clean and to move those unwanted items downstream—out of sight. But were these unwanted items really out of sight? To those who threw them away, yes. To others who settled downstream from those settlements, no.

Time marched on, and with its passage came the advent of the Industrial Revolution in Great Britain. More industry brought in more people, and more people accumulated more unwanted items to throw into the legendary Thames River. But now the Thames could handle only so much of the increased input of waste it received on a continuous basis. The limit was eventually reached. Through human actions, the

Thames had been changed from a river into an open cesspool. It was still used as a depository for unwanted items, but the items were no longer out of sight. Instead, the Thames was a floating mess, a water supply deadly with disease and rank with a horrendous, unbearable stench. Eventually, Londoners had had enough; something had to be done to clean up the Thames.

This river contamination scenario has been repeated many times in many places throughout the world, and in some places it continues. Rivers have the physical capability to clean themselves and to maintain water quality, but only to a point. Humans always seem to reach that "point," one way or another.

Response Scenario 15.2. The Willamette River

Have pollution levels improved for the Willamette River? In 1998, Brent Walth of the *Oregonian* pointed out in an article:

> The Willamette River is so polluted where it flows through Portland that the federal government is considering naming a 5.5-mile stretch as a Superfund site . . . . Tars, pesticides and other toxic chemicals cake the Willamette's sediment after decades of industrial activity in Portland Harbor, running downstream from Swan Island to Sauvie Island . . . .
>
> The threat of listing Oregon's heartland river as a Superfund site has chilled state officials and alarmed businesses along the river whose properties may have contributed to the contamination . . . .
>
> Among them are companies that own oil terminals along the river, including GATX, Time Oil and Tosco. Some companies—including Tosco, an oil terminal operator; Gunderson, a maker of rail cars; and Elf Atochem, a chemical manufacturer—inherited the industrial pollution when they bought the sites.
>
> Still others—including the Port, ship repair operator Cascade General and gas utility NW Natural—might be on the hook for pollution caused by their own operations . . . .
>
> Given that it's often difficult to tell where sedimentation contamination comes from, assessing responsibility can be a continuous process that DEQ officials hope to avoid with the group's voluntary cooperation.
>
> "We're not stepping forward to say we are particularly responsible for any of the problems," said Dean Marriott, director of the city of Portland Bureau of Environmental Services, whose sewer outfalls may have contributed to the contamination.

In 2004, "OSPIRG says river cleanup failing," Jim Feehan of the *Register-Guard* stated:

> An environmental and consumer protection organization on Saturday took Gov. Ted Kulongoski to task for his record cleaning up the Willamette River at an event about the overall health of the waterway.
>
> The Oregon Student Public Interest Research Group, or OSPIRG, believes that the governor has failed to follow up on his campaign pledge to reduce toxic emissions, increase environmental enforcement and make polluters pay for contaminating the river, according to OSPIRG toxics and clean water advocate Rhett Lawrence. . . .
>
> Each year, about 4 million pounds of dioxin, lead, arsenic, pesticides and other toxic chemicals are dumped into the Willamette, Lawrence said.

(continued)

Response Scenario 15.2. (*continued*)

An Oregon Department of Environmental Quality study of the river's Newberg Pool found that 50 percent of all fish captured had significant skeletal deformities, and in 2000, a five-mile stretch of the river in Portland was listed as a federal Superfund site, a classification reserved for the most polluted places in the country, he said. . . .

Walker said a 1972 cover story in National Geographic hailed the river as having been restored from environmental degradation.

Three decades later, the river is a "cesspool of toxin . . . a river of death," she said.

Obviously, problems are still there—and they are related to funding and enforcement. Since 70% of the Oregon population lives near the Willamette, the river's pollution levels are of extreme concern.

Visit www.willamette-riverkeeper.org/superfund/ for current Willamette River clean-up status.

Any river's water quality is at least in part a reflection of those who live and work close by. The history of the people and communities along a river are written on the river, for those who know how to read it. The Willamette's history is clear for us all to read in the following chronology:

1840 Willamette River dredging begins.
1859 Willamette River supplements water from Caruther's Creek in Portland.
1861 Willamette flood crests at 47 feet.
1863 Willamette Falls dammed.
1866 Oregon commercial fishery begins.
1871 Portland citizens protest water quality and rates.
1872 Municipal water system proposed in Portland; many cities follow.
1872 Legislature passes laws against using explosives or poisons to take salmon.
1878 Canning industry builds nation's first Columbia Basin hatchery on a Clackamas River tributary.
1878 State regulates fishing seasons.
1878 Oregon Fish Commission established.
1873 Oregon City locks open to river traffic.
1881 Willamette flood crests at 44.3 feet.
1884 Portland citizens hold protests over the condition of their drinking water.
1885 Portland's takeover of water system.
1886 Columbia River chinook stocks showing visible depletion.
1886 City of Salem moves Willamette water facilities upstream to avoid pollution.
1887 State board of commissioners established to enforce fish and game laws.
1892 State establishes a hatchery fund.
1895 Portland abandons Willamette; Bull Run new drinking water source.
1890 Willamette flood crests at 45.1 feet.
1894 Willamette flood crests at 26.9 feet.
1901 Willamette flood crests at 31.5 feet.
1901 First coho fry released in Oregon.
1902 Reclamation Act enacted.
1903 Willamette flood crests at 28.6 feet.
1907 Willamette flood crests at 31.3 feet.
1909 Willamette flood crests at 30.5 feet.
1909 State requires fishing licenses.

1911 State board of health describes Willamette as an "open sewer"; citizens using "boiling cans" and enduring typhoid epidemics.

1916 Willamette flood crests at 26 feet.

1918 Willamette River closed to commercial salmon fishing.

1919 Portland approves floodplain ordinance.

1920s Willamette River off-limits to swimmers.

1923 Willamette flood crests at 30.3 feet.

1926 State board of health holds Willamette River conference on pollution, initiates scientific study, and starts Anti-Pollution League.

1927 City of Portland initiates careful study of river's pollution, finds oxygen level inadequate to support aquatic life.

1927 Fish wheels banned on the Columbia in Oregon.

1928 Portland's City Club releases a report finding sewage outfall worst polluter within city limits.

1928 Construction begins on Portland's nearly mile-long sea wall.

1929 State passes law requiring screening of irrigation ditches.

1930 Willamette Valley Dam Project lobbying begins.

1932 Army Corps says Willamette River flood control is unnecessary.

1933 State study finds Willamette pulp mills major source of river's pollution.

1934 Portland's sewer outfall report finds sludge and decaying matter on the river's surface. Portland citizens approve sewage treatment plants.

1936 Pulp mills pollution study made public.

1936 Congress approves federal Flood Control Act; authorizes Army Corps' role in flood control, erosion control, and hydropower development.

1937 State approves water pollution control act.

1937 Army Corps report recommends Willamette Valley Project (WVP) dams for navigation, flood control, irrigation, hydropower, and pollutant flushing.

1938 Governor vetoes legislative attempt to strengthen water pollution control act.

1938 *E. coli* bacteria found in Willamette; water purification initiative approved by state voters, authorizes State Sanitary Authority (SSA).

1938 Congress authorizes funds to build 13 Willamette Valley dams and reservoirs.

1941 1st WVP dam, Fern Ridge, complete.

1943 Willamette flood crests at 30.6 feet.

1944 Scientists find river below Oregon City Falls totally devoid of oxygen.

1944 2nd WVP dam, Cottage Grove, complete.

1944 United States enters World War II; industrial development intensifies along Portland Harbor.

1949 3rd WVP dam, Dorena, complete.

1949 Drag seines, traps, and nets prohibited in Oregon.

1950 State questions need for additional federal dam construction in Oregon.

1952 SSA orders pulp mills to stop dumping wastes into river; industry does not comply.

1953 Willamette flood crests at 37.78 feet.

1953 4th & 5th WVP dams, Detroit and Big Cliff, complete.

1954 6th & 7th WVP dams, Dexter and Lookout Point, complete

1957 State strengthens antipollution laws.

1957 Oregon Fish Commission studies the problems fish have in scaling Willamette Falls.

(*continued*)

Response Scenario 15.2. (*continued*)

1960 Governor Mark Hatfield seeks to protect salmon beds from sand and gravel dredging.

1961 8th WVP dam, Hills Creek, complete.

1962 Tom McCall produces Willamette River documentary, *Pollution in Paradise*.

1963 State empowers SSA to shut down polluting industries.

1963 9th WVP dam, Cougar, complete.

1964 Tom McCall elected governor, takes on pulp mills and other polluting industries by enforcing antipollution requirements.

1964 Willamette flood crests at 37.78 feet.

1964 Citizens defeat initiative petition banning commercial fishery on Willamette.

1965 Fewer than 100 fall chinook reach Willamette Falls.

1966 State orders cities and industries to reduce pollution and begin to manage and plan for growth; Willamette River clean-up begins.

1968 Idaho, Oregon, and Washington governors establish Columbia River Fisheries Advisory Council. This later becomes the Columbia Basin Fish & Wildlife Authority.

1966 10th WVP dam, Fall Creek, complete.

1966 Willamette flood crests at 26.88 feet.

1967 Governor Tom McCall proposes Willamette River Greenway.

1968 11th & 12th WVP dams, Foster and Green Peter, complete.

1969 13th WVP dam, Blue River, complete.

1972 Congress Approves Clean Water Act.

1972 *National Geographic* magazine writes article on miraculous Willamette River clean-up.

1972 Willamette flood crests at 30.23 feet.

1972 Oregon Forest Practices Act passed.

1973 Endangered Species Act passed.

1974 Willamette flood crests at 32.32 feet.

1974 Sockeye salmon fishery closed; Oregon Fish Commission and Wildlife Commission merge to create Oregon Department of Fish and Wildlife (ODFW).

1975 By initiative petition, Oregon citizens prohibit the sale of steelhead by non-Indians.

1976 Columbia River spring chinook fishery closed.

1977 Oregon Department of Fish and Wildlife establishes its first native fish policy as a result of citizen efforts.

1980 Congress passes NW Power Act, placing salmon protection and enhancement on a par with power production in the Columbia Basin.

1985 State increases river monitoring. Separation of combined sewer outfall programs begins in many Willamette Valley cities. Stormwater management planning begins to address polluted runoff from roads and lands.

1985 United States and Canada sign a salmon interception treaty after 20 years of negotiation.

1986 Coho salmon in the Snake River become extinct.

1987 NW Power Planning Council adopts Protected Areas Program, placing 44,000 miles of salmon and steelhead streams off limits to hydroelectric dam development.

1991 Senator Mark Hatfield organizes the first Salmon Summit.

1992 Portland experiences water shortage; Willamette River comes under serious discussion as drinking water source.

1992 ODFW revises its wild fish policy, setting out gene conservation measures for wild fish management; public advocacy rather than agency initiative effected this change.

1993 Oregon Department of Environmental Quality (DEQ) study finds 80% of sampled Willamette fish have deformed gills.

1994 Adopt a River Program signed by Governor Barbara Roberts.

1996 Willamette River Water Quality Task Force formed by Governor Kitzhaber.

1996 Willamette flood crests at 44.5 feet.

1996 Army Corps and Oregon Water Resources Department initiate Willamette Basin Reservoir Study to plan future management of WVP system.

1997 Army Corps of Engineers report suggests removal of four Snake River Dams.

1997 Willamette flood crests at 29.45 feet.

1998 Willamette from Springfield to Portland designated an American Heritage River.

1998 Portland Harbor threatened with federal Superfund listing.

1998 Voters approve Willamette River as drinking water source in some south Portland suburbs.

1998 METRO adopts Title III, restricting floodplain development.

1998 Native steelhead in the Lower Columbia River Basin are listed as a threatened species by the National Marine Fisheries Service.

1998 Panel recommends withholding federal funds for new hatcheries.

1999 In protest against Title III, Metropolitan Homebuilders Association calls for development boycott in Portland metropolitan area.

1999 Contaminated sediments at Ross Island released. EPA refuses Oregon's proposed water temperature standards for the Willamette River.

1999 Willamette Valley spring chinook and winter steelhead listed as protected species.

1999 Bull trout and cutthroat trout endangered species listing anticipated.

Source: http://www.oregonwri.org/RiverCityConference/presentations/betimeline.pdf.

RESPONSE

(i) Based on a review of the time line provided above for the Willamette River, what is your assessment of the environmental condition of the river through 1999?

REFERENCES

Feehan, Jim. (2004, February 22). "OSPIRG Says River Cleanup Failing." *Register-Guardian.* http://www.registerguard.com/news/2004/02/22/c1.cr.willamette.0222.html.

Walth, B. (1998, October 23). "River Risks a Superfund Listing: The State Plans a Cleanup of the Willamette through Portland to Avoid the Federal Status." *Oregonian.* www.oregononline.com/oregonian

Rivers and Self-Purification

Normally, rivers maintain a balance between plant and animal life—with considerable interdependence among the various life forms. In a healthy river, when organic matter enters, bacteria metabolizes it and converts it into carbon dioxide, ammonia, sulfates, nitrates, and so forth, which are in turn used by algae and plants to produce oxygen and carbohydrates. Microscopic animals (rotifers and protozoa) feed on the plant life and in turn provide food for insects, worms, crustaceans, and fish. Even the wastes produced by organisms living in the river environment provide a source of food (which assists the bacterial degradation process) for some river organisms.

However, when excessive quantities of pollutants are dumped into the river, they can upset this natural balance in a number of ways and may eventually lead to the river's death. Changes in pH or excessive quantities of organic material may cause rapid bacterial growth and depletion of the DO resources of the river. Generally, very large numbers of relatively few species and the absence of higher forms characterize polluted rivers. If they could not naturally self-clean, they would have long ago turned into nothing more than slowly (if at all) moving masses of stagnating filth.

How do rivers self-clean? When pollutants enter a river system, the system works to reduce the concentration of pollutants by dilution, precipitation, bacterial oxidation, and other natural processes. Given enough time, these processes reestablish the normal cycle and distribution of life forms within the river system. In river systems, water quality standards are based on the maintenance of minimum dissolved oxygen concentrations, nontoxic concentrations of specific chemical species, and a near-neutral pH (McGhee, 1991). A healthy river has a natural assimilative capacity to assist in waste treatment without adversely affecting downstream users.

Before we begin our discussion of river **self-purification**, you must understand two terms important for their impact on river pollution:

1. Dissolved oxygen (DO) is the amount of oxygen dissolved in a river. It indicates the river's degree of health and its ability to support a balanced aquatic ecosystem. As DO drops below 5 mg/L, the forms of life that can survive are reduced. In extreme cases, when anaerobic conditions exist, higher forms of life are killed or driven off, and noxious conditions prevail. The deoxygenation caused by microbial decomposition of wastes and oxygenation by re-aeration are competing processes that are simultaneously removing and adding oxygen to a river (Masters, 1991). Oxygen comes from the atmosphere by solution and from photosynthesis of water plants. In fast rivers, oxygen is added primarily through re-aeration from the atmosphere in rapids, waterfalls, and cascades (see Figures 15.5 and 15.6). Dissolved oxygen concentrations are usually higher and more uniform from surface to bottom in streams than in lakes.
2. **Biochemical oxygen demand (BOD)** is the amount of oxygen required to biologically oxidize the organic waste over a stated period of time. BOD is important in the self-purification process, because to estimate the rate of deoxygenation in the river, the five-day and the ultimate BOD must be known.

Figure 15.5. Waterfall in a river system, aiding reaeration of water. Dawn Mist Falls, Belly River, Glacier National Park. Photo by F. R. Spellman

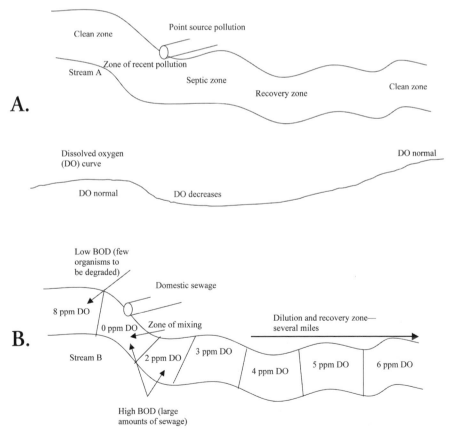

Figure 15.6. A: Changes that occur in a river after it receives excessive amounts of raw sewage; B: Effects of waste on DO. Adapted from Enger et al. *Environmental Science: The Study of Interrelationships*, 1989, p. 411

When a river receives an excessive amount of organic wastes, it exhibits various changes, which can be differentiated and classified into zones. Upstream, before a single point of pollution discharge, the river is defined by having a **clean zone** (Figure 15.6A). At the point of waste discharge, the water becomes turbid; this is the **zone of recent pollution**. Not far below the discharge point, the level of DO falls sharply and in some cases may fall to zero; this is called the **septic zone**.

After the organic waste has been largely decomposed, the dissolved oxygen level begins to rise in the **recovery zone**. Eventually, given enough time and no further waste discharges, the river returns to conditions similar to those in the clean zone.

Figure 15.6B shows the effect of organic wastes on dissolved oxygen in a river and the results of organic waste being attacked by organisms that use oxygen in the degradation process. Obviously, an inverse relationship exists between oxygen and organic matter in the river. The greater the BOD, the less desirable the river is for human use.

Aquatic Organisms and Their Role in Self-Purification

The self-purification process in rivers is similar to the purification process of secondary sewage treatment, which employs biological and chemical processes to remove most organic matter. In this discussion, we address the biological process.

In the biological self-purification process, certain factors indicate water quality. Four important ones are *coliform bacteria count, concentration of DO, BOD*, and the *biotic index* (the biota that exist at various stages in the self-purification of a river are direct indicators—a biotic index—of the water conditions).

Aquatic organisms degrade or decompose organic wastes. The river exhibits a change in the type of organisms present as the strength of the waste decreases. As the river receives the organic wastes, a very large number of bacteria predominate, because they thrive on the energy they receive from the organic waste. Some of these bacteria are normally found in rivers. Others, such as enteric microbes (coliform bacteria, found in great numbers in the intestines and thus in the feces of humans and other animals), are not normally found in the stream environment. While the growth of normal stream bacteria is greatly enhanced by organic nutrients, coliforms and pathogens generally die out within a few days, perhaps because of predation and unfavorable conditions. The bacteria predominate during the zone of recent pollution to near the end of the septic zone. If the organic load is high, the bacterial type changes from aerobic (those requiring oxygen) to anaerobic (those not requiring oxygen), because of similar changes in conditions that affect bacteria.

As stabilization continues, bacterial food declines because of consumption by high bacterial populations. Protozoans start to increase and eventually predominate. The one-celled protozoans (amoeba, paramecium, and other ciliates) feed on bacteria. As their food supply diminishes, protozoans decrease in population and are in turn consumed by rotifers and crustaceans in the recovery zone. During this period, turbidity decreases and algal growth increases.

Aquatic insects are also affected in a polluted river. In the septic zone, for example, intolerant insects such as the mayfly nymph disappear. Only air-breathing or specially adapted insects such as mosquito larvae can survive in the low DO levels present in the septic zone. When the river has completely purified the organic waste, algae return. Higher life organisms such as insects eat the algae, and they serve as food for fish. This entire process, known as **general biological succession**, is critical to the river self-purification process.

Groundwater

On average, approximately three feet of water fall each year on every square foot of the Earth. Approximately six inches of this go back to the sea. Another two feet are lost to evaporation. The remaining six inches seep through interstices, voids, hollows, and cavities into the sponge-like soil. In its journey downward through the soil, water may go only a few feet or several hundred feet before it joins the subterranean stores of liquid that make up the Earth's groundwater supply—literally, an ocean below our feet.

The groundwater supply is a colossal reservoir that feeds all the natural fountains and springs of Earth. At times and in certain places, it bubbles up in cool, blue pools, and in other places, too deep to imagine, it heats up, forms steam, and bursts back to the surface in geysers and hot springs.

Most of the Earth's groundwater supply lies just beneath the surface and can easily be reached by drilling a borehole or well to the level of the **water table**. This practice has gone on for millennia and is accelerating as more and more people inhabit Earth. In this way, groundwater has served as a reliable source of potable water for millions of people, and if used with moderation, groundwater should remain a viable source for years to come.

GROUNDWATER USES AND SOURCES

Large cities are supplied primarily by surface water, whereas most small communities use groundwater. This situation helps to explain why a larger portion of the U.S. population is supplied by surface water, but the total number of communities supplied by groundwater is four times that supplied by surface water.

Groundwater has several characteristics that make it desirable as a water supply source: (1) A groundwater system provides natural storage, eliminating the need for human-made impoundments; (2) because the groundwater supply is usually available at point of demand, the cost of transmission is reduced significantly; and (3) because groundwater is filtered by natural geologic strata, it usually appears clearer to the eye than surface water (McGhee, 1991). For these reasons, groundwater is generally preferred as a source of municipal and industrial water supplies.

Historically, because groundwater has been considered to be safe to drink, many water utilities delivered it untreated to their customers. We are quickly learning, however, that using groundwater does have some disadvantages. These include the possibility of contamination by toxic or hazardous materials leaking from waste treatment facilities, natural sources, or landfills that may not be evident to either the public or regulatory agencies. Also, when groundwater becomes contaminated, restoring it is difficult, if not impossible. Recent discoveries of contaminated groundwater in some areas have led to the shutdown of thousands of potable water wells across the United States.

AQUIFERS

In the simplest terms, the charging of the subsurface with water that then becomes groundwater occurs when surface water seeps down from the rain-soaked surface, sinks to a certain level, collects above an impermeable layer, and fills all the pores and cracks of the permeable portions. The top of this **saturated zone** is called the water table.

Figure 15.7 illustrates that the groundwater system is a bit more complex and complicated than this description. Groundwater occurs in **unconfined aquifers** in two different zones, distinguished by whether or not water fills all the cracks and pores between particles of soil and rock. The **unsaturated zone** lies just beneath the land surface and is characterized by crevices that contain both air and water. The unsaturated zone contains water (**vadose water**) that is essentially unavailable for use. When an impermeable layer does not overlie an aquifer, it is unconfined (Figure 15.7 shows an unconfined aquifer situated above a confined bed). A **confined aquifer** consists of a water-bearing layer sandwiched between two less permeable layers. Water flow in a confined aquifer is restricted to vertical movement only. In contrast, water flow in an unconfined aquifer has more freedom and is similar to flow in an open channel.

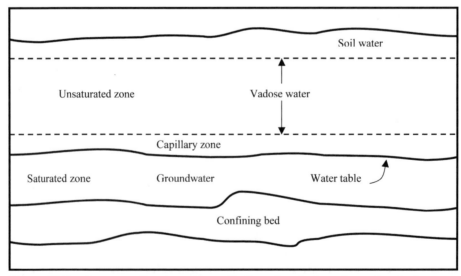

Figure 15.7.   An unconfined aquifer with its saturated and unsaturated zones. To remove water from the water table, a well would have to penetrate the saturated zone.

GROUNDWATER FLOW

Whether groundwater flow occurs in the open channel-like flow of an unconfined aquifer or the vertical-only (pipe-like) flow of a confined aquifer, for the water have any flow at all, a **hydraulic gradient** must exist. Simply stated, the hydraulic gradient is the difference in hydraulic head divided by the distance along the fluid flow path. For our purposes, what you need to understand is that groundwater moves through an aquifer in the direction of the hydraulic gradient and at a rate proportional to the gradient and inversely related to the permeability of the aquifer. The steeper the slope and the more permeable the substrate, the more rapidly the water flows.

Contrary to popular belief, groundwater does not flow like a river. Instead, it percolates downward, moving from high elevations to lower elevations, at a variable rate. It sometimes moves slowly and sometimes surprisingly fast, from less than an inch to a few feet a day.

Groundwater aquifers are important sources of water. As stated previously, they supply a large portion of the U.S. population, and almost all of the rural population. Demand for groundwater use continues to increase, and with this increase both the quantity and quality of this vast resource are threatened. Two important points you should remember about groundwater are that (1) we do not have an inexhaustible groundwater supply, and (2) groundwater is not completely purified as it percolates through the ground—it is not exempt from surface contamination.

Chapter Summary

The interconnectedness of the hydrological cycle works to our advantage in self-purification, but with persistent pollutants, the processes integral to the water cycle can trap toxins, complicating efforts to clean them up. Although the natural processes that clean our water as it travels through the hydrological cycle worked well for centuries in many places, humans have overloaded the capacity of the water cycle to self-purify. We are now cleaning up problems created by past environmental abuse and ignorance. Inevitably, we will create problems that future generations will have to clean up, because of unforeseen problems with the solutions we try now, but we have no excuse for re-creating past mistakes. Our water system is too valuable—in fact, priceless. We must no longer discount the risks involved.

Discussion Questions and Problems

1. Explain eutrophication.
2. Explain self-purification in streams and rivers.
3. Explain lake turnover.
4. Explain thermal stratification in lakes.
5. Explain the differences between confined and unconfined aquifers.
6. Explain pond succession.

7. Why do rivers flood?
8. If you drilled a well on your property, would you expect the well water to be of less or better quality than tap water?

Suggested Research Topics and Projects

- Examine the role of water as the dominant feature of Earth.
- Explore how local environmental conditions affect freshwater supplies.
- Examine the water cycle as a manifestation of Earth's heat engine.
- Map your local watershed.
- Classify a local lotic water system by eutrophic category; chemical, physical, and biological aspects; habitat; stage of development; zones; and the uses the community makes of the body of water.
- Classify a local lentic water system by eutrophic category; chemical, physical, and biological aspects; habitat; stage of development; zones; and the uses the community makes of the body of water body.
- Explore the similarities and differences between ponds and lakes.
- Research the problems specific to lakes related to phosphorus.
- Research stratification and turnover.
- Research the natural lake succession process.
- Create and extended definition of cultural eutrophication.
- Create and extended definition of river.
- Create a network analysis model.
- Examine river life span.
- Research river power, both tame (e.g., for example) and wild (e.g., flooding).
- Research land–water interchange.
- Examine habitat and organism adaptation for rapid zones.
- Examine habitat and organism adaptation for pool zones.
- Explore human activities that affect runoff.
- Research water quality and self-purification.
- Research the problems associated with lakes, pollution, and turnover.
- Examine the past quality of a local river system—how did the CWA affect it?
- Examine the Industrial Revolution's environmental impact on water systems and quality.
- Examine aquatic organisms and their place in self-purification.
- Explore how groundwater gets into and out of the ground.
- Research local groundwater sources and their quality.
- Create an extended definition of groundwater.

References and Recommended Reading

Amos, W. H. (1969). *Limnology: An Introduction to the Fresh Water Environment.* Chestertown, MD: LaMotte Company.

Davis, M. L., & Cornwell, D. A. (1991). *Introduction to Environmental Engineering.* New York: McGraw-Hill, Inc.

Laws, E. A. (1993). *Aquatic Pollution: An Introductory Text.* New York: John Wiley & Sons, Inc.

Masters, G. M. (1991). *Introduction to Environmental Engineering and Science.* Englewood Cliffs, NJ: Prentice-Hall.

McGhee, T. J. (1991). *Water Supply and Sewerage.* New York: McGraw-Hill, Inc.

NALCO. (1988). *The NALCO Water Handbook.* 2nd ed. New York: McGraw-Hill, Inc.

Odum, E. P. (1971). *Fundamentals of Ecology.* Philadelphia: Saunders College Publishing.

Smith, R. L. (1974). *Ecology and Field Biology.* New York: Harper & Row Publishers.

Spellman, F. R. (1996). *Stream Ecology and Self-Purification: An Introduction for Wastewater and Water Specialists.* Lancaster, PA: Technomic Publishing Company.

Tchobanoglous, G., & Schroeder, E. D. (1987). *Water Quality.* Reading, MA: Addison-Wesley Publishing Company.

U.S. EPA. (1989, June 29). "Surface Water Treatment Regulations." *Federal Register* tit. 54, pt. 124, 27486.

U.S. EPA. (2011a). "Classifying Lakes and Ponds." Accessed June 6, 2011, http://www.epa.gov/bioweb1/aquatic/classify.html.

U.S. EPA. (2011b). "Lakes, Ponds, and Reservoirs." Accessed June 7, 2011, http://www.epa.gov/bioweb1/aquatic/lake-r.html.

Watson, L. (1988). *The Water Planet: Celebration of the Wonder of Water.* New York: Crown Publishers, Inc.

Wetzel, R. G. (1983). *Limnology.* New York: Harcourt Brace Jovanovich College Publishers.

CHAPTER 16

Water Pollution and Control

Is it not enough for you to drink clean water?
Must you also muddy the rest with your feet?

—Ezekiel 34:18

Two million tons of waste, estimated to equal two or more billion tons of wastewater is being discharged daily into rivers and seas spreading disease to humans and damaging key ecosystems such as coral reefs and fisheries.

—United Nations, 2010

Chapter Objectives

After studying this chapter, you should be able to:

- Define and discuss PPCPs.
- Define and determine significant sources of water pollutants.
- Distinguish between point and nonpoint source pollutants and describe the differences.
- Discuss the common industrial sources of water pollution and the forms it takes.
- Discuss the problems associated with hazardous waste disposal.
- Describe the results of the environmental damage and pollutants produced by mining.
- Discuss the common pollutants agricultural practices can produce and describe their effects.
- Define acid rain and discuss the effects it has on surface water bodies.
- Describe the potential risks to our groundwater supply of surface pollutants and discuss the related wetland problems.

- Identify and discuss the political and social issues at work behind the creation, enforcement, amendment, and revision of state and federal water pollution control regulations.
- Describe the effects of federal water pollution regulations on the U.S. water supply.
- Identify and discuss the problems inherent in regulation enforcement.
- Discuss and describe the practices used to control contaminants in water treatment.
- Define and describe the characteristics and problems associated with five common sources of and types of wastewater.
- Define and describe the seven steps involved in wastewater treatment.
- Identify the common methods of thermal pollution treatment.
- Discuss the problems USTs have caused.
- Identify the principle problems inherent in UST cleanup.
- Describe the EPA requirements for remediated and new USTs and the commonly used methods of remediation.
- Define the problems associated with groundwater remediation and discuss the methods used for remediation of organic and inorganic contaminants.

Chapter Outline

- Definition: PPCPs
- Definition: water pollution
- Definition and description: point and nonpoint source pollution
- Definition and description: industrial water pollution sources, bioaccumulation, and thermal pollution
- Definition and description: hazardous waste disposal
- Definition and discussion: pollutants associated with mining operations
- Definition and discussion: pollutants associated with agricultural practices
- Discussion: acidic deposition impacts
- Discussion: groundwater pollution and drainage basin pollution
- Discussion: the recent history of environmental concerns and the regulations designed to control water supply contamination
- Discussion: the SWDA and U.S. EPA standards and priorities
- Discussion: the CWA's effectiveness and the increasing complexity of the concerns it addresses
- Description and discussion: how regulations work to prevent water pollution; factors that inhibit regulatory effectiveness and the place of science in determining critical concerns
- Description and discussion: water treatment processes
- Description and discussion: wastewater treatment, the various types of commonly treated wastes and their sources, wastewater physical and chemical characteristics, and the steps in the process
- Description and discussion: treating thermal pollution
- Definition, description and discussion: the enormity of the contamination and mitigation problems created by leaking, aging, and abandoned USTs; the treatment

practices and requirements for new USTs; the compliance schedules for meeting current regulations; spill response requirements; and the commonly used technologies for treating petroleum-contamination problems
- Description and discussion: the special problems associated with treating contaminated groundwater, LNAPLS and DNAPLS, and organic and inorganic contaminant treatment practices

Key Terms

acid mine drainage

acid rain

advanced wastewater treatment

agricultural sources

animal wastes

biological treatment

biosolids treatment

carbon adsorption

chemical precipitation

Clean Water Act (CWA)

combined wastewater

cooling tower method

dewatering

dense nonaqueous-phase liquids (DNAPLs)

disinfection

domestic wastewater

extraction well

Federal Water Pollution Control Act

fertilizers

groundwater

hazardous waste stream

incineration

industrial wastewater

irrigation

leaking underground storage tank (LUST)

nitrates

nonpoint sources

pesticides

phosphates

point sources

thermal pollution

water pollutants

water pollution

Introduction

Unless you swim in a body of water best described as a cesspool or drink water that smells foul and tastes worse, ultimately making you ill, you may think that **water pollution** is relative and find it difficult to define. Once you come up with a definition (it might have something to do with physical characteristics and negative impact), you may also consider the idea that freshwater pollution is not a new phenomenon. Only the issue of freshwater pollution as a major public concern is relatively new.

Natural forms of pollutants have always been present in surface waters. Many of the pollutants we have discussed in previous chapters were being washed from the air, eroded from land surfaces, leached from the soil, and ultimately found their way into surface water bodies long before humans walked on Earth. After all, floods and dead animals pollute, but their effects are local and generally temporary. In prehistoric times, and even in more recent times, natural disasters have contributed to surface water pollution. Cataclysmic events—earthquakes, volcanic eruptions, meteor impacts, transitions from an ice age to an interglacial age to an ice age—have all contributed to surface water pollution. Over time, natural purification processes were able to self-clean surface water bodies. We can accurately say that without these self-purifying processes, the water-dependent life on Earth could not have developed as it did (Peavy, Rowe, & Tchobanoglous, 1985).

For our purposes, we define *water pollution* as the presence of unwanted substances in water beyond levels acceptable for health or aesthetics. **Water pollutants** may include organic matter (living or dead), heavy metals, minerals, sediment, bacteria, viruses, toxic chemicals, and volatile organic compounds. In this chapter, we discuss the sources of water pollutants, both **point** and **nonpoint sources**, which include industrial sources, hazardous waste disposal, **acid mine drainage**, **agricultural sources**, and **acid rain**. We also discuss **groundwater** pollution. Finally, we address the major concerns of water pollution: the health effects for humans and how to mitigate pollution's effects on potable water systems.

Sick Water

The term *sick water* was coined by the United Nations in a 2010 press release addressing the need to recognize that it is time to arrest the global tide of sick water. The gist of the UN's report was that transforming waste from a major health and environmental hazard into a clean, safe, and economically attractive resource is a key challenge in the 21st century. As practitioners of environmental health, we certainly support the UN's view on this important topic.

However, when we discuss sick water in the context of this text and in many others we have authored on the topic, we go a few steps further than the UN in describing the real essence and tragic implications of potable water that makes people or animals sick or worse or at least can be classified as sick; again, in our opinion.

Water that is sick is actually a filthy medium, wastewater—a cocktail of **fertilizer** runoff and sewage disposal alongside animal, industrial, agricultural, and other wastes. In addition to these listed wastes of concern, other wastes are beginning to garner attention; they certainly have caught our attention in research on the potential problems related to these "other" wastes.

So, what are these other wastes? We are referring to any waste or product we dispose of in our waters, that we flush down the toilet, dispose of in the sink or bathtub, or pour down the drain of a worksite deep sink. To illustrate our point, consider the following example of "pollutants" we discharge into our wastewater treatment plants or septic tanks that we do not often consider waste products, but in reality are.

Each morning a family of four wakes up and prepares for the workday for the two parents and school for the two teenagers. Fortunately, this family has three upstairs bathrooms to accommodate their need to prepare via the morning natural waste disposal, shower and soap usage, cosmetic application, hair treatments, vitamins, sunscreen, fragrances, and prescribed medications. In addition, in this particular family, the overnight deposit of cat and dog waste is routinely picked up and flushed down the toilet. Let's fashion a short inventory of what this family of four has disposed of or has applied to themselves as they prepare for their day outside the home:

- Toilet-flushed **animal wastes**
- Prescription and over-the-counter therapeutic drugs
- Veterinary drugs
- Fragrances
- Soap
- Shampoo
- Body lotion
- Cosmetics
- Sunscreen products
- Diagnostic agents
- Nutraceuticals (e.g., vitamins, medical foods, functional foods, etc.)

Even though these bioactive substances have been around for decades, today we group all of them (the exception being animal wastes), substances and/or products, under the title of *pharmaceuticals and personal care products* (PPCPs) (see Figure 16.1).

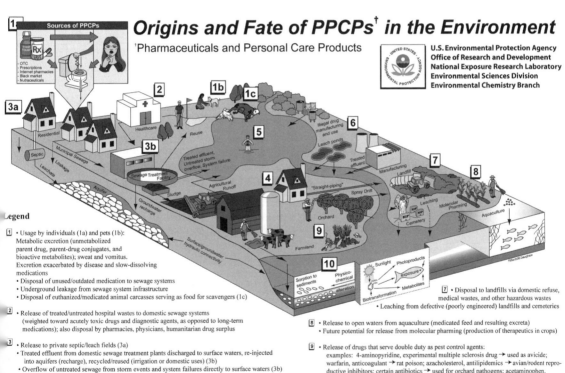

Figure 16.1. Origins and fate of PPCPs in the Environment. EPA accessed 06/09/11 @ http://epa .gov/nerlesd1/chemistry/pharma/

We pointed to the human activities of the family of four in contributing PPCPs to the environment, but there are other sources of PPCPs that should also be recognized. For example, residues from pharmaceutical manufacturing; residues from hospitals; illicit drug disposal (i.e., police knock on the door, and the user flushes the illicit drugs down the toilet and into the wastewater stream); veterinary drug use, especially antibiotics and steroids; and agribusiness use are all contributors of PPCPs in the environment

In regard to personal deposit of PPCPs into the environment and the local wastewater supply, let's return to our family of four. After having applied or taken in the various substances mentioned, the four individuals add these products, PPCPs, to the environment through excretion (the elimination of waste material from the body) and while bathing after returning home; in addition, they may dispose of any unwanted medications into sewers or trash. How many of us have found old medical prescriptions in the family medicine chest and decided they were no longer needed? How many of us have grabbed such unwanted medications and simply disposed of them with a single toilet flush? Many of these medications, such as antibiotics, are not normally found in the environment.

Previously, we stated that wastewater is a cocktail of fertilizer runoff and sewage disposal alongside animal, industrial, agricultural, and other wastes. When we add PPCPs to this cocktail, we can state analogously that we are simply adding mixer to the mix.

The questions about our mixed cocktail of waste are obvious: Does the disposal of antibiotics and/or other medications into the local wastewater treatment system cause problems for anyone or anything else "downstream?" When we ingest locally treated water, are we also ingesting flushed-down-the-toilet or -the-drain antibiotics, other medications, illicit drugs, animal excretions, cosmetics, vitamins, sunscreen, diagnostic agents, crankcase oil, grease, oil, fats, and veterinary drugs each time we drink a glass of tap water?

Well, the jury is still out on these questions. Simply, we do not know what we do not know about the fate of PPCPs or their impact on the environment once they enter our wastewater treatment systems, the water cycle, and eventually our drinking water supply systems. This is the case even though some PPCPs are easily broken down and processed by the human body or degraded quickly in the environment. Moreover, since the time of the mythical hero Hercules, arguably the world's first environmental engineer, who cleaned out King Augeas's stables. Hercules, faced literally with a mountain of horse and cattle waste in the stable area, had to devise some method to dispose of the waste, so he diverted a couple of river streams to the inside of the stable area so that all the animal waste could simply be deposited into the river: out of sight, out of mind. The waste simply flowed downstream. Hercules understood the principal point in pollution control technology, pertinent to this very day: *Dilution is the solution to pollution.*

The fly in the ointment for Hercules's solution is today's modern PPCPs. Although he was able to dispose of animal waste into a running water system, where eventually the water's self-purification process would clean the stream, he did not have to deal with today's personal pharmaceuticals and hormones, which are given to many types of livestock to enhance their health and growth.

The simple truth is that studies have shown that pharmaceuticals are present in our nation's water bodies. Further research suggests that certain drugs may cause ecological harm. The EPA and other research agencies are committed to investigating this topic and developing strategies to help protect the health of both the environment and the public. To date, scientists have found no evidence of adverse human health effects from PPCPs in the environment. Moreover, others might argue that even if PPCPs were present today or in ancient (and mythical) times, the amount present in water systems would represent only a small fraction (10^{-12} ppt, parts per trillion) of the total volume of water. And the critics would be quick to point out that when we are speaking of parts per trillion, we are speaking of a proportion equivalent to one-twentieth of a drop of water diluted into an Olympic-size swimming pool. A student in one of our environmental health classes stated that he did not think the water should be termed "sick water," because it was evident to him that if the water contained so many medications, how could it be sick? Instead it might be termed "well water."

It is important to point out that the term *sick water* can be applied to not only PPCP-contaminated water but also any filthy, dirty, contaminated, polluted, pathogen-filled drinking water source. The fact is that dirty or sick water means more people now die from contaminated and polluted water than from all forms of violence, including wars (UN, 2010). The United Nations also points out that dirty or sick water is a key factor in the rise of deoxygenated dead zones that have been emerging in seas and oceans across the globe.

Point and Nonpoint Sources of Pollution

Because of the need to control and regulate sources of water pollution, environmental scientists established a means to distinguish between point sources and nonpoint sources of water pollution from human activities. A point source (usually easy to identify) discharges pollution (or any effluent) from an identifiable, specific source or point. Pipes that discharge waste into streams and smokestacks that emit smoke and fumes into the air are point sources of pollution. Industries or facilities usually identified as point sources include factories, electric power plants, sewage treatment plants, factory farms, coal mines, offshore oil wells, and oil tankers.

Nonpoint source pollution (much more difficult to identify) cannot be traced to a specific source, but rather comes from multiple generalized sources, contributed from throughout an area, and can include runoff into surface water and seepage into groundwater from croplands, livestock feedlots, logged forests, construction areas, roadways, parking lots, and urban and suburban lands. Because it is so much harder to identify than point source pollution, nonpoint source pollution is consequently much more difficult to control.

Response Scenario 16.1. Dishonorable Discharge

Table 16.1.   The Most Polluted Waters: U.S. Waters Receiving the Greatest Amounts of Toxic Pollution (1990 to 1994)

Rank	River/Water Body	States with Toxic Discharges Contributing to Water Pollution	Total Pounds of Direct Toxic Discharges to Water
1	Mississippi River	TN, AR, LA, MO, IL, MN, WI, IA, KY, MS	702,496,748
2	Pacific Ocean	OR, HI, CA	35,195,908
3	Ohio River	IL, IN, OH, KY, WV, PA	22,072,491
4	Tennessee River	KY, TN, AL	22,031,743
5	Houston Ship Channel	TX	18,235,338
6	Ward Cove	AK	14,261,169
7	Savannah River	GA, SC	13,968,965
8	Delaware River	DE, PA, NJ	13,329,248
9	Thames River	CT	13,312,639
10	Grays Harbor	WA	10,840,795
11	Rock River	IL, WI	8,165,469
12	Straits of Juan De Fuca	WA	7,899,229
13	Amelia River	FL	7,461,070
14	Gravelly Run	VA	6,330,209
15	Calcasieu River	LA	5,427,508
16	Ouachita River	AR, LA	4,925,933
17	Mobile River	AL	4,572,055
18	Columbia River	WA, OR	4,368,387
19	Holston River	TN	4,098,240
20	Genesee River	NY	3,672,733
21	Kansas River	KS	3,420,965
22	Martins Creek	MS	3,339,065
23	Indiana Harbor Ship Canal	IN	2,578,038
24	Brazos River	TX	2,442,430
25	Cuyahoga River	OH	2,427,663
26	Patapsco River	MD	2,329,123
27	Kanawha River	WV	2,320,910
28	Susquehanna River	PA, NY	2,144,339
29	Quinnipiac River	CT	2,105,384
30	Fenholloway River	FL	1,896,369
31	Cedar River	IA	1,881,803
32	Everett Harbor	WA	1,749,650
33	Hudson River	NJ, NY	1,729,084
34	Missouri River	NE, KS, MO, ND, IA	1,727,759
35	Neches River	TX	1,645,307
36	Alabama River	AL	1,613,809
37	Escambia Bay	FL	1,568,522
38	Wisconsin River	WI	1,553,152

39	Wabash River	IL, IN, OH	1,532,308
40	Blackwater River	VA	1,488,346
41	Detroit River	MI	1,449,750
42	Little Attapulgus Creek	GA	1,431,183
43	Androscoggin River	ME, NH	1,388,133
44	Escatawpa River	MS	1,358,148
45	Pigeon River	NC	1,325,423
46	Cook Inlet	AK	1,322,140
47	Cape Fear River	NC	1,319,953
48	Des Moines River	IA	1,270,304
49	Tombigbee River	MS, AL	1,210,471
50	Willamette River	OR	1,202,737

Source: Environmental Working Group. (1996). "Dishonorable Discharge: The 50 Most Polluted Rivers in the Country." http://www.ewg.org/node/20399. (Compiled from U.S. Environmental Protection Agency, *Toxics Release Inventory 1990–1994*.)

RESPONSE

(i) What is the overwhelming implication(s) of the information provided in Table 16.1?

Industrial Sources of Water Pollution

The disposal of noxious industrial wastes into rivers and streams has been a common industrial practice for many years and ranks as one of the most serious forms of water pollution. In the past, industrial pollutants were dumped into rivers and streams in smaller quantities, and stream flows were adequate to dilute and carry away the wastes with minimal environmental damage. But as industry and population increased, stream flows could no longer handle the waste load, and industrial pollution became serious.

Industry is the largest U.S. water user, with nearly 250,000 industries in the United States using more than 260 billion gallons of water per day. The organic chemical and plastics industries are the country's largest sources of toxic chemical pollution. The iron and steel and metal finishing industries are next. Other significant sources of pollutants include metal foundries, petroleum refineries, and the pulp and paper industry.

Spills are one of the most troublesome sources of industrial contamination. Chemical and oil spills are particularly difficult, because they can never be completely

---

Did You Know?

At least 1.8 million children under five years of age die every year from water-related disease, which is one child every 20 seconds (UN, 2010).

removed or cleaned up. Consider, for example, oil dispersed by several routes into a large body of surface water (e.g., a lake). The largest percentage, the insoluble fraction, is lighter than water and gradually spreads and thins to form an ever-widening oil slick on the water's surface. Approximately 30% of the components in crude oil immediately begin to evaporate into the atmosphere. In areas that experience wind action that produces waves, the oil is whipped into an oil-water emulsion. If the spill occurs near the lakeshore, the wind and waves transport the oil to recreational beach areas, which become coated with oil. With time the emulsion is distributed throughout the upper layer of the water. Bacteria break down a portion of the emulsion. That portion not degraded by bacterial action collects to form floating tar balls. Crude oil, heavier than water, sinks to the bottom, where it coats and kills the organisms there.

Unfortunately, such toxic discharges are fairly commonplace. In the United States alone, more than 20 major oil spills occur every year. Spellman, et al. (2001) reported that a study by the EPA in the late 1980s documented nearly 7,000 accidents involving hazardous substances between 1980 and 1985.

Certain chemical contaminants are highly dangerous environmental threats, because they **bioaccumulate** through food webs—a serious matter. Persistent toxic substances like nutrients pass from one trophic level to the next. If such substances are not excreted or broken down by the organism, they remain in its tissues. If the organism continues to ingest contaminated materials, the chemical concentrations rise and are passed up to the next trophic level when that organism itself is ingested. In this way, persistent pollutants enter food webs and become considerably more concentrated—and dangerous—by the time they reach the highest trophic level. As a result, organisms feeding at the highest trophic levels are exposed to the highest doses of toxic substances. In aquatic webs, which usually consist of four to six trophic levels, accumulation is especially pronounced. The ultimate upper trophic level occupant—human beings—runs the risk of ingesting the largest concentrations of toxic substances.

Another form of industrial pollution occurs because many industries use water for cooling. **Thermal pollution** occurs when industry returns heated water to its source. Generation of electricity, for example, requires enormous quantities of water for cooling. That water is usually drawn from major rivers and large lakes, then circulated through hot electricity-generating machinery.

The heat transfers to the water, raising its temperature. When heated water discharges into its water body, it can adversely effect aquatic ecosystems by causing organisms to respond by elevated respiration rates, while simultaneously the elevated water temperature reduces DO content by decreasing the solubility of oxygen in water.

Hazardous Waste Disposal

Because only a small fraction of industrial waste is recycled, detoxified, or destroyed, the rest must go somewhere. Unfortunately, in many cases **hazardous waste streams** end up in surface water bodies and groundwater. Almost 80,000 disposal sites exist in the United States alone. Many of these waste streams are produced by industrial, municipal, agricultural, and mining activities and as brines from oil and gas extraction. Other toxic pollutants enter water supplies from nonpoint sources, including runoff from mining activities, farms, and urban areas. Urban runoff from streets, for example, carries heavy metals (cadmium and lead) as well as other pollutants. Chemicals containing cyanide are used to deice streets, and herbicides used in agriculture are all potential sources of pollution (Concern Inc., 1986, 1–4).

Did You Know?

It is estimated that close to 90% of diarrhea cases, killing some 2.2 million people every year, is caused by unsafe drinking water and poor hygiene (UN, 2010).

Acid Mine Drainage

Several environmental and human health costs are associated with extracting minerals. Miners are at risk for diseases caused by the substances with which they work (e.g., black lung disease from coal dust). Miners are also at risk from mine collapse, underground explosions and fires, and other safety hazards. Mining disturbs soil and overlying vegetation, which disrupts ecosystems, reduces productivity, and leads to soil erosion. Mining causes siltation of streams, lakes, and rivers by eroding soil. It can diminish or reduce productivity of land. It also degrades water used in mining processes. Finally, mining produces tailings and mine drainage, which can contaminate soil and water. This last environmental cost is the focus of this discussion.

Mining operations to uncover deposits of coal, copper, nickel, zinc, and lead can lead to surface water (and groundwater) pollution. When any of these ores are uncovered, they are exposed to air. Because these ores contain sulfides, the air + sulfide combination leads to oxidation, and that process is often catalyzed by certain strains of bacteria. When water filters through those oxidized minerals, it becomes more acidic (water + oxidized sulfides = sulfuric acid), which increases the solubility of metals in the water that filters through (is leached from) the newly aerated deposits and runs off into the streams below the mine. Such water often contains harmful levels of toxic materials. This pollution, known as acid mine drainage, kills fish and disrupts normal aquatic life cycles. Quigg (1976) pointed out that drainage from mining operations pollutes several thousand miles of streams in the United States, and mine drainage can be expected to grow with the world's increasing reliance on coal as an energy source.

Did You Know?

Over 50% of malnutrition cases globally are associated with diarrhea or intestinal worm infections. Diarrheal diseases come second after respiratory infections in labor productivity lost due to illness (UN, 2010).

Agricultural Sources of Surface Water Pollution

Surface water pollution from both organic and inorganic agricultural sources is usually caused by **pesticide**s, fertilizers, and animal wastes. All these enter bodies of water via runoff and groundwater absorption in areas of agricultural activity.

Pesticides include insecticides, herbicides, and fungicides. Their purpose is to kill unwanted plant species and insects to protect crops. Because of the ever-expanding worldwide population, pesticides have become essential to production of food and other crops to get the yield required to feed the increasing population.

Natural pesticides are biodegradable and thus less harmful to the environment. Nonbiodegradable pesticides (e.g., DDT) can accumulate in the environment and have been proven harmful to human health.

When pesticide pollution is present in appreciable concentrations in aquatic environments, it poses a serious health hazard for organisms that inhabit the water body and those who use the water as a drinking supply. Although pesticides are normally sold to combat a specific pest, they often kill nonpest species and have side effects on the growth and reproduction of birds and fish.

Response Scenario 16.2.
The Lotka-Volterra Predator–Prey Principle

Insects come in carnivore and herbivore, just like other creatures, and the two main categories have their own set of characteristics. Aphids, Japanese beetles, caterpillars, and grasshoppers are a few of the plant eaters. Ladybugs, spiders, cicada killers, praying mantis, and sawflies are a few that eat other insects.

Herbivores reproduce fast. Predator bugs, as a rule, reproduce more slowly and in smaller numbers than the herbivore bugs. When nature is left alone, this balances properly, because one predator eats many herbivores, just as predator mammals need a plentiful supply of rabbits and mice to keep them going. The herbivores have to reproduce quickly and in quantity to stay even.

LOTKA-VOLTERRA PREDATOR–PREY MODEL

Although the Lotka-Volterra equations are too simple for practical use without changes that reflect specific conditions, this simple model is an interesting starting point. This Lotka-Volterra model is based on two simple propositions:

1. The predator (N_1) birth rate (B_1) increases as the number of prey increases; and
2. The prey (N_2) death rate (D_2) increases as the number of predators increases.

The model uses two equations. Equation 1 calculates predator population growth:

$$dN_1/dt = (B_1 N_2 - D_1) N_1 \tag{1}$$

Where

B_1 = the birth rate of the predator
D_1 = the death rate of the predator

The individual birth rate of the prey is not directly dependent on the abundance of the predator, but its death rate is dependent upon the predator's density. Thus, the birth rate (B_2) of the prey is a constant.

Equation 2 describes the prey population growth rate:

$$dN_2/dt = (B_2 - D_2N_1) \, N_2 \qquad (2)$$

where

D_2 = the death rate of the prey.

The predator birth rate depends on the food (prey) supply available, and the death rate (D_1) of the predator is not dependent on the prey density.

Of course, predation is only one of several agents that cause population cycles. Other factors implicated include mass emigration, physiological stress from overcrowding, and genetic changes in the population.

Accurate population cycles are difficult to achieve in the field or laboratory. Usually the predators search out every one of the prey and then become extinct from lack of food.

How this concept works is something that pesticide companies would just as soon farmers didn't figure out, because the Lotka-Volterra Predator–Prey Principle can accurately describe how natural balances are disturbed by applying broad-spectrum pesticides.

Using a broad-spectrum pesticide to control crop damage actually increases the number of herbivores, increasing the pest problem. Broad-spectrum pesticides kill both prey and predator. If the carnivores and herbivores are balanced to begin with and are poisoned to the same degree, the surviving pests have the advantage, with their quick and plentiful reproduction. They bounce back rapidly. The remaining predators, however, have lost their food supply, so they actually become further depleted. Between sprayings, the balance, now disrupted, becomes more and more disturbed.

The answer? Organic growers are using a number of techniques that are far less ecologically damaging and invasive than pesticides. Marigolds planted around the base of tomato plants prevent nematodes. Bt (bacillus thuringiensis, a bacterium) applied to garden plants gives hornworms and cabbage loopers terminal indigestion, without hurting useful predators or adding poisons that will eventually be ingested by humans. Sometimes these methods are more time-consuming; sometimes they add cost—however, the extra price people are willing to pay for organic produce is an important consideration. One of the biggest obstacles in using these techniques is fear—of taking risks, of doing something unfamiliar, of change.

RESPONSE

(i) Do you think the change mentioned in the scenario is a risk?

Fertilizers, like pesticides, are used to increase food production. Agricultural water pollution results primarily from the **phosphates** and **nitrates** present in the fertilizers, which enter the water supply through erosion of topsoil and water runoff.

Nitrates can be toxic to animals and humans in high enough concentrations. Nitrates can be reduced to nitrites, which interfere with the transport of oxygen by hemoglobin in the blood. Phosphates and nitrates both contribute to the excessive growth of microscopic plant algae in lakes, a condition that affects the local ecosystem.

Animal wastes are a source of water pollution with potential health hazards. High waste concentration areas—barnyards, land treated with animal wastes, feedlots—are a major threat to water supplies when rainfall runoff carries them into streams, lakes, and rivers. The problem of animal waste disposal is magnified when animals are raised in feedlots. To gain an appreciation for how serious a problem disposal problems can be for animal feedlots, consider that the U.S. Soil Conservation Service points out that while a human being produces 0.33 pound per day of human waste, a cow produces 52.0 pounds per day. A sewage treatment plant will probably process the human's waste; the cows' wastes often remain untreated.

In the past, animal waste was a benefit to farmers and others because it was used as fertilizer. However, compared to modern chemical fertilizers, the benefits of soil fertilization from animal wastes do not justify the costs of hauling and application. Thus, the livestock owner must contend with a daily supply of animal waste that cannot be sold, burned, or given away, and that may cause water pollution in water runoff. When such runoff enters rivers and streams (carrying with it nitrates, phosphates, and ammonia), microorganisms, which use up oxygen in the process, break down the organic matter. As we have said, streams have the potential to self-clean, but a high degree of organic pollution cannot be handled by the stream and creates problems for most aquatic life. The most critical effect of agricultural water pollution on human beings is the possibility of waterborne bacterial diseases: cholera, typhoid fever, and dysentery.

Sidebar 16.1.
Concentrated Animal Feeding Operations (CAFOs)

The advent of corporate farming has created giant livestock operations—literally animal factories—that house thousands of animals. CAFOs are a national public health threat, because of the problems they cause with both air and water pollution.

Although the air pollution problems that CAFOs cause are less critical than the water pollution, CAFOs are a huge contributor to CO_2 emissions and are part of the climate change issue. Other air pollution problems caused by CAFOs include respiratory distress caused by airborne manure dust inhalation and incidental production of hydrogen sulfide that travels into adjacent areas, affecting people nearby.

One of the biggest water pollution problems associated with CAFOs is disposal of animal wastes. Typically, these operations store waste in lagoons. For an operation that houses 10,000 hogs, the daily waste output equals that of a town of 25,000 people. The waste for that town, however, must be treated. Regulations concerning animal waste are far less stringent. The result has been manure spills, fishkills, and worst, poisoned water supplies. Rural communities are especially hard hit, with tap water supplies affected in many southeastern and midwestern towns. In the Midwest, the Mississippi River carries a heavy load of the pollution from Midwest CAFOs; those pollutants end up in the Gulf of Mexico, resulting in a dead zone as big as New Jersey.

CAFOs concentrate huge quantities of waste in relatively small areas. While the nitrogen and phosphorus from animal waste provide a useful fertilizer when applied at the proper levels, overapplication to land, manure spills, and lagoon leaks release these chemicals to the environment, where they can enter groundwater, rivers, and lakes, and thus the water supply.

The EPA, the CDC, and the U.S. Committee on Agriculture have the following statistics on the pollution that CAFOs cause:

- The 22 states that categorized specific types of agricultural pollution concluded that animal wastes pollute about 35,000 of the river miles they assessed (U.S. EPA/USDA, 1998).
- Animal manure is a greater contributor than point sources (i.e., municipal or industrial discharges) to in-stream total nitrogen in 1,802 (88%) of the 2,056 watershed outlets in the United States, based on a national modeling effort by the U.S. Geological Survey (EPA, 1998).
- In Milwaukee, Wisconsin, in 1993, Cryptosporidium contamination of public water supply caused more than 100 deaths and an estimated 403,000 illnesses. The source of the contamination was not confirmed, but runoff from cow manure is a suspected source (EPA, 1998).
- In 1993, the LaGrange (Indiana) County Health Department identified a cluster of women living near a hog operation who experienced miscarriages after drinking water with high levels of nitrates from their private wells (Centers for Disease Control, 1996).
- In Iowa, Minnesota, and Missouri, which account for 36% of hog production, 20 spills in 1992 killed at least 55,000 fish. By 1996, the number of spills had doubled, resulting in 670,000 dead fish (U.S. Senate Committee on Agriculture, 1997).
- The National Oceanic and Atmospheric Administration estimated that animal feedlots contributed to the impairment of 110 shellfish beds in 1995 (EPA, 1998).
- Blooms of toxic estuarine organisms, such as the dinoflagellate pfiesteria piscicida, are associated with nutrient over-enrichment. Since 1995, pfiesteria have killed more than a billion fish in the estuaries and coastal areas of North Carolina and the Maryland and Virginia tributaries to the Chesapeake Bay. CAFOs contribute significant nitrogen and phosphorus to these waters (EPA, 1998).
- A 1995 North Carolina State University study found severe seepage of nitrogen from more than half of the lagoons included in their survey (U.S Senate Committee on Agriculture, 1997).
- Seventeen states have experienced groundwater contamination from livestock feedlots (EPA, 1998).
- A North Carolina study of nearly 1,600 wells adjacent to hog and poultry operations showed that ten percent of the wells tested were contaminated with nitrates above the drinking water standard, and 34 percent were contaminated with some level of nitrates (U.S Senate Committee on Agriculture, 1997).

(continued)

Sidebar 16.1. (*continued*)

Family farms and rural communities are hit hard by CAFOs. Individually, small farms can't compete—the costs are too high. They go under, or end up in lease-use arrangements that frequently shift the waste burden onto the shoulders of small farmers. Property values for homeowners close to a factory farm plummet, and small businesses in the nearby towns suffer, because CAFOs generally buy their supplies from corporately owned suppliers.

That a corporate operation that produces as much animal waste as a town produces human waste should have to follow the same CWA regulations as a town seems basic, but since CAFOs are a fairly recent idea, and because the giant agribusiness concerns that own them have heavy political clout, putting regulations in place to control them has been slow, and the weakened and underfunded EPA can't keep up. Enforcement of existing regulation has been stymied in many states, as well.

The Sierra Club offers reasonable solutions to the water pollution problem:

- Place a moratorium on new and expanding factory farms until all existing facilities have **Clean Water Act** permits and new pollution control rules are in place.
- Require factory farms to obtain individual, site-specific Clean Water Act permits, including comprehensive nutrient management plans, to provide nationally consistent protections.
- Mandate full public participation in all aspects of Clean Water Act permitting and enforcement.
- Ban new open-air manure lagoons and aerial spraying of liquid wastes and phase out existing lagoon/sprayfield operations.
- Place legal and financial responsibility for waste disposal and cleanup on the corporations that own the livestock animals. (http://www.sierraclub.org/factoryfarms/factsheets/water.asp)

REFERENCES

http://www.sierraclub.org/factoryfarms/faq.asp.

http://www.sierraclub.org/factoryfarms/factsheets/water.asp.

Centers for Disease Control (1996, July 5). "Spontaneous Abortions Possibly Related to Ingestion of Nitrate-Contaminated Well Water—LaGrange County, Indiana, 1991–1994." *Morbidity and Mortality Weekly Report* 45, no.26.

U.S. Environmental Protection Agency (EPA) (1998, December 31). Preliminary Data Summary: Feedlots Point Source Category Study.

U.S. Environmental Protection Agency and Department of Agriculture (U.S. EPA and USDA) (1998, September 11). Draft Unified National Strategy for Animal Feeding Operation.

Committee on Agriculture, Nutrition & Forestry, U.S. Senate (1997, December). *Animal Waste Pollution in America: An Emerging National Problem. Environmental Risks of Livestock & Poultry Production.* Report compiled by the minority staff for Senator Tom Harkin.

Another agricultural practice that contributes to water pollution is **irrigation**. Obviously, irrigating crops to ensure their growth is important, but a problem arises when water used to irrigate crops becomes contaminated with salt, which through runoff contaminates streams, lakes, and rivers. In the western United States, where water from the Colorado River is withdrawn for irrigation and later returns to the river, the water leaches large quantities of salts from the irrigated land and adds them to the river. Pimentel (1989) points out that in other western U.S. locations (e.g., the Red River area in Oklahoma and Texas) where the same irrigation practices are used, during dry periods, river water becomes saltier than seawater.

Acid Rain

We previously discussed acid rain or *acidic deposition* in Chapters 8 and 13. This section concentrates on acid rain effects on lakes, streams, and rivers. To understand how acid rain affects surface water bodies, you need to recall a few important facts. Acid rain is normally formed when atmospheric water picks up acidic particles from the air; reacts with them to form acids; then falls as rain, snow, or other precipitation. Acid rain, more precisely defined, is rain with a pH below 5.6. It can produce pH values as low as vinegar or lemon juice (pH of 2.8 and 2.3, respectively).

One of the most obvious effects of acid rain is dead or crippled lakes. The damage from acid rain in lakes begins when the smaller organisms die off, leaving the larger organisms to starve to death. As a lake becomes more acidic, sometimes the larger organisms (e.g., fish) are killed directly. High acid levels in lakes dissolve heavy metals like mercury, lead, zinc, and especially aluminum, leading to concentrations at toxic and often lethal levels.

Acid rain can also impact human health. It can poison reservoirs and water supply systems by dissolving toxic metals from soils and bedrock in watersheds. A 1988 *New York Times* article based on an EPA survey reported that more than 4% of the streams surveyed in the Middle Atlantic states were acidic, and roughly half had a low capacity to neutralize acidic rain.

Did You Know?

Over half the world's hospital beds are occupied by people suffering from illnesses linked with contaminated water (UN, 2010).

Groundwater Pollution

Groundwater, the ocean of freshwater beneath Earth's surface, is one of the most precious—and least protected—resources. In the United States, groundwater is the drinking water source for half the population, most of it used directly from the ground without any treatment. Groundwater pollution can be a very serious problem.

Through experience and study, environmental practitioners have determined that any pollutant that comes in contact with the ground may contaminate groundwater. As water enters the ground, it filters naturally through the soil, and in some soils, that process quite effectively removes many substances, including suspended solids and bacteria. Some chemicals bind themselves to the surface of soil particles (phosphates) and thus are removed. In some areas, though, industrial and municipal wastes are sprayed on the ground surface so that they will filter through the soil, become purified in the process, and recharge the groundwater reservoir. Though natural purification of water as it passes through the soil is beneficial, it is a slow process, because the water is not readily diluted and has no access to air.

The same drainage-basin activities that pollute surface waters can also contaminate groundwater. Septic tanks, agriculture, industrial waste lagoons, underground injection wells, underground storage tanks, and landfills can all lead to groundwater contamination (see Figure 16.2). A major problem occurs when waste disposal sites are sited in unsuitable soils and even directly over fractured dolomites and limestone. When located directly on top of such rock, polluted water finds its way into wells. Unfortunately, at least 25 percent of the usable groundwater (from wells) is already contaminated in some areas (Draper, 1987).

Did You Know?

Almost 900 million worldwide people currently lack access to safe drinking water, and an estimated 2.6 billion people lack access to basic sanitation. South Asia and sub-Saharan Africa have the highest numbers, with around 221 million and 330 million people, respectively, living without basic sanitation (UN, 2010).

Groundwater contamination occurs in several ways. Increasing occurrences of groundwater contamination from saltwater, microbiological contaminants, and toxic organic and inorganic chemicals are being observed. The disposal of toxic industrial wastes is the major source of groundwater contamination in the United States. This type of contamination is magnified any time waste disposal sites are not protected by some type of lining; when disposal sites are located in permeable materials lying above usable water aquifers; and when these sites are located in proximity to a water supply well. The Conservation Foundation reported in 1982, that groundwater contamination was responsible for the closing of hundreds of wells in the United States (110).

Groundwater supplies are routinely replenished and purified by wetlands. Wetland plants absorb excess nutrients and immobilize pesticides, heavy metals, and other toxins, preventing them from moving up the food chain. In some locations, wetlands have been used to treat sewage. However, the capacity of wetlands to cleanse polluted

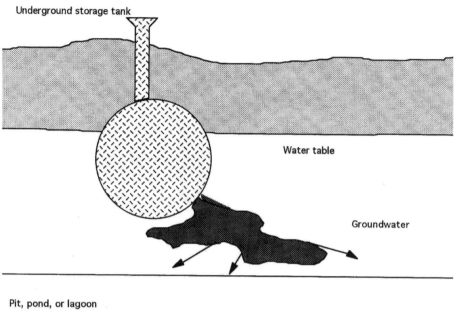

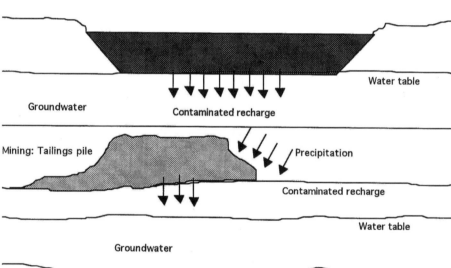

Figure 16.2.   Common activities that can lead to groundwater contamination: leaky underground storage tank, surface pits, ponds, or lagoons, and mining tailings contributing to acid mine discharge.

water is limited, and many have been overwhelmed by pollution. The United States, for example, has already lost half its wetlands to urban and agricultural development (Goldsmith & Hildyard, 1988).

Water Pollution Control

In the early 1970s, the public, environmentalists, and legislators came to the realization that something had to be done to protect and clean up our water resources, specifically our traditional freshwater supplies: lakes, streams, and rivers. Actually, environmentalists were well aware of our water resource problems years before legislation was enacted. However, in the 1950s and 1960s, when environmentalists were voicing their environmental concerns, most people ignored them; polluters simply played their standard trump card and declared them to be weirdoes, flower children, potheads, and bleeding heart liberals. Fortunately for the rest of us, we woke up and put pressure on Congress to enact two important regulations intended to protect our water resources. Let's look briefly at these two major regulations specifically designed to protect the nation's water resources: the **Safe Drinking Water Act** of 1974 and the **Federal Water Pollution Control Act** of 1972.

SAFE DRINKING WATER ACT (SDWA)

The Safe Drinking Water Act (SWDA) of 1974 came about when federal legislators became aware of the sad (and unhealthy) condition of many local drinking water supplies and the reluctance of local and state officials to remove pollutants from their wastewater. The act set national drinking water standards, called maximum contaminant levels (MCLs), for pollutants that might adversely affect public health and welfare. The first standards went into effect three years later and specifically covered every public water supply in the country serving at least 15 service connections, or 25 or more people. Because more than 200 contaminants from hazardous wastes injected into the soil were identified in groundwater, the SDWA also established standards to protect groundwater from such practices. Specifically, it requires establishment of programs to protect critical groundwater sources of drinking water, to protect areas around wells that supply public drinking water systems, and to regulate the underground injection of wastes above and below drinking water sources.

Later, in 1982 and 1983, the U.S. EPA established a priority list for setting regulations for more than 70 substances. These substances were listed because they are toxic and likely to be found in drinking water. In 1986, when Congress reauthorized the SWDA, it amended the act and directed the EPA to monitor drinking water for unregulated contaminants and to inform public water suppliers about which substances to look for. The 1986 reauthorization also instructed the EPA to set standards within 30 years for all 70+ substances on its priority list. By the end of 1994, the priority list had been expanded, and the EPA had set standards for more than 80 substances.

Under the SWDA, local public water systems are required to monitor their drinking water periodically for contaminants with MCLs and for a broad range of other contaminants as specified by the EPA. Enforcement of the standards, monitoring, and reporting are the responsibility of the individual states, but the 1986 amendments require the EPA to act when a state fails to act or is too slow to do so and authorizes substantial civil penalties against the worst violators.

The SWDA and its amendments also authorize the EPA to set secondary drinking water standards regarding public welfare, by providing guidelines regarding the taste, odor, color, and aesthetic aspects of drinking water that do not present a health risk. These guidelines are nonenforceable and are called suggested levels. The EPA recommends these levels to the states as reasonable goals, but federal law does not require water systems to comply with them, though some individual states have enforceable regulations regarding these concerns.

The 1996 amendments also ban all future use of lead pipe and lead solder in public drinking water systems and require public water systems to tell their users of the potential sources of lead contamination, its health effects, and the steps they can reasonably take to mitigate lead contamination.

FEDERAL WATER POLLUTION CONTROL ACT

In 1972, Congress enacted the Federal Water Pollution Control Act, commonly called the Clean Water Act (CWA). The CWA stems originally from a much-amended 1948 law aiding communities in building sewage treatment plants. It is "the" keystone of environmental law and is credited with significantly cutting the amount of municipal and industrial pollution fed into the nation's water bodies.

Through the 1970s and 1980s, the primary aim of the CWA was to make national waters fishable and swimmable. Specifically, it sought to eliminate discharge of untreated municipal and **industrial wastewater** into waterways (many of which are used as sources of drinking water), providing billions of dollars to finance building of sewage treatment plants.

The 1987 amendments (the Water Quality Act, which reauthorized the original Clean Water Act) focused on updating standards for dealing with toxic chemicals, since much of the toxic pollution still fouling the nation's surface water bodies came from companies that had installed 1970s-era pollution control technologies. For the first time, the law also attempted to deal with water pollution stemming from nonpoint sources (e.g., city streets and croplands), requiring states to identify waters that do not meet quality standards and develop programs to deal with the problem. The 1987 amendments also granted the U.S. Army Corp of Engineers the authority to regulate the dredging and filling of wetlands.

Effect of Regulations on Preventing Water Pollution

On the surface, we might assume that the laws passed since the early 1970s, designed to protect our water resources, are adequate in themselves to ensure water quality. We would be wrong, of course. When Kennedy (1997) expressed shock that "a government agency, charged with protecting the public from pollution, could so blatantly intervene to protect a polluter from the public and the law," he made a valid point: You can make all the laws you want, but requirement does not necessarily mean enforcement. Many factions have criticized the EPA for failing to properly enforce the Safe Drinking Water Act and the Clean Water Act. Another problem has developed in protecting groundwater supplies: Those programs have been underfunded or entirely unfunded. In addition, many environmentalists have criticized the EPA for exempting from the SDWA requirements over 100,000 public water systems as not serving year-round residents, although these systems include schools, factories, seasonal resorts, summer camps, roadside restaurants, and hospitals.

Simply stated, regulations designed to protect the environment and at the same time protect public health and welfare are only the first step across the bridge between pollution and prevention. Once in place, regulations must be complied with and enforced. Then the effort shifts from determining direction, objectives, and goals to implementation. In this implementation phase, technology comes into play—in the key role. Remember, a society can have all kinds of plans, objectives, goals, and regulations to stipulate what needs to be done to correct or mitigate an environmental problem, but none of these will bring about positive results unless the means (technology) is available to accomplish the requirements. With the "means" must also come a certain amount of common sense. Only solid, legitimate, careful scientific analysis may provide the answers and the solutions to environmental problems.

One thing is certain. Before we leap into ill-advised decisions based on emotion or strictly monetary considerations, or on anything but sound science, making decisions that "feel" good, or "feel" right, but don't truly solve the problem, we need to step back and size up the situation, through proper scientific methodology. Too much is at stake to rely on uninformed choices made by politicians with political axes to grind, supported financially by industry through PAC funding. The future of our water supply shouldn't be left to dysfunctional bureaucracy and hare-brained so-called analysis or to the results of such analysis.

Obviously—no question about it—we need to stop polluting our surface and groundwater water bodies. We shouldn't do anything to our environment until science supports our investment. We need to replace the timeworn and frustrating position that "we must start somewhere." We are fortunate in one way: The technology needed to protect and clean up our water resources the right way is available. Advances in water pollution technology are ongoing. In a number of cases, to facilitate installation, much of the technology needed to protect and/or treat water and wastewater has been funded by the federal government.

In the sections that follow, we briefly discuss traditional treatment technologies (water, wastewater, thermal, underground storage tanks and groundwater) currently available and widely used.

Response Scenario 16.3 When Government Intervened to Protect a Polluter

Using the state's freedom-of-information law, we quickly obtained the sludge hauling and alum [aluminum sulfate] purchasing records for the town of Newburgh's Chadwick Lake filtration plant. Those records showed that while the plant had produced over a million gallons of alum sludge during 1984, none had been hauled away. It could only have been dumped into the creek. Records from the previous five years also showed giant discrepancies between alum sludge produced and the amount hauled away. We immediately informed the DEC [Department of Environmental Conservation] about the illegal dumping, hoping for a criminal prosecution against the town.

It was disappointing to me [Robert F. Kennedy Jr.] that the DEC responded instead by writing the town a temporary permit to discharge alum backwash into the creek. I had read just enough environmental law by then to recognize that the purported permit was utterly illegal under the Clean Water Act. The permit had not been subject to public notice or comment, as the act requires, and it allowed discharges of pollutants that the act flatly forbade. There were no penalties and no requirement that the town clean up the creek . . . . I was still naive enough to be shocked that a government agency, charged with protecting the public from pollution, would so blatantly intervene to protect a polluter from the public and the law. (Cronin & Kennedy, 1997, 107)

RESPONSE

(i) What do you think of Cronin and Kennedy's disappointment with the regulators in this case? Is their dismay and shock warranted?

Water Treatment

Municipalities normally control contaminants in drinking water supplies by following established treatment procedures. Before distribution to local destinations (homes, schools, businesses, and hospitals), water withdrawn from its source (lake, river, or aquifer) undergoes treatment. Initial water quality determines the needed degree of treatment. Most water systems, large or small, include certain basic treatment steps. Alum (aluminum sulfate) or lime is added to water supplies to create floc (small gelatinous particles—insoluble precipitates), which gather dirt and other solids. Gentle mixing of the water causes floc particles to join and form larger particles; floc and sediment fall to the bottom and are eventually removed as sludge. The water is then filtered through a granular material (sand or carbon—crushed anthracite coal). Chlorine, sodium hypochlorite, or ultraviolet light is added to kill bacteria and other organisms, and a chemical (usually lime) is added to raise pH (reduce acidity) in water and prevent corrosion in city and household pipes. Many municipal plants also add fluoride to water supplies to prevent tooth decay.

Treated water is sent through a network of pipes (distribution system) to customers. To ensure its quality, water must be monitored and tested by licensed operators throughout the treatment and delivery process. Generally, surface water is more complicated to treat than groundwater, because contamination is more likely. However, sometimes groundwater is hard (containing calcium or magnesium), which means an additional step is added to the treatment process (softening by using alum and lime) to remove hardness.

Wastewater Treatment

What is *wastewater*? Where and how is it generated, and how is it treated? Five major sources generate wastewater, and each source's wastewater presents specific characteristics:

1. **Human and animal wastes:** Considered by many to be the most dangerous from a human health viewpoint. Contain the solid and liquid discharges of humans and animals, and millions of bacteria, viruses, and other organisms, some pathogenic.
2. **Household wastes:** The wastes, other than human and animal wastes, discharged from the home. Contain paper, household cleaners, detergents, trash, garbage, and any other substance that the average homeowner may decide to discharge into the sewer system.
3. **Industrial wastes:** All materials that can be discharged from industrial processes into the collection system are included in this category. May contain chemicals, dyes, acids, alkalies, grit, detergents, and highly toxic materials. Characteristics are industry specific and cannot be determined without detailed information on the specific industry and processes used.
4. **Stormwater runoff:** If the collection system is designed to carry both the wastes of the community and the stormwater runoff, wastewater can, during and after storms, contain large amounts of sand, gravel, road salt, and other grit as well as excessive amounts of water.
5. **Groundwater infiltration:** If the collection system is old or not sealed properly, groundwater may enter the system through cracks, breaks, or unsealed joints. This can add large amounts of water to the wastewater flows, as well as additional grit.

Did You Know?

In developing countries, 90% of the wastewater discharged daily is untreated. Most marine pollution—80%—is land based, most of it wastewater, damaging coral reefs and fishing grounds (UN, 2010).

Wastewater can be classified according to the sources of the flow:

1. **Domestic wastewater (sewage):** Domestic wastewater consists mainly of human and animal wastes, household wastes, small amounts of groundwater infiltration, and perhaps small amounts of industrial wastes.
2. **Sanitary wastewater:** Consists of domestic wastes and significant amounts of industrial wastes. In many cases, the industrial wastes can be treated without special precautions. In some cases, the industrial wastes require special precautions or a pretreatment program to ensure the wastes do not cause compliance problems for the plant.
3. **Industrial wastewater:** Often industries will determine that treating their wastes independently of domestic wastes is more economical.
4. **Combined wastewater:** A combination of sanitary wastewater and storm water runoff. All the wastewater and stormwater of the community is transported through one system and enters the treatment system.
5. **Stormwater:** Many communities have installed separate collection systems to carry stormwater runoff. Stormwater flow should contain grit and street debris, but no domestic or sanitary wastes.

Did You Know?

People in the industrialized world generate five times more wastewater per person than in developing countries, but treat over 90% of the wastewater compared, to only a small percentage in developing countries (UN, 2011).

Wastewater contains many different substances that can be used to characterize it. Depending on the source, the specific substances present will vary, as will the amounts or concentration of each. For this reason, wastewater characteristics are normally described for average domestic wastewater. Other sources and types of wastewater can dramatically change the characteristics.

The physical characteristics of wastewater include the following:

Color: Typical wastewater is gray and cloudy. Wastewater color will change significantly (to black) if allowed to go septic.
Odor: Fresh domestic wastewater has a musty odor. This odor will change significantly if septic. Septic wastewater develops the rotten egg odor associated with hydrogen sulfide production.
Temperature: Wastewater temperature is normally close to that of the water supply. Significant amounts of infiltration or stormwater flow can cause major temperature changes.
Flow: The volume of wastewater is normally expressed in terms of gallons per person per day. Most treatment plants are designed using an expected flow of 100 to 200 gallons per person per day. This figure may have to be revised to reflect the

degree of infiltration or stormwater flow the plant receives. Flow rates will vary throughout the day. This variation, which can be as much as 50% to 200% of the average daily flow, is known as the **diurnal flow variation**.

Wastewater chemical characteristics are as follows:

Alkalinity: A measure of the wastewater capability to neutralize acids. Measured in terms of bicarbonate, carbonate, and hydroxide alkalinity, it is essential to buffer (hold the neutral pH) wastewater during the **biological treatment** process.
Biochemical oxygen demand (BOD): A measure of the amount of biodegradable matter in the wastewater. Normally measured by a five-day test conducted at 20°C. The BOD_5 domestic waste is normally in the range of 100 to 300 mg/L.
Chemical oxygen demand (COD): A measure of the amount of oxidizable matter present in the sample. The COD is normally in the range of 200 to 500 mg/L. The presence of industrial wastes can increase this significantly.
Dissolved gases: Gases that are dissolved in wastewater. The specific gases and normal concentrations are based on the composition of the wastewater. Typical domestic wastewater contains oxygen (relatively low concentrations), carbon dioxide, and hydrogen sulfide (if septic conditions exist).
Nitrogen compounds: The type and amount of nitrogen present varies from raw wastewater to treated effluent. Nitrogen follows a cycle of oxidation and reduction. Most of the nitrogen in untreated wastewater will be in the form of organic nitrogen and ammonia nitrogen, presence and levels determined by laboratory testing. The sum of these two forms of nitrogen is also measured and is known as total Kjeldahl nitrogen (TKN). Wastewater normally contains 20 to 85 mg/L of nitrogen. Organic nitrogen is normally in the range of 8 to 35 mg/L and ammonia nitrogen in the range of 12 to 50 mg/L.
pH: A method of expressing the acid condition of wastewater. For proper treatment wastewater, pH should normally be in the range of 6.5 to 9.0.
Phosphorus: Essential to biological activity, phosphorus must be present in at least minimum quantities, or secondary treatment processes will not perform. Excessive amounts can cause stream damage and excessive algal growth. Phosphorus is normally in the range of 6 to 20 mg/L. The removal of phosphate compounds from detergents has had a significant impact on the amounts of phosphorus in wastewater.
Solids: Most pollutants found in wastewater can be classified as solids. Wastewater treatment is generally designed to remove solids or to convert solids to a more stable form that can easily be removed. Solids can be classified by their chemical composition (organic or inorganic) or by their physical characteristics (settleable, floatable, colloidal). Concentration of total solids in wastewater is normally in the range of 350 to 1,200 mg/L.
Water: Always the major component of wastewater. In most cases water makes up 99.5 to 99.9% of wastewater. Even in the strongest wastewater, the total amount of contamination present is less than 0.5% of the total, and in average strength wastes, it is normally less than 0.1%.

Wastewater treatment is designed to use the natural purification processes to the maximum level possible and to complete these processes in a controlled environment rather than over many miles of stream. Removing contaminants not addressed by natural processes and treating the solids generated by the treatment steps are further tasks of wastewater treatment. The specific goals wastewater treatment plants are designed to accomplish include

- protecting public health,
- protecting public water supplies,
- protecting aquatic life,
- preserving the best uses of the waters, and
- protecting adjacent lands.

Wastewater treatment is accomplished by applying up to seven principal treatment steps to the incoming waste stream. The processes and equipment for each step are specific to the task. The major categories of treatment steps used in many treatment plants include preliminary treatment, primary treatment, secondary treatment, advanced waste treatment, **disinfection**, and **biosolids treatment**.

Preliminary treatment removes materials (wood, rocks, and other forms of debris) that could damage treatment plant equipment or would occupy treatment capacity without being treated.

Primary treatment removes larger particles by filtering through screens, and settleables and floatable solids in ponds or lagoons. Water is removed from the top of the settling lagoon and released. Water that has been treated in this manner has had its sand and grit removed, but it still carries a heavy load of organic matter, dissolved salts, bacteria, and other microorganisms. Primary treatment removes up to about 60% of suspended solids. In larger cities, where several cities a few miles or less from each other take water and return it to a stream, primary wastewater treatment is not adequate.

Secondary treatment usually follows primary treatment and is designed to remove BOD_5 and dissolved and colloidal suspended organic matter by biological action. Organics are converted to stable solids, carbon dioxide, and more organisms by holding the wastewater until the bacteria and other microorganisms have degraded the organic material. Secondary treatment removes up to 90% of the oxygen-demanding wastes by using either *trickling filters*, where aerobic bacteria degrade sewage as it seeps through a large vat bed filled with media (rocks, plastic media, etc.) covered with bacterial growth, or an *activated sludge process*, in which the sewage is pumped into a large tank and mixed for several hours with bacteria-rich biosolids and air to increase bacterial degradation. To optimize this action, large quantities of highly oxygenated water for aerating water are added directly by a blower system.

Advanced wastewater treatment (tertiary sewage treatment) uses physical, chemical, and biological processes to remove additional BOD_5, solids, and nutrients. Advanced wastewater treatment is normally used in facilities that have unusually high amounts of phosphorus and nitrogen present.

Biosolids treatment works to stabilize the solids removed from the wastewater during treatment, inactivates pathogenic organisms, and/or reduces the volume of the biosolids by removing water (**dewatering**).

Did You Know?

Agriculture accounts for some 70–90% of all water consumed, mainly for irrigation. But large amounts also return to rivers in runoff: Nearly half of all organic matter in wastewater comes from agriculture (UN, 2010).

Thermal Pollution Treatment

Approximately half of the water withdrawn in the United States is used for cooling large power-producing plants. The most common method (because it is easiest and cheapest) is to withdraw cold water from a lake or river, pass it through heat exchangers in the facility, and return the heated water to the same body of water. The warm water discharge raises the receiving body's temperature, lowers DO content, and causes aquatic organisms to increase their respiration rates and consume the already depleted oxygen faster.

We can minimize the harmful effects of excess heat on aquatic ecosystems in a number of ways. Two of the most commonly used methods are the cooling tower and dry tower methods.

In the **cooling tower method**, the heated water is sprayed into the air and cooled by evaporation. The obvious disadvantage of this treatment method is the loss of large amounts of water to evaporation. Production of localized fogs is another disadvantage.

The **dry tower method** does not release water into the atmosphere. Instead, the heated water is pumped through tubes, and the heat is released into the air, which is similar to the action performed by an automobile's radiator. The disadvantage of the dry tower method is its high cost, both to construct and to operate.

Underground Storage Tanks (USTs)

Recent estimates have ranged from five to six million, but no one is quite sure just how many underground storage tanks (USTs) containing hazardous substances or petroleum products are in use in the United States. Compounding the issue, no one can even guess how many USTs are no longer being used (abandoned USTs), from which the contents have been oozing (and sometimes pouring), fouling water, land, and air. Another potential problem is just biding its time; USTs that are not leaking today will probably leak soon, in the near future. One thing is certain, however: Environmental contamination from leaking USTs poses a significant threat to human health and the environment.

Besides the obvious problem of fouling environmental media (water, soil, and air), ironically, many of these leaking USTs also pose serious fire and explosion hazards.

The irony is in the fact that USTs came into common use primarily as a fire and explosion prevention measure (the hazard was buried under the ground). Today, however, the hazards we worked to protect ourselves from are finding ways and means to present themselves in different ways.

The problem with leaking USTs goes beyond fouling the environment (especially groundwater, upon which 50% of the U.S. population relies for drinking water) and presenting fire and explosion hazards. Products released from these leaking tanks can damage sewer lines and buried cables and poison our crops.

What are USTs? The U.S. EPA, under the *Resource Conservation and Recovery Act* (RCRA), defines USTs as tanks with 10% or more of their volume (including piping) underground. The largest portion of the USTs regulated by the EPA are petroleum storage tanks owned by gas stations; another significant percentage are petroleum storage tanks owned by a group of other industries (airports, trucking fleets, farms, manufacturing operations, and golf courses) that store petroleum products for their own use.

In 1986, the U.S. Congress established a UST clean-up fund known as **Leaking Underground Storage Tank (LUST)** trust fund. The EPA, tasked with the responsibility of exploring, developing, and disseminating new clean-up technologies and developing funding mechanisms, must still leave the primary job of cleaning up LUST sites to the various state and local governments. Owners and operators of tank facilities are liable for clean-up costs and damage caused by their tanks—not a small matter in any way. The average cost for remediating a site containing petroleum contamination of the soil and groundwater is on the order of $200,000 to $350,000 (present worth), depending on the lateral and vertical extent of the contamination and the required clean-up target levels. In some cases, the cost of clean-up may exceed the value of the property.

When the EPA and other investigators initially investigated the problems with leaking USTs in 1985, they found that many of the existing USTs were more than 20 years old or of unknown age. Compounding the problem of tank age, these older tanks were often constructed of bare steel, not protected against corrosion, and nearing the end of their useful lives (Holmes, Singh, & Theodore, 1993). Exacerbating the problem, many of the old tanks were found to have already leaked or were right on the verge of leaking. Many of these old tanks were found in abandoned gas stations (shut down because of the oil crisis in the 1970s).

Because of the findings of the EPA and others on the scope of the problem with USTs, regulatory requirements were put into place. The requirements for USTs depend on whether the system is an existing or a new installation. An existing installation is defined as one that was installed prior to 1988.

Specific requirements for USTs must now be met. All existing USTs (in current use) must have overfill and spill protection. In addition, corrosion protection and leak detection systems must be installed in accordance with the schedule mandated by the federal regulations. The compliance schedule ensures that the oldest tanks (those with the greatest potential for failure) are addressed first.

Under Federal Regulations (40 C.F.R. 280), all existing tanks must have corrosion protection and spill and overfill prevention devices installed. Both pressured and suction piping installed prior to December 1988 should have had corrosion protection in place by December 1998.

To evaluate the integrity of an installed UST, all owners must abide by certain regulatory requirements (minimum requirements). The specific requirements are listed and explained in Table 16.1.

Under federal law, facilities with USTs that contain petroleum and hazardous substances must respond to a leak or spill within 24 hours of release or within another reasonable period of time as determined by the implementing agency. Responses to releases from USTs are site-specific and depend on several factors. Corrective action usually involves two stages. Stage one (initial response) is directed toward containment

Table 16.1. UST Requirements: What You Have to Do

Leak Detection

For New Tanks	Must be monitored monthly. These checks may be made by using automatic tank gauging, vapor monitoring, interstitial (secondary containment) monitoring, groundwater monitoring, and other approved methods.
Or You May	Monthly inventory control and tank tightness testing every 5 years (only for up to 10 years after installation).
for Existing Tanks	Monthly monitoring, or monthly inventory control and annual tank tightness testing (can only be used until December 1998), or monthly inventory control and annual tank tightness testing every 5 years (this choice can only be used for 10 years after adding corrosion protection and spill/overfill prevention, or until December 1998, whichever date is later).
New & Existing Pressurized Piping	Choice of one of the following: • automatic flow restrictor • annual line testing • automatic shutoff device & monthly monitoring (except automatic tank gauging) • continuous alarm system
New & Existing Suction Piping	Choice of monthly monitoring (except automatic tank gauging) or line testing every 3 years.

Corrosion Protection

New Tanks	Choices: Coated and cathodically protected steel. Fiberglass. Steel tank clad with fiberglass.
Existing Tanks	Choices: Same options as for new tanks. Add cathodic protection system. Interior lining and cathodic protection.
New Piping	Choices: Coated and cathodically protected steel. Fiberglass
Existing Piping	Choices: Same options as for new piping. Cathodically protected steel.

Spill/Overfill Protection

All Tanks	Catchment basins and • Automatic shutoff devices or • Overfill alarms or • Ball float valves

Source: 40 C.F.R. 280 (1988).

and collection of spilled material. Stage two (permanent corrective response) involves technical improvements designed to ensure that the incident does not occur again. Preventive-action technology usually includes employing containment, diversion, removal, or treatment protocols. The choice of which technology to employ in spill prevention and correction depends on its suitability, life span, ease of implementation, and ease of performing required maintenance checks.

The EPA issued *Cleanup of Releases from Petroleum USTs: Selected Technologies* in 1988, which has become the standard reference for deciding which technology to employ for use in clean-up of releases from petroleum USTs. Although only a limited number of technologies are available to clean environmental media of the contaminants associated with gasoline, their practicality, removal efficiencies, limitations, and costs are well documented.

For recovering free product from the water table, two technologies are presently used to limit the migration of floating gasoline across the water table: the trench method and the pumping well method. For recovering the free product using the trench method, a variety of equipment is available, including skimmers, filter separators, and oil/water separators. For the pumping well method, both single- and dual-pump systems are available.

When the water table is no deeper than 10–15 feet below the ground surface, the *trench method* is most effective. The advantages of this method include the ease with which the trench can be excavated and the ability to capture the entire leading edge of the plume. The disadvantage in using the trench method is that it does not reverse groundwater flow, which means it may not be appropriate for use when a potable well supply is threatened. The cost of this system is about $150 per cubic yard of soil excavated.

When a spill is deep (water table depth exceeds 20 feet below the ground surface), a *pumping well system* is the preferred method used to recover free product from the water table. The major advantage of using this system is that it can reverse the direction of groundwater flow. Including the cost of labor and engineering, this system ranges from about $150 to $300 per foot for 4- to 10-inch gravel-packed galvanized steel wells (U.S. EPA, 1988).

Because gasoline spilled onto the soil may eventually find its way to groundwater, removal of gasoline from unsaturated soils is an essential component of any corrective action plan. A number of removal techniques are available that vary in effectiveness and cost. The most widely used corrective action is excavation and disposal. Other methods include volatilization, **incineration**, venting, soil washing/extraction, and microbial degradation.

The advantage of using excavation and disposal is that it can be 100% effective. The main disadvantages are that usually only a small portion of the contaminated soil can be removed because of high cost, the limitations of the excavation equipment (backhoes normally only reach down to about 16 feet), that landfills may not accept the contaminated soil, and the lack of uniform guidelines for the proper disposal of contaminated soil.

Volatilization will effectively remove about 99% of volatile organic compounds (VOCs), but the process does not have an extensive track record (because it is little used) to make definitive statements about its efficiency and/or effectiveness in the field.

Incineration, like volatilization, will remove approximately 99% of gasoline constituents in soil. Having proven itself highly reliable, incineration of gasoline-contaminated soil is widely practiced. The practice does have a few limitations, however: (1) The soil must be brought to the surface, increasing the risk of exposure; (2) incineration is usually appropriate only when toxics other than volatiles are present; and (3) unfortunately, permitting delays (fighting the bureaucratic paper chase) may cause further spread of contamination.

The big advantage of using *venting*, which can be up to 99% effective, is that it allows for the removal of gasoline without excavation. However, because critical parameters have not yet been defined, venting is not widely used in the field. Venting is relatively easy to implement, but its effectiveness is uncertain, because soil characteristics may impede free movement of vapors and could even lead to an explosion.

Soil washing and extraction works to leach contaminants from the soil into a leaching medium, after which the extracted contaminants are removed by conventional methods. Under ideal conditions, up to 99% of VOCs can be removed. If the contaminated soil contains high levels of clay and silt, they may impede the separation of the solid and liquid after the washing phase. The soil's suitability to be decontaminated using this method should be verified first, before this procedure is implemented.

Microbial degradation, theoretically, can remove up to 99% of the contaminants. This method is still in the research mode, with field-testing still in progress; thus, its cost effectiveness and overall effectiveness have not been verified. If further testing supports its viability for use in the field, the advantage will be that *in situ* treatment is possible, with volatiles completely destroyed.

Groundwater Remediation

As you should recall, groundwater is an important water source, supplying a significant percentage of the water used for drinking. For many years, groundwater was not only the only source of potable water available in certain areas, it was the source of choice even when other sources were available, because of people's perception of groundwater as pure. Most people thought that groundwater was safer for many years, that it only needed disinfecting before being sent to the household tap. Most people knew groundwater was supplied from precipitation in the form of rain, sleet, and snow. Once on the surface, precipitation entered rock and soil and filtered its way through Earth's strata to the water table, where it was held in a "clean" state, and by the nature of its confinement there, it was protected from surface contamination.

There are problems with this view of groundwater, however. In the first place, because groundwater is so widely used, and the populations using it have increased at a steady pace, many groundwater supplies have been either depleted or lowered to the point in coastal areas where saltwater intrusion takes place. Second, groundwater supplies may become polluted.

Both groundwater depletion and groundwater pollution may be irreversible. Depletion can cause an aquifer to consolidate, diminishing its storage capacity. Both naturally occurring and artificial materials may contaminate groundwater. Just about anything water comes into contact with will be dissolved in or mixed with the flow. If contaminated, the water is likely to remain that way.

Of particular concern in groundwater pollution are *nonaqueous-phase liquids* (NAPLs). NAPLs are classified as either *light* (LNAPLs) or **dense (DNAPLs)**. LNAPLs include such products (referred to as products because of their potential for commercial reuse) as gasoline, heating oil, and kerosene. Because of the widespread use of underground storage tanks, these products are common in many soils. Because LNAPLs are light, they tend to float on the groundwater, penetrating the capillary fringe and depressing the water surface. Even when the source of the spill is controlled, the soil will remain contaminated, and the floating layer will serve as a long-term source of contamination (McGhee, 1991).

From a health standpoint, DNAPLs are a much more serious problem. They include trichloroethane, carbon tetrachloride, creosote, dichlorobenzene, and other chemicals. Because these compounds are toxic, have low viscosity, have great density, and have low solubility, they are not only health hazards but are also very mobile in groundwater, spreading quickly throughout a localized aquifer.

In contaminated groundwater mitigation and treatment, usually only localized areas of an aquifer need reclamation and restoration, because the spread of contaminants is usually confined to the *plume*. Experience has shown, however, that even after the original source of contamination is removed, clean-up of a contaminated aquifer is often costly, time-consuming, and troublesome. Problems with clean-up include difficulty in identifying the type of subsurface environment, locating potential contamination sources, defining potential contaminant transport pathways, determining contaminant extent and concentration, and choosing and implementing an effective remedial process (Davis & Cornwell, 1991, 712).

Clean-up is possible, but not simple. Some methods have proven successful in some cases (especially where groundwater has been pumped from the subsurface). These efforts have been refined from processes used to treat industrial wastes. However, attempting to treat site-contaminated groundwater using these methods is often confusing. The contaminants themselves may also dictate what methodologies should work for mitigation. When the contaminant is a single chemical, the treatment system employed may be simple—but in cases involving multiple contaminants, treatment can be extremely complex. To determine which treatment should be employed, only representative samples and laboratory analysis provide the needed information. Clean-up technologies commonly used for groundwater containing organic contamination include air stripping and activated carbon. The **chemical precipitation** process is used for inorganics in groundwater. We describe each of these treatment processes in the following discussion.

In *air stripping* (a relatively simple mass transfer process), a substance in solution in water is transferred to solution in a gas. Air stripping uses four basic equipment configurations: diffused aeration, countercurrent packed columns, cross-flow towers, and coke tray aerators. The countercurrent packed tower system has significant advantages (provides the most liquid interfacial area and high air-to-water volume ratios) over the other systems and is most often used in removing volatile organics from contaminated groundwater.

Carbon adsorption occurs when an organic molecule is brought to the activated carbon surface and held there by physical and/or chemical forces. When activated carbon particles are placed in water containing organic chemicals and mixed to give adequate contact, adsorption of the organic chemicals occurs. Activated carbon adsorption has been successfully employed for removing organics from contaminated groundwater.

Biological treatment (a new technology still under evaluation by pilot studies) removes or reduces the concentration of organic and inorganic compounds. To undergo biological treatment, contaminated groundwater must first be pretreated to remove toxins that could destroy microorganisms needed to metabolize and remove the contaminants.

When removing inorganic contaminants, the established and commonly used methodology is chemical precipitation. Accomplished by the addition of carbonate, hydroxide, or sulfide chemicals, chemical precipitation has successfully removed heavy metals from groundwater.

When groundwater near a potable water system (well) is contaminated, the most common way to protect the water from an approaching plume of contaminated groundwater is to use some combination of **extraction wells** and **injection wells**. Extraction wells are used to lower the water table, creating a hydraulic gradient that draws the plume to the wells. Injection wells raise the water table and push the plume away. Working in combination, extraction well and injection well pumping rates can be adjusted to manipulate the hydraulic gradient, which helps keep the plume away from the potable water well, drawing it toward the extraction well. Once extracted, the contaminated water is treated and either reinjected back into the aquifer, reused, or released into the local surface water system (Masters, 1991).

Chapter Summary

Clean-up of contaminated water supplies presents a complex problem. The contaminated areas are often out of sight and difficult to clearly define. The technologies, though becoming more effective, are also costly. Without the U.S. EPA as guardian and enforcer, without the Safe Drinking Water Act and the Federal Water Pollution Control Act, without pressure from concerned citizens about the condition and quality of our resources, an attitude related to "not in my backyard" creeps in: "Ignore it. It's someone else's problem." Fortunately, people are becoming more aware that contaminated water supplies will affect us all.

As the world's population grows, we are forced by circumstances we have ourselves created to face the realization of our resources' limitations. Many of us in the United States have always been fortunate enough to have enough of whatever we need, and even whatever we want. When something we like breaks or wears out, we throw it away and buy a new one, and often we don't even make an attempt to fix the first one. We neglect basic maintenance until we damage our belongings beyond repair, and we expect that we will always have enough. But some things are beyond our control, beyond our power or financial ability to replace or repair. Our water supply is one of these. Without concern, without attention, without preventive maintenance and reclamation, our water supply will not be able to support the needs of the future.

Discussion Questions and Problems

1. List the principal components of wastewater.
2. Describe the components of (a) primary, (b) secondary, and (c) tertiary treatment.
3. Should the injection of hazardous wastes into deep underground wells be banned? Why?
4. How does irrigation increase salinity?
5. Why is stormwater management more of a problem in an urban area than a rural area?
6. What is thermal pollution? How can it be controlled?
7. How does groundwater become contaminated? Describe three technologies used to control groundwater contamination.
8. Both activated biosolids waste treatment and natural resources in streams and bodies of water remove degradable materials by biodegradation. Is activated biosolids treatment more efficient than a stream's self-purification process? Explain.
9. How is hard water softened in the water treatment process?
10. Describe the three ways to meet corrosion protection standards for underground storage tanks.
11. Environmental contamination from leaking underground storage tanks poses a significant threat to human health and environment. Explain.
12. What is one of the chief sources of water pollution?
13. What is acid mine drainage? Describe its cause, source, and effects.
14. How do fertilizers contribute to water pollution?
15. Distinguish between point and nonpoint sources of pollutants.
16. What is thermal pollution, and what are its sources and effects?
17. Explain soil salinity from irrigation.
18. Explain the significance of bioaccumulation.

Suggested Research Topics and Projects

- Examine organizations concerned with environmental preservation and protection: Riverkeepers, the Sierra Club, Greenpeace, etc.
- Examine the need for and the effects of the Safe Water Drinking Act (1974).
- Examine the need for and the effects of the Clean Water Act (the Federal Water Pollution Control Act, 1972).
- Research the problems associated with regulation enforcement.
- Examine the control of contaminants in drinking water.
- Examine your community for sources of wastewater. Categorize and classify those sources and their possible waste production by what they do and by possible physical and chemical contaminants.
- Tour a wastewater facility and trace the seven steps involved in treatment.
- Underground storage tanks present a serious threat to our water supply. Examine the problems involved in remediation.

- Research the abandoned UST problem; What are some possible solutions to the problem?
- Research the petroleum industry's response to UST problems.
- Calculate the costs involved (estimate) in cleaning up a UST site.
- Examine the processes used to clean up a petroleum product spill.
- Research venting as an effective remediation technique for gas contamination.
- Research the problems associated with groundwater contamination remediation.
- What point and nonpoint pollution sources are prevalent in your area? Where do they come from, and where do they end up?
- Research clean-up technologies for oil spills.
- Analyze the effect thermal pollution has on stream organisms.
- Research the environmental and/or human health concerns related to the mining industry.
- Research modern agricultural practices and their environmental effects.
- How have acid rain levels and effects changed since the issue first arose? What's the current status? What happened to those dead lakes?
- Research the importance of wetlands within environmental ecosystems.
- Research wetland destruction and protection.

References and Recommended Readings

Concern Inc. (1986). *Drinking Water: A Community Action Guide*. Washington, DC: Concern, Inc.

Conservation Foundation (1982). *State of the Environment 1982*. Washington, DC: Conservation Foundation.

Conservation Foundation (1987). *Groundwater Pollution*. Washington, DC: Conservation Foundation.

Council on Environmental Quality (1981). *Contamination of Groundwater by Toxic Organic Chemicals*. Washington, DC: U.S. Government Printing Office.

Cronin, J., & Kennedy, R. K., Jr. (1997). *The Riverkeepers*. New York: Scribner.

Davis, M. L., & Cornwell, D. A. (1991). *Introduction to Environmental Engineering*. 2nd ed. New York: McGraw-Hill.

Draper, E. (1987, Fall). "Groundwater Protection." *Clean Water Action News*, 4.

Goldsmith, E., & Hildyard, N., eds. (1988). *The Earth Report: The Essential Guide to Global Ecological Issues*. Los Angeles: Price Stern Sloan.

Holmes, G., Singh, B. R., & Theodore, L. (1993). *Handbook of Environmental Management & Technology*. New York: John Wiley & Sons.

Hunt, C. A., & Garrels, R. M. (1972). *Water—The Web of Life*. New York: W.W. Norton.

King, Jonathan (1985). *Troubled Water*. Emmaus, PA: Rodale Press.

Masters, G. M. (1991). *Introduction to Environmental Engineering and Science*. Englewood Cliffs, NJ: Prentice-Hall.

McGhee, T. J. (1991). *Water Supply and Sewerage*. 6th ed. New York: McGraw-Hill.

National Research Council (1986). *Groundwater Quality Protection*. Washington, DC: National Academy Press.

Peavy, S., Rowe, D. R., & Tchobanoglous, G. (1985). *Environmental Engineering*. New York: McGraw-Hill.

Pimentel, D. (1989). "Waste in Agriculture and Food Sectors." Unpublished manuscript, Cornell University, College of Agriculture and Life Sciences.

Rice, R. G. (1985). *Safe Drinking Water. The Impact of Chemicals on a Limited Resource.* Chelsea, MI: Lewis Publishers.

New York Times (1988, May 22). Report Reveals Higher Acidity in Eastern Streams, A16.

Quigg, P. W. (1976). *Water: The Essential Resource.* New York: National Audubon Society.

Spellman, F. R., Drinan, J., & Whiting, N. E. (2001). *Transportation of Hazardous Materials: A Practical Guide to Compliance.* Rockland, MD: Government Institutes.

UN (2011). Accessed January 11, 2011 at www.unep.org/documents.nultilingual/default.asp?document

U.S. EPA (1988, April). *Cleanup of Releases from Petroleum USTs: Selected Technologies,* Washington, DC: EPA.

World Resources Institute, Natural Resources Consumption (1994). *World Resources 1994–95.* New York: Oxford University Press.

World Resources Institute, Water (1994). *World Resources 1994–95.* New York: Oxford University Press.

Worldwatch Institute (1995). *State of the World Resources 1994–95.* New York: W. W. Norton & Company.

Part IV

SOIL QUALITY

One can make a day of any size, and regulate the rising and setting of his own sun and the brightness of its shining.

—John Muir, 1875

The Walrus and the Carpenter
Were walking close at hand;
They wept like anything to see
Such quantities of sand:
"If this were only cleared away,"
They said, "it would be grand!"
"If seven maids with seven mops
Swept it for half a year,
Do you suppose," the Walrus said,
"That they could get it clear?"
"I doubt it," said the Carpenter,
And shed a bitter tear.

—Lewis Carroll, *Through the Looking-Glass and What Alice Found There*, 1871

CHAPTER 17

Soil Characteristics, Pollution, and Pollution Control

Every soil-atom seems to yield enthusiastic obedience to law—bowlders [sic] and mud-grains moving to music as harmoniously as the far-whirling planets.

—John Muir, 1874

The sediments are a sort of epic poem of the Earth. When we are wise enough, perhaps we can read in them all of past history.

—Rachel Carson, *The Sea Around Us*

Chapter Objectives

After studying this chapter, you should be able to:

- Identify the stages of bare rock succession and describe the process.
- Discuss soil's importance as an environmental medium.
- Describe the various soil layers, what comprises them, and how they are formed.
- Identify and discuss soil properties and describe how they are interrelated.
- Describe in detail how soil is formed and discuss the information soil horizon can provide.
- Identify and discuss the primary problems related to soil fertility.
- Identify the primary sources of soil contamination.
- Identify and distinguish between sources of surface soil pollution and of industrial pollution.
- Discuss soil pollution as a problem of developed countries.
- Describe and discuss how air pollutants affect soil quality.
- Describe and discuss the chief ways water pollutants contaminate soil.
- Discuss how biosolids disposal can affect soil quality.

- Discuss stockpiling (from mines and other sources) and concentrations of contaminants and the ways the contaminants enter the soil.
- Discuss old and new dumping practices and determine how they affect soil quality.
- Discuss urban salt use and soil contamination.
- Discuss and describe how animal feedlots affect soil quality.
- Identify and describe the problems fertilizers and pesticides can cause in soil.
- Define and discuss the rule of thumb that governs the impact and extent of accident spills and soil contamination.
- Describe how yard-waste composting can sometimes cause soil pollution.
- Identify the common industrial practices that can lead to soil contamination.
- Describe and discuss in detail the petroleum industry's impact on soil contamination, the primary pollutant sources, how location affects remediation, and the continuing problems related to underground storage tanks (USTs).
- Describe the special problems organic chemical pollution can cause.
- Discuss geothermal energy as a pollution source and identify the contamination problems related to it.
- Discuss the polluting by-products from the coal gasification process.
- Describe and discuss how mining operations adversely affect soil quality.
- Discuss and describe the deliberate contamination created as an act of environmental terrorism in the First Gulf War.
- Discuss how CERCLA and RCRA have affected remediation research and technology.
- Identify the problems associated with USTs, discuss how USTs affect soil and groundwater, and describe the common reasons USTs leak.
- Determine the common causes of UST failure.
- Define common elements that can lead to failure of new tanks.
- Describe how improper installation of tank and piping can affect tank integrity.
- Identify the consequences of spillage and overfilling.
- Identify the problems associated with incompatible tank type and content.
- Identify and discuss the process used for risk assessment of hydrocarbon spillage or disposal.
- Identify and determine the human and environmental exposure pathways associated with hydrocarbon contamination.
- Identify and determine the preliminary testing and sampling processes in remediation of contaminated soils under EPRI/USWAG.
- Identify and describe the accepted in situ and non-in situ practices for soil remediation, including volatilization, biodegradation, leaching and chemical reaction, passive remediation, isolation/containment, land treatment, thermal treatment, asphalt treatment, extraction by groundwater and chemical means, and excavation.
- Discuss the factors that affect these processes, their advantages and disadvantages, and their environmental effectiveness.
- Discuss the ongoing trends in soil remediation techniques and how venture capitalism and regulation affect progress and change.

Chapter Outline

- Description: bare rock succession
- Definition and discussion: soil and soil use classifications
- Definition and discussion: soil layers
- Definition and discussion: how soil texture, slope, tilth, and organic matter affect soil quality
- Definition and discussion: the physical, chemical, and biological interactions of soil formation
- Discussion: problems with soil fertility and the common causes: agricultural impact, erosion, and soil pollution
- Description and discussion: soil contamination from surface sources, regulation, and the extent of the problem
- Discussion: how air pollutants contaminate soil
- Discussion: how water pollutants contaminate soil
- Discussion: how solid and liquid waste disposal can contaminate soil
- Discussion: how mining, roadwork, and excavation can contaminate soil
- Discussion: dumping sites and soil contamination
- Discussion: deicing and soil pollution
- Discussion: farm animal wastes and soil pollution
- Discussion: agricultural practices of fertilization and pesticide control and how they affect soil pollution
- Discussion: accidental release of contaminant materials and soil pollution
- Discussion: small-scale composting of chemically treated yard wastes
- Discussion and description: industrial sources of soil pollution
- Discussion: oil field sites and petroleum products as primary soil contaminants
- Discussion: organic chemicals and soil contamination
- Discussion: soil contamination from geothermal energy sources
- Discussion: coal gasification and soil contamination
- Discussion: how mining practices induce soil contamination
- Discussion: the First Gulf War and environmental pollution as a weapon of terrorism
- Discussion: remediation research and technology and venture capitalism
- Discussion: USTs and the extent of the environmental damage
- Description and discussion: USTs, corrosion, and faulty construction
- Description: how a new UST can fail
- Description and discussion: USTs, faulty installation, piping failures, and spills
- Description and discussion: USTs and content incompatibility
- Description and discussion: hydrocarbon spillage and disposal risk assessment
- Description and discussion: primary and secondary pathways for direct human exposure and environmental exposure
- Description and discussion: remediation processes, regulations, and in situ and non-in situ technologies

- Description: in situ volatilization techniques; how soil, environmental, and chemical factors affect success; and the environmental effectiveness of the process
- Description: in situ biodegradation techniques; how soil, environmental, and chemical factors affect success; and the environmental effectiveness of the process
- Description: in situ leaching and chemical reaction techniques and their environmental effectiveness
- Description: in situ vitrification techniques and their environmental effectiveness
- Description: in situ passive remediation techniques and their environmental effectiveness
- Description: in situ isolation/containment techniques and their environmental effectiveness
- Description: non-in situ technologies
- Description: land treatment techniques and the advantages and disadvantages of the process
- Description: thermal treatment techniques and the advantages and disadvantages of the process
- Description: asphalt, cement, and brick incorporation techniques and the advantages and disadvantages of the process
- Description: solidification/stabilization techniques and the advantages and disadvantages of the process
- Description: chemical extraction techniques
- Description: excavation techniques and the advantages and disadvantages of the process
- Discussion: present trends in innovative clean-up technologies

Key Terms

accidental spills
acid mine drainage
accidental spills
adsorption site density
aggregate
air pollutants
airborne contaminants
animal feedlots
asphalt incorporation
bare rock succession
parent material
pedologist
peds
piping failure

primary exposure pathways
recycling technology
reuse
risk assessment
sheet piling
slope
slurry walls
soil
soil forming process
soil horizon
soil profile
soil structure (tilth)
soil texture
subsoil

surfactant   toxicological evaluation
tailings   water content
thermal treatment   weathering
topsoil   zone of weathering

Introduction

If modern humans were transported back in time, we would instantly recognize the massive structure before us, even though we might be taken aback at what we saw: a youthful mountain range with considerable mass, steep sides, and a height that certainly reached beyond any cloud. We would instantly relate to one particular peak—the tallest, most massive one. The polyhedron-shaped object, with its polygonal base and triangular faces culminating in a single sharp-tipped apex would have looked familiar—comparable in shape, though larger in size, to the largest of the Great Pyramids of Egypt, though they were originally covered in a sheet of limestone, not the thick, perpetual sheet of solid ice and snow that cover the mountain peak.

But if people walked this same site in modern times, if we knew what had once stood upon this site, the changes would be obvious and startling—and entirely relative to time. What stood as an incomparable mountain peak eons ago, today cannot be seen in its ancient majesty. In fact, we wouldn't give it a second thought as we walked across its remnants and through the vegetation that grows from its pulverized and amended remains.

Some 300 million years ago, the pyramid-shaped mountain peak stood in full, unchallenged splendor above the clouds, wrapped in a cloak of ice, a mighty fortress of stone, seemingly vulnerable to nothing, tallest of all—higher than any mountain ever stood—or will ever stand—on Earth.

And so it stood, for millions upon millions of passings of the Earth around the sun. Born when Mother Earth took a deep breath, the pyramid-shaped peak stood tall and undisturbed until millions of years later, when Mother Earth stretched. Today we would call this stretch a massive earthquake—humans have never witnessed one of such magnitude. Rather than registering on the Richter scale, it would have destroyed it.

But when this massive earthquake shattered the Earth's surface, nothing we would call intelligent life lived on Earth—and it's a good thing.

During this massive upheaval, the peak shook to its very foundations, and after the initial shockwave and the hundred plus aftershocks, the solid granite structure had fractured. This immense fracture was so massive that each aftershock widened it and loosened the base foundation of the pyramid-shaped peak itself. Only 10,000 years later (a few seconds relative to geologic time), the fracture's effects totally altered the shape of the peak forever. During a horrendous windstorm, one of an intensity known only in Earth's earliest days, a sharp tremor (emanating from deep within the Earth and shooting up the spine of the mountain itself, up to the very peak) widened the gaping wound still more.

Decades of continued tremors and terrible windstorms passed (no present-day structure could withstand a blasting from such a wind), finally, the highest peak of that time, of all time, fell. It broke off completely at its base, and following the laws of gravity (as effective and powerful a force then as today, of course), tumbled from its pinnacle position and fell more than 20,000 feet, straight down. It collided with the expanding base of the mountain range, the Earth-shattering impact destroying several thousand acres. It finally came to rest (what remained intact) on a precipitous ledge, at 15,000 feet in elevation. The pyramid-shaped peak, much smaller now, sat precariously perched on the precipitous ledge for about 5 million years.

Nothing, absolutely nothing, is safe from time. The most inexorable natural law is that of entropy. Time and entropy mean change and decay—harsh, sometimes brutal, but always inevitable. The bruised, scarred, truncated, but still massive rock form, once a majestic peak, was now a victim of Nature's way. Nature, with its chief ally, time, at its side, works to degrade anything and everything that has substance and form. For better or for worse, Nature is ruthless, sometimes brutal, and always inevitable—but never without purpose.

While resting on the ledge, the giant rock, over the course of that 5 million years, was exposed to constantly changing conditions. For several thousand years, Earth's climate was unusually warm—almost tropical—everywhere. Throughout this warm era, the rock was not covered with ice and snow, but instead baked in intense heat; steamed in hot rain; and seared in the gritty, heavy windstorms that arose and released their abrasive fury, sculpting the rock's surface each day for more than 10,000 years.

Then came a pause in the endless windstorms and upheavals of the young planet, a span of time when the weather wasn't furnace-hot or arctic-cold, but moderate. The rock was still exposed to sunlight, but at lower temperatures; to rainfall at increased levels; to fewer but more furious windstorms. The climate remained that way for some years, then the cycle repeated itself: arctic cold, moderately warm, furnace hot—and the cycle continued.

During the last of these cycles the rock, considerably affected by physical and chemical exposure, was reduced in size and shape even more. Considerably smaller now than when it landed on the ledge, and a mere pebble compared to its former size, it fell again, 8,000 feet to the base of the mountain range, coming to rest on a bed of talus. Reduced in size still more, it remained on its sloping talus bed for several thousand more years.

Somewhere around 15,000 BC, the rock form, continuously exposed to chemical and mechanical weathering, its physical structure weakened by its long-ago falls, fractured, split—broke into rocks of ever-decreasing size, until the largest intact fragment left from the original rock was no bigger than a four-bedroom house. But change did not stop, and neither did time, rolling on until (about the time the Egyptians were building their pyramids) the rock was reduced, by this long, slow decaying process, to roughly 10 feet square.

Over the next thousand years, the rock continued to decrease in size, wearing, crumbling, flaking away, surrounded by fragments of its former self, until it was about the size of a beach ball. Covered with moss and lichen, a web of fissures, tiny crevices, and fractures were now woven through the entire mass.

Over the next thousand or so years, via **bare rock succession**, what had once been the mother of all mountain peaks, the highest point on Earth, was reduced to nothing more than a handful of soil.

How did this happen? What is "bare rock succession?"

If a layer of soil is completely stripped off land by natural means (water, wind, etc.), anthropogenic means (tillage plus erosion), or cataclysmic occurrence (a massive landslide or earthquake), only after many years can a soil-denuded area return to something approaching its original state or a bare rock be converted to soil. But given enough time—perhaps a millennium—the scars heal over, and a new, virgin layer of soil forms where only bare rock once existed. We call the series of events that take place in this restoration process bare rock succession. It is indeed a true "succession," with identifiable stages. Each stage in the pattern dooms the existent community as it succeeds the state that existed before.

Bare rock, however it is laid open to view, is exposed to the atmosphere. The geologic processes that cause weathering break down the surface into smaller and smaller fragments. Many forms of weathering exist, and all effectively reduce bare rock surface to smaller particles or chemicals in solution.

Lichens appear to cover the bare rock first. These hardy plants grow on the rock itself. They produce weak acids that assist in the slow weathering of the rock surface. The lichens also trap wind-carried soil particles, which eventually produce a very thin soil layer—a change in environmental conditions that gives rise to the next stage in bare rock succession.

Mosses replace lichens, growing in the meager soil the lichens and weathering provide. They produce a larger growing area and trap even more soil particles, providing a moister bare rock surface. The combination of more soil and moisture establishes abiotic conditions that favor the next succession stage.

Now the seeds of herbaceous plants invade what was once bare rock. Grasses and other flowering plants take hold. Organic matter provided by the dead plant tissue is added to the thin soil, while the rock still weathers from below. More and more organisms join the community as it becomes larger and more complex.

By this time, the plant and animal community is fairly complicated. The next major invasion is by weedy shrubs that can survive in the amount of soil and moisture present. As time passes, the process of building soil speeds up as more and more plants and animals invade the area. Soon trees take root, and forest succession is evident. Many years are required, of course, before a climax forest will grow here, but the scene is set for that to occur (Tomera, 1989).

Today, only the remnants of the former, incomparable, pyramid-shaped peak are left. Soil: packed full of organic humus, that looks like mud when wet, and that when dry most people would think was just a handful of dirt.

Soil: What Is It?

In any discussion about soil (the third environmental medium), we must initially describe, explain, and define exactly what it is and why it is so important to us. Having stated the obvious, we must also clear up a major misconception about soil. People often confuse soil with dirt, but soil is not dirt. Dirt is misplaced soil—soil where we don't want it, contaminating our hands or clothes, tracked in on the floor. Dirt we try to clean up, and to keep out of our environment.

But **soil** is special—almost mysterious, critical to our survival, and whether we realize it or not, essential to our existence. We have relegated soil to an ignoble position. We commonly degrade it—we consider only feces a worse substance. But soil deserves better.

Before we move on, let's take another look at that handful of "dirt" our modern man is holding after the mountain peak was crafted into soil by the sure hand of Mother Nature over millions and millions of years.

What do we really have in hand when we reach down and grab a handful of "dirt?" We make the point that it isn't dirt, it's soil. But what is soil?

Perhaps nothing causes more confusion in communication among various groups of laypersons and professionals—environmental scientists, environmental engineers, specialized groups of Earth scientists, and engineers in general—than the word *soil.* Why? From the professional's perspective, the problem lies in the reasons that various groups study soils.

Pedologists (soil scientists) are interested in soil as a medium for plant growth. A corresponding branch of engineering soils specialists (soil engineers) look at soil as a medium that can be excavated with tools. *Geologists'* view of soil falls between those of pedologists and soil engineers—they are interested in soils and the weathering processes as past indicators of climatic conditions and in relation to the geologic formation of useful materials ranging from clay deposits to metallic ores.

How do we clear up the confusion? To answer, let's view that handful of soil from a different, but much more basic and revealing, perspective. Consider the following descriptions of soil to better understand what soil is, and why it is so important to us all:

1. A handful of soil is alive, a delicate, living organism, as lively as an army of migrating caribou and as fascinating as a flock of egrets. Literally teeming with life of incomparable forms, soil deserves to be classified as an independent ecosystem or, more correctly stated, as many ecosystems.
2. When we reach down and pick up a handful of soil, exposing Earth's stark bedrock surface, it should remind us, maybe startle some of us to the realization, that without its thin living soil layer, Earth is a planet as lifeless as our own moon.

If you still prefer to call soil dirt, that's okay. Maybe you view dirt in the same way as 1996 Newbery Award winner E. L. Konigsburg's character Ethan does:

> The way I see it, the difference between farmers and suburbanites is the difference in the way we feel about dirt. To them, the Earth is something to be respected and preserved, but dirt gets no respect. A farmer likes dirt. Suburbanites like to get rid of it. Dirt is the working layer of the Earth, and dealing with dirt is as much a part of farm life as dealing with manure: neither is user-friendly, but both are necessary (64).

Response Scenario 17.1.
Biomass Growth

Soils are crucial to life on Earth . . . soil quality determines the nature of plant ecosystems and the capacity of land to support animal life and society. As human societies become increasingly urbanized, fewer people have intimate contact with the soil, and individuals tend to lose sight of the many ways in which they depend upon soils for their prosperity and survival. The degree to which we are dependent on soils is likely to increase, not decrease, in the future. Of course, soils will continue to supply us with nearly all of our food and much of our fiber. On a hot day, would you rather wear a cotton shirt or one made of polyester? In addition, biomass grown on soils is likely to become an increasingly important source of energy and industrial feedstocks, as the world's finite supplies of petroleum are depleted over the coming century. The early signs of this trend can be seen in the soybean oil-based inks, the corn-starch plastics, and the wood alcohol fuels that are becoming increasingly important on the market. (Brady & Weil, 1996, 2)

RESPONSE

(i) Do you agree with the authors' assertion that biomass feedstocks may be the solution to our future energy needs?

Soil Basics

Soil is the layer of bonded particles of sand, silt, and clay that covers the land surface of the Earth. Most soils develop multiple layers. The topmost layer (**topsoil**) is the layer in which plants grow. This layer is actually an ecosystem composed of both biotic and abiotic components: inorganic chemicals, air, water, decaying organic material that provides vital nutrients for plant photosynthesis, and living organisms. Below the topmost layer (usually no more than a meter in thickness) is the **subsoil**, which is much less productive, partly because it contains much less organic matter. Below that is the **parent material**, the bedrock or other geologic material from which the soil is ultimately formed. The general rule of thumb is that it takes about 30 years to form one inch of topsoil from subsoil; it takes much longer than that for subsoil to be formed from parent material, the length of time depending on the nature of the underlying matter (Franck & Brownstone, 1992).

SOIL PROPERTIES

From the environmental scientist's viewpoint (regarding land conservation and remediation methodologies for contaminated soil remediation through reuse and recycling), four major properties of soil are of interest: texture, slope, structure, and organic matter. **Soil texture** is a given and cannot be easily or practically changed in any significant way. It is determined by the size of the rock particles (sand, silt, and clay particles) in the soil. The largest soil particles are gravel, which consists of fragments larger than 2.0 mm in diameter. Particles between 0.05 and 2.0 mm are classified as sand. Silt particles range from 0.002 to 0.05 mm in diameter, and the smallest particles (clay particles) are less than 0.002 mm in diameter. Though clays are composed of the smallest particles, those particles have stronger bonds than silt or sand, although once broken apart, they erode more readily. Particle size has a direct impact on erodibility. Rarely does a soil consist of only one single size of particle—most are a mixture of various sizes.

The **slope** (or steepness of the soil layer) is another given, important because the erosive power of runoff increases with the steepness of the slope. Slope also allows runoff to exert increased force on soil particles, which breaks them apart more readily and carries them farther away.

Soil structure (**tilth**) should not be confused with soil texture—they are different. In fact, in the field, the properties determined by soil texture may be considerably modified by soil structure. Soil structure refers to the way various soil particles clump together. The size, shape, and arrangement of clusters of soil particles called **aggregates** form larger clumps called **peds**. Sand particles do not clump; sandy soils lack structure. Clay soils tend to stick together in large clumps. Good soil develops small *friable* (easy to crumble) clumps. Soil develops a unique, fairly stable structure in undisturbed landscapes, but agricultural practices break down the aggregates and peds, lessening erosion resistance.

The presence of decomposed or decomposing remains of plants and animals (organic matter) in soil helps not only fertility, but also soil structure, and especially the soil's ability to store water. Live organisms—protozoa, nematodes, earthworms, insects, fungi, and bacteria—are typical inhabitants of soil. These organisms work to either control the population of organisms in the soil or aid in the recycling of dead organic matter. All soil organisms, in one way or another, release nutrients from the organic matter, changing complex organic materials into products that can be used by plants.

SOIL FORMATION

Soil is formed as a result of physical, chemical, and biological interactions in specific locations. Just as vegetation varies among biomes, so do the soil types that support that vegetation. The vegetation of the tundra and rain forest differs vastly from each other and from vegetation of the prairie and coniferous forest; soils differ in a like manner.

In the **soil forming process**, two related but fundamentally different processes occur simultaneously. The first is the *formation of soil parent materials* by weathering of rocks, rock fragments, and sediments. This set of processes is carried out in the **zone of weathering**. The end point is to produce parent material for the soil to develop in, referred to as C horizon material (see Figure 17.1). These processes apply in the same way to glacial deposits as to rocks. The second set of processes is the *formation of the soil profile* by soil forming processes, which changes the C horizon material into A, E, and B horizons. Figure 17.1 illustrates two soil profiles, one on hard granite and one on a glacial deposit.

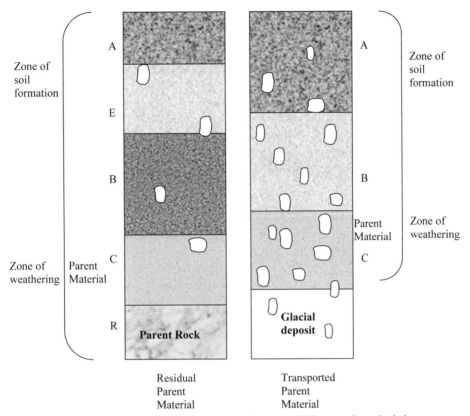

Figure 17.1. Soil profiles on residual and transported parent materials

Soil development takes time and is the result of two major processes: weathering and morphogenesis. **Weathering**, the breaking down of bedrock and other sediments that have been deposited on the bedrock by wind, water, volcanic eruptions, or melting glaciers, happens physically, chemically, or through a combination of both.

Physical weathering involves the breaking down of rock primarily by temperature changes and the physical action of water, ice, and wind. When a geographical location is characterized as having an arid desert biome, the repeated exposure to very high temperatures during the day, followed by low temperatures at night, causes rocks to expand and contract and eventually to crack and shatter. At the other extreme, in cold climates, rock can crack and break as a result of repeated cycles of expansion of water in rock cracks and pores during freezing and contraction during thawing. Another example of physical weathering occurs when various vegetation types spread their roots and grow, and the roots exert enough pressure to enlarge cracks in solid rock, eventually splitting the rock. Plants such as mosses and lichens also penetrate rock and loosen particles.

In addition to physical weathering, bare rocks are subjected to *chemical weathering*, which involves chemical attack and dissolution of rock. Accomplished primarily through oxidation via exposure to oxygen gas in the atmosphere, acidic precipitation (after having dissolved small amounts of carbon dioxide gas from the atmosphere), and acidic secretions of microorganisms (bacteria, fungi, and lichens), chemical weathering speeds up in warm climates and slows down in cold ones.

Physical and chemical weathering don't always (if ever) occur independently of each other. Instead, they normally work in combination, and the results can be striking. A classic example of the power of their simultaneous actions can be seen in the ecological process known as bare rock succession. The final stages of soil formation consist of the processes of **morphogenesis**, or the production of a distinctive **soil profile** with its constituent layers or **horizons** (see Figure 17.1). The soil profile (the vertical section of the soil from the surface through all its horizons, including C horizons) gives the environmental scientist critical information. When properly interpreted, soil horizons can provide warning of potential problems in using the land and tell much about the environment and history of a region. The soil profile allows us to describe, sample, and map soils.

Soil horizons are distinct layers, roughly parallel to the surface, that differ in color, texture, structure, and content of organic matter (see Figure 17.1). The clarity with which horizons can be recognized depends on the relative balance of the migration, stratification, aggregation, and mixing processes that take place in the soil during morphogenesis. In **podzol-type soils,** striking horizonation is quite apparent; in **vertisol-type soils**, the horizons are less distinct. When horizons are studied, they are each given a letter symbol to reflect the genesis of the horizon (see Figure 17.1).

Certain processes work to create and destroy clear soil horizons. Formation of soil horizons that tend to create clear horizons by vertical redistribution of soil materials include the leaching of ions in the soil solutions, movement of clay-sized particles, upward movement of water by capillary action, and surface deposition of dust and aerosols. Clear soil horizons are destroyed by mixing processes that occur because of organisms, cultivation practices, creep processes on slopes, frost heave, and swelling and shrinkage of clays, which are all part of the natural soil formation process.

Soil Pollution

Soil fertility is a major concern, not only throughout the United States but worldwide. The impacts on soil fertility of agricultural practices (erosion, salination, and waterlogging) are well known, well studied, and well documented. Remediation practices are also known and are actually in place in many locations throughout the globe. Indeed, solving problems related to soil fertility has received considerable attention, driven not only by a growing and hungry worldwide population, but also by economics. However, one major problem related to soil fertility has only recently become apparent, important, and critical in the human population's continuing fight to maintain soil for its primary purpose (as pointedly and correctly stated by the World Resource Institute: "its ability to process nutrients into a form usable by plants"). This "recent" problem is soil contamination or pollution.

Soil pollution generated by industrial contamination, management of Superfund sites, exploration and production, mining, and nuclear industrial practices, among others, is having impacts on soil quality that we have only recently begun to comprehend. Complicating the problem is that soil pollution remains difficult to assess. However, some evidence clearly indicates the impact of a few industrial practices related to soil pollution. For example, we know that petroleum-contaminated soil affects the largest number of sites and is the largest total volume of contaminated material. However, the volume of petroleum-contaminated soil that is either discovered or is generated each year is not consistently tracked on a local basis, so this total is unknown. We also know, from the evidence (e.g., in Oklahoma, contaminated soil accounts for about 90% of the waste generated as a one-time occurrence), that the overall amount of contaminated soil generated can be staggering (Testa, 1997).

Pollution of soil and water is a problem common to all human societies. Throughout the history of civilization, people have probably had little problem recognizing surface water contamination. Treatment of surface water for drinking became common in the late 19th century, and health problems linked to impure drinking water in developed countries are now rare. Underdeveloped countries, however, are still faced with a lack of safe drinking water.

Only in the past several decades has a new problem come to light, literally and figuratively: contamination of the soil and its underground environment. In developed countries, this problem is much more serious because of their history of industrialization and the wide range of hazardous materials and other chemicals that have been introduced, either by design or accident, to the underground environment. Ignorance—more than intent—is the culprit. We were ignorant in the sense that we did not comprehend the degree to which contaminants could migrate through the soil, the damage they could do to the soil medium and the groundwater under its "protective" surface, or the difficulty we would encounter in tracing and removing most contaminants after discovery.

Starting with the most contaminated sites, the response in developed countries to underground contamination has been a massive effort to define the extent of contamination and to remediate the subsurface. This response has been driven by governmental regulations dealing with waste handling and disposal and many other potentially contaminating activities.

The range of activities that cause underground contamination is much larger than most environmental scientists would have guessed even a few years ago. We briefly discuss these activities in the sections that follow.

Soil quality problems originating on the surface include natural atmospheric deposition of gaseous and airborne particulate pollutants; infiltration of contaminated surface water; land disposal of solid and liquid waste materials; stockpiles, tailing, and spoil; dumps; salt spreading on roads; animal feedlots; fertilizers and pesticides; **accidental spills**; and composting of leaves and other yard wastes.

Though we do not discuss them in detail in this text, note that other sources of soil contamination relate to petroleum products. These other sources include direct disposal of used oils on the ground by individuals or industries; seepage from landfills, illegal dumps, and unlined pits, ponds, and lagoons; and spills from transport accidents. Even auto accidents make contributions to the soil burden (Tucker, 1989).

In this section, we focus on both the **surface origins** of soil contaminants and the **industrial practices** that can contaminate soil; in the next section we focus on the concepts of remediation and resource recovery.

Note: The following discussion (also presented in chapter 3 and is repeated here due to its importance) focuses on contamination originating on the land surface. However, note that soil and subsurface contamination may also originate below ground, but above the water table, from septic tanks, landfills, sumps and dry wells, graveyards, USTs, leakage from underground pipelines, and other sources. In addition, soil, the subsurface, and groundwater contamination may also originate below the water table from mines, test holes, agricultural drainage wells and canals, and other sources.

GASEOUS AND AIRBORNE PARTICULATE POLLUTANTS

We don't commonly associate soil with being a prominent member of the biogeochemical cycles—carbon, nitrogen, and sulfur cycles—but we should, because it is. Not only is soil a prominent part of the rapid, natural cycles of carbon, nitrogen, and sulfur, but along with these cycles, soil has a strong and important interface with the atmosphere. Consider the nitrogen cycle, in which nitrates and ammonium ions in rainwater are absorbed by plant roots and soil microorganisms and converted into amino acids or gaseous N_2 and N_2O, which diffuse back to the atmosphere. N_2 uptake and conversion to amino acids (**nitrogen fixation**) by **symbiotic** and free-living soil microorganisms balances this loss of gaseous nitrogen. NO, NO_2, and NH_3 (other nitrogen gases) are also emitted and absorbed by soils. Soil reactions are major determinants of trace gas concentrations in the atmosphere.

Air pollutants—sulfur dioxide, hydrogen sulfide, hydrocarbons, carbon monoxide, ozone, and atmospheric nitrogen gases—are absorbed by soil. Because the reactions are subtle, they have often been discounted in importance when environmentalists assess air pollution damage. Sulfur dioxide in arid regions is probably the most obvious example of direct soil absorption. The basicity of arid soils makes them an active sink for sulfur dioxide and other acidic compounds from the atmosphere.

Two classic examples of **airborne particulate soil contamination** are the accumulation of heavy metals around smelters and soils in urban areas that are contaminated by exhaust fumes associated with auto emissions. These two soil polluters are serious in localized areas, but otherwise are generally thought to be minor.

INFILTRATION OF CONTAMINATED SURFACE WATER

Often wells are intentionally installed near streams and rivers to induce recharge from the water body and to provide high yield with low drawdowns. Occasionally, if the stream or river is polluted, contamination of the soil-water well field can result. This process normally occurs when a shallow water supply well draws water from the alluvial aquifer adjacent to the stream. The cone of depression imposed by pumping the well or well field creates a gradient on the water table directed toward the well, pulling or drawing the polluted water through and contaminating the well field and well.

LAND DISPOSAL OF SOLID AND LIQUID WASTE MATERIALS

Land disposal, stockpiling, or land-applying wastes or materials, including liquid and sludge (biosolids) wastes from sewage treatment plants (nearly half of the municipal sewage biosolids produced in the United States is applied to the soil, either for agricultural purposes or to remediate land disturbed by mining and other industrial activities), food processing companies, and other sources, have become common practices. The purpose is twofold: to serve as a means of disposal and provide beneficial use/reuse of such materials as fertilizers for agricultural lands, golf courses, city parks, and other areas. The objective is to allow biological and chemical processes in the soil, along with plant uptake, to break down the waste products into harmless substances. In many cases, such practices are successful. However, a contamination problem may arise if any of the wastes are water-soluble and mobile, which could allow them to be carried deep into the subsurface. If the drainage or seepage area is underlain by shallow aquifers, a groundwater contamination problem may arise.

STOCKPILES, TAILINGS, AND SPOILS

Stockpiles of certain chemical products can contribute to soil and subsurface contamination. Stockpiling road salt, for example, is a common practice used by many local highway departments and some large industries as a precautionary measure to treat snow- and ice-covered surfaces in winter. **Tailings** are usually produced by mining activities and commonly contain materials (asbestos, arsenic, lead, and radioactive substances) that present a health threat to humans and other living organisms. Remember that tailings from mining operations may contain contaminants, including sulfide, which, when mixed with precipitation, form sulfuric acid. As the chemically altered precipitation runs off or is leached from the tailing piles, it infiltrates the surface layer, contaminates soil, and ultimately may reach groundwater. **Spoil** is generally the result of excavations such as road-building operations, where huge amounts of surface cover are removed, excavated, and piled, then moved somewhere else. Problems with spoil are similar to the tailing problems: Precipitation removes materials in solution from the spoil by percolating (leaching) any contaminants from the spoil. Those contaminants find their way into the soil and ultimately into shallow aquifers.

DUMPS

Until recently, a common waste disposal practice was to take whatever we didn't want anymore and just dump it somewhere, anywhere out of sight. Today, uncontrolled dumping is prohibited in most industrialized countries, but the "old" dumping sites can contain just about anything and may still constitute a threat of subsurface contamination. Another problem that is still with us is "**midnight dumping**." Because dumping today is controlled and regulated, many disposers attempt to find ways to "get rid of junk." Unfortunately, much of this "junk" consists of hazardous materials and toxins that end up finding their way into and through soil to aquifers. Another illegal disposal practice has developed in some industries because of the high cost involved with proper disposal. This practice, commonly called "immaculate conception," involves leaving unmarked drums or other containers of unknown wastes on loading docks or elsewhere in industrial facilities. These vessels of toxic junk end up being thrown out with the common trash, and their contents eventually percolate through the soil to an aquifer.

SALT SPREADING ON ROADS

In northern climates, especially in urban areas, spreading deicing salts on highways is a widespread practice. In addition to causing deterioration of automobiles, bridges, and the roadway itself and adversely affecting plants growing alongside a treated highway or sidewalk, salt contamination quickly leaches below the land surface. Because most plants cannot grow in salty soils, the productivity of the land decreases. Continued use can lead to contamination of wells used for drinking water.

ANIMAL FEEDLOTS

Animal feedlots are a primary source of nonpoint surface water pollution. They are also significant contributors to groundwater pollution. Because animal waste in feedlots literally piles up and is stationary (sometimes for extended periods), runoff containing contaminants may not only enter the nearest surface water body, but may also seep into the soil, contaminating it. If the contaminated flow continues unblocked through the subsurface, the flow may eventually make its way into shallow aquifers.

FERTILIZERS AND PESTICIDES

Fertilizers and pesticides have become the mainstays of high-yield agriculture. They have also had significant impacts on the environment, with each yielding different types of contaminants.

When we apply fertilizers and pesticides to our soil, are we treating the soil—or poisoning it? This question is relatively new to us, one we are still trying to definitively answer. One thing is certain: With fertilizer and pesticide application and the long-term effects of such practices, the real quandary is that we do not know what we do not know. We are only now starting to see and understand the impact of using these chemicals. We have a lot to learn. Let's take a look at a few of the known problems with using chemical fertilizers and pesticides.

Nitrogen **fertilizers** are applied to stimulate plant growth, but often in greater quantities than plants can use at the time of application. Nitrate, the most common chemical form of these fertilizers, can easily leach below the plant root zone through rainfall or irrigation. Once it moves below the root zone, it usually continues downward to the water table.

When we put total dependency upon chemical fertilizers, they can change the physical, chemical, and biotic properties of the soil—another serious problem.

Pesticides (any chemicals used to kill or control populations of "unwanted" animals, fungi, or plants) are not as mobile as nitrate, but they are toxic at much lower concentrations. The perfect pesticide would be inexpensive, affect only the target organism, have a short half-life, and break down into harmless substances. However, as of yet we have not developed the perfect pesticide, and herein lies a multifaceted problem. Pesticides used in the past—and some of those being used today—are very stable, are very persistent, and can become long-term problems. They may also be transported from the place of original application to other parts of the world by wind or ocean currents.

Another problem associated with persistence in use of pesticides is that they may accumulate in the bodies of organisms in the lower trophic levels. Recall that when a lower trophic level animal receives small quantities of certain pesticides in its food and cannot eliminate them, the concentration within the organism increases. When lower trophic level organisms accumulate higher and higher amounts of materials within their bodies, **bioaccumulation** takes place. Eventually, this organism may pass on its accumulation to higher trophic level organisms, and those bioaccumulated toxins pass up the food chain to the highest levels.

ACCIDENTAL SPILLS

Accidental spills of chemical products can be extremely damaging to any of the three environmental media—air, water, and soil. Disturbingly common, chemical spills in the soil medium that are not discovered right away may allow the contaminant to migrate into and through the soil (contaminating it) to the water table. As an oversimplified general rule of thumb, we can say that the impact of a chemical spill in soil (or any other medium) is directly related to the concentration present at the point and time of release, the extent to which the concentration increases or decreases during exposure, and the time over which the exposure continues.

COMPOSTING OF LEAVES AND OTHER WASTES

Composting, a common practice of many homeowners (especially gardeners), has proven its worth as an environmentally friendly way to dispose of, or beneficially reuse, common waste products. When the feed material (leaves, twigs, and other organics) have been treated with chemical pesticides and some fertilizers, however, composting this material may be harmful to the soil. In the composting process, the organic material is degraded via a curing process that occurs over time. When water is intentionally added with a garden hose or by precipitation, any chemicals present can be washed or leached from the decaying organic material and drain into the soil, contaminating it.

Industrial Practices and Soil Contamination

Industrial practices that can contaminate soil include use of underground storage tanks (USTs) and contamination from oil field sites; chemical sites; geothermal sites; manufactured gas plants; mining sites; many other industrial activities; and, as a result of the First Gulf War, environmental terrorism.

CONTAMINATION FROM OIL FIELD SITES

People often repeat two clichés: "The past has a way of catching up with us" and "If we don't learn from past mistakes, we are doomed to repeat them." But sayings become clichés by being true. And they are certainly true when we consider the problems with soil contamination from oil field sites, a source of large volumes of hydrocarbon-contaminated soil resulting from past and existing oil fields. The extent of the impact of this problem is location-specific. For example, past and present-day oil exploration and production activities in remote parts of Oklahoma and Texas are not highly visible and thus not subject to public scrutiny. In these remote locations, disposing of hydrocarbon-contaminated soil is easy and inexpensive.

However, in highly urbanized locations (e.g., Los Angeles County, California, where more than 3,000 acres of prime real estate is being or has been exploited for petroleum), developers sit back and eagerly wait until existing fields reach their productive ends. When this occurs, the developers move right in and redevelop the prime real estate (prime in the sense of location and shortage of available real estate). The ill-informed developer quickly finds out, however, that just because the well runs dry does not mean that the land can immediately be developed for marketing. In these areas, disposal of contaminated soils has emerged as a serious and expensive undertaking.

On or near petroleum-producing properties, the primary sources of soil contamination include oil wells, sumps, pits, dumps, leakage from aboveground storage tanks, and leakage and/or spillage. Secondary sources include USTs, transformers, piping ratholes, well cellars, and pumping stations. In addition, the large stationary facilities used for the refining of petroleum have the potential to cause chronic pollution by the discharge of hydrocarbon-laden wastewaters and frequent small spills. The primary hazardous constituents associated with oil field properties include drilling mud and constituents, methane, and crude oil. When crude contains certain constituents above maximum contaminant levels—arsenic, chloride, chromium, lead, polychlorinated biphenols (PCBs)—and has a flash point less than the minimum standard set by American Society for Testing and Materials (ASTM) for recycled products, it may be considered a hazardous waste.

Close to many oil fields are complete handling and processing ancillaries—refineries, terminals, and pipelines—which also contribute to the overall volume of contaminated soil generated. Of primary concern are contaminants such as crude oil, refined products, and volatile organic compounds (VOCs).

CONTAMINATION FROM CHEMICAL SITES

The 1979 PEDCO-Eckhardt Survey (commonly referred to as the Eckhardt Survey) of more than 50 of the largest manufacturing companies in the United States reported that 16,843 tons of organic generated wastes were disposed. Of this total, more than 10 million tons were untreated (residing in landfills, ponds, lagoons, and injection wells). Approximately 0.5 million tons were incinerated, and approximately 0.5 million tons were either recycled or reused. The volume of contaminated soil as a result of one-time occurrence was not addressed in this survey.

Soil contamination from organic chemicals is a serious matter. Some of these compounds are biologically damaging even in small concentrations. When they do find their way into the soil, certain organic chemicals may kill or inhibit sensitive soil organisms, which can undermine the balance of the soil community. Once in the soil, the contaminant may be transported from the soil to the air, water, or vegetation, where it may be inhaled, ingested, or contacted, over a wide area, by a number of organisms. Because of their potential harm, controlling the release of organic chemicals and understanding their fate and effects in the soil are imperative.

CONTAMINATION FROM GEOTHERMAL SITES

Geothermal energy is natural heat generated beneath the Earth's surface. The Earth's mantle, 15 to 30 miles below the crust, is composed of a semimolten rock layer. Beneath the mantle, intense pressure, caused by molten rock of iron and nickel and decaying radioactive elements, helps warm the Earth's surface. Geothermal energy generally lies too deep to be harnessed, but in certain areas, where the molten rock has risen closer to the Earth's surface through massive fractures in the crust, underground reservoirs of dry steam, wet steam, and hot water are formed. As with oil deposits, these deposits can be drilled and their energy used to heat water, drive industrial processes, and generate electricity.

Generally, geothermal resources are more environmentally friendly than nuclear energy or fossil fuels. However, several drawbacks to geothermal energy use adversely impact the environment. As with oil field operations, geothermal operations provide another example of the close relationship between site usage and the potential for adverse environmental impact. The two constituents associated with geothermal plants that may be considered hazardous are brine and lead-mine scale (Testa, 1997).

Disposal of wastewater from geothermal wells containing **brine** (geothermal mineralizing fluids composed of warm to hot saline waters containing sodium, potassium, chloride, calcium, and minor amounts of other elements that may be harmful to plants and animals) is a major problem. The problem with **lead-mine scale** is more directly related to equipment failures—from scale buildup in pipes and other equipment—than environmental problems. However, when scale buildup leads to equipment failure (e.g., pipe rupture), this may lead to geothermal fluid spills, with the ultimate result of soil, air, and/or water contamination.

CONTAMINATION FROM MANUFACTURED GAS PLANTS

The manufacture of gas is not a new process. Since the late 1890s, manufactured gas plants (approximately 3,000 of them in the United States) have been in operation, been upgraded, or been completely redeveloped in one way or another. The environmental soil pollution problem associated with manufactured gas plants is the production and disposal of tarry substances, primarily produced in the coal gasification processes: coal carbonization, carburetted waste gas, natural gas, or a combination.

Other than the obvious mess that the production of any tar-like substance can produce, the main environmental problem with tars is that they are known to contain organic and inorganic compounds that are known or suspected carcinogens. The average volume of tar-contaminated soil averages 10,000 yd^3 per site (Testa, 1997).

CONTAMINATION FROM MINING SITES

According to the U.S. Departments of the Interior and Agriculture, since the mid-1860s, more than 3 million acres of land in the United States have been surface-mined for various commodities. Leading the list of commodities in acreage is mined coal, followed by sand and gravel, stone, gold, phosphate rock, iron ore, and clay.

Mining operations can give rise to land and water pollution. Sediment pollution via erosion is the most obvious problem associated with surface mining. Sediment pollution to natural surface water bodies is well documented. The Chesapeake Bay, for example, is no longer the fertile, oyster-producing environment it once was. Many environmentalists initially blamed the bay's decline on nutrient-rich substances and chemical pollutants. Recent studies of the bay's tributaries and the bay itself, however, indicate that oysters may be suffering (literally suffocating) from sedimentation rather than nutrient contamination.

Less known, because less studied, is the effect mining sediments and mining wastes (from mining, milling, smelting, and leftovers) have had and are having on soil. Typical mining wastes include acid produced by oxidation of naturally occurring sulfides in mining waste, asbestos produced in asbestos mining and milling operations, cyanide produced in precious metal heap-leaching operations, **leach liquors** produced during copper-dump leaching operations, metals from mining and milling operations, and radionuclides (radium) from uranium and phosphate mining operations.

One soil contaminant source is well known and well documented: **acid mine drainage**. Recall that acid formations occur when oxygen from the air and water reacts with sulfur-bearing minerals to form sulfuric acid and iron compounds. These compounds may directly affect the plant life that absorbs them or have an indirect effect on the flora of a region by affecting the soil minerals and microorganisms.

Another problem with mining is solid wastes. Metals are always mixed with material removed from a mine. These materials usually have little commercial value and thus must be discarded somewhere. The piles of rock and rubble are not only unsightly, they are also prone to erosion, and leaching releases environmental poisons into the soil.

CONTAMINATION FROM ENVIRONMENTAL TERRORISM

Many human activities that have resulted in environmental contamination have been the result of accidents or poor planning, poor decision making, inferior design, shoddy workmanship, ignorance, or faulty equipment. Whenever the public reads, hears about, or witnesses environmental contamination, we could assume that some human error was behind the contamination—at least until 1991.

Certainly the First Gulf War changed this perception. After the war, almost half of Kuwait's 1,500 oil wells were releasing oil into the environment. An estimated 11 million barrels of oil were either being burned or spilled each day in 600 wells. After the well capping operation got under way, and after more than 200 wells had been capped, this amount was reduced to approximately 6 million barrels by the end of summer. The harmful effects on the atmosphere and Persian Gulf were only part of the problem, however. Numerous pools of oil formed, some of them up to four feet deep, collectively containing an estimated 20 million barrels of oil (Andrews, 1992).

Response Scenario 17.2. Brownfields

The EPA defines brownfields as "property, the expansion, redevelopment, or reuse of which may be complicated by the presence or potential presence of a hazardous substance, pollutant, or contaminant" or as "abandoned, idled, or under-used industrial and commercial facilities where expansion or redevelopment is complicated by real or perceived environmental contamination." Plenty of sites are available for restoration; the EPA estimates that there are over 400,000 brownfields in the United States. Suitable restoration sites typically are contaminated at lower levels than those on the EPA's National Priority List of sites containing hazardous substances.

Restoring brownfield sites helps to slow down the development of "greenfield" sites for urban growth. Building on suburban and rural sites away from city centers encourages urban sprawl, and leaving the abandoned industrial sites vacant contributes to urban decay, causing economic, environmental, and social problems in the adjacent areas. However, liability concerns, concerns over expected clean-up levels, and delays in approved permits make redevelopment of brownfield sites a challenge for the public and private entities that wish to take on such projects.

Successful projects encourage others, however. The EPA has programs to support brownfield site development, and the Brownfield Revitalization Act of 2002 provides tools for the public and private sectors to promote sustainable brownfields clean-up and reuse through pilot programs and grants. This is proving to be an economically sound investment for many communities. The EPA's outlay for the Brownfields Program (under $700 million) resulted in leveraging more than $5 billion in brownfields clean-up and redevelopment funding from the private and public sectors and has created around 25,000 new jobs (http://www.epa.gov/brownfields/about.htm, March 23, 2004).

RESPONSE

(i) In your opinion, is the EPA's approach to cleaning up brownfields correct, or is some other methodology better suited for such mitigation?

The larger long-term problem of this blatant act of terrorism is twofold: the presence of the oil pools and huge volumes of petroleum-contaminated soil.

Soil Pollution Control Technology

Soil or **subsurface remediation** is a still-developing branch of environmental science and engineering. Because of the regulatory programs of the Comprehensive Environmental Response, Compensation, and Liabilities Act of 1980 (CERCLA; known as **Superfund**) and the Resource Conservation and Recovery Act of 1976 (RCRA; known as the "**cradle to grave act**"), remediation has not only been added to the environmental vocabulary, but also has become common and widespread. Just how common and widespread? To best answer this question, we note the response of venture capitalists in their attempts to gain a foothold in this new technological field. MacDonald points out:

> In the early 1990s, venture capitalists began to flock to the market for groundwater and soil cleanup technologies, seeing it as offering significant new profit potential. The market appeared large; not only was $9 billion per year being spent on contaminated site cleanup, but existing technologies were incapable of remediating many serious contamination problems. (1997, 560)

Note: From MacDonald's comments, soil remediation technology appears to be a booming enterprise, with unlimited potential, virtually a "can't miss" proposition—but inherent problems limit its potential. Remediation technology is a double-edged sword, as we discuss later.

Since CERCLA and RCRA were passed, numerous remediation technologies (also commonly known as **innovative clean-up technologies**) have been developed and become commercially available. We discuss these technologies in this chapter, especially those designed and intended to clean up sources of subsurface contamination caused by underground storage tanks (USTs). We focus on technology used in contamination from failed USTs, primarily because these units have been the cause of the majority of contamination events and remediation efforts to date. As a result, enormous volumes of information have been recorded on this remediation practice, by both regulators and the private industries involved with their clean-up.

Keep in mind that no matter what the contaminant, removing every molecule of contamination and restoring the landscape to its natural condition is highly unlikely (though it likely is the goal of the regulatory agency monitoring a particular UST clean-up effort).

USTs: THE PROBLEM

Previously we mentioned USTs and the subsurface contamination problems associated with them. In this section, we take a closer, more in-depth look at USTs and the remediation technologies used to clean up the contamination they produce.

No one knows for sure the exact number of UST systems installed in the United States. However, all present-day estimates range in the millions. Several thousand of these tanks—including ancillaries such as piping—are currently leaking.

Why are so many USTs leaking? They leak for several reasons: (1) corrosion, (2) faulty tank construction, (3) faulty installation, (4) piping failure, (5) overfills and spills, and (6) incompatibility of UST contents.

Corrosion Problems

The most common cause of tank failure is corrosion. Many older tanks were constructed of single shell, unprotected bare steel, and have leaked in the past (and have been removed, hopefully), are leaking at present, or (if not removed or rehabilitated) will leak in the future. If undetected or ignored, such a leak (even a small one) can cause large amounts of petroleum product to be lost to the subsurface.

Faulty Construction

As with any material item, USTs are only as good as their construction, workmanship, and materials. If a new washing machine is improperly assembled, it will likely fail, sooner rather than later. If a ladder is made of a material not suited to handle load bearing, it may fail, resulting in injury. You can probably devise your own list of possible failures resulting from poor or substandard construction or poor workmanship. We all have such a list, some lengthier than others.

USTs are no different than any other manufactured item. If they are not constructed properly, if workmanship is poor, they will fail. It's that simple, although the consequences of such failure are not so simple.

Response Scenario 17.3. Roundaway Tanks

AJ Roundaway Tank Company, located in Southport, Virginia, had been in the tank building business for 60 years. Roundaway built all sorts of tanks—large square tanks, rectangular tanks, round tanks, even special order, uniquely designed tanks.

In its earliest days, Roundaway exclusively built bare, unprotected steel tanks, until government agencies moved in with new regulations concerning tank leakage problems. When this occurred, Roundaway saw the writing on the wall. Building tanks that wouldn't rust or corrode would be best. So Abe Parsons, owner of Roundaway, did a little research and came up with the idea of retrofitting his plant, changing from making bare steel tanks (the old standbys) and bringing on line a relatively new process for making a tank out of new materials—materials that could not corrode, could not rust—and in the grand tradition of the *Titanic*—couldn't possibly leak.

The new tank building material Abe incorporated into his process is known as fiberglass reinforced plastic (FRP). Abe knew that other tank building companies had already started to manufacture and sell FRP tanks, so he had some catching up to do.

(continued)

Response Scenario 17.3. (*continued*)

He also had to modify his plant and train his fourteen employees in the new techniques. And that's what he did. Retrofitting the plant took about six months, and during this process his employees were thoroughly trained in all aspects of constructing FRP tanks.

Abe sold FRP tanks for several years, and his customers were pleased with his products. No complaints. Not yet, that is. Abe was pleased.

Abe's pleasure was soon shattered, however. A week before the Christmas holiday in 1991, with most of Abe's full-time employees on vacation, a skeleton crew of four workers was manning the plant. During this week, Roundaway received an order for 18 round 6,000-gallon fuel tanks for a petroleum storage facility. At first, Abe thought he could wait to start this project until after the first of the year. However, the customer made it clear that it needed delivery ASAP, and the sequence of events leading to "ultimate" failure began.

With only four workers on hand, Abe had to make a decision. Should he call in his other employees from their vacations so that they could fabricate their normal three tanks at one time—a fabrication process that would take them all day—or should he use the people he had on hand to fabricate one tank at a time? Unfortunately, Abe made the latter choice.

Of the four employees Abe had available, two were material formers who had about the same length of experience (less than two years); the other two employees were apprentices with only limited experience in FRP fabrication. Abe wasn't worried, though, because he would be right there to supervise the operation, and the workers would simply follow his directions.

This scenario might have worked, except that while Abe was definitely the owner of the company, he was not an expert in FRP tank fabrication, although he thought he was.

He gathered his four workers together and laid out his plan and instructions. "We'll be able to get a good head start on this order—and by the time the regulars get back, the ball will be rolling," he told them.

The ball got rolling in good fashion. Two of the workers worked the press forming devices used to form the plastic half-shells; another worker trimmed and measured the seams between the halves to ensure proper tolerance; the fourth worker, the newest member of the workforce with exactly three weeks' experience, mainly watched the other three at work.

After forming the pieces, the four workers fitted each piece in place, preliminary to the heat fusion process that binds the halves into a whole and the fiberglass wrap and resin treatment that came next. After wrapping the tank with fiberglass cloth over a bed of resin and letting it set up, three of the more experienced workers went back to starting the tank fabrication process on another tank, while the newest worker was given a pot of resin and tape pieces and told to place fiberglass and resin at the critical joint sections, smooth them out, and let them set before grinding off the rough edges.

The new employee was enthusiastic about being given the responsibility for doing something, anything—especially in this case, because making sure the joints are properly sealed is the most important part of the job. Abe, of course, kept his eagle eye on his young prodigy, just to make sure he didn't foul things up. It would have helped, however, if Abe had had some notion of just how the joints should be properly sealed.

The trouble began when they got to the fourth tank, on Christmas Eve day. The workers (including Abe) were anxious to finish the day's work and get home to their families.

Abe let the first worker leave early, at about ten o'clock that morning. He reasoned that the fourth tank's half-shells were already formed (they looked good to him). It just made good sense to let one of the tank formers go. He kept the assistant materials former a while longer, but let him go an hour later.

Abe and the other two workers went ahead and put the pieces together and taped them in place. The three of them worked to seal the top joint section first (a mistake—Abe's experienced workers would have worked both sides at once, ensuring a tight fit) until about 2:00 p.m. Then Abe decided that they would turn the tank over to the other side and let the rookie do a couple of hours more work on the second and final set of joints, while he and the other worker left for the holiday.

The rookie fabricator wanted to go home, too. But since he was new on the job, he reckoned that it was best to say nothing and do as he was told. Besides, he was proud. The owner must trust him, he reasoned. He would put the finishing touches on the tank all by himself, with no one looking over his shoulder.

The rookie worked alone and quite diligently. But then a problem developed. When he tried to force the other seam of the two half shells together tighter (to decrease the gap between them), they wouldn't budge more than half an inch or so. What was he going to do? At first he didn't know. Then, while sitting on a stool in front of the tank, drinking eggnog his girlfriend had fixed him, the solution dawned on him.

"I'll form a narrow plastic wedge and put it in the gap and use a bit more fiberglass and a bunch more resin. Then wait until it sets up, then I'll take off the rough spots—that's what I'll do." And that's what he did.

He filled in the three-quarter-inch gap with a thin strip of plastic held in place with a liberal dabbing of resin, then placed fiberglass cloth strips the entire length of the gap and heaped on several coats of resin. A couple of hours later, the rookie had a tank that was completely sealed—to the eye, anyway.

The rookie looked at his watch; noticed it was about two hours later than his regular quitting time, and moved quickly to put what he considered to be the last touches on the tank. He would come back after Christmas, grind down the rough spots, and coat it again.

The day after Christmas, the four workers who were not on extended vacation reported back to work. The rookie made sure that Abe and the workers got a look at his handiwork on the misfitted tank. They gave it only a cursory look, because at a glance it looked okay—and because they had other tanks to start on before the full shift reported to work the day after New Year's.

Abe told the rookie to go ahead, grind off the rough spots and add some more resin where needed, then they would move the tank out of the way and let it cure. Abe also told the rookie to stamp the tank with the stencil set. Part of the tank fabricating process included giving each tank a stenciled number and born-on date.

The rookie did as instructed, and after several more coats of resin, he hooked the tank to the overhead lift and moved it to the temporary curing and storage trunnions. Once it was on the trunnions, he applied the stenciled information as directed: Tank # 91-606—12/24/91 (meaning the 606th tank of 1991).

(continued)

Response Scenario 17.3. (continued)

Tank 91-606 cured for about a week, then the regular tank inspector, back from vacation, inspected it the day after New Year's. He noticed that the quality of workmanship didn't seem to be up to normal standards, but through bloodshot eyes it looked okay to him. His next move was to set the tank up for a hydrostatic (hydro) test to ensure that it didn't leak and that it could withstand a standard amount of pressure.

During the hydro, the inspector noticed that the air compressor had some type of problem—after the accumulator (where air is stored for ready use) emptied too soon, the compressor came on for a while and shut down before the accumulator filled, and it had to be restarted each time. He did restart it several times, but lunchtime was five minutes away and he had a heck of a hangover (New Year's Eve had been rough), so he told himself that the tank was okay—and besides, he would have to call an electrician to check out the compressor. He went to lunch.

After lunch, the inspector had seen just about all he wanted to see of tank 91-606, so he stamped it "inspected," signed the paperwork, and decided to take a smoke break and another aspirin.

Later that day, tank 91-606 was moved to the warehouse and put alongside the other tanks that would later be shipped to the petroleum storage facility when all 18 tanks were finished.

Two weeks passed, and the 18 tanks were completed, shipped, and delivered to the petroleum storage facility.

Tank 91-606 was the fifth tank put into the ground. Unfortunately, the contractor installing all the tanks (including 91-606) was more interested in getting the job done quickly, so he could move on to bigger and better things.

When 91-606 was craned from its storage pallet, it was jerked about, banged against the ground and two other tanks (slightly breaking the bond and forming a hairline crack in the patch that sealed the three-quarter-inch gap), and then unceremoniously deposited (dumped) into the ground—ground that had not been properly prepared, of course. Once the tank was semilevel and all pipes were connected, the backhoe moved in and buried it, then moved on to another tank.

Within two hours of having been filled with diesel fuel, tank 91-606 began to leak. At first the contents just seeped out of a slight crack in the section with the uneven three-quarter-inch gap, the one the rookie had filled to the hilt with fiberglass cloth and resin. About an hour later the slight crack enlarged to a gaping crack running the entire length of the tank along the uneven seam.

The petroleum storage facility noticed the leak within two days. Their regulation-required leak detection equipment had done its job; it had sounded an alarm, shown an indication that the tank was leaking. The problem was that the tank had not just leaked—but had emptied.

The petroleum storage facility had an environmental nightmare on its hands—6,000 gallons of diesel fuel were now in the ground. Complicating the situation, beneath the tank, the subsurface was composed of unconsolidated material that abruptly ended at a clay interface (aquitard). The clay stopped the flow of oil vertically, but did not stop it horizontally. The oil, following the path of least resistance, flowed horizontally (actually downgradient) until it came out at an outcropping a few feet above Cedar Creek, where it emptied, contaminating Cedar Creek.

Today, AJ Roundaway Tank Fabricating Company is no longer in business. The lawsuit—with litigation costs, the resulting penalty costs, and fines from local, state, and federal officials—finally sank the company.

RESPONSE

(i) Was the lawsuit really the cause of the company's failure, or was the causal factor something else? You be the judge; what is your opinion?

Faulty Installation

In Response Scenario 17.3, during installation of tank 91-606, we referred to mishandling the tank during installation and improper site preparation. Along with careful handling of the tank itself and any appurtenances, the tank bed must be specially prepared to receive the tank for burial.

Probably the most important step in tank installation is to ensure that adequate backfilling is provided to ensure that no possible movement of the tank can occur after it is placed in the ground. Any such movement might not only damage the tank (especially FRP tanks), but also could also jar loose any pipe connections or separate pipe joints. In our experience, failure to use special care in this installation process results in leaks.

Care must also be taken to ensure that underground leak detection devices are carefully and correctly installed. Obviously, if a tank is leaking, knowing it as soon as possible is best—so that remediation can be initiated quickly, before a minor spill turns into a nasty environmental contamination incident.

Piping Failures

We have mentioned tank-piping **failure** resulting from improper installation, but piping can fail in other ways as well. Before we discuss them, note that the U.S. Environmental Protection Agency (EPA) and other investigators clearly indicate that piping failure is one of the most common causes of "larger" UST spills.

If metal piping is used for connecting tanks together, to delivery pumps, to fill drops, or for whatever reason, the danger of corrosion from rust or from electrolytic action is always present. Electrolytic action occurs because threaded pipes (or other metal parts made electrically active by threading) have a strong tendency to corrode if not properly coated or otherwise protected. To prevent electrolytic action, usually **cathodic protection** is installed to negate the electrolytic action.

Piping failures are caused equally by poor workmanship, which usually appears around improperly fitted piping joints (both threaded and PVC types), incomplete tightening of joints, construction accidents, and improper installation of cover pad.

Spills and Overfills

All UST facilities are subject to environmental pollution occurring as the result of spills and overfill—usually the result of human error. Although the EPA has promulgated tank filling procedures in its 40 C.F.R. §280 regulations, and the National Fire Protection Association (NFPA) has issued its NFPA-385 Tank Filling Guidelines, spills from overfilling still occur frequently. Overfilling a UST is bad enough in itself, but the environmental contamination problem is further compounded when such actions occur repeatedly. Petroleum products or hazardous wastes can literally saturate the spill area and can intensify the corrosiveness of soils (Blackman, 1993).

How do UST spills from overfilling usually occur? We pointed out previously that the most common cause is human failure. See Response Scenario 17.4 for an example (an actual occurrence, but names and locations have been changed).

Response Scenario 17.4. Human Error

The tanker truck arrived at the plant site early Monday morning. The driver stopped her truck, got out, and walked over to the plant office. At the office, the plant clerk greeted her and asked how he could help. The driver stated that she had a load of #2 fuel oil to deliver and asked for directions to the receiving tank. The clerk said that it would be easier for the truck driver to follow him in her truck, and he walked to the tank and showed her exactly where it was located.

At the tank, the driver parked the truck, got out, and ran the filling hose from the truck to the filling port. She uncapped the filling port and inserted the measuring stick to determine the amount of fuel that was in the tank. After determining that the 5,000-gallon tank was almost empty, she inserted the hose nozzle into the fill port and then walked back to the truck, where she activated the truck's filling pump, which in turn charged the hose to the tank. When she had verified that the hose was secure (not leaking and in proper position), she activated the hose nozzle trigger device, and the tank began to fill.

She stood at the nozzle for a minute or two and then returned to the truck, got into the cab, lit up a cigarette, and peered off into space, in deep thought. If her eyes had been focused on objects in front of her, she would have seen the warning sign mounted to a five-foot pole just in front of her. However, she did not see the sign, and after a few puffs on the cigarette, she decided to rest her eyes. Within a few minutes, she was fast asleep.

Meanwhile, the tank steadily filled.

The sign shown in Figure 17.4 is a standard warning sign used at some facilities to alert delivery truck drivers that the facility is well aware of NFPA-385, which provides a list of guidelines directed at the proper procedures to use in the tank filling process. The driver was aware of these guidelines. She'd seen them (and even followed them properly) many times before—the ones stating that the driver must stay alert and in control of the filling process at all times and must stand within reach of the emergency shut-off device in case the tank overfills. She was aware of these requirements and usually paid attention to what she was doing, but familiarity with them—and confidence in her own abilities—lessened their power. She had never had a tank-overfilling problem in her six years on the job, so the guidelines weren't all that important to her anymore. And besides, her mind was elsewhere—soon lost in a fog called sleep.

About 30 minutes later, while the driver snored away, the tank filled to capacity and then overflowed to the only place it could, the grass-covered ground surrounding the tank area. Not until approximately 16,000 gallons of #2 fuel oil had overflowed and created a small lake around the filling area did anyone (a plant operator who just happened to walk by) notice that a lake of fuel oil was now covering what used to be a grassy area.

At first the operator just stood there, shocked. Surprised (to say the least) and somewhat hesitant about what to do, she quickly realized she needed to find out where the truck driver was—and she did. The operator found the driver laid out in the front seat of the truck cab—still sound asleep.

The operator yelled at the driver, shook her vigorously into consciousness (semiconsciousness), and stated the problem. The driver, a bit groggy, jumped from the truck and tripped the emergency switch to shut off the pump. It was too late, of course, but better late than wait until the entire truckload emptied.

The aftermath of this spill was routine. The plant manager, somewhat upset (as you might have guessed), informed the pertinent state regulatory agencies about the spill, while the plant superintendent called out the plant's HazMat team to respond to the spill.

The HazMat team (well-trained under NFPA 472-473 guidelines and OSHA's HAZWOPER standard) did the best they could to first contain the leak by using the plant's oil boom (too short to surround the entire leak area; subsequently they augmented it by shoveling dirt to build an earthen dike system surrounding the spill) and by using hand pumps and 55-gallon drums to pump the liquid pool dry—but most of the spill seeped into the ground.

The plant manager, after having notified all key parties about the spill, called in a local HazMat contractor to help with the clean-up. For the next three days, the contractor excavated the soil, which was deposited into dump truck after dump truck and hauled away for disposal, and when excavation had removed what appeared to be all of the contaminated soil, the 20-foot deep excavation was left open to "air out."

While the excavation was open, the plant manager hired a tank inspection company to come in and do a complete inspection of the tank. The tank integrity was still fine, so about a week later, the contractor came back with several loads of fill material and packed it in the excavated area. The plant manager ordered the plant superintendent to plant more grass and add a couple of young trees to the new soil. The total monetary cost of this particular incident was $19,855. The plant paid the bill and was later reimbursed by the fuel truck company. The truck driver was fired. Rumor has it that she found a new job within a week. She's working in a service station, pumping gas into cars.

RESPONSE

(i) That the incident described above could actually occur may seem silly to some, ridiculous to others, criminal to regulators, and embarrassing to those involved. Isn't this often the case whenever human error comes into play? However you describe this incident, a few things are certain: It happened—and it continues to happen. It will happen again. How would you prevent such an incident from occurring in the future?

Compatibility of Contents and UST

Obviously, materials must be stored in containers that will contain and hold them. We must not forget that placing highly corrosive materials into containers not rated to contain them is asking for trouble. New chemicals (including fuels) are being developed all the time. Usually the motive for developing such fuels is to achieve improved air quality, but improving air quality does little good at the expense of the other two environmental media (water and soil)—if a new fuel that is incompatible with a particular storage tank threatens them.

Many of the USTs presently in use are FRP tanks put in place to replace the old, unprotected, bare steel tanks. FRPs are rated (or can be modified using a different liner) to safely store the fuel products now in common use. The problem occurs when a new, exotic blend of fuel is developed and then placed in an incompatible FRP-type tank.

Common incompatibility problems that have been observed include blistering, internal stress, cracking, or corrosion of the underfilm. To help prevent FRP-constructed or -lined tank problems, the American Petroleum Institute has created a standard that should be referred to whenever existing tanks are to be used for different fuel products.

Risk Assessment

The problems associated with hydrocarbon spillage or disposal are complex. This complexity is somewhat eased by using the **risk assessment process**, which enables scientists, regulatory officials, and industrial managers to evaluate the public health risks associated with hydrocarbon releases (or any other toxic chemical release) to soil and groundwater. The risk assessment process consists of the following steps:

1. **Toxicological evaluation (hazard identification):** This should answer the question: "Does the chemical have an adverse effect?" The factors that should be considered during the toxicological evaluation for each contaminant include routes of exposure (ingestion, absorption, and inhalation), types of effects, reliability of data, dose, mixture effects, and the strength of evidence supporting the conclusions of the toxicological evaluation.
2. **Dose–response evaluation**: Once a chemical has been toxicologically evaluated and the result indicates that it is likely to cause a particular adverse effect, the next step is to determine the potency of the chemical. The **dose–response** curve is used to describe the relationship between degree of exposure to a chemical (dose) and the magnitude of the effect (response) in the exposed organism.
3. **Exposure assessment:** This is conducted to estimate the magnitude of actual and/ or potential human exposures, the frequency and duration of these exposures, and the pathways by which humans will potentially be exposed.
4. **Risk characterization:** The final step in risk assessment, this is the process of estimating the incidence of an adverse health effect under the conditions of exposure found and described in the exposure assessment (Ehrhardt et al, 1986; ICAIR, 1985; Blackman, 1993).

Exposure Pathways

Along with performing and evaluating the findings from the four steps involved in risk assessment, it is important to determine exposure pathways resulting from the performance of the remediation option chosen to mitigate a particular UST leak or spill. Exposure pathways may be encountered during site excavation, installation, operations, maintenance, and monitoring. They consist of two categories: (1) direct human exposure pathways and (2) environmental exposure pathways. These two categories are subdivided into primary and secondary exposure pathways.

Primary exposure pathways directly affect site operations and personnel (e.g., skin contact during soil sampling) or directly affect clean-up levels, which must be achieved by the remedial technology (e.g., when soil impact is the principal issue at a site, soil impact sets the clean-up level and corresponding time frame when clean-up will cease).

Secondary exposure pathways occur as a minor component during site operations (e.g., wind blown dust) and exhibit significant decreases with time as treatment progresses (EPRI-EEI, 1988).

Remediation of UST-Contaminated Soils

Before petroleum-contaminated soil from a leaking UST can be remediated, preliminary steps must be taken. **Soil sampling** is important, not only to confirm that a tank is actually leaking, but also to determine the extent of contamination. Any petroleum product remaining within a UST should be pumped out into above-ground holding tanks or containers before the tank area is excavated and the tank removed. Any residual fuel is removed before excavation because of potential damage to the tank during removal.

When site sampling is completed, the range and extent of contamination determined, and the UST removed, the type of remediation technology to employ in the actual clean-up effort must be determined.

Various organizations, environmental industries, and regulatory agencies have performed technical investigations and evaluations of the various aspects of remediation methods for petroleum hydrocarbons in soil, fate and behavior of petroleum hydrocarbons in soil, and economic analyses. Certainly one of the industries in the forefront of conducting such studies is electric utilities. This particular industry owns and operates many USTs, as well as facilities for using, storing, or transferring petroleum products, primarily motor and heating fuels.

The EPA has developed federal regulations for reducing and controlling environmental damage from UST leakage, and many state and localities have developed and implemented strict regulations governing USTs and remedial actions for product releases to soil and groundwater. As a result, the Electric Power Research Institute (EPRI), the Edison Electric Institute (EEI), and the Utility Solid Waste Activities Group (USWAG), in a cooperative effort, conducted a technical investigation. From their findings, they developed a report entitled *Remedial Technologies for Leaking Underground Storage Tanks* (1988), which focuses on one of the major components of the technical investigation. The report describes and evaluates available technologies for remediating soil and groundwater that contain petroleum products released from a UST leak.

The EPRI-EEI/USWAG report provides a general introduction to state-of-the-art clean-up technology and serves as a reference for determining feasible methods, a description of their basic elements, and discussion of the factors to be considered in their selection and implementation in a remedial program.

The available technologies for remediating soil and groundwater containing petroleum products listed by EPRI-EEI/USWAG are divided into two categories: in situ treatment and non-in situ treatment. **In situ** treatment refers to treatment of soil in place. The remedial technologies are further subdivided into the following categories:

- **In Situ Technologies**
  Volatilization
  Biodegradation
  Leaching and chemical reaction
  Passive remediation
  Isolation/containment
- **Non-In Situ Technologies**
  Land treatment
  Thermal treatment
  Asphalt treatment
  Solidification/stabilization
  Chemical extraction
  Excavation

We briefly describe each of these remedial technologies in the following sections, using information adapted from the EPRI-EEI/USWAG study (the standard reference since 1988).

IN SITU TECHNOLOGIES

The remedial technologies discussed in the following subsections are only those that can be used in place at the site. Because no excavation is required, exposure pathways are minimized to those that result from the actual streams produced by the in situ technologies, not those associated with the handling and transport involved in the non-in situ technologies discussed in the subsequent section.

In Situ Volatilization

In situ volatilization (ISV)—or in situ air stripping—uses forced or drawn air currents through in-place soil to remove volatile compounds. It has a successful track record for both effectiveness and cost efficiency.

A common ISV system used to enhance subsurface ventilation and volatilization of volatile organic compounds consists of the following operations:

1. A pre-injection air heater warms the influent air to raise subsurface temperatures and increase the volatilization rate.
2. Injection and/or induced draft forces establish airflow through the unsaturated zone.
3. Slotted or screened pipe allows airflow through the system and restricts entrainment of soil particles.
4. A treatment unit (usually activated carbon) recovers volatilized hydrocarbon, minimizing air emissions.
5. Miscellaneous airflow meters, bypass and flow control valves, and sampling ports incorporated into the design facilitate airflow balancing and system efficiency assessment.

Certain factors influence volatilization of hydrocarbon compounds from soils. These factors fall into four categories: soil, environment, chemical, and management (Jury, 1986).

Soil Factors

Soil factors include water content, porosity/permeability, clay content, and adsorption site density:

1. **Water content** influences the rate of volatilization by affecting the rates at which chemicals diffuse through the vadose zone. An increase in soil water content decreases the rate at which volatile compounds are transported to the surface via vapor diffusion.
2. **Soil porosity** and **permeability** factors relate to the rate at which hydrocarbon compounds volatize and are transported to the surface. A function of the travel distance and cross-sectional area available for flow, diffusion distance increases and cross-sectional flow area decreases with decreasing porosity.
3. **Clay content** affects soil permeability and volatility. Increased clay content decreases soil permeability, which inhibits volatilization.
4. **Adsorption site density** refers to the concentration of sorptive surface available from the mineral and organic contents of soils. An increase in adsorption sites indicates an increase in the ability of the soils to immobilize hydrocarbon compounds in the soil matrix.

Environmental Factors

Environmental factors include temperature, wind, evaporation, and precipitation:

1. **Temperature** rise increases the volatilization of hydrocarbon compounds.
2. **Wind** increase decreases the boundary layer of relatively stagnant air at the ground–air interface, which can assist volatilization.

3. **Evaporation** of water at the soil surface is a factor controlling the upward flow of water through the unsaturated zone, which can assist volatilization.
4. **Precipitation** provides water for infiltration into the vadose zone.

Chemical Factors

Not surprisingly, **chemical factors** are critical players in affecting the way in which various hydrocarbon compounds interact with the soil matrix. Solubility, concentration, octanol-water participating coefficient, and vapor pressure are the primary chemical properties that affect the susceptibility of chemicals to the in situ volatilization process.

Management Factors

Management factors related to soil management techniques (fertilization, irrigation) decrease leaching, increase soil surface contaminant concentrations, assist volatilization, or maximize soil aeration.

Environmental Effectiveness of ISV

Site-specific conditions (soil porosity, clay content, temperature, and so forth) drive the effectiveness of in situ volatilization techniques. Pilot studies and actual experience confirm the following:

- In situ volatilization has been successful for remediation in unsaturated zones containing highly permeable, sandy soils with little or no clay.
- Recovery periods are typically on the order of 6 to 12 months.
- Gasoline (which is light and volatile) has the greatest recovery rate.
- In situ volatilization can be used in conjunction with product recovery systems.
- Because ultimate clean-up levels are site-dependent and cannot be predicted, they are usually set by regulatory agencies.

In Situ Biodegradation

In situ biodegradation uses the naturally occurring microorganisms in soil to degrade contaminants to another form. Most petroleum hydrocarbons can be degraded to carbon dioxide and water by microbial processes (Grady, 1985). For hydrocarbon removal, stimulating their growth and activities (primarily through the addition of oxygen and nutrients) enhances this process. Factors such as temperature and pH influence their rate of growth.

Based on documentation and significant background information related to successful land treatment of refinery waste, biodegradation has proven its worth as an efficient and cost-effective method for the reduction of hydrocarbons in soil.

Heyse, James, and Wetzel (1986) describe the biodegradation process as follows:

1. A submersible pump transports groundwater from a recovery well to a mixing pump.

2. Nutrients, including nitrogen, phosphorus, and trace metals, are added to the water in a mixing tank. These nutrients are then transported by the water to the soil, supporting microbial activity.
3. Hydrogen peroxide is added to the conditioned groundwater from the mixing tank just prior to reintroduction to the soil. As hydrogen peroxide decomposes, it provides the needed oxygen for microbial activity.
4. Groundwater pumped to an **infiltration gallery** and/or injection well reintroduces the conditioned water to the aquifer or soils.
5. Groundwater flows from the infiltration galleries or injection wells through the affected area, then back to the recovery wells. The flow of the water should contact all soils containing degradable petroleum hydrocarbons.
6. The water is drawn to the recovery well and pumped to the mixing tank to complete the treatment loop.
7. Groundwater in which hydrocarbon concentrations have been reduced to very low levels is often sent through a carbon adsorption process for removal of the residual hydrocarbons.

Environmental Factors

The environmental factors that influence biodegradation in soils are temperature and microbial community:

1. **Temperature** is important in biodegradation of contaminants in soils. In general, biodegradation of petroleum fraction increases as temperatures increase (up to 104°F) from increased biological activity (Bossert & Bartha, 1984).
2. A **microbial community** capable of degrading the target compound is important in the biodegradation process. Most in situ biodegradation schemes make use of existing microbial populations; however, attempts have been made to supplement these populations with additional organisms or engineered organisms.

Chemical Factors

While biodegradation is impossible if substrate concentrations are too high, it relies on a substantial substrate (target compound) presence to ensure that microbes metabolize the target compound. Biodegradation is also limited by the solubility of a compound in water, because most microbes need moisture to acquire nutrients and avoid desiccation.

Soil Factors

The degradation of hydrocarbons in soil requires proper aerobic conditions. Moisture is also essential for microbial life—however, too much moisture (saturation) limits oxygen levels and can hinder biological activity. Bossert and Bartha (1984) report that moisture content between 50 and 80% of the water-holding capacity is considered optimal for aerobic activities. In the in situ biodegradation processes, oxygen transfer is a key factor; soils must be fairly permeable to allow this transfer to occur.

Another important soil factor is pH, which directly affects the microbial population supported by the soil. Biodegradation is usually greater in a soil environment with a pH of 7.8. Optimal biodegradation of petroleum hydrocarbons requires nutrients (nitrogen and phosphorus) in the proper amounts.

Environmental Effectiveness

The effectiveness of in situ biodegradation depends on the same site-specific factors as other in situ technologies, but the historical record for this technology is limited. However, several case studies suggest the following:

- In situ biodegradation is most effective for situations involving large volumes of subsurface soils.
- Significant degradation of petroleum hydrocarbons normally occurs in the range of 6 to 18 months (Brown, Norris, & Estray, 1986).
- In situ biodegradation has most often been used for the remediation of groundwater impacted by gasoline.
- Research suggests limited biodegradation of benzene or toluene may occur under anaerobic conditions (Wilson et al., 1986).
- In soils, the remedial target for in situ biodegradation could be in the low mg/L (ppm) level for total hydrocarbons (Brown, Norris, & Estray, 1986).

In Situ Leaching and Chemical Reaction

The **in situ leaching and chemical reaction** process uses water mixed with a surfactant (a surface-active substance—soap) to increase the effectiveness of flushing contaminated soils in the effort to leach the contaminants into the groundwater. The groundwater is then collected downstream of the leaching site through a collection system, for treatment and/or disposal.

Environmental Effectiveness

The in situ leaching and chemical reaction process is not commonly practiced. Little performance data on its environmental effectiveness exist.

In Situ Vitrification

The **in situ vitrification** process employs electrical current passed through electrodes (driven into the soil in a square configuration), which produces extreme heat and converts soil into a durable glassy material. The organic constituents are pyrolized in the melt and migrate to the surface, where they combust in the presence of oxygen. Inorganics in the soil are effectively bound in the solidified glass (Johnson & Cosmos, 1989).

Environmental Effectiveness

Organic materials are combusted and/or destroyed by the high temperatures encountered during the vitrification process. The in situ vitrification process is a developing technology. The jury is still out on whether it is environmentally effective.

In Situ Passive Remediation

The **in situ passive remediation process** is the easiest to implement and the least expensive, mainly because it involves no action at the site; however, it is generally unacceptable to the regulatory agencies. It relies on several natural processes to destroy the contaminant, including biodegradation, volatilization, photolysis, leaching, and adsorption.

Environmental Effectiveness

Because passive remediation depends on a variety of site-specific and constituent-specific factors, the environmental effectiveness of passive remediation must be decided on a case-by-case basis.

In Situ Isolation/Containment

As the name implies, isolation/containment methods are directed toward preventing migration of liquid contaminant or leachates containing contaminants. Accomplished by separating the contamination area from the environment and by installation of impermeable barriers to retain liquid containments within the site, successful application of these methods is usually contingent on the presence of an impervious layer beneath the contaminant to be contained and the attainment of a good seal at the vertical and horizontal surfaces.

In our experience, the containment devices discussed in this section adequately isolate the contamination. However, destruction of the contaminant is not accomplished.

Containment Methods

- **Slurry walls:** fixed underground physical barriers formed in an excavated trench by pumping slurry, usually a bentonite or cement and water mixture.
- **Grout curtains:** (similar to slurry walls) suspension grouts composed of Portland cement or grout, injected under pressure to form a barrier.
- **Sheet-piling:** rigid sheets, pilings of wood, steel, or concrete physically driven into the ground to form a barrier.

Environmental Effectiveness

Isolation/containment systems are effective in physically preventing or impeding migration, but the contaminant is not removed or destroyed.

NON-IN SITU TECHNOLOGIES

Unlike in-situ techniques, **non-in situ techniques** require the removal (usually by excavation) of contaminated soils. These soils can either be treated on-site or hauled off-site and treated. Another difference that must be taken into consideration when employing non-in situ techniques is the exposure pathways associated with the handling and/or transport of contaminated soil. The non-in situ technologies for soils discussed in this section include land treatment, thermal treatment, asphalt incorporation, solidification/stabilization, chemical extraction, and excavation.

Land Treatment

Land treatment or **land farming** is the process by which affected soils are removed and spread over an area to enhance naturally occurring processes, including volatilization, aeration, biodegradation, and photolysis. The land treatment process involves tilling and cultivating soils to enhance biological degradation of hydrocarbon compounds.

- The area used for land treatment is prepared by removing surface debris, large rocks, and brush.
- The area is graded to provide positive drainage and surrounded by a soil berm to contain runoff within the land treatment area.
- The pH is adjusted with lime (if necessary) to provide a neutral pH.
- If the site is deficient in nutrients, fertilizer is added.
- The petroleum-contaminated soil is spread uniformly over the surface of the prepared area.
- The contaminated material is incorporated into the top six to eight inches of soil (to increase contact with microbes) with a tiller, disc harrow, or other plowing device.
- More soils that contain petroleum products are applied at proper intervals to replenish hydrocarbon supply.
- Hydrocarbon and nutrient levels and soil pH are monitored to ensure that the hydrocarbons are properly contained and treated in the land treatment area.

Environmental Effectiveness

The effectiveness of land treatment or land farming is highly dependent on site-specific conditions. Several years of experience with treating petroleum compounds using this technology confirm the following:

- Land treatment is an effective means of degrading hydrocarbon compounds.
- Continuous treatment of petroleum-laden soils can result in accumulation of metals in the soil matrix.
- Ultimate degradation rates are site-dependent and cannot be predicted.

Thermal Treatment

Thermal treatment of contaminated soils requires special equipment, but is capable of providing complete destruction of the petroleum-laden contaminant. Affected soils are removed from the ground and exposed to excessive heat in one of various types of incinerators currently available. These include rotating kilns, fluidized bed incinerators, fixed kilns or hearths, rotating lime or cement kilns, and asphalt plants.

Environmental Effectiveness

High-temperature incineration for destruction of petroleum-product-laden soil is well documented. Destruction and removal efficiencies of 99% can be expected.

Asphalt Incorporation and Other Methods

Asphalt incorporation is a recently developed technology that goes beyond remediation, in the sense that the asphalt incorporation technique is actually a **reuse** and/or **recycling technology**, whereby the contaminant entrained in soil is employed in **beneficial reuse** (to make asphalt, cement products, and bricks), not just destroyed or disposed of.

Asphalt incorporation and other reuse/recycling technologies involve assimilation of petroleum-laden soils into hot or cold asphalt processes, wet or dry cement production processes, or brick manufacturing. During these processes, the petroleum-laden soils are mixed with other constituents to make the final product. In turn, the petroleum contaminants are either volatilized during some treatments or trapped within the substance, thereby limiting contaminant migration.

Asphalt Incorporation

The conversion of asphalt into asphalt concrete or bituminous concrete involves producing a material that is plastic when being worked and sets up to a specified hardness sufficient for its end use. The incorporation of contaminated soil into bituminous end products is accomplished by two conventional processes: **cold-mix asphalt** (CMA) and **hot-mix asphalt** (HMA) processes (Testa, 1997).

Cold-Mix Asphalt Processes (CMA)   The **cold-mix asphalt process** (commonly referred to as environmentally processed asphalt) is a mobile or in-place process. It uses soils contaminated with a variety of contaminants (including petroleum hydrocarbons) to serve as the fine-grained component in the mix, along with asphalt emulsion and specific aggregates to produce a wide range of cold-mix asphaltic products. The mix is usually augmented with lime, Portland cement, or fly ash to enhance stability of the end product. The mixing or incorporation method is accomplished with physically mixed-in-place methods for large quantities and windrowing for smaller quantities.

The CMA process has several advantages: (1) A variety of contaminants can be processed; (2) large volumes of contaminated soil can be incorporated; (3) it possesses flexible mix design and specifications; (4) it is a mobile process; (5) it has minimal weather restrictions; (6) it is cost effective; (7) the product can be stockpiled and used when needed; and (8) processing can occur on-site. The limitations of CMA are that (1) any volatiles present must be controlled, and (2) small volumes of contaminated soil may not be economically viable for mobile plants.

Hot-Mix Asphalt Processes (HMA)   The **hot-mix asphalt process** involves the incorporation of petroleum-laden soils into hot asphalt mixes as a partial substitute for aggregate. This mixture is most often applied to pavement. HMA is conventionally produced using either batch or drum mixing processes. In both of these processes, both mixing and heating are used to produce pavement material.

During the incorporation process, the mixture, including the contaminated soils (usually limited to 5% of the total aggregate feed at any one time), is heated. This causes volatilization of the more-volatile hydrocarbon compounds at various temperatures. Compound migration is limited by incorporating the remainder of the compounds into the asphalt matrix during cooling.

The advantages associated with using the HMA process are that (1) the time required to dispose of hydrocarbon-laden material is limited only by the size of the batching plant (material may be excavated and stored until it can be used); and (2) it can process small volumes of affected soil easily. The disadvantages include that (1) the compound must be applied immediately after processing; (2) it has potential for elevated emissions; (3) it has emission restrictions; and (4) incomplete burning of light-end hydrocarbons can affect the quality of end product.

Cement Production Process   Raw materials such as limestone, clay, and sand are incorporated into the **cement production process**. Once incorporated, these materials are usually fed into a rotary kiln. Contaminated soil may be introduced along with the raw materials or dropped directly into the hot part of the kiln. The mix is then heated to up to 2,700°F. Petroleum-laden soil chemically breaks apart during this process, whereas the inorganic compounds recombine with the raw materials and are incorporated into a clinker. The clinker results in dark, hard, golf-ball-sized nodules of rapidly formed Portland cement, which is mixed with gypsum and ground to a fine powder (Testa, 1997).

The advantages of the cement production process include that (1) the technology is in place and has been tested; (2) raw materials are readily available; (3) it involves relatively low water solubility and low water permeability; and (4) it can accommodate a wide variety of contaminants and material. The disadvantages include (1) odorous material limitations; (2) a wide range of volume increase; and (3) material restrictions both technically and aesthetically.

Brick Manufacturing Processes   Petroleum-laden soil has been used as an ingredient in the production of bricks. The contaminated soil replaces either the shale and/or firing clay normally used in the **brick manufacturing process**. Generally, clay and shale are incorporated into a plasticized mixture, then extruded and molded into brick. When dried, the brick is fired in a kiln at temperatures ranging up to 2,000°F for three days. When contaminated soil is added to the process, it is mixed with clay and shale, molded into brick, dried, and preheated. Then the brick is fired at 1,700° to 2,000°F for approximately 12 hours in the kiln. While in the kiln, the high temperature and residence time destroy organics and incorporate inorganics into the vitrified end product.

The advantages associated with using the brick manufacturing process to reuse or recycle contaminated soils are that (1) fine-grained, low permeability soils can be accommodated; (2) the technology is in place and has been tested; and (3) processing can occur on-site. The disadvantage is that (1) this process is restricted primarily to petroleum hydrocarbons and fly ash.

Solidification/Stabilization

Solidification/stabilization of petroleum-laden soils is used to immobilize contaminants by either encapsulating or converting them, but does not change the physical nature of the contaminant. This is not a commonly used practice for soils, because ultimate destruction of the contaminants does not occur.

Solidification/stabilization processes can be performed either on- or off-site. Various stabilizers and additives are mixed with the material. For example, one procedure consists of a generalized process for the manufacture of pozzolanic material (burnt shale or clay resembling volcanic dust that will chemically react with calcium hydroxide at ordinary temperature to form compounds possessing cementitious properties) using fly ash (Mehta, 1983; Transportation Research Board, 1976).

More commonly used to stabilize oily wastes and sludges contained in surface impoundments, solidification/stabilization processes accomplish this in two ways. In in situ surface impoundments, the stabilizing agent is added directly to the impoundment and thoroughly mixed. Treated in sections, as each solidifies, it is used as a base that allows the equipment to reach further out into the impoundment.

The second method involves excavation of the sludges contained in the impoundment, following this procedure:

• Earth-moving machines level piles of kiln dust into 6- to 12-inch-deep layers.
• A machine lifts the sludge from the impoundment and places it on top of the kiln dust.
• Machines then mix the two materials together, and a pulverizing mixer is driven over the mixture until homogeneity is achieved.
• The mixture is allowed to dry for about 24 hours, then compacted and field tested (Musser & Smith, 1984).
• Usually, the layers are then stacked to build an in-place landfill, or the semisolidified sludge can be trucked to another landfill location.

Chemical Extraction

Chemical extraction is the process in which excavated contaminated soils are washed to remove the contaminants of concern. This washing process typically is accomplished in a washing plant that uses a water/surfactant or a water/solvent mixture to remove the contaminants. This method is very similar to the in-situ leaching process. The primary difference is that by removing the soil from the ground, wash mixtures can be used that do not expose the environment to further contamination. This process increases product recovery and is a proven method for the removal of hydrocarbon contaminants from the soil.

Excavation

Excavation involves the safe physical removal (e.g., using trench boxes) of the contaminated soil for disposal at a hazardous waste or other disposal landfill site. This process has been the mainstay of site remediation for several decades, but recently it has been discouraged by newer regulations that favor alternative waste treatment technologies at the contaminated site. Today, excavation is generally considered a storage, not a treatment, process and raises issues of future liability for the responsible parties regarding the ultimate disposal of the soils. One of the factors contributing to the regulators pushing for on-site treatment methodologies versus landfilling is that landfills are quickly reaching their limits, with fewer and fewer new landfilling sites authorized for construction and operation.

The EPA (1985) points out both the positive and negative aspects of excavation. On the positive side, excavation takes little time to complete and allows for complete clean-up of the site. The negative aspects are the necessary worker/operator safety considerations; the production of dust and odor; and the relatively high costs associated with the excavation, transportation, and ultimate disposal of the soil.

Chapter Summary

When we talk about learning something from practical experience, we say we need to get in there and get our hands dirty. Increasing urbanization means increasing separation from practical knowledge in many areas of land use—from getting our hands dirty. American society has reached the point where "fresh air kids" are sent from New York to what amounts to smaller cities for a week in the "country." Many members of our society have never grown anything but houseplants potted in soil that comes packaged in plastic from a store—a packaged, sterile experience of what soil is and does.

But soil doesn't begin wrapped in plastic, any more than do the meat and produce people buy at the supermarket. When we forget that we are reliant on what our Earth produces out of the fertility of that thin, fine layer of topsoil, we become wasteful—and we put ourselves at risk. We underestimate the value of our soil. We clear-cut it, we pave it over, we expand our communities needlessly on it, and through carelessness and unconcern we poison it—in short, we waste it.

As awareness of the serious soil pollution problems we must now mitigate and remediate grows, as we work to develop effective methods to reuse and recycle contaminated soil, we still have a tendency to think of soil pollution only as it affects our water supply. Again, we undervalue soil. We should not lose sight of the mountains of stone and eternity of time that went into making the soil under our feet.

In many respects, soil pollution was to environmental science in the 1990s what water and air pollution were to earlier decades—the pressing environmental problem at hand. While developing methods to control air and water was difficult, socially and politically, once the regulations were in place and working effectively, the problems confronting the environmentalists were relatively easy to locate.

Soil pollution, however, presents us with a new problem. These contamination sites, especially those from old underground sources (e.g., USTs), create a difficult game of contamination "hide and seek." Although new techniques for handling the contamination show signs of promise, and we have no shortage of sites in need of remediation, we must also remember that hidden sites are still affecting us beneath our feet.

Soil pollution has come to our attention at a time when regulation to begin remediation is in place, and the public knows the importance of mitigating the contaminated areas; however, political attacks have weakened regulatory agencies' ability to clean up contaminated sites.

Discussion Questions and Problems

1. Select a natural topographical feature formed by physical and chemical weathering in your locality and describe its formation.
2. Describe how soil is formed.
3. Define soil texture and soil structure.
4. Why is there confusion or disagreement about the use of the term *soil*?
5. Explain how organic matter alters both the physical and chemical nature of soils.
6. What is soil pollution? Explain.
7. Distinguish between natural soil pollution and anthropogenically caused pollution.
8. List at least five origins of soil contaminants.
9. Which industry (presently) is most responsible for soil pollution?
10. How do contaminants infiltrate soil? What is the effect of contaminant infiltration? Explain.
11. Explain why USTs have been and remain an environmental problem.
12. In soil remediation projects, why is it important to perform a risk assessment?
13. What are exposure pathways? What are the routes of exposure for human beings?
14. Why do some spill sites require in situ treatment and others require non-in situ treatment?
15. What are the soil factors that come into play with remediation using in-situ volatilization?
16. Explain in-situ biodegradation.
17. Discuss the drawback(s) of remediation by excavation.

Suggested Research Topics and Projects

• Chart the characteristics in each stage of bare rock succession.
• Choose a site in your area that demonstrates bare rock succession in action. Research its history.
• Create an extended definition of *soil*.
• Choose a location in your area. Analyze the soil by the four principal properties: texture, slope, structure, and organic matter.
• Examine the soil formation process for a specific geological region—e.g., rain forest, desert, tundra, plains, or mountain.
• Research soil fertility in your area.
• Research soil fertility problems in a developing country.
• Research crop rotation and no-till farming in light of soil fertility improvement.
• Examine soil remediation practices for soil fertility.
• Research information on best estimates of the extent of soil pollution in the United States.
• Examine the other petroleum product sources of contamination: direct disposal of used oils on the ground by individuals or industries; seepage from landfills, illegal

dumps, unlined pits, ponds, and lagoons; and spills from transport accidents or auto accidents.

- Examine sources of soil and subsurface contamination below the ground but above the water table: septic tanks, landfills, sumps and dry wells, graveyards, USTs, and leakage from underground pipelines.
- Examine how soil reactions help determine trace gas concentrations.
- Explain and draw how contamination problems may arise from land disposal of water-soluble waste materials in areas with shallow aquifers.
- Research incidents of "midnight dumping."
- Examine current agricultural practices that cause non-point source pollution problems.
- Research the effects of pesticides in food webs.
- Research reclaimed real estate development of petroleum sites.
- Examine the PEDCO Eckhardt Survey figures for waste disposal. Research and estimate the current levels of waste disposal.
- Research the environmental advantages and disadvantages of geothermal energy.
- Examine the effects of sedimentation on water quality.
- Examine the pollution problems associated with mining.
- Research the environmental problems caused by First Gulf War environmental terrorism and how remediation efforts are progressing.
- Research (through local records, old city maps, newspaper articles and ads, aerial photographs, and neighborhood interviews) possible locations for "missing" old UST locations. Using the information you've gathered, assess the probable and possible degree of site contamination and what the contaminants might be.
- Examine newspaper archives (either for your local paper, or for a city newspaper on file at your library) for information on (1) local development or use of innovative clean-up technologies, (2) HazMat incidents and clean-ups, or (3) local and state attention to environmental hazard issues. What does this tell you about your local government's response to environmental issues?
- Research one of the "famous" environmental contamination incidents/scandals (Times Beach or Love Canal, for example). Write about the political, social, or environmental ramifications.
- Analyze stock performance over the last 10 years for several innovative clean-up technology companies. Who survived? Why?
- Research one large corporation's response to accusations of environmental contamination.
- Research current tank retrofitting techniques.
- Analyze a specific site for possible UST installation.
- Research an old HazMat incident. Apply modern risk assessment procedures to that situation. What would today's regulations and standards require?
- Examine the differing regulation requirements of the EPA, CERCLA, and RCRA.

References and Recommended Reading

American Petroleum Institute. (1980). *Landfarming: An Effective and Safe Way to Treat/Dispose of Oily Refinery Wastes*. Solid Waste Management Committee.

Andrews, J. S., Jr. (1992). "The Cleanup of Kuwait." In Kostecki, P. T., et al., eds., *Hydrocarbon Contaminated Soils*, Vol. II. Boca Raton, FL: CRC/Lewis Publishers.

Blackman, W. C., Jr. (1993). *Basic Hazardous Waste Management*. Boca Raton, FL: Lewis Publishers.

Bossert, I., & Bartha, R. (1984). "The Fate of Petroleum in Soil Ecosystems." In Atlas, R. M., ed., *Petroleum Microbiology*. New York: Macmillan.

Brady, N.C., & Weil, R.R. (1996). *The Nature and Properties of Soils*. 11th ed. New York, Prentice-Hall.

Brown, R. S., Norris, R. D., & Estray, M. S. (1986). *In Situ Treatment of Groundwater*. Baltimore, MD: HazPro 86: Professional Certification Symposium and Exposition.

Ehrhardt, R. F., Stapleton, P. J., Fry, R. L., & Stocker, D. J. (1986). *How Clean Is Clean?—Cleanup Standards for Groundwater and Soil*. Washington, DC: Edison Electric Institute.

EPRI-EEI. (1988). *Remedial Technologies for Leaking Underground Storage Tanks*. Chelsea, MI: Lewis Publishers.

Franck, I., & Brownstone, D. (1992). *The Green Encyclopedia*. New York: Prentice-Hall.

Grady, P. C. (1985). "Biodegradation: Its Measurement and Microbiological Basis." *Biotechnology and Bioengineering* 27: 660–74.

Heyse, E., James, S. C., & Wetzel, R. (1986). "In Situ Aerobic Biodegradation of Aquifer Contaminants at Kelly Air Force Base." *Environmental Progress*, 207–211.

ICAIR, Life Systems, Inc. (1985). *Toxicology Handbook*. Washington, DC: U.S. EPA.

Johnson N. P., & Cosmos, M. G. (1979, October). "Thermal Treatment Technologies for HazWaste Remediation." *Pollution Engineering*, 79.

Jury, W. A. (1986). "Volatilization from Soil." In *Guidebook for Field Testing Soil Fate and Transport Models—Final Report* Washington, DC: U.S. EPA.

Kehew, A. E. (1995). *Geology for Engineers & Environmental Scientists*. 2nd ed. Englewood Cliffs, NJ: Prentice Hall.

Konigsburg, E. L. (1996). *The View from Saturday*. New York: Scholastic Books.

MacDonald, J. A. (1997, December). "Hard Times for Innovation Cleanup Technology." *Environmental Science & Technology* 31, no. 12: 560–63.

Mehta, P. K. (1983). "Pozzolanic and Cementitious By-Products as Miner Admixtures for Concrete—A Critical Review." In Malhotra, M., ed., *Fly Ash, Silica Fume, Slag, and Other Mineral By-Products in Concrete*, Vol. 1. American Concrete Institute.

Musser, D. T., & Smith, R. L. (1984). "Case Study: In Situ Solidification/Fixation of Oil Field Production Fluids—A Novel Approach." In *Proceedings of the 39th Industrial Waste Conference*. Purdue University.

National Research Council. (1997). *Innovations in Groundwater and Soil Cleanup: From Concept to Commercialization*. Washington, DC: National Academy Press.

Pacific Northwest Laboratories. (1986). "Application of In Situ Vitrification to PCB-Contaminated Soils." Paper prepared for Electric Power Research Institute, EPRCS-4834, RP1263-24.

PEDCO. (1979). *PEDCO Analysis of Eckhardt Committee Survey for Chemical Manufacturer's Association*. Washington, DC: PEDCO Environmental Inc.

Testa, S. M. (1997). *The Reuse and Recycling of Contaminated Soil*. Boca Raton: FL: CRC/Lewis Publishers.

Tomera, A. N. (1989). *Understanding Basic Ecological Concepts*. Portland, ME: J. Weston Walch.

Transportation Research Board. (1976). *Lime-Fly Ash: Stabilized Bases and Subbases*. TRB-NCHRP Synthesis Report 37.

Tucker, R. K. (1989). "Problems Dealing with Petroleum Contaminated Soils: A New Jersey Perspective." In Kostecki, P. T., & Calabrese, E. J., eds., *Petroleum Contaminated Soils*, Vol. I. Boca Raton, FL: CRC/Lewis Publishers.

U.S. EPA. (1984). *Review of In-Place Treatment Techniques for Contaminated Surface Soils; Volume 1: Technical Evaluation.* EPA/540/2-84-003. Washington, DC: Environmental Protection Agency.

USEPA. (1985). *Remedial Action at Waste Disposal Sites* (revised). Washington, DC: Environmental Protection Agency.

Weston, R. F. (1986). "Underground Storage Tank Leakage Prevention Detection and Correction." Report prepared for Petroleum Marketers Association of America.

Wilson, J. T., Leach, L. E., Benson, M., & Jones, J. N. (1986). "In Situ Biorestoration as a Ground Water Remediation Technique." *Ground Water Monitoring Review*, 56–64.

World Resources Institute. (1992). *World Resources 1992–93.* New York: Oxford University Press.

Part V

SOLID AND HAZARDOUS WASTES

There are thousands of different chemicals in the environment that may cause adverse human health effects. Little is known about the toxicological properties of most of these chemicals . . . [and their associated waste products].

—U.S. Environmental Protection Agency, 1987

CHAPTER 18

Solid/Hazardous Wastes
and Control

Unfortunately, man is in the woods, and waste and pure destruction are already making rapid headway.

—John Muir, 1877

Chapter Objectives

After studying this chapter, you should be able to:

- Describe and discuss the problems associated with solid waste disposal.
- Identify the possible problems our society may face because of our solid waste pro-
  duction and disposal practices.
- Define and describe municipal solid waste (MSW).
- Identify and discuss the principal regulations governing waste disposal and their
  purposes.
- Identify and describe solid waste characteristics.
- Identify and discuss the biggest sources of solid waste in the United States.
- Discuss the ramifications of the sheer mass of waste we generate in the United States
  each year.
- Identify and discuss the sources of MSW in the United States.
- Identify and discuss the effects of Rachel Carson's *Silent Spring*.
- Identify and discuss the problems associated with hazardous waste, environmentally
  and societally.
- Discuss America as a "throwaway" society.
- Define and discuss hazardous substance, hazardous material, hazardous waste, ex-
  tremely hazardous substance, toxic chemicals, and hazardous chemicals.
- Discuss RCRA, CERCLA, and the U.S. EPA's distinction between them and how
  their regulations affect industry and the environment.
- Identify and discuss RCRA's four characteristics of hazardous substances.

- Identify the nine categories used in the United Nations Hazard Class Number System.
- Define and discuss TCLP and how it functions.
- Identify the point at which hazardous materials become hazardous waste.
- Identify and discuss the three hazardous waste categories.
- Identify the principal sources and generators of hazardous waste.
- Identify and discuss the chief concerns about hazardous waste.
- Discuss the effect hazardous waste legislation has had on the environment and industry.
- Discuss RCRA's regulation areas and CERCLA's requirements.
- Define and discuss the ramifications of RCRA's Waste Management Hierarchy.
- Identify, describe and discuss waste minimization methods, including substitution of inputs, process modification, and good operating practices.
- Discuss the advantages and disadvantages of recycling or recovering materials or energy from the waste stream.
- Identify, describe, and discuss treatment technologies and their effectiveness, including biological treatment, thermal processes, activated carbon sorption, electrolytic recovery techniques, air stripping, stabilization and solidification, and filtration and separation.
- Identify, define, and discuss ultimate solutions for hazardous waste disposal and their advantages and disadvantages, including deep-well injection, surface impoundments, waste piles, and landfills.

Chapter Outline

- Definition and discussion: anthropogenically produced wastes and waste disposal
- Discussion: municipal, federal, and state regulation of solid waste disposal
- Description and discussion: classification and volume of solid wastes
- Discussion: solid waste sources: residential, commercial, institutional, construction, municipal services, and treatment plant wastes
- Discussion: Rachel Carson and *Silent Spring*
- Discussion: American's waste generation habits and their effects on human health and the environment
- Definition and discussion: hazardous substance, hazardous material, hazardous waste, extremely hazardous substance, toxic chemicals, and hazardous chemicals
- Discussion: RCRA's four characteristics of hazardous substances
- Definition and discussion: the Toxicity Characteristics Leaching Procedure (TCLP) and concentrations of toxicity
- Discussion: hazardous material into hazardous waste and U.S. EPA's classification
- Discussion: USEPA's categories and criteria for their hazardous substance standards
- Discussion: hazardous waste generators and the waste they create
- Discussion: public concern, public action, and hazardous waste
- Discussion and example: Bhopal

- Discussion: hazardous waste legislation and what this legislation covers—RCRA and the Cradle to Grave management system; CERCLA and Superfund
- Discussion: RCRA's five management areas for hazardous waste
- Discussion CERCLA's key requirements for NPL site remediation and the Community Right-to-Know Act
- Discussion: America's hazardous waste disposal dilemma and the RCRA's Waste Management Hierarchy
- Discussion and definition: waste minimization and the chemical process audit
- Discussion: techniques for minimization: substitution of inputs, process modification, and good operating practices
- Discussion: recycling industrial wastes and energy
- Discussion and definition: treatment technologies—biological treatment, thermal processes, activated carbon sorption, electrolytic recovery techniques, air stripping, stabilization and solidification, and filtration and separation
- Discussion and definition: permanent land disposal techniques: deep-well injection, surface impoundments, waste piles, and landfills

Key Terms

adsorption

aerobic processes

biodegradable

commercial sources of MSW

commercial chemical products

control of disposal

construction and demolition sources of MSW

garbage

extraction procedure

hazardous chemical

hazardous material

hazardous substance

hazardous waste

institutional sources of MSW

Interstate Commerce Clause

landfills

litter

manifest

middens

municipal services sources of MSW

municipal solid waste (MSW)

nonspecific source wastes

oxidation-reduction

permitting system

reactive

recycle

refuse

residential sources of MSW

Resource Conservation and Recovery Act (RCRA)

Rivers and Harbor Act (1899)

rubbish

solid waste

Solid Waste Disposal Act (1965)

solid waste stream

Superfund Law

surface impoundment

trash

treatment plant site sources of MSW

toxic chemical

toxicity

tracking system

waste piles

wetland

white goods

Introduction

In the final part of this text, we discuss a growing and significant problem facing not only all practitioners of environmental science, but also all of humanity: *anthropogenically produced wastes*. We are faced with daunting questions: What are we going to do with all the wastes we generate? What are the alternatives? What are the technologies available to us at present to mitigate the "waste problem," a problem that grows with each passing day?

Before beginning our discussion, we focus on an important question: When we throw waste away, is it really gone? Remember, though we are faced today and in the immediate future with growing mountains of wastes we produce (and we are running out of places on Earth to dispose of them), an even more pressing, twofold problem is approaching—one related to the waste's toxicity and persistence.

We discuss waste and the toxicity problem later, but now, think about the persistence of the wastes that we discard. For example, when we excavate a deep trench and place within it several 55-gallon drums of liquid waste, then bury the entire sordid mess, are we really disposing of the waste in an Earth-friendly way? Are we disposing of it permanently at all? What happens a few years later, when the 55-gallon drums corrode and leak? Where does the waste go?

What are the consequences of such practices? Are they insignificant to us today because they are tomorrow's problems?

We need to ask ourselves these questions and determine the answers now. If we are uncomfortable with the answers we come up with now, shouldn't we feel the same about the answers someone else (our grandchildren) will have to come up with later, when it is far too late?

Waste is not easily disposed of. We can hide it. We can mask it. We can move it from place to place. We can take it to the remotest corners of the Earth. But because of its persistence, waste is not always gone when we think it is. It has a way of coming back, a way of reminding us. How persistent is waste? Very, very persistent, as thousands of documented cases make clear.

In this section, we define and discuss solid wastes. In particular, we focus on a significant portion of solid wastes, **municipal solid wastes** (MSW), because people living in urban areas where many of the problems associated with solid waste occur generate these wastes. In addition, we discuss another significant waste problem: hazardous wastes. We also discuss waste control technologies related to waste minimization, treatment, and disposal.

Solid Waste Regulatory History (United States)

For most of the nation's history, municipal ordinances (rather than federal regulatory control) were the only solid waste regulations in effect. These local urban governments controlled solid waste almost from the beginning of each settlement, because of the inherent severe health consequences of street disposal. Along with prohibiting dumping of waste in the streets, municipal regulations usually stipulated requirements for proper disposal in designated waste dump sites and mandated that owners remove their waste piles from public property.

The federal government did not begin regulating solid waste dumping until the nation's harbors and rivers were either already overwhelmed with raw wastes or headed in that direction. The government used its constitutional powers under the **Interstate Commerce Clause** of the constitution to enact the **Rivers and Harbors Act** in 1899. The U.S. Army Corp of Engineers was empowered to regulate, and in some cases prohibit, private and municipal dumping.

Not until 1965 did Congress finally get into the picture (as a result of strong public opinion), adopting the **Solid Waste Disposal Act**, which became the responsibility of the U.S. Public Health Service to enforce. The act was to achieve the following purposes:

1. Promote the demonstration, construction, and application of solid waste management and resource recovery systems that preserve and enhance the quality of air, water, and land resources.
2. Provide technical and financial assistance to state and local governments and interstate agencies in the planning and development of resource recovery and solid waste disposal programs.
3. Promote a national research and development program for improved management techniques; more effective organizational arrangements; new and improved methods of collection, separation, recovery, and recycling of solid wastes; and the environmentally safe disposal of nonrecoverable residues.
4. Provide for the promulgation of guidelines for solid waste collection, transport, separation, recovery, and disposal systems.
5. Provide for training grants in occupations involving the design, operation, and maintenance of solid waste disposal systems (Tchobanoglous, Theisen, & Vigil, 1993).

After Earth Day 1970, Congress became more sensitive to waste issues. In 1976, Congress passed solid waste controls as part of the **Resource Conservation and Recovery Act** (RCRA). "Solid waste" was defined as any garbage, refuse, sludge from a waste treatment plant, water supply treatment plant, or air-pollution control facility, and other discarded material.

In 1980, the **Comprehensive Environmental Response, Compensation and Liability Act** (CERCLA) was enacted to provide a means of directly responding to and funding the activities to respond to, problems at uncontrolled hazardous waste disposal sites. Uncontrolled MSW landfills are facilities that have not operated or are not operating under RCRA (U.S. EPA, 1989).

Many other laws that apply to the control of solid waste management problems are now in effect. Federal legislation and associated regulations have encouraged implementation of solid waste management programs at the state level of government. Apparently, legislation will continue to be an important part of future solid waste management.

Solid Waste Characteristics

Solid waste (also called **refuse**, **litter**, **rubbish**, **waste**, **trash**, and [incorrectly] **garbage**) refers to any of a variety of materials that are rejected or discarded as being spent, useless, worthless, or in excess. Table 18.1 provides a useful waste classification system.

Table 18.1. Classification of Solid Waste

Type	Principal Components
Trash	Highly combustible waste paper, wood, cardboard cartons, including up to 10% treated papers, plastic or rubber scraps; commercial and industrial sources.
Rubbish	Combustible waste, paper, cartons, rags, wood scraps, combustible floor sweepings; domestic, commercial, and industrial sources.
Refuse	Rubbish and garbage; residential sources.
Garbage	Animal and vegetable wastes; restaurants, hotels, markets; institutional, commercial, and club sources.

Source: Adapted from Davis & Cornwell, 1991, 585.

Solid waste is probably more correctly defined as "any material thing that is no longer wanted." O'Reilly (1992) points out that defining solid waste is tricky, because solid waste is a series of paradoxes:

personal in the kitchen trash can—but impersonal in a landfill;

what one individual may deem worthless (an outgrown or out-of-fashion coat, for example) and fit only for the trash can—another individual may find valuable;

of little cost concern to many Americans—yet very costly to our society in the long term;

an issue of serious federal concern—yet a very localized problem from municipality to municipality.

The popular adage is accurate: Everyone wants waste to be picked up, but no one wants it to be put down. It goes almost without saying that the other adage, "not in my back yard" (NIMBY) is also accurate. The important point, though, is that whenever a material object is thrown away, regardless of its actual or potential value, it becomes solid waste.

Garbage (with its tendency to decompose rapidly and create offensive odors) is often used as a synonym for solid waste, but actually refers strictly to animal or vegetable wastes resulting from handling, storage, preparation, or consumption of food.

The collective and continual production of all refuse (the sum of all solid wastes from all sources) is referred to as the **solid waste stream**. As stated previously, an estimated 6 billion metric tons of solid waste are produced in the United States each year. The two largest sources of solid wastes are agriculture (animal manure, crop residues, and other agricultural by-products) and mining (dirt, waste rock, sand and slag, the material separated from metals during the smelting process). About 10% of the total waste stream is generated by industrial activities (plastics, paper, fly ash, slag, scrap metal, and sludge or biosolids from treatment plants).

In Figure 18.1, we see that paper and paperboard account for the largest percentage (about 29%) of refuse materials by volume of MSW. Yard wastes account for almost 14%. Glass and metals make up almost 14% of MSW, food wastes just under 15%, and plastics about 12.3%.

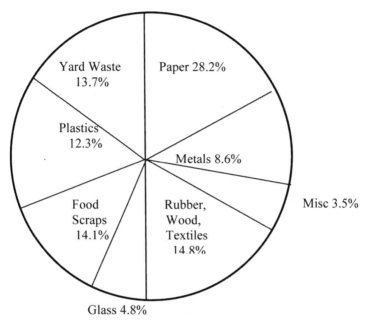

Figure 18.1. Composition of municipal solid waste discarded in a typical day by each American. EPA, Meeting the Environmental Challenge, 2009; Characterization of Municipal Solid Waste in U.S.; 2009 Update, EPA/530-5-019

The U.S. EPA (2009) reports that approximately 243 million metric tons of MSW were generated in the United States in 2009, equivalent to a bit more than 5 pounds per person per day. The EPA estimated that by the year 2010, waste generation in the U.S. would rise to more than 250 million metric tons annually, almost 5.5 pounds per person per day.

Response Scenario 18.1. Waste

Humans have always been known for their garbage. Ancient garbage dumps (called **middens**) provide us with a wealth of information about our human ancestors and their lives. From the historical perspective, this human garbage trail has allowed archaeologists to study people from their earliest days, discovering many fascinating facts about them (us). From the garbage record, for example, we've determined that at every stage, humans have always lived with enormous amounts of garbage, underfoot and all around

(continued)

Response Scenario 18.1. (*continued*)

them. Still true in the poorest parts of developing countries, this all-too-human habit poses a significant hazard to human health and to the environment, today and always.

Ah! But don't panic. Modern Man can solve any problem. Right?

Is this really the case? Let's look at the record—the record we will leave behind us—maybe it will provide us with some insight or answers.

By the 20th century, most industrialized countries (with their modern approaches to sanitation) were removing garbage and other human waste from many living and working environments. But how about the other environment, the one we abuse or rarely think about (the one that sustains our lives), in which we live with its air, soil, and water, which are all critical to our very existence—the natural world?

We stated previously that people can put up with just about anything, until it displeases them. Then, of course, the source of displeasure must be removed—the old "out of sight, out of mind" syndrome. So what did we do? What do we do today?

We transferred or diverted our garbage from our immediate living and working areas into waterways, we heaped and often burned it in garbage dumps (today called **surface impoundments**), or we dumped it into areas called **landfills** (often former **wetlands** were filled in for anticipated future use).

The result has been so massive as to overwhelm and sometimes directly kill life in local environments. Each year, in the United States alone, about 10 billion metric tons of nonagricultural solid waste is generated. Municipal solid waste alone accounts for more than 150 metric tons each year. An average U.S. citizen discards about four pounds of waste each day—that's nearly 1,500 pounds per person, each year.

But what is new and threatening about modern garbage is not entirely the amount (great as it is), but its toxicity and persistence. Most waste in earlier times was **biodegradable**—that is, it could and did break down in the environment as part of natural processes (via biogeochemical cycles). However, today humans routinely use products made from or that produce toxic chemicals, as well as many other hazardous substances. Many of these are poisonous to start with; others become poisonous under certain conditions—for example, when they are burned, or when they come into contact with certain other chemicals to form a chemical brew of unknown toxicity. This chemical brew also enters the food chain and is passed along in concentration in the bodies of larger organisms. Many of these waste products, pesticides and plastics especially, persist in the environment for years, decades, and beyond.

RESPONSE

(i) Nearly 20 years ago, the *Wall Street Journal*, the *Washington Post*, and the *Christian Science Monitor* all called the garbage disposal situation in America a "crisis" (Peterson, 1987; Tongue, 1987; Richards, 1988). Have we weathered the crisis since then? Can it be solved, or will we continue to expand the historical garbage trail, leaving future archaeologists a record to study that will paint our generation as one of folly, total disregard, deliberate misuse—capable only of poor judgment—where conscience and the problem is for the other guy—for other generations?

Sources of Municipal Solid Wastes (MSW)

Sources of municipal solid wastes in a community are generally related to land use and zoning. MSW sources include residential, commercial, institutional, construction and demolition, municipal services, and treatment plants.

RESIDENTIAL SOURCES OF MSW

Residential sources of MSW are generated by single and multifamily detached dwellings and apartment buildings. The types of solid wastes generated include food wastes, textiles, paper, cardboard, glass, wood, ashes, tin cans, aluminum, street leaves, as well as special bulky items like yard wastes collected separately, **white goods** (refrigerators, washers, dryers, etc.), batteries, oil, tires, and household hazardous wastes.

COMMERCIAL SOURCES OF MSW

Commercial sources of MSW are generated in restaurants, hotels, stores, motels, service stations, repair shops, markets, office buildings, and print shops. The types of solid wastes generated include paper, cardboard, wood, plastics, glass, special wastes such as white goods and other bulky items, and hazardous wastes.

INSTITUTIONAL SOURCES OF MSW

Institutional sources of MSW are generated in hospitals, schools, jails and prisons, and government centers. The types of solid wastes generated by institutional sources are the same as those generated by commercial sources.

CONSTRUCTION AND DEMOLITION SOURCES OF MSW

Construction and demolition sources of MSW are generated at new construction sites, the razing of old buildings, road repair/renovation sites, and broken pavement. The types of solid wastes generated by construction and demolition sources are standard construction materials such as wood, steel, plaster, concrete, and soil.

MUNICIPAL SERVICES SOURCES OF MSW

Municipal services (excluding treatment plants) sources of MSW are generated in street cleaning, landscaping, parks and beaches, recreational areas, and catch basin maintenance and cleaning activities. The types of solid wastes generated by municipal services are rubbish, street sweepings, general wastes from parks, beaches, and recreational areas, and catch basin debris.

TREATMENT PLANT SITE SOURCES OF MSW

Treatment plant site sources of MSW are generated in water, wastewater, and other industrial treatment processes (e.g., incineration). The principal types of solid wastes generated by treatment plant sites are sludges or biosolids, fly ash, and general plant wastes.

Response Scenario 18.2.
Problem Wastes: Tire Disposal

Since the invention of the automobile, what to do with wornout tires has presented a disposal problem. America's love affair with cars means that hundreds of millions of tires are discarded every year. Stockpiles across the country store billions of tires. Some of these stockpiles are legal, others are not, but all present us with problems, including the risk of catastrophic fire and the creation of prime breeding habitat for mosquitoes, some varieties of which carry encephalitis or West Nile virus.

In recent years, tire fires have received national attention. They are particularly difficult to extinguish. Water used as an extinguishing agent can cause oily runoff, and burning tires emit toxic black smoke, causing pollution problems for air, surface, and groundwater supplies and soil. Smothering them with dirt and sand appears to be the most cost-effective and efficient way to control burning tire stockpiles. However, sometimes more unusual problems occur with tire fires.

In January 1996, a major road in Ilwaco, Washington, began to heat up, and two months later, created a major oil leak, the result of a massive underground fire. Although response teams immediately contained the oil, they were forced to allow the fire to smolder while they figured out how to even get to it.

Using scrap tires as subgrade road base is probably the most successful effort at recycling used tires, along with using shredded tires as supplemental fuel for modern, scrubber-equipped boilers. However, the chances of further episodes of burning roads, which could create contamination problems in all environmental media, means that the risks associated with using scrap tires are great. As more states enact legislation prohibiting disposal of tires in landfills, recycling, stockpiling, and waste tire dumps will increase, until we can properly manage, store, and process these wastes.

With the advent of West Nile virus, another serious problem with tires has surfaced, one related to international shipping. In the past, shipping techniques and reliance on human labor meant that items shipped internationally by boat were en route and in port for long periods of time. Mechanized loading and unloading practices and modern shipping containers have drastically shortened shipping times—in general, a positive. Serious speculation about how the virus arrived in the United States suggests that a likely culprit is the international market in used tires: Mosquito larvae (infected or not) living in water in the tires can survive container shipment, because the trip is too short to kill off the disease-carrying insects. Whether or not West Nile virus came to the United States this way, shipping used tires poses a recognized threat to public health.

RESPONSE

(i) How would you solve the used tire disposal problem?

America: A Throwaway Society

To this point in this text we have painted a small portrait of American society—a fairly accurate portrayal of an American habit. The portrait and portrayal displays and underscores a characteristic that might be described as habit, trend, custom, or practice: the tendency we have to discard those objects we no longer want. We simply throw them away—so much, and so often, so that we even refer to ourselves as a "throwaway society."

When something is no longer of value because it is broken, worn out, out of style, or no longer needed for whatever reason, we feel that discarding it should not be a big issue. But it is—particularly when the item we throw away is a hazardous substance—persistent, nonbiodegradable, and poisonous.

What is the magnitude of the problem with hazardous substance/waste disposal? Let's take a look at a few facts:

- Hazardous substances—including industrial chemicals, toxic waste, pesticides, and nuclear waste—are entering the marketplace, the workplace, and the environment in unprecedented quantities.
- The United States produces almost 300 million metric tons of hazardous waste each year—with a present population of more than 320 million, this amounts to more than one ton for every person in the country.
- Through pollution of air, soil, and water supplies, hazardous wastes pose both short- and long-term threats to human health and environmental quality.

What Is a Hazardous Substance?
A Hazardous Waste?

Hazardous wastes can be informally defined as a subset of all solid and liquid wastes that are disposed of on land rather than being shunted directly into the air or water, and which have the potential to adversely affect human health and the environment. We have the tendency to think of hazardous wastes as resulting mainly from industrial activities, but households also play a role in the generation and improper disposal of substances that might be considered hazardous wastes. Hazardous wastes, via Bhopal and other disastrous episodes, have been given much attention, but surprisingly little is known of their nature and the actual scope of the problem. In this section, we examine definitions of hazardous materials, substances, wastes, and so forth, and attempt to bring hazardous wastes into perspective as a major environmental concern.

Unfortunately, defining a **hazardous substance** is largely a matter of "pick and choose," with various regulatory agencies and pieces of environmental legislation defining that term and related terms somewhat differently. Many of the terms are used interchangeably. Even experienced professionals in environmental health and safety fields, like certified hazardous materials managers (CHMMs), sometimes interchange these terms, though the terms are generated by different federal agencies and by different pieces of legislation and have somewhat different meanings, depending on the nature of the problem addressed. To understand the scope of the dilemma we face in defining *hazardous substance*, let's take a look at the terms commonly used today, used interchangeably, and often thought to mean the same thing.

HAZARDOUS MATERIAL

A **hazardous material** is a substance (gas, liquid, or solid) capable of causing harm to people, property, and the environment. The U.S. Department of Transportation (DOT) uses the term *hazardous materials* to cover nine categories identified by the *United Nations Hazard Class Number System*, including the following:

- Explosives
- Gases (compressed, liquefied, dissolved)
- Flammable liquids
- Flammable solids
- Oxidizers
- Poisonous materials
- Radioactive materials
- Corrosive materials
- Miscellaneous materials

HAZARDOUS SUBSTANCES

The term *hazardous substance* is used by the U.S. EPA for chemicals that, if released into the environment above a certain amount, must be reported, and depending on the threat to the environment, for which federal involvement in handling the incident can be authorized. The EPA lists hazardous substances in 40 C.F.R. Part 302, Table 302.4.

The Occupational Safety and Health Administration (OSHA) uses the term *hazardous substance* in 29 C.F.R. § 1910.120 (which resulted from Title I of SARA and covers emergency response) differently than does the EPA. Hazardous substances (as defined by OSHA) cover every chemical regulated by both the DOT and the EPA.

EXTREMELY HAZARDOUS SUBSTANCES

Extremely hazardous substance is a term used by the EPA for chemicals that must be reported to the appropriate authorities if released above the *threshold reporting quantity* (RQ). The list of extremely hazardous substances is identified in Title III of the *Superfund Amendments and Reauthorization Act* (SARA) of 1986 (40 C.F.R. Part 355). Each substance has a threshold reporting quantity.

TOXIC CHEMICALS

The EPA uses the term **toxic chemical** for chemicals whose total emissions or releases must be reported annually by owners and operators of certain facilities that manufacture, process, or otherwise use listed toxic chemicals. The list of toxic chemicals is identified in Title III of SARA.

HAZARDOUS WASTES

> The most alarming of all man's assaults upon the environment is the contamination of air, Earth, rivers, and sea with dangerous and even lethal materials. This pollution is for the most part irrecoverable; the chain of evil it initiates not only in the world that must support life but in living tissues is for the most part irreversible. In this now universal contamination of the environment, chemicals are the sinister, and little-recognized partners of radiation in changing the very nature of the world—the very nature of life. (Carson, 1962)

Rachel Carson was able to combine the insight and sensitivity of a poet with the realism and observations of science more adeptly than anyone before her. Famous for her classic and highly influential book *Silent Spring*, it seems strange to us today that after the publication of her magnum opus such a visionary was ostracized, vilified, laughed at, lambasted, and disregarded. To those guilty of the sins that she revealed, Rachel Carson was an enemy to be discredited—and silenced. She was not, however, disregarded by those who understood. To these concerned folks with conscience, her message was clear: Waste, if not properly treated and handled, not only threatens human life in the short term, but the environment as a whole in the long term. Her plea was also clear: Stop poisoning the Earth.

Examined with the clear vision of retrospect, the environmental missionary Rachel Carson was well ahead of her time. The fears she expressed in 1962 were based on limited data, but have since been confirmed. Rachel Carson was right.

The EPA uses the term *hazardous wastes* for chemicals regulated under the RCRA (40 C.F.R. § 261.33). Hazardous wastes in transportation are regulated by the DOT (49 C.F.R. Parts 170–179).

For the purposes of this text, we define a hazardous waste as any hazardous substance that has been spilled or released to the environment. For example, chlorine gas is a hazardous material. When chlorine is released to the environment, it becomes a hazardous waste. Similarly, when asbestos is in place and undisturbed, it is a hazardous material. When it is broken, breached, or thrown away, it becomes a hazardous waste.

HAZARDOUS CHEMICALS

OSHA uses the term *hazardous chemical* to denote any chemical that poses a risk to employees if they are exposed to it in the workplace. Hazardous chemicals cover a broader group of chemicals than the other chemical lists.

Response Scenario 18.3.
Spills of Hazardous Materials

Quick and well-trained response in emergency situations is essential to protect human health and safety, as well as the environment. Consider the possible negative outcomes in the following situation.

At 6:30 p.m. on Monday, October 5, 1998, 16 railroad cars derailed on the Buffalo and Pittsburgh Railroad at the edge of the Allegheny National Forest, near the Clarion River, near Erie, Pennsylvania. One of the derailed cars spilled its load of toxic sulfuric acid.

Emergency workers contained the spill about eight hours after the accident occurred, and the leaking tank car was sealed about three hours later. Once the tank was sealed, the acid, which had hung in the air in a light mist, dissipated. No injuries were reported, but 100 people were evacuated from their homes in nearby Portland Mills overnight. Route 949 was closed while workers from a remediation company finished cleaning up the spill. Emergency workers had been concerned about acid contamination of the Clarion River, but the spill's flow had been contained in a ditch between the tracks and the road. None of the sulfuric acid had reached the river.

Plans for possible emergency situations put into place in real emergency situations prevent human and environmental exposure to pollutants or toxins. Even if the source of the emergency is not local, such planning works to the community's and the environment's benefit. HazCom (actually the MSDS) provides procedures to follow in the event of a chemical spill. In this case, HazMat responders were able to determine the correct response and mitigation procedures to follow to prevent the spread of the spilled acid and to confine it, preventing further environmental pollution.

RESPONSE

(i) How would you prevent the derailing of, or lessen the danger of derailed, chemical tanker cars?

Again, What Is a Hazardous Substance?

To form the strongest foundation for understanding the main topic of this chapter (hazardous waste), and because RCRA's definition of a hazardous substance can also be used to describe a *hazardous waste*, we use the RCRA's definition. The RCRA defines something as a *hazardous substance* if it possesses any of the following four characteristics: *reactivity, ignitability, corrosiveness,* or *toxicity.* Briefly:

- *Ignitability* refers to the characteristic of being able to sustain combustion and includes the category of flammability (ability to start fires when heated to temperatures less than 140°F or less than 60°C).
- *Corrosive* substances (or wastes) may destroy containers, contaminate soils and groundwater, or react with other materials to cause toxic gas emissions. Corrosive

materials present a specific hazard to human tissue and aquatic life where the pH levels are extreme.

• Reactive substances may be unstable or have a tendency to react, explode, or generate pressure during handling. Pressure-sensitive or water-reactive materials are included in this category.

• Toxicity is a function of the effect of hazardous materials (or wastes) that may come into contact with water or air and be leached into the groundwater or dispersed in the environment.

Toxic effects on humans, fish, or wildlife are the principal concerns here. Until 1990, toxicity was tested using a standardized laboratory test, called the **extraction procedure** (EP Toxicity Test). The EP Toxicity test was replaced in 1990 by the *Toxicity Characteristics Leaching Procedure* (TCLP), because the EP test failed to adequately stimulate the flow of toxic contaminants to drinking water. The TCLP test is designed to identify wastes likely to leach hazardous concentrations of particular toxic constituents into the surrounding soils or groundwater as a result of improper management.

The TCLP extracts constituents from the tested waste in a manner designed to simulate leaching actions that occur in landfills. The extract is then analyzed to determine if it possesses any of the toxic constituents listed in Table 18.2. If the concentrations of the toxic constituents exceed the levels listed in the table, the waste is classified as *hazardous*.

What Is Hazardous Waste?

Recall our general rule of thumb, that any hazardous substance spilled or released to the environment is no longer classified as a hazardous substance, but as a hazardous waste. The EPA uses the same definition for hazardous waste as it does for hazardous substance. The four characteristics described in the previous section (reactivity, ignitability, corrosivity, and toxicity) can be used to identify hazardous substances as well as hazardous wastes.

Note that the EPA lists substances that it considers hazardous wastes. These lists take precedence over any other method used to identify and classify substances as hazardous (i.e., if a substance is listed in one of the EPA's lists, legally it is a hazardous substance, no matter what).

EPA LISTS OF HAZARDOUS WASTES

EPA-listed hazardous wastes are organized into three categories: **nonspecific source wastes**, **specific source wastes**, and **commercial chemical products**; all listed wastes are presumed hazardous regardless of their concentrations. The EPA developed these lists by examining different types of wastes and chemical products to determine whether they met any of the following criteria:

• Exhibit one or more of the four characterizations of a hazardous waste.
• Meet the statutory definition of hazardous waste.

Table 18.2. Maximum Concentration of Contaminants for TCLP Toxicity Test

Contaminant	Regulatory Level (mg/L)
Arsenic	5.0
Barium	100.0
Benzene	0.5
Cadmium	1.0
Carbon tetrachloride	0.5
Chlordane	0.03
Chlorobenzene	100.0
Chloroform	6.0
Chromium	5.0
Cresol	200.0
2,4-D	10.0
1,4-Dichlorobenzene	7.5
1,5-Dichloroethane	0.5
2,4-Dinitrololuene	0.13
Endrin	0.02
Heptachlor	0.008
Hexachlorobnezene	0.13
Hexachloroethane	3.0
Lead	5.0
Lindane	0.4
Mercury	0.2
Methoxychlor	10.0
Methyl ethyl ketone	200.0
Nitrobenzene	2.0
Pentachlorophenol	100.0
Pyridine	5.0
Selenium	1.0
Silver	5.0
Tetrachloroethylene	0.7
Toxaphene	0.5
Trichloroethylene	0.5
2,4,5-Trchlorophenol	400.0
2,4,6-Trchlorophenol	2.0
2,4,5-TP (Silvex)	1.0
Vinyl chloride	0.2

Source: U. S. EPA, 1990.

- Are acutely toxic or acutely hazardous.
- Are otherwise toxic.

The three categories briefly, are defined as follows:

- **Nonspecific source wastes:** generic wastes, commonly produced by manufacturing and industrial processes. Examples from this list include spent halogenated solvents used in degreasing and wastewater treatment sludge from electroplating processes, as well as dioxin wastes, most of which are "acutely hazardous" wastes because of the danger they present to human health and the environment.

- **Specific source wastes:** wastes from specially identified industries such as wood preserving, petroleum refining, and organic chemical manufacturing. These wastes typically include sludge, still bottoms, wastewaters, spent catalysts, and residues, for example, wastewater treatment sludge from pigment production.
- **Commercial chemical products:** also called "P" or "U" list wastes because their code numbers begin with these letters. wastes from specific commercial chemical products, or manufacturing chemical intermediates. This list includes chemicals such as chloroform and creosote, acids such as sulfuric and hydrochloric, and pesticides such as DDT and kepone (40 C.F.R. 261.31, .32 & .33).

Note that the EPA ruled that any waste mixture containing a listed hazardous waste is also considered a hazardous waste and must be managed accordingly. This applies regardless of what percentage of the waste mixture is composed of listed hazardous wastes. Wastes derived from hazardous wastes (residues from the treatment, storage, and disposal of a listed hazardous waste) are considered hazardous waste as well (U.S. EPA, 1990).

Where Do Hazardous Wastes Come From?

Hazardous wastes are derived from several waste generators. Most are in the manufacturing and industrial sectors and include chemical manufacturers, the printing industry, vehicle maintenance shops, leather products manufacturers, the construction industry, metal manufacturing, and others. These industrial waste generators produce a wide variety of wastes, including strong acids and bases, spent solvents, heavy metal solutions, ignitable wastes, cyanide wastes, and many more.

Why Are We Concerned about Hazardous Wastes?

From the environmental scientist's perspective, any hazardous waste release that could alter the environment in any way is of major concern. The specifics of their concern lie in acute and chronic toxicity to organisms, bioconcentration, biomagnification, genetic change potential, etiology, pathways, change in climate and/or habitat, extinction, persistence, and esthetics (visual impact).

Remember that when a hazardous substance or material is spilled or released into the environment, it becomes a hazardous waste. Since specific regulatory legislation is in place regarding hazardous wastes; responding to hazardous waste leak/spill contingencies; and for proper handling, storage, transportation, and treatment of hazardous wastes, this distinction is important—the goal being, of course, to protect the environment and ultimately, ourselves.

Why so much concern about hazardous substances and wastes? This question is relatively easy to answer because of hard lessons we have learned in the past. Our answers are based on experience. Actual hazardous materials incidents that we know of, that we have witnessed, have resulted in tragic consequences, not only to the environment, but also to human life. Consider an example in Spellman (1998, pp. 77–78). It may provide a better explanation of why the control of hazardous substances and wastes is critical for us all.

Hazardous Waste Legislation

A few people (Rachel Carson for one) could have predicted that a disaster on the scale of Bhopal was ripe to occur, but humans are strange in many ways. We may know that a disaster is possible, is likely, could happen, is predictable. We predict it—but do we act? Do we act before someone dies? No. Not often. Not often enough. We don't think about the human element. We forget the victims of hazardous materials spills—that is, until they're gone, after they suffer, after they die, after we can no longer help them.

Is this fair? We all know it isn't, but ideally, we strive to make it more so. Is it right? So what do we do about it? We legislate, of course.

Because of Bhopal and other similar (but less catastrophic) chemical spill events, the U.S. Congress (pushed by public concern) developed and passed certain environmental laws and regulations to regulate hazardous substances/wastes in the United States. This section focuses on the two regulatory acts most crucial to the current management programs for hazardous wastes. The first (mentioned several times throughout the text) is the Resource Conservation and Recovery Act (RCRA). Specifically, the RCRA provides guidelines for prudent management of new and future hazardous substances/wastes. The second act (more briefly mentioned) is the Comprehensive Environmental Response, Compensation, and Liability Act (CERCLA), otherwise known as **Superfund**, which deals primarily with mistakes of the past: inactive and abandoned hazardous waste sites.

RESOURCE CONSERVATION AND RECOVERY ACT

The RCRA is the single most important U.S. law dealing with the management of hazardous waste. The law and its amendment, the *Hazardous and Solid Waste Act* of 1984 (HSWA), deal with the ongoing management of solid wastes throughout the country, with emphasis on hazardous waste. Keyed to the waste side of hazardous materials, rather than broader issues dealt with in other acts, the RCRA is primarily concerned with land disposal of hazardous wastes. The goal is to protect groundwater supplies by creating a "cradle-to-grave" management system with three key elements: a **tracking system**, a **permitting system**, and **control of disposal**:

1. The tracking system requires that a **manifest** accompany any waste that is transported from one location to another.
2. The permitting system helps ensure safe operation of facilities that treat, store, or dispose of hazardous wastes.
3. The disposal control system controls and governs the disposal of hazardous wastes onto, or into, the land (Masters, 1991).

The RCRA regulates five specific areas for the management of hazardous waste (with the focus on *treatment*, *storage*, and *disposal*):

1. Identifying what constitutes a hazardous waste and providing classifications of each.
2. Publishing requirements for generators to identify themselves, which includes notification of hazardous waste activities and standards of operation for generators.
3. Adopting standards for transporters of hazardous wastes.
4. Adopting standards for treatment, storage, and disposal facilities.
5. Providing for enforcement of standards through a permitting program and legal penalties for noncompliance (Griffin, 1989).

Arguably, the RCRA is our single most important law dealing with the management of hazardous waste—it certainly is the most comprehensive piece of legislation that the EPA has promulgated to date.

COMPREHENSIVE ENVIRONMENTAL RESPONSE, COMPENSATION, AND LIABILITIES ACT (CERCLA)

The mission of CERCLA (Superfund) is to clean up hazardous waste disposal mistakes of the past and to cope with emergencies of the present. More often referred to as the Superfund law, as a result of its key provisions a large trust fund (about $1.6 billion) was created. Later, in 1986, when the law was revised, this fund was increased to almost $9 billion. The revised law is designated the Superfund Amendments and Reauthorization Act of 1986 (SARA). The key requirements of CERCLA include the following:

1. CERCLA authorizes the EPA to deal with both short-term (emergency situations triggered by a spill or release of hazardous substances) and long-term problems involving abandoned or uncontrolled hazardous waste sites for which more permanent solutions are required.
2. It has set up a remedial scheme for analyzing the impact of contamination on sites under a hazard ranking system. From this hazard ranking system, a list of prioritized disposal and contaminated sites is compiled. This list becomes the *National Priorities List* (NPL) when promulgated. The NPL identifies the worst sites in the nation, based on such factors as the quantities and toxicity of wastes involved, the exposure pathways, the number of people potentially exposed, and the importance and vulnerability of the underlying groundwater.
3. CERCLA also forces those parties who are responsible for hazardous waste problems to pay the entire cost of clean-up.
4. Title III of SARA requires federal, state, and local governments and industry to work together in developing emergency response plans and reporting on hazardous chemicals. This requirement is commonly known as the *Community Right-To-Know Act*, which allows the public to obtain information about the presence of hazardous chemicals in their communities and releases of these chemicals into the environment.

Waste Control Technology

How to handle society's toxic chemical waste now ranks among the top environmental issues in most industrial countries. Without concerted efforts to reduce, recycle, and reuse more industrial waste, the quantities produced will overwhelm even the best treatment and disposal systems. (Postel, 1987, 37)

One of the most challenging and pressing current environmental concerns (dilemmas) confronting environmental scientists (and many others) is what to do with all of the solid and hazardous wastes our throwaway society produces. In simple (and simplistic) terms, we could say that we should shift from a throwaway society to a recycling one, which would help restore a gain in our living standards. We could also say that since disposing hazardous waste is so expensive and risky, to make the situation better we should follow RCRA's Waste Management Hierarchy (in descending order of desirability): (1) stop producing waste in the first place; (2) if we cannot avoid producing it, then produce only minimum quantities; (3) recycle it; (4) if it must be produced, but cannot be recycled, then treat it: (5) if it cannot be rendered nonhazardous, dispose of it in a safe manner; and (6) once it is disposed of, continuously monitor it to ensure there are no adverse effects to the environment.

All of these suggestions have merit. But are they realistic? To a point, yes. We have developed several strategies to curb the spread of hazardous substances/wastes. One approach is treatment of hazardous wastes to neutralize them or make them less toxic. However, again, a better strategy would be to reduce or eliminate the use of toxic substances and the generation of hazardous waste. We can accomplish this to a degree, but to think that we can simply do away with all our hazardous materials, processes that use hazardous materials, and processes that produce hazardous materials is wishful thinking.

What we need to do is refine our waste reduction programs as much as possible and develop technologies that will better treat waste products that we are not able to replace, do away with, or reduce. We have such technologies and/or practices available to us today. Environmental science and technology can be put to work to develop and use measures and practices by which hazardous chemical wastes can be minimized, recycled, treated, and disposed of. We review these measures, practices and technologies in the following sections.

Waste Minimization

Waste minimization (or using *source reduction measures*) is accomplished in a variety of ways and includes feedstock or input substitution, process modifications, and good operating practices. Note that before any source reduction measure can be put into place, considerable amounts of information must be gathered.

One of the first steps to be taken in the information-gathering process is determining the exact nature of the waste produced. The waste must initially be characterized and categorized by type, composition, and quantity, a task accomplished by performing a *chemical process audit* or *survey* of the chemical process. Keep in mind that during this information-gathering survey, it is important to look closely for any off-specification input materials that might produce defective outputs; any inadvertent contamination of inputs, process chemicals, and outputs; and any obsolete chemicals (which should be properly disposed of).

During the survey, particular attention should be given to problem areas: excessive amounts of waste per unit of production, excessive process upsets or bad batches, or frequent off-specification inputs. The effect of process variables on the waste stream created, and the relationship of waste stream composition to the input chemicals and process methods used, should be examined. For example, determine exactly how much process water is used. Can the amount of water used be reduced? Can process water be reused? Questions like these should be addressed during the chemical process survey (Lindgren, 1989).

To determine the feasibility of reuse, recycling, materials recovery, waste transfer, or proper methods of waste disposal, the exact nature of the waste must also be determined. Usually accomplished through sampling the waste stream, then analyzing the sample in the laboratory, the nature of the waste can yield valuable information about the industrial process and the condition of process equipment.

SUBSTITUTION OF INPUTS

After completing the chemical process survey, the information gathered may suggest or justify the substitution of certain chemicals, process materials. or feedstock to enable the process hazardous wastes to be reduced in volume or no longer be produced. Note that input substitutions are often inseparable from process modifications. A few specific examples of possible input substitutions are

- use of synthetic coolants in place of emulsified oil coolants,
- use of water-based paints instead of solvent-based paints,
- use of noncyanide-based electroplating solutions, and
- use of cartridge filters in lieu of Earth filters.

PROCESS MODIFICATIONS

One of the key benefits derived from performing a chemical process audit or survey is that audits often point to or suggest modifications to production systems that work to minimize hazardous waste stream production. Whenever a chemical process can be made more efficient, a reduction in the volume and toxicity of the residuals usually results.

GOOD OPERATING PRACTICES

Reducing wastage, preventing inadvertent releases of chemicals, and increasing the useful lifetime of process chemicals are all directly related to *good operating practices*.

Ensuring good operating practices by workers can only be accomplished through effective worker training. This training should include not only proper process operations, but also effective spill response training.

Recycling

Various strategies have been developed to **recycle** (and thus minimize) the volume of hazardous wastes to dispose of. These strategies recover or recycle resources, either materials or energy, from the waste stream. The key point to note in chemical process recycling is that the product must receive some processing before reuse. Wastes generally recognized as having components of potential value include

- flammable and combustible liquids,
- oils,
- slags and sludge,
- precious metal wastes,
- catalysts,
- acids, and
- solvents.

From this list, we can see that one such recycling or recovery effort involves the reclamation of organic solvents. Usually accomplished by using highly effective distillation techniques, in this process solvents contaminated with metals and organics are heated to produce a liquid phase and a vapor phase. Lighter components with high volatiles rise to the top of the liquid phase and begin to vaporize. By carefully controlling the waste mixture's temperature, the desired substance can be vaporized and recovered by condensation, leaving the heavier contaminants behind. What remains is a concentrated, highly toxic mixture (far reduced in volume) referred to as *still bottoms*. Bottoms may contain usable metals and other solvents. As distillation technology improves, more of these bottom materials will be recovered and possibly reused.

Treatment Technologies

The 1984 and 1991 amendments to RCRA require that hazardous wastes must be treated prior to ultimate disposal in a landfill. Even with process modifications, material substitution, and recycling, some portions of some waste streams may still be hazardous and must be properly contained. These hazardous waste components require additional treatment. Such treatment takes place in vessels (tanks), reactors, incinerators, kilns, boilers, or impoundments.

At the present time, several technologies are available for the treatment of hazardous waste streams. In this section, we discuss a few examples, including biological treatment, thermal treatment, activated carbon sorption, electrolytic recovery techniques, air stripping, stabilization and solidification, and filtration and separation treatment systems.

Note: Some of these treatment techniques were previously covered in greater detail (in situ and non-in situ soil contamination treatment); some technologies combine two of more of these basic technologies.

BIOLOGICAL TREATMENT

Several biological treatment processes are available for treating "liquid" hazardous waste streams (contaminated soils and solids are more difficult to treat), including activated sludge, aerobic lagoons, anaerobic lagoons, spray irrigation, trickling filters, and waste stabilization ponds. These processes are normally associated with biological treatment of municipal and industrial wastewater and are generally used for removal of organic pollutants from wastewater. Generally effective on wastewater with low-to-moderate concentrations of simple organic compounds and lower concentrations of complex organics, these are generally ineffective in attacking mineral components and are useless against heavy metals.

Biological treatment of toxic organic components requires considerably more sophisticated operational control (including pretreatment) than is necessary with nontoxic wastewaters. Microorganisms used in biological treatment processes can easily be destroyed by rapid increases in rate of feed. Acclimation and development of a functional population of biota may require considerable time, and the system is continuously subject to upset (Blackman, 1993).

The two biological processes used for treatment of toxic waste are **aerobic processes** (treatment in the presence of oxygen—conventional aeration) and anaerobic processes (treatment in the absence of oxygen—in a simple septic tank).

In aerobic treatment, organisms require both an energy source and a carbon source for growth, and both affect what type of organisms will grow in a particular environment. Many hazardous waste streams satisfy both basic requirements, and if appropriate nutrients are present, a thriving organic population for waste treatment can exist. Under these conditions, if pH and temperature are controlled, substances that are toxic to the active organisms can be eliminated.

The most important aspect limiting the applicability of aerobic biological treatment of hazardous waste is the biodegradability of the waste—its conversion by biological processes to simple inorganic molecules and biological materials. Biodegradability of a particular waste is very system-specific, and the correct conditions for successful treatment (detoxification or biological conversion of a toxic substance to one less toxic) must be maintained to encourage the correct microbe mixture.

Anaerobic treatment of toxic waste streams has been effectively practiced on many different types of toxic waste streams. This form of treatment is basically a fermentation process, in which organic waste is both oxidized and reduced.

THERMAL PROCESSES

Thermal treatment processes (incineration) are commonly used to treat both liquids and solids to either destroy the hazardous components or allow disposal of the process residue or treated waste in an EPA-approved hazardous waste landfill.

During incineration, carbon-based (organic) materials are burned at high temperatures, typically ranging from 1,500°F to 3,000°F, to break them down, chiefly into hydrogen, carbon, sulfur, nitrogen, and chlorine. These constituent elements then combine with oxygen to form inorganic gases like water vapor, carbon dioxide, and nitrogen oxides. After combustion, the gases pass through a pollution control system to remove acidic gases and particulate matter prior to being released to the atmosphere.

The advantages of hazardous wastes incineration are twofold: (1) It permanently reduces or eliminates the hazardous character of the waste; and (2) it substantially reduces the volume of the waste being disposed of.

Waste characteristics and treatment requirements determine the incinerator design to accommodate liquid or solid wastes. Temperature, turbulence, and retention time (commonly known as the 3 Ts of incineration) are the prime factors determining incineration treatment design for both solid and liquid wastes.

Hazardous waste incinerators are regulated by the EPA and require a permit for operation. To receive an operating permit, an incineration facility must demonstrate a 99.99% destruction and removal efficiency (DRE) for each principal organic hazardous constituent in the feed material.

Non-in situ thermal processes (primarily incinerators) include designs such as liquid injection and boilers, rotary kilns, fluidized beds, and catalytics. More sophisticated and less common types of thermal treatment systems include wet oxidation, pyrolytic, and plasma processes. Some of these can be conducted in situ, with steam injection, radio frequency heating, and vitrification (molten glass treatment) processes.

ACTIVATED CARBON SORPTION

Organic substances may be removed from aqueous hazardous waste streams with *activated carbon* by *sorption*. Sorption is the transfer of a substance from a solution to a solid phase. In **adsorption** (a final chemical reaction that forms a cementitious precipitated sludge, not to be confused with *absorption*, which is defined as a physical process that does not chemically stabilize a waste material), chemical substances are removed from the waste stream onto a carbon matrix. The carbon may be used in either granular or powdered form, depending on the application.

The effectiveness of activated carbon in removing hazardous constituents from aqueous streams is directly proportional to the amount of surface area of the activated carbon; in some cases it is adequate for complete treatment. It can also be applied to pretreatment of industrial hazardous waste streams prior to follow-up treatment. Activated carbon sorption is most effective for removing from water those hazardous waste materials that are not water-soluble.

ELECTROLYTIC RECOVERY TECHNIQUES

The *electrolytic recovery technique* (used primarily for recovery of metals from process streams, to clean process waters, or to treat wastewaters prior to discharge) is based on the **oxidation-reduction** reaction, wherein electrode surfaces are used to collect the metals from the waste stream.

Typically, an electrolytic recovery system consists of a treatment vessel (tank, etc.) with electrodes, an electrical power supply, and a gas handling and treatment system. Recovered metal must be removed from the electrodes periodically when the design thickness is achieved for the recovered metal.

AIR STRIPPING

The *air stripping* technique for removing hazardous constituents from waste streams, although not particularly effective, has been used for many years. *Stripping* is a means of separating volatile components from less volatile ones in a liquid mixture by partitioning the more volatile materials to a gas phase of air or steam. In air stripping, the moving gas is usually ambient air, which is used to remove volatile dissolved organic compounds from liquids, including groundwater and wastewater. Additional treatment must be applied to the exhaust vapors to destroy and/or capture the separated volatiles. The process is driven by the concentration gradient between air and liquid phase equilibrium for particular molecules according to **Henry's Law**, which states that at constant temperature, the weight of gas absorbed by a given volume of a liquid is proportional to the pressure at which the gas is supplied.

STABILIZATION AND SOLIDIFICATION

Stabilization and *solidification* are techniques used to convert hazardous waste from the original form to a physically and chemically more stable material. Accomplished by reducing the mobility of hazardous compounds in the waste prior to its land disposal, stabilization and solidification are particularly useful when recovery, removal, or converting hazardous components (as required by RCRA) from waste prior to disposal in a landfill is not possible.

A wide variety of stabilization and solidification treatment processes use Portland cement as a binding agent. Waste/concrete composites can be formed that have exceptional strength and excellent durability and that retain wastes very effectively (Blackman, 1993). Stabilization and solidification treatment processes improve handling and physical characteristics and result in a reduction of solubility or limit the leachability of hazardous components with a waste.

FILTRATION AND SEPARATION

Filtration and *separation* hazardous waste treatment processes are physical processes. Filtration (the separation of solid particles from a liquid stream through use of semiporous media) is driven by a pressure difference across the media. This pressure difference is caused by gravity, centrifugal force, vacuum, or elevated pressure.

Filtration applied to hazardous waste treatment falls into two categories—clarification and dewatering. *Clarification* takes place when liquids of less than 200 ppm are placed within a clarifier, and the solids are allowed to settle out, producing a cleaner effluent. *Dewatering* is performed on slurries and sludge. The goal of dewatering is to concentrate the solids into a semisolid form for further treatment or land disposal.

Ultimate Disposal

Most of us are familiar with open dumps. However, you might not be familiar with some of the dumping practices that were developed because of environmental legislation in the 1970s, which placed increasingly stringent controls on releases to the atmosphere and to the nation's waterways. To protect our atmosphere and our waterways, the 1970s legislative mindset drove us to dump hazardous materials into open dumps. Why not? Land disposal is safer and proper. Isn't it?

No, it is not. But we didn't realize this until the tragic consequences of these practices became apparent to us later—and today, we're still cleaning up the resulting mess.

We are now well aware that the land is not a bottomless sink that can be used to absorb all of our discards. We've learned that we must pretreat our wastes to detoxify them, to degrade them, to make them less harmful, to make them more Earth-friendly—before we deposit them on or in the ground, the soil, the land—our Earth.

Regardless of the treatment, destruction, and immobilization techniques used, some residue(s) that must be contained somewhere will always remain from hazardous wastes. This "somewhere" is burial in land, deep-well injection, surface impoundments, waste piles, and landfills. In this section we discuss the last four methods.

DEEP-WELL INJECTION

The practice of *deep-well injection* is not new; it was used in the 1880s by the petroleum industry to dispose of saltwater produced when drilling for oil. However, disposing of hazardous materials by deep-well injection is a relatively recent development. The EPA estimates that about 9 billion gallons of all the hazardous waste produced in the United States (about 22% of the total produced) is injected deep into the ground. Most of the deep-well injection sites are located in the Great Lakes region and along the Gulf Coast.

Deep-well injection involves the injection of liquid waste under pressure into underground strata isolated by impermeable rock, where geologists believe they will be contained permanently, isolated from aquifers, typically at a depth of more than 700 m below the surface. A high-pressure pump forces the hazardous liquids into pores in the underground rock, where they displace the water, oil, and gases originally present. Sandstone and other sedimentary rock formations are used because they are porous and allow the movement of liquids.

In theory, when properly constructed, operated, and monitored, deep-well injection systems may be the most environmentally sound disposal method for toxic and hazardous wastes currently available. However, as with anything else that in theory is "perfect" or affords us the "best available technology," deep-well injection has its problems. For example, though constructed at a depth below the groundwater table, fractures in the underground geology could allow waste to go where it is not wanted; namely, into the groundwater. The biggest problem with deep-well injection concerns the unknown. We are not certain of the exact fate of hazardous substances after injection—another example of the "we don't know what we do not know" syndrome.

Because of our uncertainty about the results of our hazardous waste disposal practices, the 1984 amendments to RCRA ban unsafe, untreated wastes from land disposal. For those land disposal facilities allowed to accept hazardous substances, the EPA (1986) implemented restrictions

- Banning liquids from landfills;
- Banning underground injection of hazardous waste within one-quarter mile of a drinking water well;
- Requiring more stringent structural and design conditions for landfills and surface impoundments, including two or more liners, leachate collection systems above and between the liners, and groundwater monitoring;
- Requiring clean-up or corrective action if hazardous waste leaks from a facility;
- Requiring information from disposal facilities about pathways of potential human exposure to hazardous substances; and
- Requiring location standards that are protective of human health and the environment.

SURFACE IMPOUNDMENTS

Surface impoundments are diked or excavated areas used to store liquid hazardous wastes (see Figure 18.2). Because most surface impoundments are temporary, relatively cheap to construct, and allow easy access for treatment, they have been popular for many years.

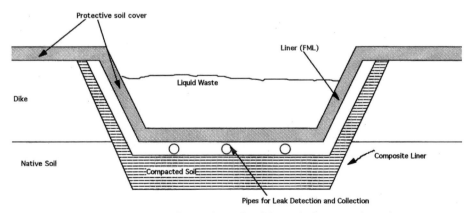

Figure 18.2. Cross-section of a surface liquid waste impoundment.

Unfortunately, in the past surface impoundments were poorly constructed (literally quickly dug out or diked and put into operation), poorly sited (built on a thin layer of permeable soil that allowed leachate to infiltrate to groundwater), located too close to sources of high-quality drinking water (wells or running water sources), and either not monitored at all or poorly monitored. In 1984, the EPA estimated that of the more than 180,000 surface impoundments surveyed, prior to 1980 only about 25% were lined, and fewer than 10% had monitoring systems.

Because of the problems associated with poor siting, construction, and management of the early surface impoundments, EPA regulations have toughened the requirements for construction of new surface impoundments. Under the *Hazardous and Solid Waste Amendments* (HSWA) of 1984, for example, the EPA now requires new surface impoundments to include

- the installation of two or more liners;
- a leachate collection system between liners; and
- groundwater monitoring.

Provisions must also ensure prevention of liquid escaping from overfilling or run-on and prevention of erosion of dams and dikes. During construction and installation, liners must be inspected for uniformity, damage, and imperfections. These liners must also meet permit specifications for materials and thickness.

WASTE PILES

Waste piles are normally associated with industrial sites, where it was a common practice for years to literally pile up industrial waste, and later, when the pile became "too large," dispose of it in a landfill. Industrial practice has been to list such piles as "treatment" piles, and even 40 C.F.R. 264/265 subpart L refers to such piles as treatment or storage units.

The environmental problem with such piles is similar to the problems we discussed related to mining waste. Like mining waste, industrial waste piles are subject to weather exposure, including evaporation of volatile components to the atmosphere, and wind and water erosion. The most significant problem related to industrial waste piles is precipitation—leaching of contaminants (producing leachate), which may percolate into the subsurface.

The RCRA specifications for waste piles are similar to those for landfills (discussed in the next section) and are listed in 40 C.F.R. 264/265 subpart L. Under the RCRA guidelines, the owner or operator of a waste pile used for storage or treatment of non-containerized solid hazardous wastes is given a choice between compliance with either the waste pile or landfill requirements. If the waste pile is used for disposal, it must comply with landfill requirements. The waste pile must be placed on an impermeable surface, and if leachate is produced, a control and monitor system must be in place. Waste piles must also be protected from wind dispersion.

LANDFILLING

Landfilling wastes has a history of causing environmental problems—including fires, explosions, production of toxic fumes, and storage problems when incompatible wastes are commingled. Landfills also have a history of contaminating surface and groundwater (U.S. EPA, 1990).

Sanitary landfills are designed and constructed to dispose of MSWs only. They are not designed, constructed, or allowed to be operated for disposal of bulk liquids and/ or hazardous wastes. Landfills that can legally receive hazardous wastes are known as *secure landfills.*

Under the RCRA, the design and operation of hazardous waste landfills has become much more technically sophisticated. Instead of the past practice of gouging out a huge maw from the subsurface and then dumping countless truckloads of assorted waste materials (including hazardous materials) into it until it was full, a hazardous waste landfill is now designed as a modular series of three-dimensional control cells. Design and operating procedures have evolved to include elaborate safeguards against leakage and migration of leachates.

Secure landfills for hazardous waste disposal are equipped with double liners. Leakage detection, leachate collection and monitoring, and groundwater monitoring systems are required (see Figure 18.3). Liners used in secure landfills must meet regulatory specifications. For example, the upper liner must consist of a 10- to 100-mil thick *flexible-membrane liner* (FML), usually made of sheets of rubber or plastic. The lower liner is usually FML, but recompacted clay at 3 feet thick is also acceptable.

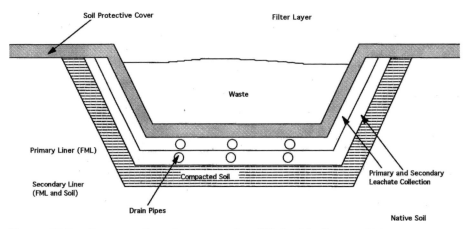

Figure 18.3.   Cross section of a secure landfill double liner system.

Secure landfills must be constructed to allow the collection of leachate (usually via perforated drainage pipes with an attached pumping system) that accumulates above each liner. Leachate control is critical. To aid in this control process (especially from leachate produced by precipitation), a low permeability cap must be placed over completed cells. When the landfill is finally closed, a cap that will prevent leachate formation via precipitation must be put in place. This cap should be sloped to allow drainage away from the wastes.

When a landfill is filled and capped, it cannot be completely abandoned, ignored, or forgotten. The site must be monitored to ensure that leachate is not contaminating the groundwater. This is accomplished by installing test wells downgradient to ensure detection of any leakage from the site.

Chapter Summary

As we examine the problems associated with solid waste disposal, whether municipal, industrial, or hazardous, the answer to a question posed in the introduction of this chapter becomes more and more apparent: When we "throw away" waste, it is not gone. Dealing with the waste permanently has only been postponed. Sometimes this postponement means that when we go back, the wastes are rendered helpful and harmless (as with some biodegradable wastes), but more often, it means that the problems we must face will be worse—increased by chemistry and entropy. That 55-gallon drum was easier to handle before it rusted out.

Amid the cries of "not in my backyard" and "pick up the trash, but don't put it down," we need to hear a more realistic and environmentally kinder truth: *There's no such thing as a free lunch.*

We pay, somehow, for what we get or use, whether we see the charges or not. The price for our solid waste habits will soon be charged to us. In some places (e.g., big cities), awareness of the size of the bill is sinking in.

Environmentally, what does that mean? In short, if we as a society are going to consume as we do, build as we do, grow as we do, we have to pay the price for our increases. And sometimes that is going to mean that our waste is going to be "in our backyard." We will have to increase the amount of solid waste we reuse and recycle; spend tax dollars to solve the problems with landfills and trash incineration; and seriously look at how we live, how the goods we buy are packaged, and how our industries deal with their wastes—because if we don't, the bill will be more than we can afford to pay.

Advancements in technology have made our lives more comfortable, safer, healthier, and in many cases more enjoyable. Some would say that progress is not without cost. This statement is correct—however, what costs do they refer to? Can we afford the consequences if these costs include more Bhopals, Times Beaches, Love Canals, or another *Exxon Valdez*? If such disasters are "to be included as a cost of progress," then we must say that the cost outweighs the gain.

What we must do to ensure a balance between technological progress and its environmental results is to use technological advances to ensure that "progress" is not too costly—or life-threatening—to both our environment and ourselves.

The RCRA's Waste Management Hierarchy sums up what could/ should/ would happen with waste—any kind of waste—in a "best of all possible worlds." But though it is idealistic and too simple to say we "should" follow these standards, in practical terms, we benefit in the long term by striving to achieve them.

Regulating problem wastes, developing safe and environmentally friendly ways to dispose of them, and using the technologies we develop to control the future of such wastes is in all our best interests.

Discussion Questions and Problems

1. Distinguish among garbage, rubbish, refuse, and trash, based on their composition and source.
2. Distinguish between persistent and nonpersistent solid wastes.
3. Why are biodegradable materials easier to dispose of than those that are not biodegradable?
4. What is municipal solid waste (MSW)?
5. List the sources of MSW.
6. What is the difference between garbage and trash?
7. What is the difference between refuse and rubbish?
8. In your own words, write a definition for each of the key terms that are listed in this chapter. Compare your definitions with those in the text and glossary.
9. In what way is hazardous waste a social problem?
10. What is bioremediation?
11. What is hazardous waste? Explain.
12. Explain the term "throwaway society." Does it apply to your hometown?
13. Differentiate among hazardous waste, hazardous substance, and toxic chemical.
14. To be a hazardous waste, does a substance have to be listed by the EPA first? Explain.
15. How are the hazardous wastes that are generated in your state disposed of?
16. How does a sanitary landfill differ from a secure landfill?
17. Summarize the various ways of disposing of hazardous wastes.
18. List the advantages and disadvantages of landfilling.
19. Can leachate leak from a secure hazardous waste landfill? If so, how?

Suggested Research Topics and Projects

- Research current landfill use in your area.
- Research the practice of solid waste disposal across state lines.
- Examine waste transportation by garbage scows and the problems associated with them.
- Research current landfill technology.
- Explore the connection between solid waste disposal and air, water, and soil contamination.
- Explore the advantages and disadvantages of "trash-to-steam" technologies.
- Examine the issues local residents have concerning solid waste disposal.
- Examine current and developing means of reusing and recycling solid wastes.
- Examine solid waste in the light of resource recovery.

- Research "not in my backyard" solid waste disposal cases.
- Agricultural and mining by-products produce the most waste. Examine possible means of reducing, reusing, or recovering significant portions of that waste.

SILENT SPRING

- Biography of Rachel Carson.
- Analysis of *Silent Spring*.
- Analysis of the changes in environmental issues since *Silent Spring* was first published.
- Analysis of *Silent Spring*'s importance.
- Analysis of public reaction to *Silent Spring*.

HAZARDOUS WASTE

- Analyze one of the big hazardous waste "incidents" (e.g., Bhopal, *Exxon Valdez*, Love Canal, First Gulf War oil well fires): environmental effects, political response, societal response, or human health effects.
- Research combinations of ordinary substances that combine for increased toxicity.
- Analyze hazardous waste as the catalyst for change in popular media (e.g., *Teenage Mutant Ninja Turtles*).
- Write an extended definition of hazardous substance, hazardous material, hazardous waste, extremely hazardous substance, toxic chemicals, or hazardous chemicals.
- Research industry practice for waste disposal.
- Evaluate your community's risk level for a hazardous incident (e.g., Harrisburg, Pennsylvania, and Three Mile Island).
- Analyze the tragedy at Bhopal: what was spilled, who was killed, who was responsible, what the long- and short-term results were, how it affected the way the rest of the world handles hazardous waste.
- Who's heading the NPL list, and why?
- How have the RCRA and/or CERCLA affected industries in your area?
- Examine the RCRA's Waste Management Hierarchy step by step and research in-place technologies to achieve those goals for a particular industry.
- Research waste minimization. Find concrete examples of industries actively seeking to achieve reduced hazardous waste by minimization.
- Explore the technologies available for waste resource recovery and reuse in the petroleum industry.
- What hazardous wastes demand which methods of pretreatment?
- Research the wastes suitable for treatment by biological treatment processes.
- Examine the wastes suitable for treatment by thermal processes.
- Examine the activated carbon sorption method for waste treatment.
- Research where and how stabilization and solidification is used to control hazardous wastes.
- Research deep-well injection.

- Research the RCRA's bans—what processes or practices it does not allow.
- Research the problems related to improper surface impoundment management.
- Examine the history of the environmental problems related to landfills.

References and Recommended Reading

49 C.F.R. Parts 170–179 (U.S. Department of Transportation)
40 C.F.R. § 261.24, USEPA (1990).
40 C.F.R. §261.31–33.
40 C.F.R. § 264.1.
40 C.F.R. § 264.52b.
40 C.F.R. § 302.4.
Blackman, W. C. (1993). *Basic Hazardous Waste Management.* Boca Raton, FL: Lewis Publishers.
Carson, R. (1962). *Silent Spring.* Boston: Houghton Mifflin Company.
Comprehensive Environmental Response, Compensation, and Liabilities Act (CERCLA). (1980). Pub. L. No. 96-510, 42 U.S.C. § 9601 et seq.
Davis, M. L., & Cornwell, D. A. (1991). *Introduction to Environmental Engineering.* 2nd ed. New York: McGraw-Hill.
Griffin, R. D. (1989). *Principles of Hazardous Materials Management.* Chelsea, MI: Lewis Publishers.
Hazardous and Solid Waste Amendments (1984). Pub. L. No. 98-616.
Lindgren, G. F. (1989). *Managing Industrial Hazardous Waste.* Chelsea, MI.
Masters, G. M. (1991). *Introduction to Environmental Engineering and Science.* New York: Prentice-Hall.
O'Reilly, J. T. (1992). *State & Local Government Solid Waste Management.* Deerfield, IL: Clark, Boardman, Callahan.
Peterson, C. (1987, April 5). "Mounting Garbage Problem." *Washington Post.* Accessed January12, 2012 at www.highbeam.com/doc/1P2.1315144.h
Postel, S. (1987). *Defusing the Toxics Threat: Controlling Pesticides and Industrial Wastes.* Worldwatch Paper 79. Washington, DC: Worldwatch Institute.
Resource Conservation and Recovery Act (1976). P.L. 94-580, 42 U.S.C. § 6901 et seq.
Richards, B. (1988, June 16). "Burning Issue." *Wall Street Journal,* B-3.
Spellman, F. R. (1998). *Surviving an OSHA Audit: A Manager's Guide.* Lancaster, PA: Technomic.
Spellman, F. R. (2007). *The Science of Water: Concepts and Applications.* Lancaster, PA: Technomic.
Superfund Amendments and Reauthorization Act (SARA) (1986). Pub. L. No. 99-499.
Tchobanoglous, G., Theisen, H., & Vigil, S. (1993). *Integrated Solid Waste Management: Engineering Principles and Management Issues.* New York: McGraw-Hill.
Tonge, P. (1987, July 6). "All That Trash." *Christian Science Monitor,* 11.
U.S. EPA (1986). *Solving the Hazardous Waste Problem: EPA's RCRA Program.* Washington, DC: EPA Office of Solid Waste.
U.S. EPA (1989). *Decision-Makers Guide to Solid Waste Management.* EPA/530-SW89-072. Washington, DC: Environmental Protection Agency.
U.S. EPA (1990). *RCRA Orientation Manual.* Washington, DC: United States Environmental Protection Agency.
U.S. EPA (1992). *Characterization of Municipal Solid Waste in U.S.: 1992 Update.* EPA/530-5-92-019. Washington, DC: Environmental Protection Agency.

Glossary

abiotic: The nonliving part of the physical environment (e.g., light, temperature, and soil structure).

absorption: (1) Movement of a chemical into a plant, animal, or soil. (2) Any process by which one substance penetrates the interior of another substance. In chemical spill clean-up, this process applies to the uptake of chemicals by capillaries within certain sorbent materials.

absorption units: Devices or units designed to transfer the contaminant from a gas phase to a liquid phase.

accidental spills: The unintended release of chemicals and hazardous compounds or materials into the environment.

acid: A hydrogen-containing corrosive compound that reacts with water to produce hydrogen ions; a proton donor; a liquid compound with a pH less than or equal to 2.

acid mine drainage: The dissolving and transporting of sulfuric acid and toxic metal compounds from abandoned underground coal mines to nearby streams and rivers when surface water flows through the mines.

acid rain: Precipitation made more acidic from falling through air pollutants (primarily sulfur dioxide) and dissolving them.

acidic deposition: *See* **acid rain**.

adiabatic: Without loss or gain of heat. When air rises, air pressure decreases and expands adiabatically in the atmosphere; since the air can neither gain nor lose heat, its temperature falls as it expands to fill a larger volume.

adiabatic lapse rate: The temperature profile or lapse rate, used as a basis of comparison for actual temperature profiles (from ground level) and hence for predictions of stack gas dispersion characteristics.

adsorption: (1) The process by which one substance is attracted to and adheres to the surface of another substance without actually penetrating its internal structure. (2) The process by which a substance is held (bound) to the surface of a soil particle or mineral in such a way that the substance is only available slowly.

adsorption site density: The concentration of sorptive surface available from the mineral and organic contents of soils. An increase in adsorption sites indicates an increase in the ability of the soils to immobilize hydrocarbon compounds in the soil matrix.

advanced wastewater treatment: Any treatment that follows primary and secondary wastewater treatment.

advective wind: The horizontal air movements resulting from temperature gradients that give rise to density gradients and subsequently pressure gradients.

aerobic: Living in the air. Opposite of *anaerobic*.

aerobic processes: Processes that are dependent on microorganisms that require oxygen for their metabolism. For example, water in an aerobic stream contains dissolved oxygen. Therefore, organisms using this process can oxidize organic wastes to simple compounds.

afterburners: A device that includes an auxiliary fuel burner and combustion chamber to incinerate combustible gas contaminants.

aggregate: Clusters of soil particles.

agricultural sources: Both organic and inorganic contaminants, usually produced by pesticide, fertilizers, and animal wastes, all of which enter bodies of water via runoff and groundwater absorption in areas of agricultural activity.

air: The mixture of gases that constitutes the Earth's atmosphere.

air currents: Currents created by air moving upward and downward.

air mass: A large body of air with particular characteristics of temperature and humidity. An air mass forms when air rests over an area long enough to pick up the conditions of that area.

air pollutants: Sulfur dioxide, hydrogen sulfide, hydrocarbons, carbon monoxide, ozone, and atmospheric nitrogen; can also include any gaseous substance that contaminates air.

air pollution: Contamination of atmosphere with any material that can cause damage to life or property.

air stripping: A mass transfer process in which a substance in solution in water is transferred to solution in a gas.

airborne contaminants: Any contaminant capable of dispersion in air and/or capable of being carried by air to other locations.

airborne particulate matter: Fine solids or liquid droplets suspended and carried in the air.

albedo: The fraction of received radiation reflected by a surface.

algae: A large and diverse assemblage of eucaryotic organisms that lack roots, stems, and leaves, but have chlorophyll and other pigments for carrying out oxygen-producing photosynthesis.

alphiatic hydrocarbon: Compound comprised of straight chain molecules as opposed to a ring structure.

alkalinity: (1) The concentration of hydroxide ions. (2) The capacity of water to neutralize acids because of the bicarbonate, carbonate, or hydroxide content. Usually expressed in milligrams per liter of calcium carbonate equivalent.

alkanes: A class of hydrocarbons (gas, solid, or liquids depending on carbon content). Its solids (paraffins) are a major constituent of natural gas and petroleum. Alkanes are usually gases at room temperature (methane) when containing less than five carbon atoms per molecule.

alkenes: A class of hydrocarbons (also called olefins); sometimes gases at room temperature, but usually liquids; common in petroleum products. Generally more toxic than alkanes, less toxic than aromatics.

alkynes: A class of hydrocarbons (formerly known as acetylenes). Unsaturated compounds characterized by one or more triple bonds between adjacent carbon atoms. Lighter alkenes, such as ethyne, are gases; heavier ones are liquids or solids.

amoebae (pl.) (sing. **amoeba**): One of the simplest living animals, consisting of a single cell and belonging to the protozoa group. The body consists of colorless protoplasm. Its activities are controlled by the nucleus, and it feeds by flowing round and engulfing organic debris. It reproduces by binary fission. Some species of amoeba are harmless parasites.

anabolism: The process of building up cell tissue, promoted by the influence of certain hormones; the constructive side of metabolism as opposed to catabolism.

anaerobic: Not requiring oxygen.

anaerobic process: Any process (usually chemical or biological) carried out without the presence of air or oxygen, for example, in a heavily polluted watercourse with no dissolved oxygen present.

analysis: The separation of an intellectual or substantial whole into its constituent parts for individual study.

animal feedlots: A confined area where hundreds or thousands of livestock animals are fattened for sale to slaughterhouses and meat producers.

animal wastes: Dung (fecal matter) and urine of animals.

anthropogenic sources: Sources generated by human activity.

anticyclone: High atmosphere areas characterized by clear weather and the absence of rain and violent winds.

apoenzyme: The protein part of an enzyme.

aqueous solution: Solution in which the solvent is water.

aquifer: Any rock formation containing water. The rock of an aquifer must be porous and permeable to absorb water.

aromatic hydrocarbons: Class of hydrocarbons considered to be the most immediately toxic; found in oil and petroleum products; soluble in water. Antonym: aliphatic.

asphalt incorporation: Soil remediation/recycling process whereby contaminated soil is removed from a site and fed into an asphalt-making process as part of the aggregated filler substance.

atmosphere: The layer of air surrounding the Earth's surface.

atom: A basic unit of physical matter indivisible by chemical means; the fundamental building block of chemical elements; composed of a nucleus of protons and neutrons, surrounded by electrons.

atomic number: Number of protons in the nucleus of an atom. Each chemical element has been assigned a number in a complete series from 1 to 100+.

atomic orbitals/electron shells: The region around the nucleus of an atom in which an electron is most likely to be found.

atomic weight: The mass of an element relative to its atoms.

auger: A tool used to bore holes in soil to capture a sample.

automatic samplers: Devices that automatically take samples from a waste stream.

autotrophic: An organism that can synthesize organic molecules needed for growth from inorganic compounds using light or another source of energy.

autotrophs: *See* **autotrophic.**

Avogadro's number: The number of carbon atoms in 12 g of the carbon-12 isotope $(6.022045 \times 10^{23})$. The relative atomic mass of any element, expressed in grams, contains this number of atoms.

bacilli (pl.) (sing: **bacillus**): Members of a group of rodlike bacteria that occur everywhere in soil and air. Some are responsible for diseases such as anthrax or for causing food spoilage.

bacteria: One-celled microorganisms.

bacteriophage: A virus that infects bacteria; often called a *phage.*

baghouse filter: A closely woven bag for removing dust from dust-laden gas streams. The fabric allows passage of the gas with retention of the dust.

bare rock succession: An ecological succession process whereby rock or parent material is slowly degraded to soil by a series of bio-ecological processes.

base: A substance that when dissolved in water generates hydroxide (OH-) ions or is capable of reacting with an acid to form a salt.

beneficial reuse: The practice of reusing a typical waste product in a beneficial manner, for example, wastewater biosolids to compost.

benthic (*benthos*): Aquatic organisms living on the bottom or on submerged vegetation. The term originates from the Greek word for bottom.

best available technology (BAT): Essentially a refinement of best practicable means whereby a greater degree of control over emissions to land, air, and water may be exercised using currently available technology.

binomial system of nomenclature: A system used to classify organisms; organisms are generally described by a two-word scientific name, the genus and species.

bioaccumulation: The biological concentration mechanism whereby filter feeders such as limpets, oysters, and other shellfish concentrate heavy metals or other stable compounds present in dilute concentrations in sea or freshwater.

biochemical oxygen demand (BOD): The amount of oxygen required by bacteria to stabilize decomposable organic matter under aerobic conditions.

biodegradable: A material capable of being broken down, usually by microorganisms, into basic elements.

biodegradation: The natural decay process breaking down human-made and natural compounds to their constituent elements and compounds, for assimilation in, and by, the biological renewal cycles; for example, wood is decomposed to carbon dioxide and water.

biogeochemical cycles: Cycles driven by energy, directly or indirectly, from the sun. *Bio* refers to living organisms and *geo* to water, air, rocks, or solids. *Chemical* is concerned with the chemical composition of the Earth.

biological oxygen demand (BOD): The amount of dissolved oxygen taken up by microorganisms in a sample of water.

biological treatment: Process by which hazardous waste is rendered nonhazardous or reduced in volume by the actions of microorganisms.

biological treatment process: Process such as activated sludge, aerated lagoon, trickling filters, waste stabilization ponds, and anaerobic digestion.

biology: The science of life.

biosolids treatment: Conditioning, thickening, dewatering, disposal by incineration, composting, land application, or land burial. *Biosolids* refers to water or sewage sludge.

biosphere: The region of the Earth and its atmosphere in which life exists, an envelope extending from as much as 6,000 meters above to 10,000 meters below sea level that embraces all life from alpine regions to the ocean deeps.

biostimulant: A chemical that can stimulate growth; for example, phosphates or nitrates in a water system.

biota: The animal and plant life of a particular region considered as a total ecological entity.

biotic: Pertaining to life or specific life conditions.

biotic index: A systematic survey of invertebrate aquatic organisms that is used to correlate with river quality, based on two principles: (1) pollution tends to restrict the variety of organisms present at a point, although large numbers of pollution-tolerant species may persist; and (2) in a polluted stream, as the degree of pollution increases, key organisms tend to disappear in this order: stone fly, mayflies, caddis fly, freshwater shrimp, bloodworms, and tubificid worms. The diversity of species in an ecosystem is often a good indicator of the presence of pollution—the greater the diversity, the lower the degree of pollution.

blastospore (or **bud**): Fungispores formed by budding.

blowby: Leakage of combustion gases between a piston and the cylinder wall into the crankcase in an automobile. Blowby occurs as gases from the piston ring area pass into the crankcase.

boiling point: The temperature at which a substance changes from a liquid to a gas.

brackish water: Water (nonpotable) containing between 100 and 10,000 ppm of total dissolved solids.

brick manufacturing process: Contaminated soil recycling/remediation process whereby contaminated soil is added to the mix used to make brick.

brine: Water containing more than 100,000 ppm of total dissolved solids (salt—NaCl), which can yield salt after evaporation.

btu: British thermal unit, a measuring unit of heat.

budding: Type of asexual reproduction in which an outgrowth develops from a cell to form a new individual. Most yeasts reproduce this way.

calorie: The amount of heat required to raise the temperature of one gram of water one degree centigrade.

capsule: Organized accumulation of gelatinous material on cell walls.

carbon adsorption: Process whereby activated carbon, known as the sorbent, is used to remove certain wastes from water by preferentially holding them to the carbon surface.

carbon cycle: Process whereby the carbon fixed by photosynthesis is eventually returned to the atmosphere as plants and animals die and the dead organic matter is consumed by the decomposer organisms. The atmosphere is a reservoir of gaseous carbon dioxide, but to be of use to life, this carbon dioxide must be converted into suitable organic compounds—"fixed"—as in the production of plant stems by the process of photosynthesis. The productivity of an area of vegetation is measured by the rate of carbon fixation.

carbon dioxide: A colorless, odorless inert gas; a by-product of combustion.

carbon monoxide: A highly toxic and flammable gas that is a by-product of incomplete combustion. Very dangerous even in very low concentrations.

carbonate hardness: Temporary hard water caused by the presence of bicarbonates; when water is boiled, the bicarbonates are converted to insoluble carbonates that precipitate as scale.

catabolism: In biology, the destructive part of metabolism in which living tissue is changed into energy and waste products.

catalysis: The acceleration (or retardation) of chemical or biochemical reactions by a relatively small amount of a substance (the catalyst), which itself undergoes no permanent chemical change, and which may be recovered when the reaction has finished.

catalyst: A substance or compound that speeds up the rate of chemical or biochemical reactions.

catalytic combustion: A process in which a preheated, contaminant-laden gas stream is passed through a catalyst bed that promotes the oxidization reaction at lower temperatures. The metal catalyst (usually platinum) is used to initiate and promote combustion at much lower temperatures than those required for thermal combustion.

catalytic converter: A device fitted to the exhaust system of a motor vehicle to reduce toxic emissions from the engine. It converts harmful exhaust products to relatively harmless ones by passing the exhaust gases over a mixture of catalysts coated on a metal or ceramic honeycomb, a structure that increases the surface area and therefore the amount of active catalyst with which the exhaust gases will have contact.

catchment: The natural drainage area for precipitation; the collection area for water supplies or a river system. The notional line, or watershed, on surrounding high land defines the area.

cell: The basic biological unit of plant and animal matter.

cell membrane (cytoplasmic membrane): The lipid- and protein-containing, selectively permeable membrane that surrounds the cytoplasm in procaryotic and eucaryotic cells; in most types of microbial cell, the cell membrane is bordered externally by the cell wall. In microbial cells, the precise composition of the cell membrane depends on the species, growth conditions, and the age of the cell.

cell nucleus: A membrane-lined body that contains chromosomes; contained within a eucaryotic cell.

cell wall: The permeable, rigid outermost layer of a plant cell, composed mainly of cellulose.

cement production process: A contaminated soil recycling/remediation technology whereby contaminated soil is added to the mix in cement production.

CERCLA: (Comprehensive Environmental Response, Compensation and Liability Act of 1980; Superfund.) A federal law that provides for clean-up and compensation and assigns liability for the release of hazardous substances into the air, land, or water.

chemical bond: A chemical linkage that holds atoms together to form molecules.

chemical change: A transfer that results from making or breaking chemical bonds.

chemical equation: A shorthand method for expressing a reaction in terms of written chemical formulas.

chemical extraction: A process in which excavated contaminated soils are washed to remove contaminants of concern.

chemical formula: A formula that indicates the kinds of atoms present in each molecule and their actual number.

chemical oxygen demand (COD): A means of measuring the pollution strength of domestic and industrial wastes based on the fact that all organic compounds, with few exceptions, can be oxidized by the action of strong oxidizing agents under acid conditions to carbon dioxide and water.

chemical precipitation: A process by which inorganic contaminants (heavy metals from groundwater) are removed by addition of carbonate, hydroxide, or sulfide chemicals.

chemical process audit/survey: A procedure used to gather information on the type, composition, and quantity of waste produced.

chemical reaction: The process whereby a substance undergoes a chemical change and is no longer the same substance; it becomes one or more new substances.

chemical weathering: A form of weathering brought about by a chemical change in the rocks affected; involves the breakdown of the minerals within a rock and usually produces a claylike residue.

chemosynthesis: A method of making protoplasm using energy from chemical reactions, in contrast to the use of light energy employed for the same purpose in photosynthesis.

chlorofluorocarbons (CFCs): Synthetic chemicals that are odorless, nontoxic, nonflammable, and chemically inert. CFCs have been used as propellants in aerosol cans, as refrigerants in refrigeration and air conditioners, and in the manufacture of foam packaging. They are partly responsible for the destruction of the ozone layer.

chlorophyll: A combination of green and yellow pigments, present in all "green" plants, which captures light energy and enables the plants to form carbohydrate material from carbon dioxide and water in the process known as photosynthesis. Found in all algae, phytoplankton, and almost all higher plants.

chloroplasts: A structure (or organelle) found within a plant cell containing the green pigment chlorophyll.

cilia: Small, threadlike organs on the surface of some cells, composed of contractile fibers that produce rhythmic waving movements. Some single-celled organisms move by means of cilia. In multicellular animals, they keep lubricated surfaces clear of debris. They also move food in the digestive tracts of some invertebrates.

clarification: The process of removing solids from water.

clay content: The amount of clay (fine-grained sedimentary rock) in a soil.

Clean Air Act: The name given to three laws passed by the U.S. government. The 1963 act dealt with the control of smoke from industrial and domestic sources. It was extended by the 1968 act, particularly to control gas cleaning and heights of stacks of installations in which fuels are burned to deal with smoke from industrial open bonfires. The 1990 Clean Air Act brought wide-ranging reforms for all kinds of pollution from large or small, mobile or stationary sources, including routine and toxic emissions ranging from power plants to consumer products.

Clean Water Act (CWA): A keystone environmental law credited with significantly cutting the amount of municipal and industrial pollution fed into the nation's waterways. More formally known as the Federal Water Pollution Control Act Amendments, passed in 1972, it stems originally from a much-amended 1948 law aiding communities in building sewage treatment plants and has itself been much amended, most notably in 1977 and 1987.

clean zone: That point in a river or stream upstream before a single point of pollution discharge.

climate: The composite pattern of weather conditions that can be expected in a given region. Climate refers to yearly cycles of temperature, wind, rainfall, and so on, not to daily variations.

coal gasification process: The conversion of coal (via destructive distillation or heated out) to gaseous fuel.

cocci (sing. **coccus**): Members of a group of globular bacteria, some of which are harmful to humans.

cofactor: A nonprotein activator that forms a functional part of an enzyme.

cold front: The leading portion of a cold atmospheric air mass moving against and eventually replacing a warm air mass.

cold-mix asphalt process: A mobile or in-place process whereby contaminated soils are recycled/remediated by serving as the fine-grained component in the asphalt-making process.

collector: *See* **cyclone collector**.

colloidal material: A constituent of total solids in wastewater; consists of particulate matter with an approximate diameter of from 1 millimicron to 1 micron.

color: A physical characteristic of water often used to judge water quality; pure water is colorless.

combined wastewater: The combination of sanitary wastewater and stormwater runoff.

combustion: The rapid combination of a substance with oxygen, accompanied by the evolution of heat and usually light. In air pollution control, combustion or incineration is a beneficial pollution control process in which the objective is to convert certain contaminants into innocuous substances such as carbon dioxide and water.

commercial chemical products: An EPA category listing of hazardous wastes (also called *P* or *U* listed wastes because their code numbers begin with these letters); includes specific commercial chemical products or manufacturing chemical intermediates.

commercial sources of MSW: Solids generated in restaurants, hotels, stores, motels, service stations, repair shops, markets, office buildings, and print shops.

Community Right-to-Know Act: A part of SARA Title III under CERCLA. Stipulates that a community located near a facility storing, producing, or using hazardous materials has a right to know about the potential consequences of a catastrophic chemical spill or release of chemicals from the site.

composite sample: A sample formed by mixing discrete samples taken at periodic points in time or a continuous proportion of the flow. The number of discrete samples that make up the composite depends on the variability of pollutant concentration and flow.

composting: A beneficial reuse biological process whereby waste (e.g., yard trimmings or wastewater biosolids) is transformed into a harmless humus-like substance used as a soil amendment.

compound: A substance composed of two or more elements, chemically combined in a definite proportion.

concentrated solution: Solute in concentration present in large quantities.

condensation: Air pollution control technology used to remove gaseous pollutants from a waste stream; a process in which the volatile gases are removed from the contaminant stream and changed into a liquid.

condenser: An air pollution control device used to condense vapors to a liquid phase by either increasing the system pressure without a change in temperature or decreasing the system temperature to its saturation temperature without a pressure change.

conduction: Flow of heat energy through a material without the movement of any part of the material itself.

confined aquifer: A water-bearing layer sandwiched between two less permeable layers; water flow is restricted to vertical movement only.

conidia: The asexual spores borne on aerial mycelia (actinomycetes bacteria).

construction and demolition sources of MSW: Generated by new construction sites, razing of old buildings, road repair/renovation sites, and broken pavement.

consumers: Organisms that cannot produce their own food and eat by engulfing or predigesting the fluids, cells, tissues, or waste products of other organisms.

contact condenser: Similar to a simple spray scrubber; it cools vapor stream by spraying liquid directly on the vapor stream.

control of disposal: A system of controls and restrictions governing the disposal of hazardous wastes onto, or into, the land. A key element of RCRA's goal of protecting groundwater supplies.

convection: Method of heat transfer whereby the heated molecules circulate through the medium (gas or liquid).

cooling tower method: A treatment method used to treat thermally polluted water by spraying the heated water into the air and allowing it to cool by evaporation.

corrosive: A substance that attacks and eats away other materials by strong chemical action.

covalent bond: A chemical bond produced when two atoms share one or more pairs of electrons.

cradle-to-grave act: *See* **Resource Conservation and Recovery Act**.

crustacean: One of a class of arthropods that includes crabs, lobsters, shrimps, wood-lice, and barnacles.

cultural eutrophication: Overnourishment of aquatic ecosystems with plant nutrients, resulting form human activities, including agriculture, urbanization, and industrial discharge.

cyclone collector: In air pollution control, a collector that removes particles from a gas stream by centrifugal force.

cytochrome: A class of iron-containing proteins important in cell metabolism.

cytoplasm: The jelly-like matter within a cell.

decomposers: Organisms such as bacteria, mushrooms, and fungi that obtain nutrients by breaking down complex matter in the wastes and dead bodies of other organisms into simpler chemicals, most of which are returned to the soil and water for reuse by producers.

decomposition: Process whereby a chemical compound is reduced to its component substances. In biology, the destruction of dead organisms either by chemical reduction or by the action of decomposers.

deep-well injection: In waste control technology, the ultimate disposal of liquid hazardous waste under pressure to underground strata isolated by impermeable rock strata to a depth of about 700 m.

density: The ratio of the weight of a mass to the unit of volume.

depletion: In evaluating ambient air quality, pertains to the fact that pollutants emitted into the atmosphere do not remain there forever.

desertification: Creation of deserts by changes in climate or by human-aided processes.

detoxification: Biological conversion of a toxic substance to one less toxic.

dewatering: The physical or chemical process of removing water from sludge or biosolids.

diatom: Microscopic single-celled alga found in all parts of the world.

diffusion: (1) Mixing of substances, usually gases and liquids, from molecular motion. (2) The spreading out of a substance to fill a space.

dilute solutions: A solution weakened by the addition of water, oil, or other liquid or solid.

dinoflagellates: Unicellular, photosynthetic protistan algae.

direct flame combustion (flaring): A process used in air pollution control technology to burn off gases (e.g., methane).

disinfection: Effective killing by chemical or physical processes of all organisms capable of causing infectious disease (chlorination is commonly employed for disinfection in wastewater treatment processes).

dispersion: The dilution and reduction of concentration of pollutants in either air or water. Air pollution dispersion mechanisms are a function of the prevailing meteorological conditions.

dissolved oxygen (DO): The amount of oxygen dissolved in a stream, river, or lake, an indication of the degree of health of the body of water and its ability to support a balanced aquatic ecosystem.

DNAPLs: Dense nonaqueous-phase liquids, including carbon tetrachloride, creosote, trichloroethane, dichlorobenzene, and others, which can contaminate groundwater supplies.

domestic wastewater: Wastewater containing mainly human and animal wastes, household wastes, and small amounts of groundwater infiltration, as well as perhaps small amounts of industrial waste.

dose–response curve: A visual means of determining, based on collected data, the percent mortality to dose administered.

dose–response evaluation: The toxicological evaluation of the potency of a chemical.

dose–response relationship: Process in which a dose is administered to test animals, and depending on the outcome, it is increased or decreased until a range is found where at the upper end all animals die, and at the lower end, all animals survive. Used by toxicologists as a basis for toxicological considerations.

drainage basin: The geographical region drained by a river or stream.

dry adiabatic lapse rate: Lapse rate (cooling) of –1-C/100m or 1-10-C/km, which results when a dry parcel of air is lifted in the atmosphere, undergoing adiabatic expansion and cooling.

dry tower method: A thermal pollution treatment technique whereby heated water is pumped through tubes and the heat is released into the air (similar to the performance of an automobile radiator).

dumps: An open location where refuse and other waste materials are disposed of in a manner that does not protect the environment; is susceptible to open burning; or is exposed to the elements, vermin, or scavengers.

dystrophic: Characterized by defective nutrition.

ecological toxicology: The branch of toxicology that addresses the effects of toxic substances, not only on the human population, but also on the environment in general, including air, soil, surface water, and groundwater.

ecology: The study of the interrelationship of an organism or a group of organisms with the environment.

ecosystem: A self-regulating, natural community of plants and animals interacting with one another and with their nonliving environment.

ecotoxicology: *See* **ecological toxicology**.

electrolytic recovery technique: A method used primarily for recovery of metals from process streams, to clean process waters, or to treat wastewaters prior to discharge; based on the oxidation-reduction reaction, wherein electrode surfaces are used to collect the metals from the waste stream.

electron: A component of an atom; travels in a distant orbit around a nucleus.

electron transport system: A series of electron carriers in metabolic transfer that operate together to transfer electrons from donors such as NADH and $FADH_2$ to acceptors such as oxygen.

electrostatic precipitation: Process using a precipitator to remove dust or other particles from air and other gases by electrostatic means. An electric discharge is passed through the gas, giving the impurities a negative electric charge. Positively charged plates are then used to attract the charged particles and remove them from the fast flow.

elements: The simplest substance that cannot be separated into more simple parts by ordinary means. There are more than 100 known elements.

emergency response: Relates primarily to OSHA's requirement under 29 C.F.R. § 1910.120 for chemical, industrial, storage, and waste sites to have a written emergency response plan for any covered chemical release or spill to the environment that could jeopardize the good health and well-being of any worker. The EPA also requires an emergency response plan for facilities handling, producing, or using covered chemicals in its risk management plan requirements. Contingencies for fire, natural disasters, terrorist attacks, and medical emergencies should also be included in emergency response plans.

emergent vegetation: A subdivision of the littoral zone of a pond; encompasses shoreline soil area and the immediate shallow water area where emergent plant life can take root under water, grow, and surface above the waterline.

emergents: *See* **emergent vegetation**.

endergonic: A reaction in which energy is absorbed.

endoplasmic reticulum: A system of membranes that ramifies through the cytoplasmic region and forms the limiting boundaries, compartments, and channels whose lumina are completely isolated from the cytoplasm; the endoplasmic reticulum is a protein-containing lipid bilayer.

energy: A system capable of producing a physical change of state.

entropy: A measure of the disorder of a system.

environment: All the surroundings of an organism, including other living things, climate and soil, etc. In other words, the conditions for development or growth.

environmental degradation: All the limiting factors that act together to regulate the maximum allowable size or carrying capacity of a population.

environmental factors: Factors that influence volatilization of hydrocarbon compounds from soils. Environmental factors include temperature, wind, evaporation, and precipitation.

environmental science: The study of the human impact on the physical and biological environment of an organism. In its broadest sense, it also encompasses the social and cultural aspects of the environment.

environmental toxicology: The branch of toxicology that addresses the effects of toxic substances, not only on the human population, but also on the environment in general, including air, soil, surface water, and groundwater.

enzymes: Proteinaceous substances that catalyze microbiological reactions such as decay or fermentation. They are not used up in the process but speed it up greatly. They can promote a wide range of reactions, but a particular enzyme can usually only promote a reaction on a specific substrate.

epilimnion: The upper layer of a lake, heated by the sun and lighter and less dense than the underlying water.

eucaryotic: An organism characterized by a cellular organization that includes a well-defined nuclear membrane.

euphotic: The surface layer of an ocean, lake, or other body of water through which sufficient sunlight reaches to allow photosynthesis.

eutrophic lake: A lake with a large or excessive supply of plant nutrients (mostly phosphates and nitrates).

eutrophication: A natural process in which lakes receive inputs of plant nutrients as a result of natural erosion and runoff from the surrounding land basin.

evaporative emissions: The evaporative emission of fuel from internal combustion systems caused by diurnal losses, hot soak, and running losses.

evapotranspiration: The combination of evaporation and transpiration of liquid water in plant tissue and the soil to water vapor in the atmosphere.

excavation: The physical removal of soil to construct a burial site for contaminants (landfill) and/or contaminated soil by mechanical means.

excavation and disposal: The removal of contaminated soil for treatment or ultimate disposal.

exergonic: Releasing energy.

exposure assessment: A measurement to estimate the magnitude of actual and/or potential human exposures, the frequency and duration of these exposures, and the pathways by which humans are potentially exposed.

exposure pathways: The means by which exposure is experienced. There are two categories: (1) direct human exposure pathways and (2) environmental exposure pathways. Both of these categories are further subdivided into primary and secondary exposure pathways. Primary pathways directly affect site operations and personnel (e.g., skin contact during soil sampling). Secondary exposure pathways occur as a minor component during site operations and exhibit significant decreases with time as treatment progresses (e.g., wind blown dust).

extraction procedure (EP): A standardized laboratory test used to test for toxicity; replaced in 1990 by the Toxicity Characteristics Leaching Procedure (TCLP).

extraction well: A well used to lower the water table, creating a hydraulic gradient that draws a plume of contamination to the well so that the contaminant can be extracted.

extremely hazardous substance: An EPA term for those chemicals that must be reported to the appropriate authorities if released above the threshold reporting quantity.

facultative: Capable of growth under aerobic and anaerobic conditions.

Federal Water Pollution Control Act (Clean Water Act)**:** Federal law concerned with controlling and regulating the amount of municipal and industrial pollution fed into the nation's water bodies.

fermentation: The decomposition of organic substances by microorganisms and/or enzymes. The process is usually accompanied by the evolution of heat and gas and can be aerobic or anaerobic.

fertilizer: Substance that adds essential nutrients to the soil and makes the land or soil capable of producing more vegetation or crops.

filtration: Technique by which suspended solid particles in a fluid are removed by passing the mixture through a filter. The particles are retained by the filter to form a residue, and the fluid passes through to make up the filtrate.

1st Law of Thermodynamics: "Law" that states that in any chemical or physical change, movement of matter from one place to another, or change in temperature, energy is neither created nor destroyed, but merely converted from one form to another.

flagella (pl.) (sing: **flagellum**)**:** Threadlike appendages extending outward from the plasma membrane and cell wall, which give some bacteria motility.

flare: *See* **direct flame combustion**.

flexible-membrane liner (FML): A rubber or plastic liner used in sanitary landfills.

floating leaf vegetation: Part of the littoral zone in a lake or pond where vegetation rooted under the surface allows stems to produce foliage that is able to reach and float on the water surface.

fluoride: Fluoride salt is added to public drinking water supplies for improving resistance to dental carries.

food chain: A sequence of transfers of energy in the form of food from organisms in one trophic level to organisms in another trophic level when one organisms eats or decomposes another.

food web: A complex network of many interconnected food chains and feeding interactions.

formula weight: The sum of the atomic weight of all atoms that comprise one formula unit.

friable: Readily crumbled in the hand.

front: In meteorology, the boundary between two air masses of different temperature or humidity.

frustules: The distinctive two-piece wall of silica in diatoms.

fumigation: What occurs when emissions from a smokestack that is under an inversion layer head downward, leading to greatly elevated downwind ground-level concentrations of contamination.

fungi (pl) (sing: **fungus**): Saprophytic or parasitic organisms that may be unicellular or made up of tubular filaments and lack chlorophyll.

garbage: The generic name for waste emanating from households, containing mostly vegetable matter and paper.

gas: In the widest sense, applied to all aeriform bodies, the most minute particles that exhibit the tendency to fly apart from each other in all directions. Normally these gases are found in that state at ordinary temperature and pressure. They can only be liquefied or solidified by artificial means, either through high pressure or extremely low temperatures.

gas laws: The physical laws concerning the behavior of gases. They include Boyle's law and Charles's law, which are concerned with the relationships among the pressure, temperature, and volume of an ideal (hypothetical) gas.

general biological succession: The process whereby communities of plant and animal species in a particular area are replaced over time by a series of different and usually more complex communities (aka *ecological succession*).

genome: A complete haploid set of chromosomes.

genus: A group of species with many common characteristics.

geology: The science of Earth, its origin, composition, structure, and history.

geophysical testing: A testing method used to evaluate the subsurface layers, locate the water table, and map contaminant contours using resistivity and conductivity meters.

geosphere: The inorganic, or nonliving, portions of the Earth that are home to all the globe's organic, or living, matter.

geothermal energy: The use of the Earth's natural heat for human purposes; a form of alternative energy that is massive but difficult to tap.

geothermal power: *See* **geothermal energy**.

global warming: The long-term increase in the average temperature of the Earth.

glycolysis: One of three phases of the catabolism of glucose to carbon and water.

grab sample: An individual discrete sample collected over a period of time not exceeding 15 minutes.

gram: The basic unit of weight in the metric system; equal to 1/1000th of a kilogram; approximately 28.5 grams equal 1 ounce.

gravity: The force of attraction that arises between objects by virtue of their masses. On Earth, gravity is the force of attraction between any object in the Earth's gravitational field and the Earth itself.

gravity settler: An enlarged chamber in which the horizontal gas velocity is slowed, allowing particles to settle out by gravity. Used for the removal of solid and liquid waste materials from gaseous streams.

greenhouse effect: The trapping of heat in the atmosphere. Incoming shortwavelength solar radiation penetrates the atmosphere, but the longwave outgoing radiation is absorbed by water vapor, carbon dioxide, ozone, and several other gases in the atmosphere and is re-radiated to the Earth, causing an increase in atmospheric temperature.

greenhouse gases: The gases present in the Earth's atmosphere that cause the greenhouse effect.

groundwater: Water collected underground in porous rock strata and soils; it emerges at the surface as springs and streams.

grout curtain: Portland cement or grout injected under pressure to form a barrier against contaminant movement in soil. Used in in-situ isolation and containment.

growth: Exponential bacterial growth.

growth curve: Plotting of bacterial growth cycles. The curve is divided into four phases: lag, exponential, stationary, and death. The lag phase, characterized by little or no growth, corresponds to an initial period of time when bacteria are first inoculated into a fresh medium. After the bacteria have adjusted to their new environment, a period of rapid growth (the exponential phase) follows. During this time, conditions are optimal and the population doubles with great regularity. As the bacteria food supply begins to be depleted, or as toxic metabolic products accumulate, the population enters the no-growth, or stationary, phase. Finally, as the environment becomes more and more hostile, the death phase is reached, and the population declines.

guano: A substance composed chiefly of the dung of sea birds or bats, accumulated along certain coastal areas or in caves and used as fertilizer.

habitat: The place or type of place where an organism or community of organisms naturally or normally thrives.

hardness: A water quality parameter. Water that does not lather easily with soap and produces scale in pots, pans, and kettles, is hard. Hardness is caused by the presence of certain salts of calcium and magnesium in the water supply.

Hazardous and Solid Waste Amendments (1984): Part of the **RCRA** that emphasizes the development and use of alternative and innovative treatment technologies that result in permanent destruction of wastes or reduction in toxicity, mobility, and volume. Land disposal is greatly restricted under the 1984 amendments.

hazardous chemical: An explosive, flammable, poisonous, corrosive, reactive, or radioactive chemical requiring special care in handling because of hazards it poses to public health and the environment.

hazardous material: A substance in a quantity or form posing an unreasonable risk to health, safety, and/or property when transported in commerce; a substance that by its nature, containment, and reactivity has the capability to inflict harm during an accident occurrence; characterized as toxic, corrosive, flammable, reactive, an irritant, or a strong sensitizer, and thereby poisonous. A threat to health and the environment when improperly managed.

hazardous substance: A U.S. EPA term used for certain listed chemicals that when released into the environment above a certain amount must be reported.

hazardous waste: Waste materials or mixtures of waste that require special handling and disposal because of their potential to damage health and the environment.

hazardous waste stream: A gaseous or liquid waste stream that contains any type of hazardous substance.

heat: A condition of matter caused by the rapid movement of its molecules. Energy has to be applied to the material in sufficient amounts to create the motion and may be applied by mechanical or chemical means.

heat balance: The constant trade-off that takes place when solar energy reaches the Earth's surface and is absorbed, then must return to space to maintain the Earth's normal heat balance.

heat islands: Large metropolitan areas where heat generated has an influence on the ambient temperature (adds heat) in and near the area.

heavy metals: A group of elements whose compounds are toxic to humans when found in the environment; examples are cadmium, mercury, copper, nickel, chromium, lead, zinc, and arsenic.

Henry's law: A "law" governing the behavior of gases in contact with water.

heterotrophic: Obtains energy by consuming the tissue of other organisms.

heterotroph: *See* **heterotrophic**.

holoenzyme: A complete enzyme consisting of an apoenzyme and a coenzyme.

horizon: In soil, a layer of soil approximately parallel to the soil surface and differing in properties and characteristics from adjacent layers below or above it.

hot soak: Evaporative emissions from heat from an internal combustion engine after it is shut off.

hot-mix asphalt process: A remedial technology whereby a contaminant entrained in soil is used in beneficial applications to make asphalt. In the hot-mix process, the petroleum-laden soil is added as part of the aggregate to hot asphalt and then mixed to make the final product.

humidity: The amount of water vapor in a given volume of the atmosphere (absolute humidity) or the ratio of the amount of water vapor in the atmosphere to the saturation value at the same temperature (relative humidity).

humus: That more or less stable fraction of the soil organic matter remaining after the major portions of added plant and animal residues are decomposed. Usually dark in color.

hydraulic gradient: The difference in hydraulic head divided by the distance along the fluid flow path. Groundwater moves through an aquifer in the direction of the hydraulic gradient.

hydrocarbon: A chemical containing only carbon and hydrogen atoms. Crude oil is a mixture largely of hydrocarbons.

hydrological cycle: The means by which water is circulated in the biosphere. Cooling in the atmosphere and precipitation over both land and oceans counterbalance evapotranspiration from the land mass plus evaporation from the oceans.

hydrosphere: The portion of the Earth's surface covered by the oceans, seas, and lakes.

hypha (pl. **hyphae**)**:** In fungi, a tubular cell that grows from the tip and may form many branches.

hypolimnion: The cold, relatively dense bottom layer of water in a stratified lake.

ideal gas law: A hypothetical gas that obeys the gas laws exactly in regard to temperature, pressure, and volume relationships.

igneous rock: Rock formed by the cooling and solidification of hot, molten material.

ignitability: One of the characteristics used to classify a substance as hazardous.

impaction: In air pollution control technology, a particle collection process whereby the center of mass of a particle diverging from a fluid strikes a stationary object and is collected by the stationary object.

impoundment: A lake classification; an artificial, human-made lake made by trapping water from rivers and watersheds.

in situ biodegradation: A process that uses naturally occurring microorganisms in soil to degrade contaminants to another form.

in situ isolation/contamination: A method of soil remediation that prevents the migration of liquid contaminant or leachates containing contaminants.

in situ leaching and chemical reaction: A soil remediation process whereby water mixed with a surfactant is used to leach contaminants from the soil into the groundwater. The groundwater is then collected downstream of the leaching site, through a collection system for treatment and/or disposal.

in situ passive remediation: The easiest to implement and least expensive remediation methodology, because it involves no action at the site; it lets nature takes its course, but is not readily or normally accepted by regulators.

in situ technologies: Remedial technologies performed in place at the site.

in situ vitrification: A treatment process that employs electrical current passed through electrodes driven into the soil that produce extreme heat and converts soil into a durable glassy material. The organic constituents are pyrolized in the melt and migrate to the surface, where they combust in the presence of oxygen. Inorganics in the soil are effectively bound in the solidified glass.

in situ volatilization: A process that uses forced air or drawn air currents through in-place soil to remove volatile compounds. Commonly known as air stripping.

incineration: The application of high temperatures (800° to 3,000°F) to break down organic wastes into simpler forms and to reduce the volume of waste needing disposal. Energy can be recovered from incineration heat.

inclusion: Storage granules often seen within bacterial cells.

industrial practices: Practices that can lead to soil contamination, including contaminants from USTs, oil field sites, chemical sites, geothermal sites, manufactured gas plants, mining sites, and environmental terrorism.

industrial wastewater: Liquid wastes produced by industry.

infiltration galleries: A technique used in in-situ biodegradation to reintroduce conditioned groundwater to the soil or aquifer.

infrared radiation: Invisible electromagnetic radiation of wavelength between about 0.75 mm and 1 mm—between the limit of the red end of the visible spectrum and the shortest microwaves.

injection well: In groundwater remediation, a process used to raise the level of the water table and to push a contaminated plume away from a potable water system (well).

innovative clean-up technology: Any new or developing soil remediation technology.

inorganic substance: A substance that is mineral in origin that does not contain carbon compounds, except as carbonates, carbides, etc.

insolation: The amount of direct solar radiation incident per unit of horizontal area at a given level.

institutional sources of MSW: Wastes generated in hospitals, schools, jails and prisons, and government centers.

interception: In particle collection technology, a process in which the particle's center of mass closely misses the object, but because of its finite size, the particle strikes the object and is collected.

Interstate Commerce Clause: The clause in the U.S. Constitution upon which the federal government enacted the Rivers and Harbors Act of 1988, enabling the U.S. Army Corp of Engineers to regulate and in some cases prohibit private and municipal dumping practices.

ionic bond: A chemical bond in which electrons have been transferred from atoms of low ionization potential to atoms of high electron affinity.

irrigation: An artificial water supply for dry agricultural areas, created by means of dams and channels.

isobar: A line drawn on maps and weather charts linking all places with the same atmospheric pressure (usually measured in millibars).

jet stream: A narrow band of very fast wind found at altitudes of 6 to10 miles in the upper troposphere or lower stratosphere.

Kelvin: A temperature scale used by scientists that begins at absolute zero and increases by the same degree intervals as the Celsius scale; that is, 0°C is the same as 273K, and 100°C is 373K.

Krebs cycle or **citric acid cycle:** The final part of the chain of biochemical reactions by which organisms break down food using oxygen to release energy (respiration).

land farming: Another name for land treatment, whereby various contaminants are spread on soil and worked into the surface and subsurface to allow biodegradation to take place.

land treatment: *See* **land farming**.

landfill: A land waste disposal site located without regard to possible pollution of groundwater and surface water resulting from runoff and leaching; waste is covered intermittently with a layer of Earth to reduce scavenger, aesthetic, disease, and air pollution problems.

landfilling: An ultimate disposal technique whereby solid and hazardous wastes are disposed of in excavated sites.

lapse rate: The rate of change of air temperature with increasing height.

latent heat of fusion: The amount of heat required to change one gram of a substance from the solid to the liquid phase at the same temperature.

latent heat of vaporization: The amount of heat required to change one gram of a substance from the liquid to the gas phase at the same temperature.

Law of conservation of mass: The "law" stating that in any ordinary physical or chemical change, matter is neither created nor destroyed, but merely changed from one form to another.

laxative effect: Loosening effect on bowels of new consumers caused by the consumption of hard water combined with magnesium sulfates.

leach liquors: Liquid leached from a substance via water circulation through or over it.

leachate: The liquid formed when rainwater percolates downward through landfilled wastes, picking up contaminants that might then enter the surrounding environment.

lead: A heavy metal, the accumulation of which in organic tissue could produce, in animals and humans, behavioral changes, blindness, and ultimately death.

lead-mine scale: Build-up of lead that occurs in geothermal process equipment such as piping, leading to process equipment failure.

Leaking Underground Storage Tanks (LUST): The 1986 U.S. UST clean-up fund.

lentic (calm waters)**:** Calm lakes, ponds, and swamps.

limited: Limiting nutrients such as carbon, nitrogen, and phosphorus.

limiting factor: Factors such as temperature, light, water, or a chemical that limit the existence, growth, abundance, or distribution of an organism.

limiting nutrient: *See* **limited**.

limnetic: The open water surface layer of a lake through which sufficient sunlight penetrates for photosynthesis.

limnology: The study of the plant and animal biology and physical properties of lakes and other bodies of open freshwater.

liquid: A state of matter between a solid and a gas.

liter: A metric unit of volume, equal to one cubic decimeter (1.76 pints).

lithosphere: The Earth's crust; the layers of soil and rock that comprise the crust.

litter: The intact and partially decayed organic matter lying on top of the soil; discards thrown about without regard to the environment.

littoral: The shallow zone of waters near the shore of a body of water.

LNAPLs: Light nonaqueous-phase liquids, including gasoline, heating oil, and kerosene.

loam: The textural-class name for soil with a moderate amount of sand, silt, and clay. Loam soils contain 7–27% clay, 28–50% silt, and 23–52% sand.

lotic: Running freshwater systems, for example, rivers or streams.

magma: The molten rock material within the Earth's core.

management factors: The management techniques (fertilization, irrigation, etc.) employed in land and soil management that decrease leaching, increase soil surface contaminant concentrations, or maximize soil aeration against volatilization.

manifest: *See* **tracking system**.

mass: The quantity of matter and a measurement of the amount of inertia that a body possesses.

mass balance equations: Equations used to track pollutants from one place to another.

materials balance: The idea that everything has to go somewhere, but is neither created nor destroyed in the process.

mature pond: A pond that reaches maturity, characterized by being carpeted with rich sediment, with aquatic vegetation extending out into open water, and a great diversity of plankton, invertebrates, and fishes.

maximum contaminant levels (MCLs): Primary drinking water standard and maximum contaminant levels allowed based on health-related criteria.

maximum sustainable yield: The highest rate at which a renewable resource can be used without impairing or damaging its ability to be fully renewed.

melting point: The temperature at which a substance changes from solid to liquid.

meromictic: Chemically stratified lakes in which different dissolved chemicals are partly mixed.

mesosome: A common intracellular structure found in the bacterial cytoplasm; an invagination of the plasma membrane in the shape of tubules, vesicles, or lamellae.

mesosphere: An atmospheric layer that extends from the top of the stratosphere to about 56 miles above the Earth.

mesotrophic lake: A term used to distinguish between an oligotrophic and an eutrophic lake.

metabolic transformation: The assembly-line-like activities that occur in microorganisms during the processing of raw materials into finished products.

metabolism: The chemical processes of living organisms; a constant alternation of building up and breaking down. For example, green plants build up complex organic substances from water, carbon dioxide, and mineral salts (photosynthesis); by digestion, animals partially break down complex organic substances ingested as food and subsequently resynthesize them in their own bodies.

metalloid: An element that exhibits the properties of both metals and nonmetals.

metals: Elements that tend to lose their valence electrons.

metamorphic rock: A type of rock that forms when rocks lying deep below the Earth's surface are heated to such a degree that their original crystal structure is lost. As the rock cools, a new crystalline structure is formed.

meteorology: The scientific observation and study of the atmosphere, so that weather can be accurately forecast.

meter: The standard of length in the metric system, equal to 39.37 inches or 3.28 feet.

methane (CH_4): The simplest hydrocarbon of the paraffin series. Colorless, odorless, and lighter than air, it burns with a bluish flame and explodes when mixed with air or oxygen. Methane is a greenhouse gas.

microbial community: The community of microbes available to biodegrade contaminants in the soil.

microbial degradation: The natural process whereby certain microbes in soil can degrade contaminants into harmless constituents.

microbiology: The study of organisms that can only be seen under the microscope.

middens: Primitive dunghills or refuse heaps.

midnight dumping: The illegal dumping of solid or hazardous wastes into the environment.

mining waste: The Earth and rock (including minerals and/or chemicals within) from a mine, discarded because the mineral or fuel content is too low to warrant extraction. This waste is an environmental problem if toxic substances leach from it into a river or stream, groundwater, or the soil.

mitochondria (pl.) (sing: **mitochondrion**): Microscopic bodies found in the cells of almost all living organisms and containing enzymes responsible for the conversion of food to usable energy.

mixture: In chemistry, a substance containing two or more compounds that still retain their separate physical and chemical properties.

mobile sources: Nonstationary sources of gaseous pollutants, including locomotives, automobiles, ships, and airplanes.

mobilization: The mobilizing of metals in soil by the acidity of precipitation.

modeling: The use of mathematical representations of contaminant dispersion and transformation to estimate ambient pollutant concentrations.

molar concentration (molarity): In chemistry, a solution that contains one mole of a substance per liter of solvent.

mole: An SI unit (symbol mol) of the amount of a substance. The amount of a substance that contains as many elementary entities as there are atoms in 12 g of the isotope carbon-12.

molecular weight: The weight of one molecule of a substance relative to ^{12}C, expressed in grams.

molecule: The fundamental particle that characterizes a compound. It consists of a group of atoms held together by chemical bonds.

monitor wells: Installed wells specifically designed to provide a means to monitor a contaminant plume in soil/groundwater.

monitoring: A process whereby a contaminant is tracked.

Montreal Protocol: An agreement requiring signatory countries to reduce their consumption of CFCs by 20% by 1993 and by 50% by 1998.

morphogenesis: The evolutionary development of the structure of an organism or part.

motility: An organism's mobility; ability to move.

municipal services sources of MSW: Wastes generated in restaurants, hotels, stores, motels, service stations, repair shops, markets, office buildings, and print shops.

municipal solid wastes (MSW): Municipally derived wastes, including paper, yard wastes, glass, metals, and plastics.

mycelium: An interwoven mass of threadlike filaments or hyphae forming the main body of most fungi. The reproductive structures, or "fruiting bodies," grow from the mycelium.

mycology: The branch of botany that deals with fungi.

National Ambient Air-Quality Standards (NAAQS): Standards established by the EPA at two levels: primary and secondary. Primary standards must be set at levels that will protect public health and include an "adequate margin of safety," regardless of whether the standards are economically or technologically achievable. Primary standards must protect even the most sensitive individuals, including the elderly and those with respiratory ailments. Secondary air quality standards are meant to be even more stringent than primary standards. Secondary standards are established to protect public welfare (e.g., structures, crops, animal, fabrics).

National Priorities List (NPL): A list that identifies the worst waste sites in the nation, based on such factors as the quantities and toxicity of wastes involved, the exposure pathways, the number of people potentially exposed, and the importance and vulnerability of the underlying groundwater.

nekton: In a water environment, the free-swimming organisms.

neustons: In a water environment, the organisms living on the surface.

neutrally stable atmosphere: An intermediate class of atmosphere between stable and unstable conditions. Will cause a smokestack plume to cone in appearance as the edges of the plume spread out in a V-shape.

neutron: Elementary particles that have approximately the same mass as protons but have no charge. They are one constituent of the atomic nucleus.

niche: The functional role of an organism within its community—the complete ecological description of an individual species (including habitat, feeding requirements, etc.).

nitrates: In freshwater pollution, a nutrient, usually from fertilizer, that enters the water system and can be toxic to animals and humans in high enough concentrations.

nitrification: The process that takes place in soil when bacteria oxidize ammonia, turning it into nitrates.

nitrogen cycle: The natural circulation of nitrogen through the environment.

nitrogen dioxide (NO_2)**:** A reddish-brown, highly toxic gas with a pungent odor. One of the seven known nitrogen oxides that participate in photochemical smog and primarily affect the respiratory system.

nitrogen fixation: A process in which bacteria "fix" nitrogen.

nitrogen oxide (NO)**:** A colorless gas used as an anesthetic; soil bacteria form it from decomposing nitrogenous material.

non-in situ technology: Remediation/recycling technology that takes place away from the contamination site.

noncarbonate hardness: A property of water; the hardness cannot be removed by boiling and is classified as permanent.

nonmetals: An element that tends to gain electrons to complete its outer shell.

nonpoint source: A source of pollution in which wastes are not released at one specific, identifiable point, but from a number of points that are spread out and difficult to identify and control.

nonpoint source pollution: Pollution that cannot be traced to a specific source, but rather comes from multiple generalized sources.

nonrenewable resources: Resources that exist in finite supply or are consumed at a rate faster than the rate at which they can be renewed.

nonspecific source wastes: Generic wastes commonly produced by manufacturing and industrial processes; for example, spent solvents.

nonvolatile: A substance that does not evaporate at normal temperatures when exposed to the air.

normal lapse rate: The rate of temperature change with height. On average, temperature decreases –65°C/100m or –6.5°C/km, the normal lapse rate.

nucleoid: The primitive nuclear region of the procaryotic cell.

nutrient cycles: *See* **biogeochemical cycles**.

nutrients: Elements or compounds needed for the survival, growth, and reproduction of a plant or animal.

nutrition: The process of nourishing or being nourished.

oligotrophic lake: A lake with a low supply of plant nutrients.

organelle: A specialized part of a cell that resembles and functions as an organ.

organic chemistry: The branch of chemistry concerned with compounds of carbon.

organic matter: Both natural and synthetic molecules containing carbon, and usually hydrogen. All living matter is made up of organic molecules.

organic substance: Any substance containing carbon.

overgrazing: Consumption of vegetation on rangeland by grazing animals to the point that the vegetation cannot be renewed or is renewed at a rate slower than consumption.

oxidation: The process by which electrons are lost.

oxidation-reduction: The (redox) process wherein electrons are lost and gained.

oxidize: To combine with oxygen.

oxygen: An element that readily unites with materials.

oxygen sag curve: The oxygen content in a stream or river system after organic pollution is introduced into the water body; organic pollution causes a profusion in growth of organisms that tends to decrease the amount (sag) of oxygen available.

ozone: The compound O_3. Found naturally in the atmosphere in the ozonosphere; a constituent of photochemical smog.

ozone holes: Holes created in the ozone layer by chemicals, especially CFCs.

packed tower: A remediation method (scrubber) employed to clean a contaminated gaseous waste stream by exposing it to biological media or chemical scrubbing agents.

parasite: A primary, secondary, or higher consumer that feeds on a plant or animal, known as a host, over an extended period of time.

parent material: The unconsolidated and more or less chemically weathered mineral or organic matter from which pedogonic processes develop the solum of soils.

particulate matter: Dust and fumes; travels easily through air.

pascal (Pa): A unit of pressure equal to one newton per square meter.

pathogen: Any disease-producing organism.

pedologist: A person who studies soils.

peds: A unit of soil structure such as an aggregate, crumb, prism, block, or granule, formed by natural processes.

pellicle: A *Euglena* structure that allows for turning and flexing of the cell.

period: An interval of geologic time that is a subdivision of an era and made up of epochs; a horizontal row of the periodic table that contains elements with approximately the same energy.

periodic law: A "law" stating that physical or chemical properties of the elements are periodic functions of their atomic weights.

periodic table: A list of all elements arranged in order of increasing atomic numbers and grouped by similar physical and chemical characteristics into "periods"; based on the chemical law that physical or chemical properties of the elements are periodic functions of their atomic weights.

permanent pond: A pond shallow enough to permit aquatic plants to penetrate the surface anywhere over its entire mass; its mass is not so great as to allow formation of large waves that could erode the shoreline; permanent ponds have no temperature layering, rather a gradient of temperatures extending from the surface to bottom. Actually a misnomer, as no pond is permanent.

permitting system: A key element of RCRA; a system designed to ensure safe operation of facilities that treat, store, or dispose of hazardous wastes.

perpetual resource: A resource such as solar energy that comes from an essentially inexhaustible source and thus will always be available on a human time scale regardless of whether or how it is used.

persistent substance: A chemical product with a tendency to persist in the environment for a long time; for example, plastics.

pesticide: Any chemical designed to kill weeds, insects, fungi, rodents, or other organisms that humans consider to be undesirable.

pH: A numerical designation of relative acidity and alkalinity; a pH of 7.0 indicates precise neutrality; high values indicate increasing alkalinity and lower values indicate increasing acidity.

phosphates: A nutrient substance obtained from fertilizers.

phosphorus cycle: A biogeochemical cycle in which phosphorus is converted into various chemical forms and transported through the biosphere.

photochemical reaction: A reaction induced by the presence of light.

photochemical smog: A complex mixture of air pollutants produced in the atmosphere by the reaction of hydrocarbons and nitrogen oxides under the influence of sunlight.

photosynthesis: A complex process that occurs in the cells of green plants whereby radiant energy from the sun is used to combine carbon dioxide (CO_2) and water (H_2O) to produce oxygen (O_2) and simple sugar or food molecules, such as glucose.

physical change: The process that alters one or more physical properties of an element or compound without altering its chemical composition. Examples include changing the size and shape of a sample of matter and changing a sample of matter from one physical state to another.

physical weathering: The physical changes produced in rocks by atmospheric agents (wind, precipitation, heat, cold, etc.).

pioneer community: The first successfully integrated set of plants, animals, and decomposers found in an area undergoing primary ecological succession.

piping failure: A common equipment component failure in many different systems; in this instance, the most common cause of UST spills.

plankton: Microscopic floating plant and animal organisms of lakes, rivers, and oceans.

planktonic: *See* **plankton**.

plasma membrane: *See* **cell membrane**.

plate towers: In absorption scrubbing, towers that contain perforated horizontal plates or trays designed to provide large liquid-gas interfacial area. The polluted air stream rises up through the perforations in each plate; the rising gas prevents liquid from draining through the openings. During continuous operation, contact is maintained between air and liquid, allowing gaseous contaminants to be removed, with clean air emerging from the top of the tower.

plume: (1) The column of noncombustible products emitted from a fire or smokestack. (2) A vapor cloud formation having shape and buoyancy. (3) A contaminant formation dispersing through the subsurface.

point source: Discernible conduits, including pipes, ditches, channels, sewers, tunnels, or vessels, from which pollutants are discharged.

point source pollution: Pollution that can be traced to an identifiable source.

pollute: To impair the quality of some portion of the environment by the addition of harmful impurities.

pond: A still body of water, smaller than a lake, often of artificial construction.

pond succession: A pond transformation process whereby a young pond is formed, develops over time to a mature pond, and then to a senescent (old) pond.

pool zone: In a body of moving water (river or stream), the quiet or still water portion.

positive crankcase ventilation (PCV): Technology used to control crankcase emissions.

preliminary treatment: (1) In wastewater, treatment prior to primary treatment. (2) In industrial applications, pretreatment of a waste stream before it becomes plant effluent and then influent into a wastewater treatment plant for further treatment.

pressure: Force per unit area.

pressure gradient force: A variation of pressure with position.

primary consumers: In the food chain, organisms that consume producers (autotrophs).

primary exposure pathways: In site remediation, the exposure pathways that directly affect site operations and personnel or the clean-up levels that must be achieved by the remedial technology.

primary pollutants: Pollutants emitted directly into the atmosphere, where they exert an adverse influence on human health or the environment. The six primary pollutants are carbon dioxide, carbon monoxide, sulfur oxides, nitrogen oxides, hydrocarbons, and particulates. All but carbon dioxide are regulated in the United States.

primary standards: The Clean Air Act (NAAQS) air quality standards covering criteria pollutants.

primary treatment: A wastewater treatment process in which mechanical treatment is employed to screen out large solids and settle out suspended solids.

procaryotic: Lacking a membrane-delimited nucleus.

producers: Organisms that use solar energy (green plant) or chemical energy (some bacteria) to manufacture their own organic substances (food) from inorganic nutrients.

profundal: The deep-water zone of a lake, not penetrated by sunlight.

proton: A component of a nucleus, 2,000 times more massive than an electron; it differs from a neutron by its positive (+1) electrical charge. The atomic number of an atom is equal to the number of protons in its nucleus.

protozoa: Single-celled microorganisms, including the most primitive forms of animal life.

pumping well system: In control technology for leaking USTs, the preferred method used to recover free product from the water table when the spill is deep.

radiation: The emitting of energy from an atom in the form of particles of electromagnetic waves; energy waves that travel with the speed of light and upon arrival at a surface are absorbed, reflected, or transmitted.

radiative inversions: A nocturnal phenomenon caused by cooling of the Earth's surface. Inversions prompt the formation of fog and simultaneously trap gases and particulates, creating a concentration of pollutants.

radioactive material: Any material that spontaneously emits ionizing radiation.

rapids zone: The turbulent zone of a stream or river in which water is agitated by subsurface obstructions causing turbulence and aeration of water.

reactive: The tendency of a material to react chemically with other substances.

recharge area: The area in which precipitation percolates through to recharge groundwater.

recovery zone: The zone in a stream or river where contamination is reduced by the self-purification process.

recycle: To recover and reuse materials from waste streams.

recycling: *See* **recycle**.

recycling technology: The technology available to recycle or reuse waste products; processes such as composting and hot- and cold-mix asphalt incorporation.

reduction: Removal of oxygen from a compound; lowering of oxidation number resulting from a gain of electrons.

refuse: Rubbish and garbage; residential sources.

relative humidity: The percentage of moisture in a given volume of air at a given temperature in relation to the amount of moisture the same volume of air would contain at the saturation point.

renewable resources: Resources that can be depleted in the short run if used or contaminated too rapidly, but that normally are replaced through natural processes.

representative sample: A sample of a universe or whole, such as a waste pile, a lagoon, or groundwater, that can be expected to exhibit the average properties of the whole.

reservoir: A large and deep human-created standing body of freshwater.

residential sources of MSW: Municipal solid wastes from households consisting primarily of paper, glass, vegetable waste, paperboard, ash, tin cans, etc.

Resource Conservation and Recovery Act (RCRA): A law passed in 1976 by Congress to control dumping of waste materials (cradle-to-grave).

resource: Something that serves a need, is useful, and is available at a particular cost.

reuse: To use a product again and again in the same form, as when returnable glass bottles are washed and refilled.

ribosomes: In bacterial cytoplasm, minute, rounded bodies made of RNA, loosely attached to the plasma membrane; they are the site of protein synthesis and are part of the translation process.

risk assessment: Evaluation of the threat to public health and the environment posed by a hazardous waste facility; considering the probability of an incident and its effects.

risk characterization: The final step in the risk assessment process whereby an estimate of the incidence of an adverse health effect under the conditions of exposure found and described in the exposure assessment is determined.

Rivers and Harbors Act (1899): A law that initiated the first legislative authority given to a federal agency (U.S. Army Corp of Engineers) to prevent dumping wastes into rivers and harbors.

rotifers: A minute multicellular aquatic organism with a wheel-like ring of cilia at the anterior end.

rubbish: Combustible waste, paper, cartons, rags, wood scraps, combustible floor sweepings; domestic, commercial, and industrial sources.

running losses: Evaporative emissions from an internal combustion engine as a result of driving; losses also occur when the fuel is heated by the road surface, and when fuel is forced from the fuel tank while the vehicle is being operated and the fuel tank becomes hot.

runoff: Surface water entering rivers, freshwater lakes, or reservoirs from land surfaces.

Safe Drinking Water Act (SDWA): A law mandating that the U.S. EPA establish drinking-water standards for all public water systems serving 25 or more people, or having 15 or more connections.

saline water: Water with excessive salt content.

salt spreading: The practice of spreading salt on roadways during winter to help reduce ice and snow accumulation; road salts contaminate soil during runoff.

sanitary landfill: A method of solid waste disposal designed to minimize water pollution from runoff and leaching; waste is covered with a layer of soil within a day after being deposited at the landfill site.

sanitary wastewater: A separate sewer system designed to remove domestic wastes from residential areas.

saprophyte: An organism that uses enzymes to feed on waste products of living organisms or tissues of dead organisms.

SARA: Superfund Amendments and Reauthorization Act of 1986. *See* **CERCLA**.

saturated zone: Subsurface soil saturated with water; the water table.

scaling: Calcium carbonate and magnesium hydroxide precipitated out of solution when carbonate hard water is heated, forming a rock-hard scale that clogs hot-water pipes and reduces the efficiency of boilers, water heaters, and heat exchangers.

science: The observation, identification, description, experimental investigation, and theoretical explanation of natural phenomena.

scientific method: A systematic form of inquiry that involves observation, speculation, and reasoning.

sea level rise: The natural increase in the sea level that occurs in cyclical patterns; may be the result of humans' impacts on global warming.

2nd Law of Thermodynamics: A natural law that dictates that in any conversion of heat energy to useful work, some of the initial energy input is always degraded to a lower-quality, more dispersed, less useful form of energy, usually low-temperature heat that flows into the environment; you can't break even in terms of energy quality.

secondary drinking water standards: The unenforceable guidelines based on both aesthetics, including taste, odor, and color of drinking water, as well as nonaesthetic characteristics such as corrosivity and hardness.

secondary exposure pathways: In on-site remediation, a minor component of site operations that exhibits significant decreases with time as treatment progresses (e.g., wind blown dust).

secondary standards: The NAAQS requirement to protect public welfare.

secondary treatment (of sewage)**:** The removal of impurities from water by the digestive action of various small organisms in the presence of air or oxygen.

secure landfill: A land site for the storage of hazardous solid and liquid wastes normally placed in containers and buried in a restricted-access area that is continually monitored. Such landfills are located above geologic strata that are supposed to prevent the leaching of wastes into groundwater.

sedimentary rock: A rock formed from materials deposited from suspension or precipitated from solution and usually more or less consolidated. The principal sedimentary rocks are sandstones, shales, limestones, and conglomerates.

sediments: Soil particles dislodged by raindrops that travel via runoff into streams, rivers, lakes, or oceans and are deposited there.

self-purification: The natural phenomenon occurring in running water systems (streams and rivers) whereby physical, chemical, and biological processes work to purify the water.

senescent pond: A pond that has reached old age.

separation: A hazardous waste treatment technology (filtration and separation) whereby filtration is used to separate solid particles from a liquid stream through use of semiporous media. Driven by a pressure difference across the media and caused by gravity, centrifugal force, vacuum, or elevated pressure.

septic zone: In the self-purification process that takes place in running water bodies (streams or rivers), the zone characterized by heavy organic pollution and low DO levels.

sheet piling: In in-situ isolation/containment technology, the physical driving of rigid sheets, pilings of wood, steel, or concrete into the ground to form a barrier for containment.

silage liquor: The liquid drained or leached from fodder prepared by storing and fermenting green forage plants in a silo.

sink: Areas, whether natural or artificial, where the products or effluents from production and consumption in one place are physically exported to another place for storage or dispersal.

slope: A soil property in which the steepness of the soil layer is directly related to the degree of erosion that may occur.

slope winds: Winds that move through a typical river valley; they flow downhill into the valley floor.

slurry walls: In situ isolation/containment, fixed underground physical barriers formed in an excavated trench by pumping slurry, usually a bentonite or cement and water mixture.

smog: Visible air pollution; a dense, discolored haze containing large quantities of soot, ash, and gaseous pollutants such as sulfur dioxide and carbon dioxide.

soft water: Water with a hardness of less than 50 ppms.

soil: A dynamic natural body in which plants grow, composed of mineral and organic materials and living forms.

soil boring: Using a boring tool (such as an auger) to take soil samples for analysis.

soil factors: In in-situ soil remediation, factors including water content, porosity/permeability, clay content, and adsorption site density.

soil fertility: The quality of a soil that enables it to provide essential chemical elements in quantities and proportions for the growth of specified plants.

soil-forming process: The mode of origin of the soil, with special reference to the processes or soil-forming factors responsible for the development of the solum, or true soil, from the unconsolidated parent material.

soil horizon: A layer of soil, approximately parallel to the soil surface, differing in properties and characteristics from adjacent layers below or above it.

soil pollution: Contamination of the soil and subsurface by the addition of contaminants or pollutants.

soil profile: A vertical section of the soil from the surface through all its horizons, including C horizons.

soil remediation: The use of various techniques or technologies to decontaminate or dispose of contaminated soil.

soil sampling: Sampling conducted to determine through analysis the type, texture, and structure of a soil; collecting of samples of contaminated soil to determine degree and extent of contamination and for analysis.

soil structure: The combination or arrangement of primary soil particles into secondary particles, units, or peds. These secondary units may be, but usually are not, arranged in the profile in such a manner as to give a distinctive, characteristic pattern. The secondary units are characterized and classified on the basis of size, shape, and degree of distinctness into classes, types, and grades, respectively.

soil texture: The relative proportions of the various soil separates in a soil.

soil washing and extraction: In pollution control technology used for USTs, a process used to leach contaminants from the soil into a leaching medium, after which the extracted contaminants are removed by conventional methods.

Solid Waste Disposal Act (1965): The first major step taken by U.S. legislators to promote (among other things) the demonstration, construction, and application of solid waste management and resource recovery systems to preserve and enhance the quality of air, water, and land resources.

solid: Matter that has a definite volume and a definite shape.

solid waste: Any normally solid material that is useless or unwanted that results from human or animal activities.

solid waste stream: A stream of solid waste materials as a whole.

solidification: A stabilization technique used to convert hazardous waste from its original form to a physically and chemically more stable material. Accomplished by reducing the mobility of hazardous compounds in the waste prior to its land disposal.

solidification/stabilization: *See* **solidification**.

solubility: The ability of a substance to mix with water.

solute: A dissolved substance in a solution.

solvent: A substance in excess in a solution.

sorption: The process of adsorption or absorption of a substance on or in another substance.

species: A group of individuals or populations potentially able to interbreed and unable to produce fertile offspring by breeding with other sorts of animals and plants.

specific gravity: The ratio of the weight of the volume of liquid or solid to the weight of an equal volume of water.

specific heat: The amount of heat energy in calories necessary to raise the temperature of one gram of the substance one degree Celsius.

specific source wastes: Wastes from specifically identified industries, including wood preserving, petroleum refining, and organic chemical manufacturing. Typically includes sludges, still bottoms, wastewaters, spent catalysts, and residues.

spirilla: Bacteria shape characterized as being nonflexible, helical, and curved.

spoil: Material removed from an excavation.

sporangiospore: Spores that form within a sac called a sporangium. The sporangia are attached to stalks called sporangiophores.

spore: The reproductive stage of fungi.

spring overturn: The lake phenomenon whereby the entire body of water within the lake overturns because of changes in water density.

stability: Atmospheric turbulence; a function of vertical distribution of atmospheric temperature.

stability class: Term used to classify the degree of turbulence in the atmosphere.

stabilization: *See* **solidification**.

stable atmosphere: Atmosphere that is marked by air that is cooler at the ground than aloft, by low wind speeds, and consequently by a low degree of turbulence.

standard temperature and pressure (STP): Standard temperature and pressure –0°C at a standard atmosphere of 760 millimeters of mercury. As the density of gases depends on temperature and pressure, defining the pressure and temperature against which the volume of gases are measured is customary. All gas volumes are referred to these standard conditions.

stationary sources: Sources of air pollution emanating from any fixed or stationary point.

still bottoms: What remains after a spent solvent is distilled (for recycling); composed of a concentrated, highly toxic mixture, far reduced in volume.

stockpile: Certain chemical products (such as road salt) kept in quantity for possible use, runoff from which may contribute to soil pollution.

stormwater: Water containing grit and street debris, but no domestic or sanitary wastes.

stratification: The temperature–density relationship of water in temperate lakes (>25 feet in depth) that leads to subsequent turnover or overturn.

stratosphere: A region of the atmosphere based on temperature, between approximately 10 and 35 miles in altitude.

stripping: A waste control technology whereby volatile compounds are separated from less volatile ones in a liquid mixture by partitioning the more volatile materials to a gas phase of air or steam.

subadiabatic: The ambient lapse rate when it is less than the dry adiabatic lapse rate.

submerged vegetation: In a pond, the submerged plants that grow where light can penetrate the water surface and reach them.

subsidence inversion: A type of inversion usually associated with a high pressure system, known as anticyclones, which may significantly affect the dispersion of pollutants over large regions.

subsoil: That part of the soil below the plow layer.

substrate: The material or substance upon which an enzyme acts.

suggested levels: Nonenforceable guidelines for secondary drinking water standards regarding public welfare.

sulfur cycle: The natural circulation of sulfur through the environment.

sulfur dioxide: A primary pollutant originating chiefly from the combustion of high-sulfur coals.

sulfurous smog: The haze that develops in the atmosphere when molecules of sulfuric acid accumulate, growing in size as droplets until they become large enough to serve as light scatterers.

summer stagnation: In lake stratification, a state that occurs in some lakes when the top layer of water is warmer than the bottom layer. It results in layers of different density, the top light, the bottom heavy. With increased temperature, the top layer becomes even lighter, and the thermocline forms. From top to bottom, the lightest and warmest is on top, medium weight and relatively warm is in the middle, and the heaviest and coldest is below, with a sharp drop in temperature at the thermocline. The water in these three layers does not mix in circulation. If the thermocline is below the range of effective light penetration, the oxygen supply becomes depleted in the hypolimnion, since both photosynthesis and the surface source of oxygen are cut off.

superadiabatic rate: The lapse rate when a parcel of air starting at 1000m at 20ºC, for example, starts moving downward and becomes cooler and denser than its surroundings. Because the ambient air is unstable, it continues to sink.

Superfund: *See* **CERCLA**.

Superfund law: *See* **CERCLA**.

surface condenser: In air pollution control technology, a type of condensation equipment, normally a shell-and-tube heat exchanger. It uses a cooling medium of air or water where the vapor to be condensed is separated from the cooling medium by a metal wall. Coolant flows through the tubes, while the vapor is passed over and condenses on the outside of the tubes and drains off to storage.

surface impoundment: (1) Another name for a garbage dump. (2) Diked or excavated areas used to store liquid hazardous wastes.

surface origins: Origins of soil contaminants that include gaseous and airborne particulates; infiltration of contaminated surface water; land disposal of solid and liquid waste materials; stockpiles, tailings, and spoils; dumps; salt spreading on roads; animal feedlots; fertilizers and pesticides; accidental spills; and composting of leaves and other wastes.

surface water: Water on the Earth's surface, exposed to the atmosphere, and mostly the product of precipitation.

surfactant: A surface-active substance (soap).

symbiotic: A close relationship between two organisms of different species; one wherein both partners benefit from the association.

synthesis: The formation of a substance or compound from more elementary compounds.

tailings: The residual fine-grained waste rejected after mining and processing of ore, usually after washing.

taste and odor: A water quality parameter.

TCLP (Toxicity Characteristics Leaching Procedure): A toxicity test that replaced the EP Toxicity Test; it is designed to identify wastes likely to leach hazardous concentrations of particular toxic constituents into the surrounding soils or groundwater.

temperature: A measure of the average kinetic energy of the molecules.

temperature inversion: A condition characterized by an inverted lapse rate.

thermal circulation: The result of the relationship based on a law of physics whereby the pressure and volume of a gas are directly related to its temperature.

thermal incinerator (or afterburner): A device used in combustion whereby the contaminant airstream passes around or through a burner and into a refractory-lined residence chamber where oxidation occurs. Flue gas from a thermal incinerator is at high temperature and contains recoverable heat energy.

thermal inversion: A layer of cool air trapped under a layer of less dense warm air, thus preventing reversing to the normal situation.

thermal NO_x: A compound created when nitrogen and oxygen in the combustion air (e.g., within an internal combustion engine) are heated to a high enough temperature (above 1000K) to cause nitrogen (N_2) and oxygen (O_2) in the air to combine.

thermal pollution: An increase in water temperature with harmful ecological effects on aquatic ecosystems.

thermal radiation: Heat energy directly radiated into space from the Earth's surface and atmosphere.

thermal treatment: In non-in situ soil pollution control technology, the complete destruction (by incineration) of petroleum-laden contaminants.

thermal treatment processes: In waste control technology, incineration of wastes.

thermocline: The fairly thin transition zone in a lake that separates an upper warmer zone from a lower colder zone.

thermosphere: A region of the atmosphere based on temperature between approximately 60 and several hundred miles in altitude.

threshold of effect: In the dose–response relationship, the level of "no effect."

threshold reporting quantity: A level set by the EPA for extremely hazardous substances, which if exceeded during spill or release to the environment must be reported to appropriate authorities.

tilth: The physical condition of soil as related to its ease of tillage, fitness as a seedbed, and impedance to seedling emergence and root penetration.

topsoil: The layer of soil moved in cultivation.

total dissolved solids: The solids residue after evaporating a sample of water or effluent, expressed in mg/liter.

total Kjeldahl Nitrogen (TKN): The total concentration of organic and ammonia nitrogen in wastewater.

toxic chemical: Term used by the U.S. EPA for chemicals whose total emissions or releases must be reported annually by owners and operators of certain facilities that manufacture, process, or otherwise use a listed toxic chemical. The list of toxic chemicals is identified in Title III of SARA.

toxic metals: Metals, including arsenic, cadmium, lead, and mercury, that are all cumulative toxins and particularly hazardous to human health.

toxic or hazardous substance: Substance that is injurious to the health of individual organisms and sometimes fatal.

toxicity: The degree of poisonousness.

toxicological evaluation: A part of risk assessment, which should answer the question: "Does the chemical have an adverse effect?"

toxin: A poison produced by a plant or animal.

tracking system: In hazardous waste management, use of manifest documents that accompany any waste transported from one location to another.

transformation: Chemical change that takes place in the atmosphere; for example, the conversion of the original pollutant to a secondary pollutant such as ozone.

trash: Highly combustible waste paper, wood, cardboard cartons, including up to 10% treated papers, plastic, or rubber scraps.

treatment plant site sources of MSW: Wastes generated in water, wastewater, and other industrial treatment processes (e.g., incineration ash, sludges or biosolids, and general plant wastes).

trench method: In pollution control technology for USTs, a method used to capture the entire leading edge of the contaminant plume.

trenching: *See* **excavation**.

trophic level: The feeding position occupied by a given organism in a food chain, measured by the number of steps removed from the producers.

troposphere: A region of the atmosphere based on temperature difference between the Earth's surface and 10 miles in altitude.

turbidity: Reduced transparency of the atmosphere, caused by absorption and scattering of radiation by solid or liquid particles other than clouds and held in suspension.

turbulence: (1) Uncoordinated movements and a state of continuous change in liquids and gases. (2) One of the 3 Ts of combustion.

turnover: The mixing of the upper and lower levels of a lake that most often occurs during the spring and fall, caused by dramatic changes in surface water temperature.

unconfined aquifer: An aquifer not underlain by an impermeable layer.

underground storage tanks (USTs): Underground tanks designed to store chemicals, especially fuels.

United Nations Hazard Class Number System: A system for designating and labeling hazardous materials that uses a dedicated number system.

unsaturated zone: An area that lies just beneath the soil surface and is characterized by crevices that contain both air and water; water contained therein is not available for use.

unstable atmosphere: Atmosphere characterized by a high degree of turbulence.

vacuole: A small cavity in the protoplasm of a cell.

vadose water: Water in the unsaturated zone that is essentially unavailable for use.

valence: The net electric charge of an atom or the number of electrons an atom can give up (or acquire) to achieve a filled out shell.

valley winds: At valley floor level, slope winds transformed, which flow down-valley, often with the flow of a river.

venting: In pollution control technology, a method of remediating hydrocarbon (gasoline) spills or leaks from USTs.

venturi: A short tube with a constricted throat used to determine fluid pressures and velocities by measurement of differential pressures generated at the throat as a fluid traverses the tube.

vernal ponds: Spring ponds, usually of short duration.

virus: An infectious agent with a simple acellular organization, a protein coat, and a single type of nucleic acid, that reproduces only with living host cells.

volatile organic compounds (VOCs): Organic compounds that evaporate and contribute to air pollution directly or through chemical or photochemical reactions to produce secondary pollutants, principally ozone.

volatile: Will evaporate at ordinary temperatures if exposed to the air.

volatilization: When a solid or liquid substance passes into the vapor state.

volume: Surface area times (X) a third dimension.

warm front: A front marking the advance of a warm air mass as it rises up over a cold one.

waste minimization: An umbrella term that refers to industrial practices that minimize the volume of products, minimize packaging, extend the useful life of products, and minimize the amount of toxic substance in products.

waste piles: Waste piled at industrial sites and then eventually disposed of in a landfill.

wastewater: A liquid waste stream primarily produced by five major sources: human and animal waste, household wastes, industrial wastes, stormwater runoff, and groundwater infiltration.

water content: In in-situ volatilization, the influence that water has on the rate of volatilization by affecting the rates at which chemicals can diffuse through the vadose zone. An increase in solid water content decreases the rate at which volatile compounds are transported to the surface via vapor diffusion.

water pollutants: Unwanted contaminants that can pollute water.

water pollution: Any physical or chemical change in surface water or groundwater that can adversely affect living organisms.

water table: The upper surface of the saturation zone below which all void spaces are filled with water.

water vapor: The most visible constituent of the atmosphere (H_2O in vapor form).

waterborne pathogens: The transmission conduit for some pathogenic microorganisms.

watershed: The region that drains into a river, river system, or body of water.

watershed divide: A ridge of high land dividing two areas drained by different river systems.

weather: The day-to-day pattern of precipitation, temperature, wind, barometric pressure, and humidity.

weathering: The chemical and mechanical breakdown of rocks and minerals under the action of atmospheric agencies.

weight: The force exerted upon any object by gravity.

wet scrubber: A treatment device (e.g., a stacked tower) in which the contaminant waste stream is passed through microorganism-laden media or a chemical spray (such as a caustic) to degrade and/or neutralize the harmful affects of the contaminant(s).

wetland: A lowland area, such as a marsh or swamp, saturated with moisture and usually thought of as natural wildlife habitat.

white goods: Large solid waste items such as household appliances (refrigerators, stoves, dishwashers, washers and dryers, etc.).

wind: Horizontal air motion.

wind and breezes: Local conditions caused by the circulating movement of warm and cold air (convection) and differences in heating.

winter kill: A condition that can occur in a lake or pond when the entire water mass is frozen, thereby killing all inhabitants.

winter stratification: In a lake in winter, the condition that occurs when the epilimnion is icebound, is at the lowest temperature and thus lightest, the thermocline is at medium temperature and medium weight, and the hypolimnion is at about 4-C and heaviest.

worms: In stream ecology, the presence of certain species of worms in bottom sediment indicates stream pollution.

xenobiotics: Any chemical present in a natural environment that does not normally occur in nature; for example, pesticides and/or industrial pollutants.

young pond: In the cycle of pond evolution, the initial or earliest phase.

zone of recent pollution: In streams or rivers, the point of pollution discharge.

Index

abiotic, 23
Abominable Snowperson, 18
absolute pressure, 369
accidental spills, 168
acid, 109, 124, 369
acid deposition, 146
acid mine drainage, 544, 551
acid precipitation, 457–459
acid rain, 95, 149, 544, 577
acid surge, 369
acidic deposition, 327–328
activated biosolids process, 215–217
activated carbon sorption, 652
adiabatic, 431
adiabatic lapse rate, 430–431
adsorption, 164
aerobic, 180
air pollution, 38, 143–144
acidity, 129
agent, 242
air currents, 380–388
air pollution events, 369
air samples, 306
air stripping, 653
airborne particulate matter, 211, 325–327
aid dispersion, 427–437
air masses, 407–408
air pollution control technology, 460–466
air stripping, 573
albedo, 370, 378–379
algae, 206–211; classification of, 207–208; description of, 207; motility of, 208; nutrients of, 208; reproduction of 209
algal cell wall, 208

algology, 206
Allee's Law, 70
aliphatic hydrocarbons, 113
alkalinity, 124, 126, 129, 492
alkanes, 113
alkynes, 113
ambient air quality, 305
amoebae, 213
anabolic, 225–226
anaerobic, 180
animal feedlots, 168, 596
anticyclones, 433
Appalachian Trail, 26–27
apparent color, 123
aquatic food chain, 61
aquifer, 291, 293, 509, 536
aqueous solutions, 106
aromatic hydrocarbons, 113
arsenic, 132
asphalt incorporation, 619
atmosphere, 137–154, 361–388; composition of, 365–374; structure of, 374–380
atmospheric change, 439–466; how measured, 444
atmospheric pollutants, 411–424
atom, 99; structure of, 99
ATP, 227
automatic samplers, 303
autotrophic bacteria, 198
Avogadro's number, 104

bacteria, 184–199, 498; chemical composition of, 197; classification of,

195; metabolism of, 198–199; shapes and forms of, 193; structure of, 194
bacterial growth, 233–240; growth curve, 234–235
bacteriological contamination, 184–192
bacteriophage, 195, 200
bare rock succession, 586–587
barrier lakes, 518
base, 109, 124
Bayes' theorem, 15–16
benthic, 206
best available technology, 477
biochemical oxygen demand (BOD), 65
biodegradation, 164
bioenergy, 347
biogeochemical cycles, 24, 47–53
biological characteristics of water, 496–500
biological oxygen demand (BOD), 330, 495
biological treatment, 651
biomass, 320, 347–348
biorefractory, 133
biosphere, 23, 58–59
biostimulent, 496
biota, 5, 23
biotic, 23, 266
binary fission, 206, 209
boiling point, 108, 127
brackish water, 491
brick manufacturing process, 620
brown algae, 210
budding, 204
buffer, 458
buffering capacity, 328

cadmium, 131
Calder's Law, 70
capsule, 195
carbon adsorption, 574
carbon cycle, 47–50
carbon dioxide, 142–143, 420
carbon monoxide, 320, 414
carbon oxides, 145
carrying capacity, 75
catabolic, 225
catalysis, 220
cation exchange capacity, 158
cell membrane, 182–183
cell nucleus, 184
cell structure, 183–184

cell walls, 184, 195–196
cells, 182–184
CFCs, 150–151
ciliates, 213
chelating agents, 132
chemical bonding, 98, 102–103
chemical changers, 98
chemical equations, 103–104
chemical extraction, 621
chemical formulas, 103–104
chemical oxygen demand, 495
chemical precipitation, 573
chemical reaction, 98
chemical site contamination, 599
chemical sties, 155
chemically stratified lakes, 516
chemotrophs, 226
chlorophyll, 208
chloroplasts, 184
cholera, 185–193
citric acid cycle, 229
classification nomenclature, 181–182
Clean Air Act, 414
clean zone, 534
climate, 370
clumped, 74
coal gasification, 338
colligative properties, 119
colloids, 121
community ecology, 68
complexes, 131
composite sample, 302
composting, 597
compounds, 96
Comprehensive Environmental Response Compensation and Liability Act, 633, 647
concentrated solution, 106
concentrating solar power, 341–342
conduction, 58
congeners, 134
conidia, 204
consensus science, 47
consumers, 24
Carson, R., 6
contagious distribution, 74
contaminated surface water, 594
convection, 58
corrosive, 642

covalent bonds, 98, 103
creeks, 525
crustaceans, 219, 499
Cryptosporidium spp., 212
cysts, 212
cytoplasm, 184, 196

Damuth's Law, 71
Darwin, C., 66
decomposers, 62
decomposition, 330
decomposers, 24
deductive inferences, 14
deep ancient lakes, 516
deep-well injection, 654–655
deforestation, 50
density, 84, 105, 127, 365
density-dependent factors, 72
density-independent, 73
desert salt lakes, 516
desertification, 36
Devils Tower, 18–20
dew point, 370
diatoms, 206
dilute solution, 106
dinoflagellates, 206, 210–211
dispersion, 74
dispersion models, 435–437; types of, 436–437
dissolved inorganics, 133
dissolved oxygen, 123, 330
dissolved solids, 122
distribution, 74
diversion, 346
dose-response, 263–265; curve for, 264–265
doubling rule, 79
drainage basin, 481
dump, 167
dynamic viscosity, 163
dystrophic lakes, 516

ecological pyramids, 54, 62–64
ecological succession, 82–83; process of, 83
ecology, 24
ecophagy, 311
ecosystem, 24
El Nino, 406
electrolytic recovery, 652–653
electron transport system, 230–231

elements, 96–98; classification of, 97–98
emergence of disease, 243–255; control of disease, 253–254
emergent vegetation, 513
emergents, 513
emigration, 72
emissivity, 370
emulsion, 121
endergonic, 227
endoplasmic reticulum, 184
endothermic process, 119
energy, 54
energy flow, 53–54
Einstein, A., 22
enthalpy, 108–109
environment, 6–10
environmental biology, 175–255
environmental carrying capacity, 77
environmental chemistry, 93–171
environmental degradation, 36
environmental media, 23, 114
environmental models, 20–21
environmental science, 6–10; components of, 7
environmental terrorism, 158, 601
environmental toxicology, 261–279; application of, 265–279
enzymes, 219–225; action of, 221; concentration of, 224; efficiency of, 223; nature of, 220
Euglenoids, 209
eukaryotic, 182
eutrophic lake, 515
eutrophication, 48, 496, 517
evapotranspiration, 291
evidence, 318
excavation, 621–622
exergonic, 227
exothermic process, 119
exposure pathways, 611
extraction procedure, 643
extraction wells, 574
extremely hazardous substances, 640–641

Federal Water Pollution Control Act, 560–561
feel-good science, 28–29
Fenchel's Law, 70
fertilizer and pesticides, 596

filtration, 653
flagellates, 213
floating leaf vegetation, 513
fluoride, 493
fog, 422
food chain, 24, 48
food web, 49, 62
fragmentation, 206
frequentists, 16
freshwater, 505–537
friability, 288
frontier science, 47
frustules, 206, 208
fumigation, 433
fungi, 181, 201–206, 499; classification of,
    202; cultivation of, 204; reproduction of,
    204

garbage, 634
gas laws, 106
gas plant contamination, 600
gaseous airborne particulate pollutants, 594
gases, 88
Generation-Time Law, 71
genome, 200
geology, 281–291
geothermal contamination, 599
geothermal energy, 155, 348–351
geothermal power, 338
geothermal sites, 15
Giardia lamblia, 212
Ginzburg's Law, 71
glacial lakes, 517
global fish harvest, 66
global warming, 146, 441–444
glycolysis, 228
golden-brown algae, 209–210
good science, 28–29
grab sample, 302
green algae, 209
greenhouse effect, 95, 290, 370
greenhouse gases 146, 441, 443–444
groundwater, 535; flow of, 537; uses and
    sources of, 535–536
groundwater, 283, 292–293, 483–484
groundwater pollution, 558–560
groundwater remediation, 572–574
growth rate, 234

habitat, 24
hardness, 126, 492
hazardous chemcials, 641–642
hazardous material, 640
hazardous substance, 639–640, 642
hazardous waste, 641, 643–648; legislation
    for, 646–648; type of, 643–645
hazardous waste stream, 550
heat, 107
heat balance, 376
heat capacity, 108, 128
heat index, 383–385
heat of fusion, 128
heat of vaporization, 128
heavy metals, 131, 458–459
herbicides, 133
heterotrophic bacteria, 199
heterotrophs, 226
host, 242
hydraulic gradient, 537
hydrogen, 113
hydrology, 282–293
hydrogen bonding, 127
hydrophilic, 121
hydrophobic, 121
hydropower, 345–347
hypha, 203
hypotheses, 16–17
hydrogen, 351–354; for fuel cell, 354;
    storage of, 353

ideal gas law, 106
ignitability, 642
igneous, 284
immigration, 72
impoundment, 346, 509
in situ biodegradation, 614–616
in situ isolation, 617
in situ leaching, 616
in situ passive remediation, 617
incineration, 652
inclusions, 197
inductive inference, 15
industrial water pollution, 549–550
injection wells, 574
inorganic matter, 124
Interstate Commerce Clause, 633
ionic bonds, 102–103

ion balance, 164
ions, 102
isopleths, 435

J-shaped curve, 77
junk science, 11–13

Krebs Cycle, 228–230

lake turnover, 518–520
lakes, 514–520; classification of, 515;
    classification of by impoundments,
    518–520
land disposal of solid wastes, 585
land treatment, 618
landfilling, 657
landscape ecology, 68
lapse rate, 371
latent heat of fusion, 108
law of conservation of mass or matter, 55
laws of thermodynamics, 54
leachate, 329
lead, 131, 322, 414, 422
leaking underground storage tanks, 539
length, 85
lentic, 509
Leopold, A., 3–5
levee lakes, 517
Liebigs Law, 70
Lily Pond Parable, 77–78
limiting factor, 51
limiting nutrient, 495
limnetic, 512
limnology, 509
liquids, 87
lithotrophs, 226
littoral, 512
loam, 283
Lord Kelvin, 22
Lotic water systems, 509, 520–533
Lotka–Volterra's Law, 70

mass, 55, 84
macronutrients, 232–233
Malthusians Law, 70
manual sampling, 302
manufactured gas plants, 157
mass balance equations, 55

mastax, 218
materials balance, 54–58
matter, 105
mature pond, 512
maximum sustainable yield, 36
melting pint, 108
mercury, 131
mesosphere, 371
mesosome, 196
mesotrophic lake, 515
metabolic transformations, 225–232
metabolism, 181, 225–232
metals, 123
metamorphic, 284
meteorology, 391–409
micelles, 121
microbial adaptation, 252
microbial nutrition, 232
microbiology, 181–182
microclimate, 404
micronutrients, 232
middens, 635
midnight dumping, 617
mining site contamination, 600
mining sites, 157
mining wastes, 338
miscible, 118
mist, 422
mitochondria, 184
molality, 117
molarity, 117
mole, 104
molecules, 102
monitor wells, 308
monoculture, 15
mortality, 72
municipal solid waste, 637–639
mycelium, 203

NAAQS, 414
natality, 72
nektons, 512
neustonic, 207
neustons, 512
niche, 24
nitrogen, 141–142
nitrogen cycle, 50–51
nitrogen oxides, 148, 414

nonaqueous-phase liquids, 573
nonpoint sources, 544
nonpoint source of pollution, 547–549
nonrenewable resources, 37
nonseptate, 203
normality, 117
nucleoid, 196–197
nutrient cycles, 47
nutrients, 495

ocean energy, 351
Ockham's Razor, 13, 18–19
oil field contamination, 598
oil field sites, 155–156
old field succession, 83
oligotrophic lakes, 515
oogonia, 209
organic air pollutants, 151–154
organic chemistry, 111–112
organic compounds, 112–113
organic matter, 124, 494–495
organometallics, 132
osmotic pressure, 120
overgrazing, 36
oxbow lakes, 57
oxygen, 140
oxygen-demanding wastes, 329–330
ozone, 141, 321, 417–420

PAHs, 153
PAN, 153
paradigm shift, 21–23
paraffins, 113
parasites, 252–253
parent material, 589
particulate matter, 144–146, 420–422
particulates, 414
pathogens, 180, 252–253
pathogenicity, 240–243; transmission of disease, 242–243
PBN, 153
pedologists, 588
peds, 590
pellicle, 207
periodic law, 99
periodic table, 100
periods, 100
perpetual resources, 36
persistent substances, 336

pesticides, 133
Pfiesteria, 178–179
pH, 1100–11, 125, 159
phase transition, 128
phenol, 152
phosphorus cycle, 52–52
phosphorylation, 228
photochemical smog, 151, 417–420
photosynthesis, 49, 366
phototrophs, 226
photovoltaics, 341
physical change, 98–99
physiology, 68
plankton, 207
plant nutrient, 335
plasma membrane, 195–196
plume, 430
point source, 544
point source pollution, 547–549
polar lakes, 517
pollute, 38
ponds, 511–514; succession of, 512; habitats of, 512
population, 47
population density, 54, 69
population ecology, 66–75
population genetics, 68
population growth, 75–81
population regulation, 72
population size, 80
population system, 67
PPCPs, 544–547
ppm, 83
pressure, 87, 106, 365
primary air pollutants, 415
primary consumers, 62–63
producers, 24
productivity, 47, 64–66
profundal, 512
prokaryotic, 182
proto-air, 366
protozoa, 181, 211–217, 498; classification of, 212–217
pumped storage, 346–347
pure substances, 97
pyruvic acid, 228

radiation, 50, 58, 432
radioactive substance, 336

radionuclides, 132
Raleigh scattering, 371
random distribution, 74
reactive, 643
recharge area, 481
recovery zone, 534
recycling, 650
reduction reaction, 227
refuse, 634
regular distribution, 74
renewable energy, 339–354
renewable resources, 36
representative sample, 299
respiration, 366
Resource Commerce and Recovery Act (RCRA), 569, 633, 646–647
ribosomes, 184
risk assessment, 610
river habitat, 525
river water quality, 525–531
Rivers and Harbors Act, 633
rivers, 522–524
road salt, 167, 596
rotifers, 213, 218–219, 499
rubbish, 634
Rule of 70, 79
runoff, 509

Safe Drinking Water Act, 560–561
saline soils, 159
saline water, 491
salinity, 129
salmon, 30–34
salt, 109, 125
sampling, 21, 297–309; for soil and groundwater, 307; location for, 301; objectives of, 301; types of, 302
saprophytes, 205–206
saturated solution, 106
saturated zone, 536
science, 6, 28
scientific method, 10
sea level rise, 444–456
secondary air pollutants, 415
sediment, 332–335
sedimentary, 284
self-purification, 532–535
separation, 653
septata, 203

septic zone, 534
shut-ins, 518
sick water, 544–547
silage liquor, 329
slime layers, 195
slope, 163
slope winds, 432
sludge, 134
smog, 320
Snow, J., 187–193
soaps, 133
soil, 284–291; characteristics of, 287–289, 581–589; enhancement of, 287; formation of, 284–287; function of, 289
soil chemistry, 154–172
soil color, 159–160
soil depth, 162–163
soil drainage, 162
soil formation, 590–592
soil horizons, 592
soil pollution, 336, 592–594
soil pollution control technology, 602–610
soil profile, 592
soil properties, 589–590; slope in, 590; texture of, 590; tilth, 590
soil remediation, 168–170
soil texture, 160, 288
soil tilth, 161, 590
solar energy, 340–342
solid waste, 629–639; characteristics of, 634
Solid Waste Disposal Act, 633
solid waste stream, 634
solidification, 620, 653
solids, 122
solubility, 105, 126
solute, 106, 115
solvent, 106, 115
species diversity, 81
specific heat, 108
specific gravity, 87
spoils, 167
spore, 203
sporangiospores, 203
S-shaped curve, 78
stability, 430
stabilization, 653
standard temperature and pressure (STP), 106
statistical inference, 15

stewardship, 6
stigma, 29
stockpiles, 167
stratification, 514–515
stratosphere, 372
stratospheric ozone depletion, 459–460
subsoil, 589
succession, 47
sulfur cycle, 53
sulfur dioxide, 147–148, 321, 414
sulfuric acid, 96
surface impoundments, 655–656
surface tension, 126
surface water, 477, 480–483, 509
surfactants, 133
suspended solids, 122
sustainability, 25
syllogisms, 14
system, 54–55

tailings, 167, 338
technology, 35, 311–354; impact on air
    quality, 319–329; impact on soil, 336–
    339; impact on water quality, 329–336
temperature, 86
temperature inversions, 432
terminal lakes, 517
thallus, 207
theories, 17–18
thermal inversion, 408–409
thermal pollution, 335
thermal pollution treatment, 568; cooling
    tower method of, 568; dry tower method
    of, 568
thermal processes, 651–652
thermal water pollution, 550
throughput, 54
tilth, 288
TMDLs, 134–135
total dissolved solids, 491
total solids, 122
toxin, 263
toxicity, 643
toxicity characteristics leaching procedure,
    643
toxicology, 263

transport, 434–435
trash, 634
treatment technologies, 650–651
troph, 226
trophic level, 48
trophozoites, 212
true color, 123
tubifix, 219
turbidity, 122–123
turbulence, 430
turbulent mixing, 431–432
topsoil, 589

ultimate carrying capacity, 54, 77
ultimate disposal, 654
unconfined aquifers, 536
underground storage tanks, 155, 568–572;
    remediation of leaks, 602–622
unidirectional flow, 61
uniform distribution, 74
units of measurement, 83–88
universal solvent, 490

vacuoles, 184
vadose water, 536
valance, 103
vapor pressure, 120
vapors, 88
Verhulst's Law, 70
volatile organic compounds, 414, 416–417
volcanic lakes, 516
volume, 85
volutin, 197
viruses, 199–201, 498

Walden Pond, 38
waste control technology, 648
waste minimization, 648–650
waste piles, 656
wastewater treatment, 564–568
water characteristics, 486–490
water chemistry, 114–137
water constituents, 122
water hardness, 129–130
water-holding capacity, 161–162
water management, 525

water molecule, 114–115
water pollution, 38, 128–129, 541–563; agricultural sources of, 552–557
water resources, 478–479; major sources of, 479
water scaling, 493
water solution, 115
water striders, 127
water table, 293
water treatment, 563–564
water use, 484–486
water vapor, 364
watershed, 510
weather, 392–407, 429–430; weather generator, 405–407
weight, 84
whole-tree harvests, 171
wind chill factors, 383
wind energy, 343–344
worms, 219, 499

About the Authors

Frank R. Spellman is a retired U.S. naval officer with 26 years of active duty, a retired environmental safety and health manager for a large wastewater sanitation district in Virginia, and retired assistant professor of environmental health at Old Dominion University, Norfolk, Virginia. He is the author or coauthor of 78 books and consults on environmental matters with the U.S. Department of Justice and various law firms and environmental entities across the world. He holds a BA in public administration, a BS in business management, and an MBA and PhD in environmental engineering. In 2011, he traced and documented the ancient water distribution system at Machu Pichu, Peru, and surveyed several drinking water resources in Coco and Amazonia, Ecuador.

Melissa L. Stoudt is a graduate of Old Dominion University with a BS in Environmental Health (Summa Cum Laude). She is a nuclear safety trainer for a New York nuclear power plant. She has co-authored four environmental science books with Frank R. Spellman.